INTERNATIONAL SERIES IN PHYSICS

LEE A. DuBRIDGE, Consulting Editor

INTRODUCTION TO ATOMIC SPECTRA

*This book is produced in full compliance
with the government's regulations for con-
serving paper and other essential materials.*

INTERNATIONAL SERIES IN PHYSICS

LEE A. DuBRIDGE, *Consulting Editor*

Dr. F. K. Richtmyer was consulting editor of the series from its inception in 1929 until his death in 1939.

INTRODUCTION
TO
ATOMIC SPECTRA

BY

HARVEY ELLIOTT WHITE, Ph.D.

*Assistant Professor of Physics, at the
University of California*

FIRST EDITION
FIFTH IMPRESSION

McGRAW-HILL BOOK COMPANY, Inc.

NEW YORK AND LONDON

1934

THE MAPLE PRESS COMPANY, YORK, PA.

TO MY WIFE

PREFACE

During the past few years students have frequently come to the author with this query, "Where can I find an elementary treatment of atomic spectra?" Further questioning has shown, in general, that, although these students have had at least one year of calculus and one or more years of college physics, they have found most treatments of atomic spectra either too brief or too highly mathematical. The desire to meet the situation has given the author the incentive and the encouragement to write this book.

In preparing a manuscript that will in some measure meet the desires of beginning students, as well as those already familiar with certain phases of atomic spectra, the author set up the following three objectives: first, to start as nearly as possible at the beginning of each subject; second, to develop each new concept so that the student with a working knowledge of elementary physics and elementary calculus should have little difficulty in following; and third, clearly to illustrate each chapter, as far as possible, with diagrams and photographs of actual spectra.

At the outset one is confronted with the problem of describing a field of scientific investigation that has developed, and still is developing, at a rapid rate. On the one hand we have the Bohr-Sommerfeld theory of an orbital atom and on the other the newer and more satisfactory theory of quantum mechanics. Believing that one can better understand the principles of quantum mechanics by first becoming well acquainted with the observed spectra and with the vector model, the orbital model of the atom is first treated in some detail. Once developed the orbital model then furnishes a very easy step to the quantum-mechanical atom as given by Schrödinger's wave equation or by the Dirac electron. At frequent intervals throughout the book both the old and new models, of orbits and probability density functions, are compared with each other.

The treatment as it is given here starts with the historical background of spectroscopy (Chap. I) and develops in the first ten chapters the old and the new quantum theories of one-valence-electron atoms. The second half of the book (Chaps. XI through XXI) deals with complex atomic systems of two or more valence electrons and includes a brief account of x-ray spectra. Believing that frequent comparison with the observed spectral lines, by giving actual reproductions of spectrograms, is all too often neglected, the author has spent a great deal of time in photographing many of the spectra used as illustrations. That photographs are an extremely important feature of any book on atomic spectra may be emphasized by pointing out that, of all the theories and knowledge concerning atoms, the spectrum lines will remain the same for all time.

For the benefit of those readers who profit greatly by the working out of examples, typical problems on each subject are given at the end of most chapters. All sections, figures, tables, and equations are assigned two numbers, the first number designating the chapter, and the second the ordinal number in the chapter. The purpose of this notation is to facilitate the finding of any section, figure, table, or equation referred to in the text. In referring to Eq. (4.9), for example, one turns to Chap. IV, using the headings at the top of each page, and then to the ninth equation in that chapter.

The author wishes to take this opportunity especially to thank Prof. Raymond T. Birge and Dr. E. Ramberg for their valuable criticism of the entire manuscript. Sincere thanks are also to be extended to Adeline Dally White for her assistance and patience in the reading of the proof, Prof. F. K. Richtmyer and S. Allison for their reading of Chap. XVI on x-ray spectra, Prof. H. N. Russell for reading Chaps. XI, XII, XIII, XIV, XV, and XIX, on complex spectra, Prof. S. Goudsmit for reading Chap. XVIII on hyperfine structure, Prof. P. S. Epstein for reading Chap. XX on the Stark effect, Prof. J. R. Oppenheimer for the reading of sections dealing with quantum-mechanical results, and Profs. R. B. Brode and F. A. Jenkins for their reading of various sections and chapters. Most sincere thanks are also extended to Drs. A. S. King and P. W. Merrill of the Mount Wilson Observatory, and Prof. D. H. Menzel of the Lick and Harvard observatories, for the original terrestrial, stellar, and solar spectrograms, and to Mr. H. D. Babcock of the Mount Wilson Observatory for the very fine Zeeman patterns of vanadium and chromium. I also wish to thank Prof. F. K. Richtmyer and Dr. F. Hirsch for the original spectrograms reproduced in Figs. 16.5 and 16.7, Prof. M. Siegbahn for the copies of the x-ray diffraction and interference patterns reproduced in Figs. 16.2 and 16.3, Prof. J. S. Foster for the Stark-effect patterns reproduced in Fig. 20.12, Profs. G. N. Lewis and C. D. Shane and Drs. F. H. Spedding and N. S. Grace for the spectrograms of H_α^1 and H_α^2 reproduced in Figs. 9.1 and 9.5. Finally I wish to thank Prof. R. B. Brode and Miss Burmann for especially photographing the x-ray absorption spectra shown in Fig. 16.9, S. S. Ballard for the photographing of the Lyman series of H^1 and H^2, reproduced in Fig. 2.12, and Dr. N. S. Grace, Dr. E. McMillan, and K. More for the original spectrograms reproduced in Fig. 18.2.

HARVEY ELLIOTT WHITE.

BERKELEY, CALIF.,
September, 1934.

CONTENTS

ix

CHAPTER XII

CHAPTER XIII

CHAPTER XIV

CHAPTER XV

CHAPTER XVI

INTRODUCTION TO ATOMIC SPECTRA

CHAPTER I

EARLY HISTORICAL DEVELOPMENTS IN ATOMIC SPECTRA

Spectroscopy as a field of experimental and theoretical research has contributed much to our knowledge concerning the physical nature of things—knowledge not only of our own earth but of the sun, of interstellar space, and of the distant stars. It may rightly be said that spectroscopy had its beginning in the year 1666 with the discovery by Sir Isaac Newton that different colored rays of light when allowed to pass through a prism were refracted at different angles. The experiments that Newton actually carried out are well known to everyone. Sunlight confined to a small pencil of rays by means of a hole in a diaphragm and then allowed to pass through a prism was spread out into a beautiful band of color. Although it was known to the ancients that clear crystals when placed in direct sunlight gave rise to spectral arrays, it remained for Newton to show that the colors did not originate in the crystal but were the necessary ingredients that go to make up sunlight. With a lens in the optical path the band of colors falling on a screen became a series of colored images of the hole in the diaphragm. This band Newton called a *spectrum*.

Had Newton used a narrow slit as a secondary source of light and examined carefully its image in the spectrum, he probably would have discovered, as did Wollaston[1] and Fraunhofer[2] more than one hundred years later, the dark absorption lines of the sun's spectrum. Fraunhofer took it upon himself to map out several hundred of the newly found lines of the solar spectrum and labeled eight of the most prominent ones by the first eight letters of the alphabet (see Fig. 1.1). These lines are now known as the *Fraunhofer lines*.

1.1. Kirchhoff's Law.—More than half a century passed in the history of spectroscopy before a satisfactory explanation of the Fraunhofer lines was given. Foucault[3] showed that, when light from a very power-

---

[1] WOLLASTON, W. H., *Phil. Trans. Roy. Soc.*, II, 365, 1802.

[2] FRAUNHOFER, J., *Gilbert s, Ann.*, **56**, 264, 1817.

[3] FOUCAULT, L., *Ann. chim. et phys.*, **68**, 476, 1860.

ful arc was first allowed to pass through a sodium flame just in front of the slit of a spectroscope, two black lines appeared in exactly the same position of the spectrum as the two D lines of the sun's spectrum. Not many years passed before evidence of this kind proved beyond doubt that many of the elements found on the earth were to be found also in the sun. Kirchhoff[1] was not long in coming forward with the theory that the sun is surrounded by layers of gases acting as absorbing screens for the bright lines emitted from the hot surfaces beneath.

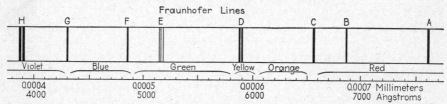

FIG. 1.1.—Prominent Fraunhofer lines. Solar spectrum.

In the year 1859 Kirchhoff gave, in papers read before the Berlin Academy of Sciences, a mathematical and experimental proof of the following law: *The ratio between the powers of emission and the powers of absorption for rays of the same wave-length is constant for all bodies at the same temperature.* To this law, which goes under Kirchhoff's name, the following corollaries are to be added: (1) *The rays emitted by a substance excited in some way or another depend upon the substance and the temperature; and* (2) *every substance has a power of absorption which is a maximum for the rays it tends to emit.* The impetus Kirchhoff's work gave to the field of spectroscopy was soon felt, for it brought many investigators into the field.

In 1868 Ångström[2] set about making accurate measurements of the solar lines and published an elaborate map of the sun's spectrum. Ångström's map, covering the visible region of the spectrum, stood for a number of years as a standard source of wave-lengths. Every line to be used as standard was given to ten-millionths of a millimeter.

1.2. A New Era.—The year 1882 marks the beginning of a new era in the analysis of spectra. Realizing that a good grating is essential to accurate wave-length measurements, Rowland constructed a ruling engine and began ruling good gratings. So successful was Rowland[3] in this undertaking that within a few years he published a photographic map of the solar spectrum some fifty feet in length. Reproductions from two sections of this map are given in Fig. 1.2, showing the sodium

[1] KIRCHHOFF, G., *Monatsber. Berl. Akad. Wiss.*, 1859, p. 662; *Pogg. Ann.*, **109**, 148, 275, 1860; *Ann. chim. et phys.*, **58**, 254, 1860; **59**, 124, 1860.

[2] ÅNGSTRÖM, A. J., Uppsala, W. Schultz, 1868.

[3] ROWLAND, H. A., *Johns Hopkins Univ. Circ.* 17, 1882; *Phil. Mag.*, **13**, 469, 1882; *Nature*, **26**, 211, 1882.

D lines, the iron E lines, and the ionized calcium H lines. With a wave-length scale above, the lines, as can be seen in the figure, were given to ten-millionths of a millimeter, a convenient unit of length introduced by Ångström and now called the *Ångström unit*. The Ångström unit

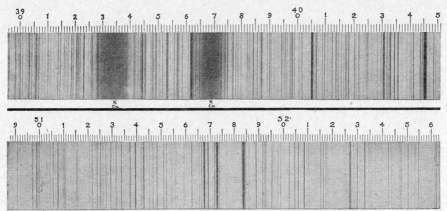

FIG. 1.2.—Sections of Rowland's solar map.

is abbreviated Å, or just A, and, in terms of the standard meter, 1 m = 10^{10} Å.

Up to the time Balmer (1885) discovered the law of the hydrogen series, many attempts had been made to discover the laws governing the distribution of spectrum lines of any element. It was well known that the spectra of many elements contained hundreds of lines, whereas the spectra of others contained relatively few. In hydrogen, for example, half a dozen lines apparently comprised its entire spectrum. These few lines formed what is now called a *series* (see Fig. 1.3).

In 1871 Stoney,[1] drawing an analogy between the harmonic overtones of a fundamental frequency in sound and the series of lines in

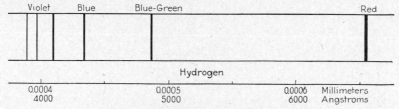

FIG. 1.3.—The Balmer series of hydrogen.

hydrogen, pointed out that the first, second, and fourth lines were the twentieth, twenty-seventh, and thirty-second harmonics of a fundamental vibration whose wave-length *in vacuo* is 131, 274.14 Å. Ten years later Schuster[2] discredited this hypothesis by showing that such a coincidence is no more than would be expected by chance.

[1] STONEY, G. J., *Phil. Mag.*, **41**, 291, 1871.
[2] SCHUSTER, A., *Proc. Roy. Soc. London*, **31**, 337, 1881.

Liveing and Dewar,[1] in a study of the absorption of spectrum lines, made the outstanding discovery that most of the lines of sodium and potassium could be arranged into series of groups of lines. A reproduction of their diagram is given in Fig. 1.4. Excluding the *D* lines of sodium, each successive group of four lines becomes fainter and more diffuse as it approaches the violet end of the spectrum. Liveing and

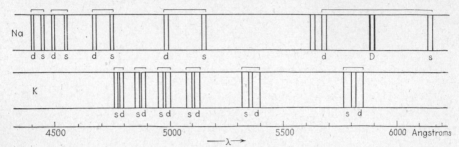

Fig. 1.4.—Schematic representation of the sodium and potassium series. (*After Liveing and Dewar.*)

Dewar say that while the wave-lengths of the fifth, seventh, and eleventh doublets of sodium were very nearly as $\frac{1}{15}:\frac{1}{16}:\frac{1}{17}$, the whole series cannot be represented as harmonics of one fundamental. Somewhat similar harmonic relations were found in potassium but again no more than would be expected by chance.

Four years later Hartley[2] discovered that the components of a doublet or triplet series have the same separations when measured in terms of frequencies instead of wave-lengths. This is now known as *Hartley's law*. This same year Liveing and Dewar[3] announced their discovery of series in thallium, zinc, and aluminum.[4]

1.3. Balmer's Law.—By 1885 the hydrogen series, as observed in the spectra of certain types of stars, had been extended to 14 lines. Photographs of the hydrogen spectrum are given in Fig. 1.5. This year is significant in the history of spectrum analysis for at this early date Balmer announced the law of the entire hydrogen series. He showed that, within the limits of experimental error, each line of the series is given by the simple relation

$$\lambda = h\frac{n_2^2}{n_2^2 - n_1^2},\tag{1.1}$$

where $h = 3645.6$ Å and n_1 and n_2 are small integers. The best agreement for the whole series was obtained by making $n_1 = 2$ throughout

[1] Liveing, G. D., and J. Dewar, *Proc. Roy. Soc. London*, **29**, 398, 1879.

[2] Hartley, W. N., *Jour. Chem. Soc.*, **43**, 390, 1883.

[3] Liveing, G. D., and J. Dewar, *Phil. Trans. Roy. Soc.*, **174**, 187, 1883.

[4] A more complete and general account of the early history of spectroscopy is to be found in Kayser, "Handbuch der Spektroscopie, Vol. I, pp. 3–128, 1900.

and $n_2 = 3, 4, 5, 6 \cdots$ for the first, second, third, fourth, $\cdots$ members of the series. The agreement between the calculated and observed values of the first four lines is shown in the following table:

TABLE 1.1.—BALMER'S LAW FOR THE HYDROGEN SERIES

Calculated wave-lengths	Ångström's observed values	Difference
$H_\alpha = \frac{9}{5}h = 6562.08$ Å	6562.10 Å	$+0.02$ Å
$H_\beta = \frac{16}{12}h = 4860.80$	4860.74	-0.06
$H_\gamma = \frac{25}{21}h = 4340.00$	4340.10	$+0.10$
$H_\delta = \frac{36}{32}h = 4101.30$	4101.20	-0.10

While the differences between calculated and observed wave-lengths for the next 10 lines are in some cases as large as 4 Å, the agreement is as good as could be expected from the existing measurements. The

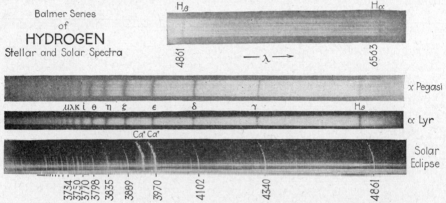

FIG. 1.5.—Stellar and solar spectrograms showing the Balmer series of hydrogen.

accuracy with which lines were then known is seen from the following measurements of five different investigators for the first member of the hydrogen series:

TABLE 1.2.—EARLY MEASURES OF THE HYDROGEN LINE H_α

6565.6	Van der Willigen
6562.10	Ångström
6561.62	Mendenhall
6560.7	Mascart
6559.5	Ditscheiner

1.4. Rydberg's Contributions.—Rydberg's early contributions to atomic spectra consisted not only in finding the laws of a number of series but also in showing that Hartley's law of constant frequency differences was applicable in cases where the doublet or triplet components were very far apart. For example, he showed that the first member of the principal series of thallium is a doublet with the enormous separation of 1574 Å, one line lying in the green at λ5350 and the other in the near ultra-violet at λ3776. This discovery proved to be of considerable importance, as it suggested the possibility that all series arising from the same element were in some simple way connected with each other.

Using Liveing and Dewar's data on the sodium and potassium series, Rydberg made for the first time the distinction between what is called a *sharp series* and a *diffuse series*. The Na and K series given in Fig. 1.4 were each shown to be in reality two series, one a series of sharp doublets (designated by *s*) and the other a series of diffuse doublets (designated by *d*).

A third type of series found in many spectra is the so-called *principal series,* involving as its first member the *resonance* or *persistence* line of the entire spectrum. Resonance or persistence lines are those relatively strong lines most easily excited. Such lines usually appear strong in a Bunsen flame. The yellow *D* lines are a good example of this.

Still a fourth type of series was discovered by Bergmann. This type of series is usually observed in the near infra-red region and is sometimes called the *Bergmann series*. Since Bergmann did not discover all such series, Hicks called them the *fundamental series*. Although this name is perhaps less appropriate than the other and is really misleading, it has after 20 years become attached to the series. New series were discovered so rapidly about this time that many different names and systems of notation arose. Three of these systems commonly used are given in the following table.

TABLE 1.3.—SERIES NOTATION USED BY DIFFERENT INVESTIGATORS

Foote and Mohler	Paschen	Rydberg
Second subordinate...................	II. Nebenserie	Sharp
Principal...........................	Hauptserie	Principal
First subordinate....................	I. Nebenserie	Diffuse
Bergmann..........................	Bergmann	Fundamental

In searching for a general series formula Rydberg discovered that if the wave-lengths λ or the frequencies ν of a series be plotted against consecutive whole numbers, a smooth curve which is approximately a displaced rectangular hyperbola is the result.[1] For a curve such as the one shown in Fig. 1.6 he attempted a solution of the form

[1] It is convenient in practice to express ν numerically not as the actual frequency but as the frequency divided by the velocity of light. Such quantities are called *wave numbers* and, since $c = \nu\lambda$, they are given by the reciprocal of the wave-length measured in centimeters. In this way a spectrum line is described by the number of waves per centimeter *in vacuo*. Wave numbers, therefore, are units with the dimensions of reciprocal centimeters, abbreviated cm^{-1}.

$$\nu_n = \nu_\infty - \frac{C}{n + \mu}, \qquad n = 2, 3, 4, 5, \cdots \infty, \tag{1.2}$$

where ν_n is the wave number of the given line n, and ν_∞, C, and μ are constants. In this equation, ν_n approaches ν_∞ as a limit, as n approaches infinity. While this formula did not give the desired accuracy for an entire series, Rydberg was of the opinion that the form of the equation could not be far from correct.

The next equation investigated by Rydberg was of the form

$$\nu_n = \nu_\infty - \frac{N}{(n + \mu)^2}, \qquad n = 2, 3, 4, 5, \cdots \infty, \tag{1.3}$$

where, as before, N and μ are constants, ν_∞ is the limit of the series, and n is the ordinal number of the line in the series. This formula proved

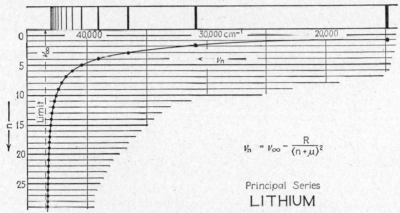

FIG. 1.6.—Frequency plot of the principal series of lithium.

to be so successful when applied to many series that Rydberg adopted it in all of his succeeding work. The important fact about the formula is that N takes the same value in all series in all elements. It is interesting to observe that, by placing $\mu = 0$, the equation reduces to Balmer's formula for hydrogen (see Sec. 1.8). Since n takes on integral values only, the hydrogen series affords a direct means of calculating this universal constant N, now known as the *Rydberg constant R*. Rydberg's equation is now written

$$\nu_n = \nu_\infty - \frac{R}{(n + \mu)^2}, \qquad n = 2, 3, 4, 5, \cdots \infty. \tag{1.4}$$

If we now let ν_n^s, ν_n^p, ν_n^d, and ν_n^f represent ν_n for the sharp, principal, diffuse, and fundamental series, respectively, then the four general series may be represented by

Sharp series:

$$\nu_n^s = \nu_\infty^s - \frac{R}{(n + S)^2}, \text{ where } n = 2, 3, 4, \cdots \infty. \tag{1.5}$$

Principal series:

$$\nu_n^p = \nu_\infty^p - \frac{R}{(n+P)^2}, \text{ where } n = 1, 2, 3, \cdots \infty. \tag{1.6}$$

Diffuse series:

$$\nu_n^d = \nu_\infty^d - \frac{R}{(n+D)^2}, \text{ where } n = 2, 3, 4, \cdots \infty. \tag{1.7}$$

Fundamental series:

$$\nu_n^f = \nu_\infty^f - \frac{R}{(n+F)^2}, \text{ where } n = 3, 4, 5, \cdots \infty. \tag{1.8}$$

Here $S, P, D,$ and F represent the values of μ, and ν_∞^s, ν_∞^p, ν_∞^d, and ν_∞^f the limits of the different series. In applying the above equations to the three chief series of lithium, Rydberg obtained the following expressions:

$$\nu_n^s = 28601.6 - \frac{109721.6}{(n+0.5951)^2}. \tag{1.9}$$

$$\nu_n^p = 43487.7 - \frac{109721.6}{(n+0.9596)^2}. \tag{1.10}$$

$$\nu_n^d = 28598.5 - \frac{109721.6}{(n+0.9974)^2}. \tag{1.11}$$

These equations show a relation that might have been anticipated from an examination of the sharp and diffuse series of Na and K in Fig. 1.4, *viz.*, that the limits of the S and D series are probably the same, *i.e.*, $\nu_\infty^s = \nu_\infty^d$. It is to be noted that the first member of the sharp series, Eq. (1.9), starts with $n = 2$. With $n = 1$ this formula gives the first member of the principal series with a negative value.

1.5. The Rydberg-Schuster Law.—Rydberg observed that if n is placed equal to unity in the sharp-series formula, Eq. (1.9), the right-hand term became approximately the limit of the principal-series formula, Eq. (1.10).

$$\frac{109721.6}{(1+0.5951)^2} = 43123.7 \cong \nu_\infty^p. \tag{1.12}$$

Similarly, if n is placed equal to unity in the principal-series formula, the right-hand term becomes approximately the limit of the sharp series:

$$\frac{109721.6}{(1+0.9596)^2} = 28573.1 = \nu_\infty^s. \tag{1.13}$$

Rydberg came to the conclusion that the calculated differences were due to experimental errors and that the sharp- and diffuse-series limits were identical. He therefore could write Eqs. (1.9), (1.10), and (1.11) in the following form:

$$\nu_n^s = \frac{R}{(1 + P)^2} - \frac{R}{(n + S)^2}, \tag{1.14}$$

$$\nu_n^p = \frac{R}{(1 + S)^2} - \frac{R}{(n + P)^2}, \tag{1.15}$$

$$\nu_n^d = \frac{R}{(1 + P)^2} - \frac{R}{(n + D)^2}. \tag{1.16}$$

It was not until 1896 that Rydberg[1] discovered, as did Schuster[2] in the same year, that the first line of the principal series in the alkalies is also the first member of the sharp series when taken with negative sign. If n is placed equal to unity in Eqs. (1.9) and (1.10), then $\nu_1^s = -\nu_1^p$. In exactly this same way it was found that the difference between the limit of the principal series and the common limit of the sharp and diffuse series is equal to the first member of the principal series:

$$\nu_\infty^p - \nu_\infty^s = \nu_1^p = -\nu_1^s. \tag{1.17}$$

These important relations are now known as the *Rydberg-Schuster law*.

Immediately upon the discovery by Bergmann, 12 years later, of the fundamental series, Runge announced that the difference between the limits of the diffuse and fundamental series is equal to the first line of the diffuse series:

$$\nu_\infty^d - \nu_\infty^f = \nu_2^d. \tag{1.18}$$

Hence, from Eqs. (1.7) and (1.18), Eq. 1.8 can be written

$$\nu_n^f = \frac{R}{(2 + D)^2} - \frac{R}{(n + F)^2}, \tag{1.18a}$$

and this equation added to the group (1.14), (1.15), and (1.16) shows that the frequency limit of every one of the four series has now been expressed in terms of the constants of some other series. For the diffuse series, n usually starts with two in place of unity.

The Rydberg-Schuster law as well as the Runge law is shown in Fig. 1.7 by plotting the spectral frequencies, in wave numbers ν, against the order number n, for the four chief series of sodium. To prevent confusion among the lines belonging to the different series each one is plotted separately. In order to show that the first member of the principal series becomes the first member of the sharp series, when taken with negative value, the scale has been extended to negative wave numbers. Unfortunately the frequency scale is too small to show the doublet nature of each line. The Rydberg-Schuster law is indicated by the intervals X_1 of the figure and the Runge law by the intervals X_2.

A study of the singlet and triplet series discovered in a number of elements shows that similar laws are to be found. This may be illus-

[1] RYDBERG, J. R., *Astrophys. Jour.*, **4**, 91, 1896.
[2] SCHUSTER, A., *Nature*, **55**, 180, 200, 223, 1896.

trated by the calcium series shown schematically in Fig. 1.8. The upper four series represent the triplets and the lower four the singlets. Intervals between certain series limits, shown at the bottom of the figure,

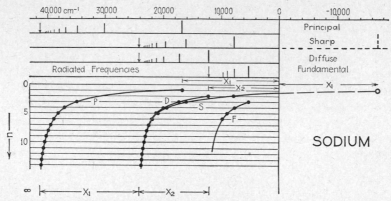

Fig. 1.7.—Schematic plot of the four chief series of sodium doublets showing the Rydberg-Schuster and Runge laws.

are observed to be the same as the frequencies of certain radiated lines. Figures such as these reveal many important relations and, as we shall see later, facilitate the formation of what are called *energy level diagrams*.

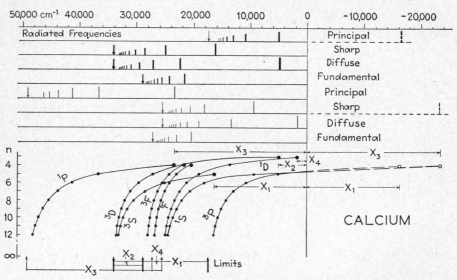

Fig. 1.8.—Schematic plot of the chief triplet and singlet series of calcium showing the Rydberg-Schuster and Runge laws.

1.6. Series Notation.—A somewhat abbreviated notation for Rydberg's formulas was employed by Ritz. This abbreviated notation, which follows directly from Eqs. (1.14), (1.15), (1.16), and (1.18a), for the four chief types of series is written as follows:

$$v_n^s = 1P - nS, \qquad v_n^d = 1P - nD.$$
$$v_n^p = 1S - nP, \qquad v_n^f = 2D - nF. \qquad\qquad (1.19)$$

In order to distinguish between singlet-, doublet-, and triplet-series systems, various schemes have been proposed by different investigators. Fowler,[1] for example, used capital letters S, P, D, etc., for singlets, Greek letters σ, π, δ, etc., for doublets, and small letters s, p, d, etc., for triplets. Paschen and Götze[2] on the other hand adopted the scheme of small letters s, p, d for both doublets and triplets, and capitals S, P, D for singlets.

A more recent scheme of spectra notation, published by Russell, Shenstone, and Turner,[3] has been accepted internationally by many investigators. In this new system capital letters are used for all series and small superscripts in front of each letter give the multiplicity (see Table 1.4).

TABLE 1.4.—SERIES NOTATION

Series	Fowler	Paschen	Adopted
Singlet	$S \quad P \quad D \quad F$	$S \quad P \quad D \quad F$	$^1S \quad ^1P \quad ^1D \quad ^1F$
Doublet	$\sigma \quad \pi \quad \delta \quad \varphi$	$s \quad p \quad d \quad f$	$^2S \quad ^2P \quad ^2D \quad ^2F$
Triplet	$s \quad p \quad d \quad f$	$s \quad p \quad d \quad f$	$^3S \quad ^3P \quad ^3D \quad ^3F$

1.7. Satellites and Fine Structure.—The appearance of faint lines, or satellites, in some series was discovered by Rydberg and also by Kayser and Runge. At first the satellites, which usually appear on the long wave-length side of the diffuse series, were considered as a secondary diffuse series until it was discovered that Hartley's law of constant frequency separations applied to the separation of the satellite and one of the strong lines of the doublet. In most diffuse doublets the strongest line lies between the satellite and the weaker line of the doublet.

This is illustrated in Fig. 1.9, where the first four members of the four chief series of caesium are plotted schematically. Plotted to a frequency scale it is seen that the outside separation of each member of the sharp and diffuse series and the first member of the principal series is exactly the same. It should also be noted that the first member of the principal series is, when inverted, the first member of the sharp series. This member is shown dotted.

Unlike other ^2F series, to be studied later, the strongest line in each F-doublet in caesium lies on the low-frequency side of the respective satellites. Like all ^2F series, however, each doublet has one interval in common with the first member of the diffuse series.

[1] FOWLER, A., "Report on Series in Line Spectra," Fleetway Press, 1922.

[2] PASCHEN, F., and R. GÖTZE, "Seriengesetze der Linienspektren," Julius Springer, 1922.

[3] RUSSELL, H. N., A. G. SHENSTONE, and L. A. TURNER, *Phys. Rev.*, **33**, 900, 1929.

Similar relations are found to exist among the triplet series of the alkaline earths. The first four members of the four chief series of calcium are shown schematically in Fig. 1.10. From the diagram it is seen, first, that the common limit of sharp and diffuse series is a triple

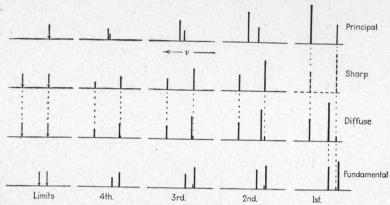

Fig. 1.9.—Frequency plot of the doublet fine structure in the chief series of caesium.

limit with separations equal to the first member of the principal series; second, that the limit of the fundamental series is a triple limit with separations equal to the separations of the strongest line and satellites of the first member of the diffuse series; and third, that the principal series has a single limit. It is to be noted in the doublet series (Figs.

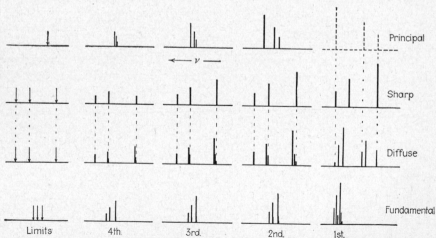

Fig. 1.10.—Frequency plot of the triplet fine structure in the chief series of calcium.

1.9 and 1.7) that, while the first principal doublet becomes the first sharp doublet when inverted, the reverse is true for the triplet series of calcium. By inverting the first sharp-series member (Fig. 1.10), the lines fall in with the principal series in order of separations and intensities.

In the development of Rydberg's formula, each member of a series was assumed to be a single line. In the case of a series where each member is made up of two or more components, the constants ν_∞ and μ of Eq. (1.4) must be calculated for each component. Rydberg's formulas for the sharp series of triplets, for example, would be written, in the accepted notation,

$$\nu_n^s = \frac{R}{(1 + {}^3P_2)^2} - \frac{R}{(n + {}^3S_1)^2} = 1^3P_2 - n^3S_1,$$

$$\nu_n^s = \frac{R}{(1 + {}^3P_1)^2} - \frac{R}{(n + {}^3S_1)^2} = 1^3P_1 - n^3S_1, \qquad (1.20)$$

$$\nu_n^s = \frac{R}{(1 + {}^3P_0)^2} - \frac{R}{(n + {}^3S_1)^2} = 1^3P_0 - n^3S_1,$$

where ${}^3S_1$, ${}^3P_0$, ${}^3P_1$, ${}^3P_2$, occurring in the denominators, are small constants. Symbolically 1^3P_2 stands for the term $R/(1 + {}^3P_2)^2$ which is one of the three limits of the sharp series. The subscripts 0, 1, and 2, used here to distinguish between limits, are in accord with, and are part of, the internationally adopted notation and are of importance in the theory of atomic structure.

A spectral line is seen to be given by the difference between two terms and a series of lines by the difference between one *fixed term* and a series of *running terms*. The various components of the diffuse-triplet series with three main lines and three satellites are designated

$1^3P_2 - n^3D_3$, first strong line; $1^3P_1 - n^3D_2$, second strong line.

$1^3P_2 - n^3D_2$, satellite; $1^3P_1 - n^3D_1$, satellite.   (1.21)

$1^3P_2 - n^3D_1$, satellite; $1^3P_0 - n^3D_1$, third strong line.

The general abbreviated notation of series terms is given in the following table along with the early schemes used by Fowler and Paschen.

TABLE 1.5.—NOTATION OF SERIES TERMS

Series	Fowler				Paschen				Internationally adopted			
Singlet	S	P	D	F	S	P	D	F	$^1S_0$	$^1P_1$	$^1D_2$	$^1F_3$
Doublet	σ	π_2	δ	φ	s	p_2	d_2	f_2	$^2S_{\frac{1}{2}}$	$^2P_{\frac{1}{2}}$	$^2D_{\frac{3}{2}}$	$^2F_{\frac{5}{2}}$
		π_1	δ'	φ'		p_1	d_1	f_1		$^2P_{\frac{3}{2}}$	$^2D_{\frac{5}{2}}$	$^2F_{\frac{7}{2}}$
Triplet	s	p_1	d	f	s	p_1	d_1	f_1	$^3S_1$	$^3P_2$	$^3D_3$	$^3F_4$
		p_2	d'	f'		p_2	d_2	f_2		$^3P_1$	$^3D_2$	$^3F_3$
		p_3	d''	f''		p_3	d_3	f_3		$^3P_0$	$^3D_1$	$^3F_2$

While the new notation is somewhat complicated by the use of superscripts and especially by half-integral subscripts, it will be seen

later that each letter and number has a definite meaning, in the light of
present-day theories of atomic structure.

**1.8. The Lyman, Balmer, Paschen, Brackett, and Pfund Series of
Hydrogen.**—It is readily shown that Balmer's formula given by Eq. (1.1)
is obtained directly from Rydberg's more general formula

$$\nu_n = \frac{R}{(n_1 + \mu_1)^2} - \frac{R}{(n_2 + \mu_2)^2} \tag{1.22}$$

by placing $\mu_1 = 0$, $\mu_2 = 0$, $n_1 = 2$, and $n_2 = 3, 4, 5, \cdots$. Inverting
Eq. (1.1),

$$\frac{1}{\lambda} = \frac{1}{a} - \frac{1}{a}\frac{n_1^2}{n_2^2} = \nu_n, \tag{1.23}$$

where $a = 3645.6$ Å. Writing $R = n_1^2/a$,

$$\nu_n = \frac{R}{n_1^2} - \frac{R}{n_2^2} = R\left(\frac{1}{n_1^2} - \frac{1}{n_2^2}\right). \tag{1.24}$$

This is the well-known form of the hydrogen-series formula.

It was Ritz, as well as Rydberg, who made the suggestion that n_2
might take running values just as well as n_1. This predicts an entirely
different series for each value assigned to n_1. For example, with $n_1 = 1$,
2, 3, 4, and 5, the following formulas are obtained:

Lyman series:

$$\nu_n = R\left(\frac{1}{1^2} - \frac{1}{n_2^2}\right), \text{ where } n_2 = 2, 3, 4, \cdots. \tag{1.25}$$

Balmer series:

$$\nu_n = R\left(\frac{1}{2^2} - \frac{1}{n_2^2}\right), \text{ where } n_2 = 3, 4, 5, \cdots. \tag{1.26}$$

Paschen series:

$$\nu_n = R\left(\frac{1}{3^2} - \frac{1}{n_2^2}\right), \text{ where } n_2 = 4, 5, 6, \cdots. \tag{1.27}$$

Brackett series:

$$\nu_n = R\left(\frac{1}{4^2} - \frac{1}{n_2^2}\right), \text{ where } n_2 = 5, 6, 7, \cdots. \tag{1.28}$$

Pfund series:

$$\nu_n = R\left(\frac{1}{5^2} - \frac{1}{n_2^2}\right), \text{ where } n_2 = 6, 7, 8, \cdots. \tag{1.29}$$

Knowing the value of R from the well-known Balmer series the positions
of the lines in the other series are predicted with considerable accuracy.
The first series was discovered by Lyman in the extreme ultra-violet
region of the spectrum. This series has therefore become known as the
Lyman series. The third, fourth, and fifth series have been discovered

where they were predicted in the infra-red region of the spectrum by Paschen, Brackett, and Pfund, respectively. The first line of these five series appears at $\lambda 1215$, $\lambda 6563$, $\lambda 18751$, $\lambda 40500$, and $\lambda 74000$ Å, respectively. It is to be seen from the formulas that the fixed terms of the second, third, fourth, and fifth equations are the first, second, third, and fourth running terms of the Lyman series. Similarly, the fixed terms of the third, fourth, and fifth equations are the first, second, and third running terms of the Balmer series; etc. This is known as the *Ritz combination principle* as it applies to hydrogen.

1.9. The Ritz Combination Principle.—Predictions by the Ritz combination principle of new series in elements other than hydrogen have been verified in many spectra. If the sharp and principal series of the alkali metals are represented, in the abbreviated notation, by

$$\text{Sharp:} \quad \nu_n = 1^2P - n^2S, \text{ where } n = 2, 3, 4, \cdots ,$$
$$\text{Principal:} \quad \nu_n = 1^2S - n^2P, \text{ where } n = 2, 3, 4, \cdots , \tag{1.30}$$

the series predicted by Ritz are obtained by changing the fixed terms 1^2P and 1^2S to 2^2P, 3^2P and 2^2S, 3^2S, etc. The resultant formulas are of the following form:

Combination sharp series:

$$2^2P - n^2S, \text{ where } n = 3, 4, 5, \cdots .$$
$$3^2P - n^2S, \text{ where } n = 4, 5, 6, \cdots . \tag{1.31}$$
$$\text{etc.}$$

Combination principal series:

$$2^2S - n^2P, \text{ where } n = 3, 4, 5, \cdots .$$
$$3^2S - n^2P, \text{ where } n = 4, 5, 6, \cdots . \tag{1.32}$$
$$\text{etc.}$$

In a similar fashion new diffuse and fundamental series are predicted by changing the fixed ^2P term of the diffuse series and the fixed ^2D term of the fundamental series.

Since all fixed terms occurring in Eqs. (1.31) and (1.32) are included in the running terms of Eqs. (1.30), the predicted series are simply combinations, or differences, between terms of the chief series. Such series have therefore been called *combination series*. Extensive investigations of the infra-red spectrum of many elements, by Paschen, have led to the identification of many of the combination lines and series.

In the spectra of the alkaline earth elements there are not only the four chief series of triplets ^3S, ^3P, ^3D, and ^3F but also four chief series of singlets ^1S, ^1P, ^1D, and ^1F. Series and lines have been found not only for triplet-triplet and singlet-singlet combinations but also *triplet-singlet* and *singlet-triplet* combinations. These latter are called *intercombination lines* or *series*.

1.10. The Ritz Formula.—The work of Ritz on spectral series is of considerable importance since it marks the development of a series formula still employed by many investigators. Assuming that Rydberg's formula for hydrogen was correct in form

$$\nu_n = R\left(\frac{1}{p^2} - \frac{1}{q^2}\right), \tag{1.33}$$

and realizing that p and q must be functions involving the order number n, Ritz obtained, from theoretical considerations, p and q in the form of infinite series:

$$\begin{aligned} p &= n_1 + a_1 + \frac{b_1}{n_1^2} + \frac{c_1}{n_1^4} + \frac{d_1}{n_1^6} + \cdots \\ q &= n_2 + a_2 + \frac{b_2}{n_2^2} + \frac{c_2}{n_2^4} + \frac{d_2}{n_2^6} + \cdots \end{aligned} \tag{1.34}$$

Using only the first two terms of p and q, Ritz's equation becomes identical with Rydberg's general formula which is now to be considered only a close approximation. In some cases, the first three terms of the expansion for p and q are sufficient to represent a series of spectrum lines to within the limits of experimental error.

1.11. The Hicks Formula.—The admirable work of Hicks[1] in developing an accurate formula to represent spectral series is worthy of mention at this point. Like Ritz, Hicks starts with the assumption that Rydberg's formula is fundamental in that it not only represents each series separately but also gives the relations existing between the different series. Quite independent of Ritz, Hicks expanded the denominator of Rydberg's Eq. (1.3) into a series of terms

$$n + \mu + \frac{a}{n} + \frac{b}{n^2} + \frac{c}{n^3} + \cdots. \tag{1.35}$$

The final formula becomes

$$\nu_n = \nu_\infty - \frac{R}{\left(n + \mu + \dfrac{a}{n} + \dfrac{b}{n^2} + \dfrac{c}{n^3} + \cdots\right)^2}. \tag{1.36}$$

This formula, like Ritz's, reduces to Rydberg's formula when only the first two members in the denominator are used.

1.12. Series Formulas Applied to the Alkali Metals.—The extension of the principal series of sodium to the forty-seventh member by Wood[2] (see Fig. 1. 11) and of the principal series of potassium, rubidium, and caesium, to the twenty-third, twenty-fourth, and twentieth members,

---

[1] HICKS, W. M., *Phil. Trans. Roy. Soc.*, **A, 210,** 57, 1910; **212,** 33, 1912; **213,** 323, 1914; **217,** 361, 1917; **220,** 335, 1919.

[2] WOOD, R. W., *Astrophys. Jour.*, **29,** 97, 1909.

respectively by Bevan[1] furnishes the necessary data for testing the accuracy of proposed series formulas. A careful investigation of these series was carried out by Birge[2] who found that the Ritz formula was to be preferred and that with three undetermined constants it would represent the series of the alkali metals of lower atomic weight with fair accuracy. Birge shows that the number of terms that need be used in

Principal Series of Sodium

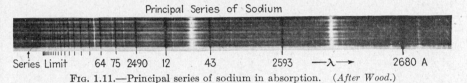

Series Limit   64 75 2490 12   43   2593   —λ→   2680 A

Fig. 1.11.—Principal series of sodium in absorption. (*After Wood.*)

the denominator depends directly on the size of the coefficients of the several terms, and that these coefficients increase with atomic weight. This increase is shown in the following table:

TABLE 1.6.—Series Coefficients
(*After Birge*)[1]

Element	Atomic weight	a	b
H	1	0	0
He	4	0.0111	0.0047
Li	7	0.047	0.026
Na	23	0.144	0.113
K	39	0.287	0.221
Rb	85	0.345	0.266
Cs	133	0.412	0.333

[1] Birge, R. T., *Astrophys. Jour.*, **32**, 112, 1910.

To illustrate the accuracy with which the Ritz formula represents series in some cases, the principal series of sodium is given in the table shown on page 18.

The Rydberg constant as calculated by Birge from the first five members of the Balmer series of hydrogen and used by him for all series formulas is $R = 109678.6$. It is to be noted that the maximum error throughout the table is only 0.1Å.

This work greatly strengthened the idea that the Rydberg constant was a universal constant and that it was of fundamental importance in series relations. The Ritz equation has therefore been adopted by many investigators as the most accurate formula, with the fewest constants, for use in spectral series. A modified but equally satisfactory form of the Ritz formula will be discussed in Sec. 1.14.

[1] Bevan, P. V., *Phil. Mag.*, **19**, 195, 1910.
[2] Birge, R. T., *Astrophys. Jour.*, **32**, 112, 1910.

Table 1.7.—The Ritz Formula Applied to the Sodium Series Observed by Wood
(Calculations after Birge)[1]

$$\nu_n = A - \frac{R}{\left(n + a + \dfrac{b}{n^2}\right)^2},$$

where $A = 41,450.083$ cm^{-1}, $R = 109,678.6$ cm^{-1}, $a = 0.144335$, and $b = -0.1130286$.

n	λ_{vac} obs.	Calc. diff.	n	λ_{vac} obs.	Calc. diff.	n	λ_{vac} obs.	Calc. diff.
2	5897.563	0.00	18	2432.08	−0.01	34	2418.03	+0.01
3	3303.895	0.00	19	30.07	−0.02	35	17.75	+0.02
4	2853.63	−0.04	20	28.37	−0.01	36	17.45	0.00
5	2681.17	+0.09	21	26.93	+0.02	37	17.21	+0.03
6	2594.67	+0.09	22	25.65	+0.03	38	16.98	+0.04
7	2544.49	−0.05	23	24.53	+0.01	39	16.76	+0.03
8	2512.90	+0.07	24	23.55	0.00	40	16.54	+0.02
9	2491.36	−0.04	25	22.69	0.00	41	16.35	+0.03
10	76.26	+0.03	26	21.93	+0.02	42	16.17	+0.02
11	65.18	+0.10	27	21.25	+0.01	43	16.02	+0.03
12	56.67	+0.05	28	20.67	+0.04	44	15.86	+0.04
13	50.11	+0.04	29	20.15	+0.07	45	15.71	+0.03
14	44.89	−0.03	30	19.65	+0.06	46	15.59	+0.05
15	40.71	+0.01	31	19.09	−0.05	47	15.43	+0.01
16	37.35	+0.06	32	18.74	0.00	48	15.29	−0.01
17	34.50	+0.04	33	18.36	−0.01	49	15.15	−0.04

[1] Birge, R. T. *Astrophys. Jour.*, **32**, 112, 1910.

1.13. Neon with 130 Series.—The first successful analysis of a really complex spectrum was made by Paschen[1] in the case of neon. Although the neon spectrum was found to contain a great many lines, Paschen was able to arrange them into 130 different series. These series, classified as 30 principal series, 30 sharp series, and 70 diffuse series, were found to be combinations between 4 series of S terms, s_1, s_2, s_3, and s_4; 10 series of P terms, p_1, p_2, p_3, . . . , p_{10}; and 12 series of D terms, d_1, d_2, d_3, . . . , d_{12}. Paschen showed that, while many of the series were regular and followed a Ritz formula, others were irregular and could not be fitted to any formula. These abnormal series will be discussed in the following section.

1.14. Normal and Abnormal Series.—Occasionally it is found that certain members of a well-established series do not follow the ordinary Rydberg or Ritz formula to within the limits of experimental error. Well-known series of this kind were pointed out by Saunders in the singlet series of Ca, Sr, and Ba, and by Paschen in certain neon series. A convenient method, employed by Paschen and others, for illustrating deviations from a normal series is to plot μ, the residual constant in the Rydberg denominator, of each term against n, the order number of the

[1] Paschen, F., *Ann. d. Phys.*, **60**, 405, 1919; **63**, 201, 1920.

term. Several of the diffuse series of terms of neon as given by Paschen are reproduced in Fig. 1.12. A normal series should show residuals that follow a smooth curve like the first nine members of the d_4 series. The curves for the d_1, d_3, and d_5 terms show no such smoothness, making it very difficult to represent the series by any type of series formula.

A series following a Rydberg formula is represented on such a graph by a horizontal line, *i.e.*, μ constant. With a normal series like d_4 of

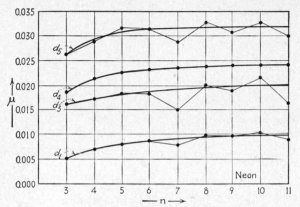

FIG. 1.12.—Four diffuse series in neon showing normal and abnormal progression of the residual μ. (*After Paschen.*)

neon, a Ritz formula with at least one added term is necessary to adequately represent the series. If T_n represents the running term of a Ritz formula, and T_1 the fixed term,

$$\nu_n = T_1 - T_n = T_1 - \frac{R}{\left(n + a + \dfrac{b}{n^2}\right)^2}. \tag{1.37}$$

Another useful form of the Ritz formula is obtained by inserting the running term itself as a correction in the denominator:

$$T_n = \frac{R}{(n + a + bT_n)^2}. \tag{1.38}$$

This term being large at the beginning of a series, the correction is correspondingly large. Formulas representing abnormal series like d_1, d_3, and d_5 in Fig. 1.12 will be treated in Chap. XIX.

Other anomalies that frequently occur in spectral series are the irregular spacings of the fine structure in certain members of the series. A good example of this type of anomaly is to be found in the diffuse triplet series of calcium. In Fig. 1.13 a normal diffuse series, as is observed in cadmium, is shown in contrast with the abnormal calcium series. The three chief lines of each triplet are designated a, b, and d, and the three satellites c, e, and f. Experimentally it is the interval between the two satellites f and c and the interval between the satellite c and the chief line a that follows Hartley's law of equal separations in both series. In cadmium it is seen that the main lines and satellites converge toward the three series limits very early in the series. In calcium, on the other hand, the lines first converge in a normal fashion, then spread out anomalously and converge a second time toward the three series limits. These irregularities now have a very beautiful explanation which will be given in detail in Chap. XIX.

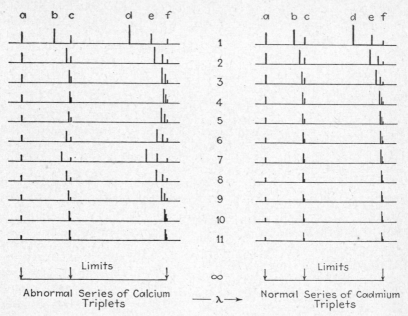

Fig. 1.13.—Diffuse series of triplets in cadmium and calcium.

1.15. Hydrogen and the Pickering Series.—In the hands of Balmer and Rydberg the historical hydrogen series was well accounted for when Pickering, in 1897, discovered in the spectrum of the star ζ-Puppis a series of lines whose wave-lengths are closely related to the Balmer series of hydrogen. Rydberg was the first to show that this new series could be represented by allowing n_2 in Balmer's formula to take both half and whole integral values. Balmer's formula for the Pickering series may therefore be written

$$\nu_n = R\left(\frac{1}{2^2} - \frac{1}{n_2^2}\right), \qquad \text{where } n_2 = 2.5, 3, 3.5, 4, 4.5, \cdots . \quad (1.39)$$

The Balmer and Pickering series are both shown schematically in Fig. 1.14. So good was the agreement between calculated and observed wave-lengths that the Pickering series was soon attributed to some new form of hydrogen found in the stars but not on the earth.

Since n_2 was allowed to take on half-integral values, Rydberg predicted new series of lines by allowing n_1 to take half-integral values.   One series, for example, could be written

$$\nu_n = R\left(\frac{1}{1.5^2} - \frac{1}{n_2^2}\right), \qquad \text{where } n_2 = 2, 2.5, 3, \cdots. \qquad (1.40)$$

All of the lines of this predicted series, except the first, are in the ultra-violet region of the spectrum.   With the appearance of a line in the spectrum of ζ-Puppis at λ4688, the position of the first line of the pre-dicted series, Rydberg's assumption was verified and the existence of a new form of hydrogen was (erroneously) established.

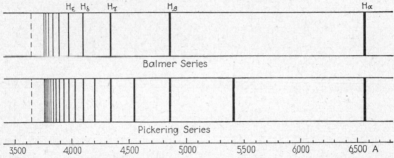

FIG. 1.14.—Comparison of the Balmer series of hydrogen and the Pickering series.

Fowler in his experiments on helium brought out, with a tube con-taining helium and hydrogen, not only the first two members of the Pickering series strongly but also a number of other lines observed by Pickering in the stars.   While all of these lines seemed to be in some way connected with the Balmer formula for hydrogen, they did not seem to be in any way connected with the known chief series of helium.   The whole matter was finally cleared up by Bohr[1] in the extension of his theory of the hydrogen atom to ionized helium.   This is the subject taken up in Chap. II.

1.16. Enhanced Lines.—Spectral lines which on passing from arc to spark conditions become brighter, or more intense, were early defined by Lockyer as *enhanced lines*.   In the discovery of series relations among the enhanced lines of the alkaline earths, Fowler[2] made the dis-tinction between three classes of enhanced lines; (1) lines that are strong in the arc but strengthened in the spark, (2) lines that are weak in the arc but strengthened in the spark, and (3) lines that do not appear in the arc at all but are brought out strongly in the spark.

Fowler discovered, in the enhanced spectra of Mg, Ca, and Sr, series of doublet lines corresponding in type to the principal, sharp, and diffuse

[1] BOHR, N., *Phil. Mag.*, **26**, 476, 1913.
[2] FOWLER, A., *Phil. Trans. Roy. Soc.*, A, **214**, 225, 1914.

doublets of the alkali metals. In an attempt to represent these series by some sort of Rydberg or Ritz formula, it was found that n_2, the order number of the series, must take on half-integral as well as integral values. The situation so resembled that of the Pickering series and the hydrogen series that Fowler, knowing the conditions under which the enhanced lines were produced, associated correctly the enhanced doublet series of Mg, Ca, and Sr with the ionized atoms of the respective elements. For such series we shall see in the next two chapters that the Rydberg constant R is to be replaced by $4R$ so that the enhanced series formula becomes

$$\nu_n = 4R\left\{\frac{1}{(n_1 + \mu_1)^2} - \frac{1}{(n_2 + \mu_2)^2}\right\}, \qquad (1.41)$$

where n_2 is integral valued only.

Problem

With the frequencies of the four chief series of spectrum lines as given for ionized calcium by Fowler, "Series in Line Spectra," construct a diagram similar to the one shown in Fig. 1.7. Indicate clearly the intervals illustrating the Rydberg-Schuster and Runge laws.

CHAPTER II

INTRODUCTION TO THE QUANTUM THEORY AND THE BOHR ATOM

The Quantum theory was first introduced by Planck in the year 1900 and is the result of an attempt by him to derive the law of black-body radiation. In order to formulate an equation which would fit the experimental data at hand Planck postulated that energy is radiated and absorbed only in whole multiples of an elementary quantum of energy,

$$E = h\nu, \tag{2.1}$$

where ν is the frequency of the emitted or absorbed radiation and h is a universal constant now known as *Planck's constant of action* ($h = (6.547 \pm 0.008) \times 10^{-27}$ erg sec.). Planck arrived at the quantum hypothesis by assuming that a simple harmonic oscillator acts as a resonator to radiation. Making use of this hypothesis Einstein developed the law of the photoelectric effect, and Bohr developed the theory of the hydrogen atom.

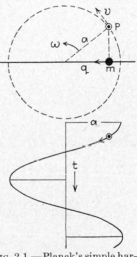

FIG. 2.1.—Planck's simple harmonic oscillator.

2.1. Planck's Simple Harmonic Oscillator.— As an introduction to the quantum theory we shall first consider Planck's simple harmonic oscillator. The term *simple harmonic oscillator* is here referred to as a single electrically charged particle of mass m free to oscillate along a straight line under the action of a force proportional to the displacement from and always directed toward a central equilibrium position. For such an oscillator the position of the *mass point* m is conveniently described in terms of the projection on any diameter of a *graph point* P moving with constant speed on the circumference of a circle of reference (see Fig. 2.1).

With the radius of the circle of reference equal to the amplitude of vibration a, the position coordinate q is given by

$$q = a \cos \omega t. \tag{2.2}$$

The momentum $m\dot{q}$ of the particle is obtained by differentiating Eq. (2.2) and multiplying through by m. This gives

$$m\dot{q} = -ma\omega \sin \omega t = p. \tag{2.3}$$

23

Squaring the resulting expressions for cos ωt and sin ωt and adding yields

$$\frac{p^2}{(ma\omega)^2} + \frac{q^2}{a^2} = 1. \tag{2.4}$$

This is the equation of an ellipse in a pq plane with a major axis a and a minor axis $ma\omega$. When sin $\omega t = 1$, then $\dot{q} = -a\omega$ and $q = 0$; the potential energy is zero and the total energy is all kinetic. Replacing the angular velocity ω by 2π times the frequency ν, the total energy of the oscillator becomes

$$W = \tfrac{1}{2}m\dot{q}^2 = 2\pi^2\nu^2ma^2. \tag{2.5}$$

Now the area of the ellipse in the pq plane is obtained by integrating the momentum p over a complete cycle, *i.e.*:

$$\text{Area} = J = \oint p \, dq = \pi ab = 2\pi^2\nu ma^2. \tag{2.6}$$

This area is, thus, equal to the total energy W divided by ν, *i.e.*:

$$\text{Area of ellipse in } pq \text{ plane} = \frac{W}{\nu}. \tag{2.7}$$

Now Planck made the drastic assumption that the total energy W of the oscillator can take only integral values of energy $h\nu$:

$$W = nh\nu, \text{ where } n = 1, 2, 3, \cdots . \tag{2.8}$$

This quantum condition expressed in terms of the area of the ellipse in phase space becomes

$$\text{Area} = J = \oint p \, dq = nh. \tag{2.9}$$

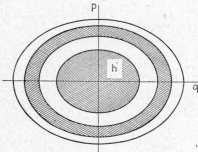

FIG. 2.2.—Phase-space diagram for a simple harmonic oscillator.

This last equation signifies that out of all the classically possible ellipses only certain discrete ones are allowed. These discrete "quantized" ellipses which represent quantized states of the linear oscillator are shown in Fig. 2.2.

According to Eq. (2.9) the total area of the first ellipse is h, the second $2h$, the third $3h$, etc., so that the area between any two consecutive ellipses is just h. The motion of the oscillator in any one of its quantized states is now represented by a graph point traversing one of the fixed ellipses in phase space. In the emission or absorption of radiation the graph point jumps to a smaller or larger ellipse with the simultaneous emission or absorption of a quantum of energy $h\nu$. The elliptic path traversed by the graph point in phase space is not to be confused with the actual path of the mass point.

With such a quantized oscillator Planck was able to derive (where the strictly classical laws of mechanics and the assumptions of statistical mechanics failed) a law of black-body radiation which agrees with experimental observations.

2.2. The Bohr Atom.—The announcement by Bohr[1] in the year 1913 of his theory for the hydrogen atom marks the beginning of a new era in spectroscopy and atomic structure.   Bohr not only gave a satisfactory account of the Balmer, Lyman, and Paschen series of hydrogen and the Pickering series of ionized helium but also calculated from purely theoretical considerations the value of the Rydberg constant.   More than this his theory gave a physical meaning to the experimental discovery that the frequency of a spectrum line is given by the difference between two terms.

Bohr adopted the theory of Rutherford[2] that an atom consists of a positively charged nucleus surrounded by a cluster of electrons.   Rutherford had just shown from experiments on large-angle scattering of α particles that each nucleus carries with it a charge that corresponds to a number of electrons approximately equal to the atomic number Z.   Making the assumption, following Rutherford, that *the number of electrons around the nucleus of a neutral atom is equal to the atomic number Z*, Bohr concluded that the hydrogen atom was made up of one electron, of charge $-e$, and one proton, of charge $+e = E$.

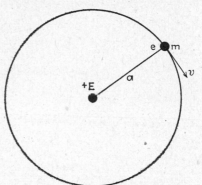

FIG. 2.3.—Bohr's atomic model.

Consider with Bohr then the simplest type of atomic system, *viz.*, that of a positively charged nucleus and an electron describing closed orbits around it.   Since the mass of the hydrogen nucleus M is approximately 2000 times the mass of the electron m, the motion will be approximately the same as the motion of an electron around a fixed central charge of infinite mass.

2.3. Bohr's First Assumption.—Bohr's first assumption was that *the electron moves in circular orbits about the nucleus under the action of a Coulomb field of force* (see Fig. 2.3).   The force of attraction between the electron of charge e and the nucleus of charge E will then be

$$F = \frac{eE}{a^2} = \frac{e^2 Z}{a^2},\qquad(2.10)$$

where a is the electron-nuclear distance, $E = Ze$, and Z is the atomic number; 1 for hydrogen, 2 for helium, *i.e.*, helium with one of its two

[1] BOHR, N., *Phil. Mag.*, **26**, 1, 476, 1913.
[2] RUTHERFORD, L. M., *Phil. Mag.*, **21**, 669, 1911.

electrons removed, 3 for doubly ionized lithium, *i.e.*, lithium with two of its three electrons removed, etc. This force is equal to the centripetal force mv^2/a, where v is the velocity and m the mass of the electron. For equilibrium conditions, then,

$$\frac{e^2Z}{a^2} = \frac{mv^2}{a},$$ (2.11)

from which

$$v^2 = \frac{e^2Z}{ma}.$$ (2.12)

The kinetic energy of the rotator becomes, therefore,

$$\text{K.E.} = \frac{1}{2}mv^2 = \frac{e^2Z}{2a} = T.$$ (2.13)

If the potential energy of the system is zero when the electron is infinitely far removed from the nucleus, then

$$\text{P.E.} = -\frac{e^2Z}{a} = -2T = V.$$ (2.14)

Now the total energy W is the sum of the kinetic energy T and the potential energy V so that, by adding Eqs. (2.13) and (2.14),

$$W = T + V = \frac{e^2Z}{2a} - \frac{e^2Z}{a} = -T.$$ (2.15)

For uniform circular motion the kinetic energy may also be written

$$T = \tfrac{1}{2}mv^2 = \tfrac{1}{2}ma^2\dot{\varphi}^2 = \tfrac{1}{2}ma^2(2\pi f)^2,$$ (2.16)

where $\dot{\varphi}$ is the angular velocity and f is the frequency of revolution.

From Eq. (2.13)

$$a = \frac{e^2Z}{2T},$$ (2.17)

which substituted in (2.16) gives

$$T = 2\pi^2 f^2 m\left(\frac{e^2Z}{2T}\right)^2.$$ (2.18)

One interesting result brought out in Eq. (2.15) is that the kinetic energy T taken with a negative sign is equal to the total energy W.

2.4. Bohr's Second Assumption.—Bohr's second assumption for the hydrogen atom may be stated as follows: *2π times the orbital angular momentum is equal to an integer times Planck's constant of action h.*

$$2\pi p_\varphi = 2\pi ma^2\dot{\varphi} = nh, \text{ where } n = 1, 2, 3, \cdots .$$ (2.19)

This assumption may be derived from Planck's quantum conditions for the harmonic oscillator by making the following substitutions: In

Bohr's rotator the angular displacement φ replaces the linear displacement q of the oscillator and the angular momentum $p_\varphi = ma\dot\varphi$ replaces the momentum $p = m\dot q$. Since the angular momentum is constant for circular motion the graph point in phase space always remains at a fixed distance from the φ axis. Now the quantum conditions are that *for one complete revolution of the electron the area under the graph-point curve in phase space is equal to an integer n times h* [see Eq. (2.9)]:

$$\text{Area} = J = \oint p_\varphi d\varphi = \int_0^{2\pi} p_\varphi d\varphi = nh. \quad (2.20)$$

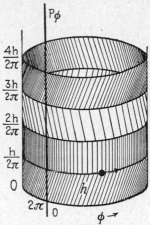

In making one complete revolution, the radius vector has turned through an angle $\varphi = 2\pi$. The phase-space diagram may therefore be represented in the form of a cylinder of circumference 2π (see Fig. 2.4) and the motion by a graph point moving with constant speed on one of the circles at a distance $nh/2\pi$ above the base of the cylinder. The area of each shaded section in the figure is equal to h. Carrying out the integration in Eq. (2.20) we obtain Bohr's second assumption, Eq. (2.19).

FIG. 2.4.—Phase-space diagram for Bohr's rotator.

Replacing $\dot\varphi$ in this equation by 2π times the frequency of revolution f, and multiplying through by f,

$$f = \frac{4\pi^2 f^2 m a^2}{nh}. \quad (2.21)$$

Substituting Eq. (2.16),

$$f = \frac{2T}{nh}. \quad (2.22)$$

Inserting this value of the frequency in Eq. (2.18), the kinetic energy

$$T = 2\pi^2 m \left(\frac{2T}{nh}\right)^2 \left(\frac{e^2 Z}{2T}\right)^2 = \frac{2\pi^2 m e^4 Z^2}{n^2 h^2} = -W. \quad (2.23)$$

The total energy of the rotator is thus *quantized* in that it is given only by integral values of the quantum number n.

It should be pointed out that contrary to the principles of classical electrodynamics, the electron in any one of its stationary orbits is not to be thought of as radiating but as continuing in the same state with the same energy.

2.5. Bohr's Third Assumption.—From Planck's quantum theory that radiation does not take place continuously but in quanta of energy, Bohr takes one more step and makes his third and, at the time, radical assumption that the *frequency of a spectrum line* $\bar{\nu}$ *is proportional to the difference between two energy states*, such that

$$h\bar{\nu} = W_2 - W_1 = T_1 - T_2, \qquad (2.24)$$

where the subscripts 2 and 1 denote the initial and final states, respectively, and h is Planck's constant of action.   With the energy expressed in terms of the kinetic energy, as it is in Eq. (2.23), the frequency becomes

$$\bar{\nu} = \frac{2\pi^2 m e^4 Z^2}{h^3}\left(\frac{1}{n_1^2} - \frac{1}{n_2^2}\right). \qquad (2.25)$$

While $\bar{\nu}$ represents the actual frequency of the radiation, *i.e.*, the number of waves in 2.99796×10^{10} cm, it is convenient in practice to express the frequency in wave numbers, *i.e.*, the number of waves in 1 cm.   The frequency in wave numbers ν is obtained by dividing $\bar{\nu}$ by the velocity of light c,

$$\nu = \frac{\bar{\nu}}{c} = \frac{1}{\lambda}, \qquad (2.26)$$

or by taking the reciprocal of the wave-length λ measured in centimeters. Expressed in wave numbers, Eq. (2.25) becomes

$$\nu = \frac{2\pi^2 m e^4 Z^2}{ch^3}\left(\frac{1}{n_1^2} - \frac{1}{n_2^2}\right) \qquad (2.27)$$

or, more briefly, by

$$\nu = RZ^2\left(\frac{1}{n_1^2} - \frac{1}{n_2^2}\right), \qquad (2.28)$$

where

$$R = \frac{2\pi^2 m e^4}{ch^3} \qquad (2.29)$$

is the Rydberg constant [see Eqs. (1.4) and (1.39)].

For hydrogen with $Z = 1$, Eq. (2.28) becomes identical with the experimental formula of Balmer for the hydrogen series, even to the value of the Rydberg constant.

2.6. Characteristics of the Bohr Circular Orbits.—Before going further, it will be of interest to determine some of the characteristics of Bohr's stationary states, as, for example, the radius of the circular orbits and the speed of the orbital electron.   From Eqs. (2.13) and (2.23)

$$\frac{e^2 Z}{2a} = \frac{2\pi^2 m e^4 Z^2}{n^2 h^2} \qquad (2.30)$$

which gives for the radius

$$a = \frac{h^2}{4\pi^2 m e^2} \cdot \frac{n^2}{Z}. \qquad (2.31)$$

Using the best known values of the physical constants,

$$m = 9.035 \times 10^{-28} \text{ g},$$
$$e = 4.770 \times 10^{-10} \text{ abs. e.s.u.,}$$
$$h = 6.547 \times 10^{-27} \text{ erg sec.,}$$

the values of a come out to be

$$a = 0.528 \times 10^{-8} \text{ cm} \times \frac{n^2}{Z} \tag{2.32}$$

The radius of the first Bohr orbit of hydrogen, $Z = 1$, $n = 1$, is therefore

$$a_1 = 0.528 \times 10^{-8} \text{ cm} = \frac{h^2}{4\pi^2 m e^2} \tag{2.33}$$

This gives the diameter of the hydrogen atom in the normal state $n = 1$, as about 1 Å, a value in good agreement with the value arrived at from

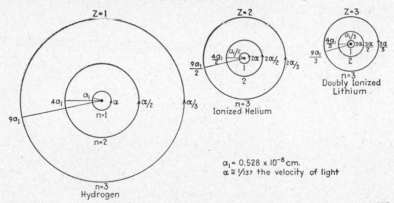

FIG. 2.5.—Relative sizes of the Bohr circular orbits for H I, He II, and Li III.

collision experiments. In general the radius of all orbits varies as n^2 and as $1/Z$. The first three orbits for (1) hydrogen $Z = 1$, (2) ionized helium $Z = 2$, and (3) doubly ionized lithium $Z = 3$ are shown in Fig. 2.5, drawn to the same scale. The helium atom with a nuclear charge $E = Ze = 2e$ and two orbital electrons is made hydrogen-like by removing one of its electrons. The resultant *ionized helium atom* is usually designated He II or He⁺. Similarly the lithium atom with a nuclear charge $E = Ze = 3e$ and three orbital electrons is made hydrogen-like by removing two of its electrons. The *doubly ionized lithium atom* is designated Li III or Li⁺⁺. (The number of plus signs in the one notation signifies the number of electrons missing, whereas the Roman numeral gives the effective nuclear charge in units of e in the other.)

The speed of the electron in its orbit is obtained directly from Eqs. (2.13) and (2.31):

$$v = \frac{2\pi e^2}{h} \cdot \frac{Z}{n} \tag{2.34}$$

As compared with the velocity of light c,

$$\frac{v}{c} = \frac{2\pi e^2}{ch} \cdot \frac{Z}{n} \qquad (2.35)$$

which for the first Bohr orbit of hydrogen gives

$$\frac{v}{c} = \alpha = \frac{2\pi e^2}{ch} = \frac{1}{137.29}. \qquad (2.36)$$

The constant α is Sommerfeld's fine-structure constant and, as we shall see later, is of importance in the study of the fine structure of the hydrogen series. Equation (2.34) shows that the speed of the electron varies as Z and as $1/n$.

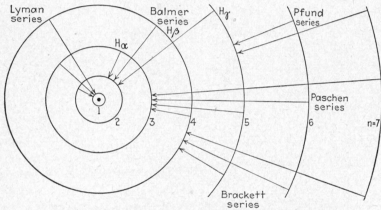

FIG. 2.6.—Bohr circular orbits of hydrogen showing series transitions.

2.7. Bohr Orbits and the Hydrogen Series.—With the Rydberg constant calculated from the best known values of e, h, c, and m, the chief series in hydrogen may be computed from Eq. (2.28). The Lyman series in the extreme ultra-violet is given by $n_1 = 1$ and $n_2 = 2, 3, 4, \cdots$, the Balmer series in the visible spectrum by $n_1 = 2$ and $n_2 = 3, 4, 5, \cdots$, the Paschen series in the near infra-red spectrum by $n_1 = 3$ and $n_2 = 4, 5, 6, \cdots$, etc.

The transition of an electron from any one of the excited states $n = 2, 3, 4, 5, \cdots$ to the first Bohr orbit $n = 1$ gives rise to a radiated spectrum line belonging to the Lyman series (see Fig. 2.6). The transition of an electron from any one of the excited states $n = 3, 4, 5, 6, \cdots$ to the second Bohr orbit $n = 2$ gives rise to a spectrum line belonging to the Balmer series, etc. (see Fig. 2.7.) Should an electron be excited by some means or other to the third Bohr orbit, it may return to the normal state $n = 1$ in one of two ways: either by two jumps $n = 3$ to $n = 2$ and then $n = 2$ to $n = 1$ with the emission of H_α and the first line of the Lyman series, or in one jump $n = 3$ to $n = 1$ with the emission of a single radiated frequency, the second member of the Lyman series. In either of the two processes here cited the total energy radiated is the same, hence the frequency radiated in the latter case is equal to the sum of the other two frequencies. When the electron is in its lowest possible energy state $n = 1$, it is said to be in the *normal state*.

The absorption of radiation by a hydrogen atom is the reverse of the process of emission and would be represented in Fig. 2.6 by the transition

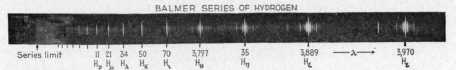

BALMER SERIES OF HYDROGEN

Series limit 11 21 34 50 70 3,797 35 3,889 —λ—→ 3,970
H_γ H_μ H_λ H_κ H_ι H_θ H_η H_ζ H_ε

FIG. 2.7.—Balmer series of hydrogen in emission. (*After Wood.*) (Each of the heavier lines shows grating ghosts.)

of the electron from the inner orbit to one of larger n. Absorption is thus a process by which atoms may be excited. It must be remembered that, while the kinetic energy increases with decreasing n, *i.e.*, smaller orbits, the total energy decreases [see Eq. (2.15)].

2.8. Series of Ionized Helium, He II (He⁺).—In the early development of atomic spectra the Pickering series, first discovered in the star ζ-Puppis by Pickering, was ascribed to some form of hydrogen. Owing to the excellent experimental work of Evans,[1] Fowler,[2] and Paschen[3] this series is now known to arise from ionized helium atoms. The experiments consisted of producing the Pickering series in pure helium and of showing that it was absent in pure hydrogen. One of the first outstanding successes of Bohr's orbital model was attributed to the accuracy with which Eq. (2.28) represented this one series.

With $Z = 2$ in Bohr's formula the Rydberg constant R is replaced by $4R$:

$$\nu = 4R\left(\frac{1}{n_1^2} - \frac{1}{n_2^2}\right). \qquad (2.36a)$$

With different values of n_1 and n_2 this formula represents all of the known series of ionized helium. The Pickering series is represented by $n_1 = 4$ and $n_2 = 5, 6, 7, \cdots$, while the so-called λ4686 series of Fowler is represented by $n_1 = 3$ and $n_2 = 4, 5, 6, \cdots$. Two other series have been found in the extreme ultra-violet spectrum of helium by Lyman.[4] These two series are given accurately by $n_1 = 2$ and by $n_1 = 1$, n_2 taking running values 3, 4, 5, . . . and 2, 3, 4, . . . , respectively. A photograph of the latter series is shown in Fig. 2.7a.

[1] EVANS, E. J., *Phil. Mag.*, **29**, 284, 1915.
[2] FOWLER, A., *Proc. Roy. Soc.*, **90**, 426, 1914.
[3] PASCHEN, F., *Ann. d. Phys.*, **50**, 901, 1916.
[4] LYMAN, T., *Astrophys. Jour.*, **23**, 181, 1906; **43**, 89, 1916.

2.9. Series of Doubly Ionized Lithium, Li III (Li⁺⁺) and Triply Ionized Beryllium, Be IV (Be⁺⁺⁺).—Lithium, atomic number $Z = 3$, next follows helium in the periodic table with three orbital electrons. By doubly ionizing the atom of lithium a structure is left which is hydrogen-like, *i.e.*, it has but one electron and a nucleus. With a nuclear charge

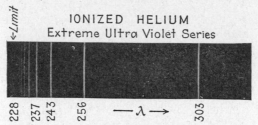

Fig. 2.7a.—Lyman series of ionized helium.   (*After Kruger.*)

three times that of the hydrogen atom, the Rydberg constant R of Eq. (2.28) must be replaced by $9R$, giving for all Li III series,

$$\nu = 9R\left(\frac{1}{n_1^2} - \frac{1}{n_2^2}\right). \qquad (2.37)$$

Beryllium, $Z = 4$, the fourth element in the periodic table is made hydrogen-like by triply ionizing the atom, *i.e.*, by removing three of its four electrons. Bohr's formula for Be IV becomes therefore

$$\nu = 16R\left(\frac{1}{n_1^2} - \frac{1}{n_2^2}\right). \qquad (2.38)$$

Placing $n_1 = 1$ and $n_2 = 2, 3, 4, \cdots$, Eqs. (2.37) and (2.38) represent extreme ultra-violet series of Li III and Be IV, the first members of which have been found by Ericson and Edlen[1] at $\lambda 135.02$Å and $\lambda 75.94$Å. respectively.

2.10. Energy Level Diagrams.—In attempting to represent the stationary states of an atom and the particular transitions giving rise to series lines, as was done in Fig. 2.6, certain difficulties arise, *viz.*, orbits with large n values, higher series members, and series limits cannot be shown. In order to incorporate these latter features into the same atomic picture, energy level diagrams are frequently drawn (see Fig. 2.8).

In an energy level diagram each Bohr orbit, or stationary state, is represented by a horizontal line plotted to an energy scale. Instead of plotting the energy directly it is customary to plot something which is proportional to it, W divided by Planck's constant h and the velocity of light c. In this way the difference between any two levels gives directly the frequency of the radiation in wave numbers, *i.e.*, in cm⁻¹. Since the energies of the quantized states are negative in value [see Eq. (2.15)] and approach zero as $n \rightarrow \infty$, the zero of energy (n infinite) is drawn at the top

---

[1] Ericson, A., and B. Edlen, *Zeits. f. Phys.*, **59**, 679, 1930.

of the figure and the other states below.   In Fig. 2.8 energy level diagrams for hydrogen and ionized helium are drawn to the same scale.   The first few members of each of the various series are also indicated.   It should be noted that each member of the Balmer series and alternate members of the Pickering series apparently have the same energy transitions.

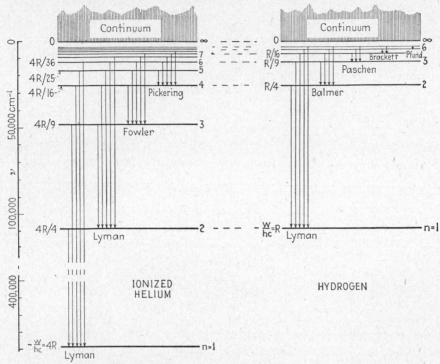

FIG. 2.8.—Energy level diagrams of hydrogen and ionized helium.

2.11. Unquantized States and Continuous Spectra.—Soon after Bohr put forward his famous theory of the hydrogen atom it became apparent that there might also be orbits with positive energy that are not quantized. That such states should exist is shown experimentally by the observation of a continuous band of radiation starting at the series limit of the Balmer series of hydrogen and extending some little distance to shorter wavelengths, *i.e.*, to higher frequencies.   These new unquantized orbits take the form of *hyperbolas* and are analogous to the paths taken by certain comets known to have passed near to our own sun never to return again. From classical electrodynamics it is readily shown that an electron moving about a nucleus in such an hyperbolic path (see Fig. 2.9) has a positive energy.   The positive energy only means that, before the approaching electron comes under the influence of the nucleus, the potential energy $V = e^2 Z/a$ is zero, and that the kinetic energy

$$T = \tfrac{1}{2}mv^2 \tag{2.39}$$

is positive.   As before, m and v are the mass and velocity of the electron, e its charge, and $Ze = E$, the nuclear charge with a the electron-nuclear distance.   The total energy of the electron at any point in its path will be

$$W = T + V = \frac{1}{2}mv^2 - \frac{e^2Z}{a}.$$ (2.40)

If at any time the electron jumps to one of the quantized Bohr orbits, energy of frequency $\bar{\nu}$, given by the difference in energy between the initial and final states, will be radiated:

$$h\bar{\nu} = \frac{1}{2}mv^2 - \frac{e^2Z}{a} + \frac{2\pi^2me^4Z^2}{n^2h^2}.$$ (2.41)

The frequency of this radiation will be greater than any frequency arising from transitions starting from any of the quantized states and

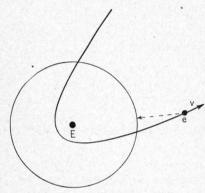

ending on the final quantized state of the series in question.   In other words, the spectrum line will lie beyond the series limit.   Since v and a take values that vary continuously through all values, the spectrum beyond the series limit will not be discontinuous but spread out into a continuous band.   In the energy level diagrams of hydrogen and ionized helium (Fig. 2.8), the continuum of energy levels is shown as starting at the series limit and extend-

Fig. 2.9.—Non-quantized orbits on the ing upward.   In this diagram, transi-
Bohr model of hydrogen.

tions may also be shown starting from any point in the continuum and ending on any of the quantized states.

2.12. The So-called "Reduced Mass" of the Electron.—In deriving all of the above equations for the Bohr orbits, or stationary states, it has been assumed that the electron of mass m rotates about a nucleus of infinite mass, *i.e.*, a stationary nucleus.   Before going further, let us consider the finite mass of the nucleus and determine its effect upon Bohr's fundamental results.   It may be shown from elementary principles of classical mechanics that the preceding equations will apply to two masses m and M rotating about their center of mass, if m be replaced by

$$\frac{mM}{m + M} = \frac{m}{1 + \dfrac{m}{M}} = \mu.$$ (2.42)

μ is called the *reduced mass* and approaches m as $M \to \infty$.

If M_p represents one-sixteenth the mass of an oxygen atom and A the atomic weight, then, to a first approximation, we may write, for any nucleus,

$$M = A \cdot M_p; \tag{2.43}$$

and, for the reduced mass,

$$\mu = \frac{m}{1 + \dfrac{m}{AM_p}}. \tag{2.44}$$

Making this substitution for the mass m in Bohr's formula, Eq. (2.27),

$$\nu = \frac{2\pi^2 me^4 Z^2}{ch^3\left(1 + \dfrac{m}{AM_p}\right)}\left(\frac{1}{n_1^2} - \frac{1}{n_2^2}\right) \tag{2.45}$$

and the Rydberg constant becomes

$$R_A = \frac{2\pi^2 me^4}{ch^3\left(1 + \dfrac{m}{AM_p}\right)} = \frac{R_\infty}{1 + \dfrac{m}{AM_p}}, \tag{2.46}$$

where R_∞ is the value of R_A for infinite mass, *i.e.*, A is infinite.

The last equation shows that the Rydberg constant is not exactly the same for all atomic nuclei. It should be made clear that the quantum conditions applied to the angular momentum of the electron in Eq. (2.19) are now applied to the atomic system, electron plus nucleus, as a whole. For convenience, however, we shall continue to speak of the quantum number n as though it were the quantum number of the electron alone.

2.13. Variation of the Rydberg Constant.—Assuming that the Rydberg constant R is exactly the same for both hydrogen and ionized helium, Eqs. (2.28) and (2.36) show that alternate members of the Pickering series ($n_2 = 6, 8, 10, \cdots$) coincide with members ($n_2 = 3, 4, 5, \cdots$) of the

TABLE 2.1.—WAVE-LENGTHS OF THE BALMER AND PICKERING SERIES
(*After Paschen*)

He II		H		$\Delta\lambda$ diff.
n_2	λ_{air}	n_2	λ_{air}	
6	6560.19	3	6562.80	2.61
7	5411.60			
8	4859.40	4	4861.38	1.98
9	4541.66			
10	4338.74	5	4340.51	1.77
11	4199.90			
12	4100.10	6	4101.78	1.68

Balmer series.   A careful experimental investigation of these lines by
Paschen has shown that the Balmer lines are not exactly coincident with
alternate lines of the Pickering series but are displaced by small intervals
to longer wave-lengths.   Paschen's measurements are given in Table 2.1
and shown graphically in Fig. 2.10.

If the frequency differences between corresponding lines are studied
(instead of $\Delta\lambda$), it is found that the series limits of the two elements must
differ by about 11 wave numbers.   This means that the Rydberg con-
stant for He II is about four times 11 cm^{-1}, or 44 cm^{-1} larger than it is
for hydrogen.   This result is in excellent agreement with theoretical
values obtained from Eq. (2.45).   Owing to the fact that the calculation
of R from theory involves knowing accurate values of the physical
constants, it is better to measure the wave-lengths of the hydrogen and

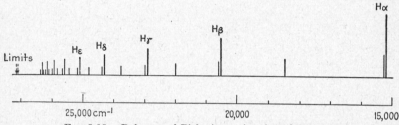

Fig. 2.10.—Balmer and Pickering series plotted together.

helium lines and from these to calculate directly the Rydberg constant.
Thus determined, the Rydberg constant furnishes one of the best relations
used in determining most probable values of the physical constants.

The most accurate spectroscopic measurements on hydrogen and
ionized helium have been made by Houston.[1]   Using Eq. (2.45) he
obtains

$$R_1 = 109677.759 \text{ cm}^{-1}, \tag{2.47}$$

and for ionized helium,

$$R_4 = 109722.403 \text{ cm}^{-1}. \tag{2.48}$$

From Eq. 2.46,

$$R_\infty = R_1\left(1 + \frac{m}{M_p}\right) = R_4\left(1 + \frac{m}{4M_p}\right). \tag{2.49}$$

Using Houston's values of R_1 and R_4, Birge[2] obtains, as the most probable
value of R_∞,

$$R_\infty = 109737.424 \text{ cm}^{-1}. \tag{2.50}$$

Values of the Rydberg constant, based upon this value of R_∞, are
given in Table 2.2 for a number of the lighter elements.   The variation

[1] Houston, W. V., Phys. Rev., **30**, 608, 1927.

[2] Birge, R. T., Phys. Rev., Supplement, **1**, 1, 1929.

of R_A with the atomic weight A is best seen from the graph, Fig. 2.11. The greatest change in R_A occurs between H^1 and H^2. In computing the positions of series lines for all hydrogen-like atoms H^1, H^2, He II, Li III, Be IV, etc., the respective constants R_1, R_2, R_4, R_7, R_9, etc., should be used. This is exemplified by the photograph of the Lyman series

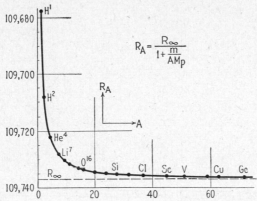

FIG. 2.11.—Variation of the Rydberg constant R as a function of the atomic weight A.

of the two hydrogen isotopes in Fig. 2.12. Photographs similar to those of the Balmer series lines were first used to detect the presence of this newly discovered isotope by Urey, Brickwedde, and Murphy.[1] It is of interest to observe (see Fig. 2.11) that the ratio between the difference

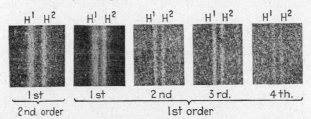

FIG. 2.12.—Photographs of the first four members of the Lyman series of the two hydrogen atoms, H^1 and H^2. (*After Ballard and White.*)

$R_\infty - R_1$ and the difference $R_\infty - R_A$ is approximately equal to the atomic weight A.

$$\frac{R_\infty - R_1}{R_\infty - R_A} = \frac{AM_p + m}{M_p + m} \cong A. \tag{2.51}$$

In passing, it should be mentioned that for atomic systems containing more than one electron the refinement in the Rydberg constant is not necessary in representing observed series. For these heavier elements it is recommended that R_∞ be used for all series and the refinements be taken care of by the constants in the Rydberg denominator [see Eq. (1.22)].

[1] UREY, H. C., F. G. BRICKWEDDE, and G. M. MURPHY, *Phys. Rev.*, **40**, 1, 1932.

Table 2.2.—Variation of the Rydberg Constant with Atomic Number

Z	Element	Atomic weight A	R_A	$R_\infty - R_A$
1	H¹	1.007	109677.759	59.665
1	H²	2.00	109707.387	30.037
2	He	4.00	109722.403	15.021
3	Li	7	109728.84	8.58
4	Be	9	109730.74	6.68
5	B	11	109731.96	5.46
8	O	16	109733.66	3.76
10	Ne	20	109734.42	3.00
21	Sc	45	109736.08	1.34
33	As	75	109736.62	0.80
∞	..	∞	109737.424	0.00

2.14. Bohr's Correspondence Theorem.—According to Planck's original quantum hypothesis, an oscillator emits only radiation of a particular frequency, *viz.*, the frequency of the oscillator itself. According to Bohr's theory of the hydrogen atom, the frequency of radiation emitted or absorbed is not equal to the frequency of the rotator in one of its stationary orbits but a frequency determined by the difference in energy between two orbital states [see Eq. (2.24)]. Attempts to find a correlation between the classical frequency of revolution in the different electron orbits and the quantum frequency of energy emission have led to Bohr's correspondence theorem. A rather brief but elementary treatment of this theorem is not out of place here.[1]

Referring to Eqs. (2.22), (2.23), and (2.29), the classical frequency of the revolution in an orbit is given by

$$f = \frac{2T}{nh} = \frac{4\pi^2 m e^4 Z^2}{n^3 h^3} = \frac{2RcZ^2}{n^3}, \qquad (2.52)$$

where R is the Rydberg constant, c the velocity of light, n the quantum number, and Z the nuclear charge in units of e. Turning now to Eqs. (2.24) and (2.25), a radiated frequency on the quantum theory is given by

$$\bar\nu = \frac{T_1 - T_2}{h} = \frac{2\pi^2 m e^4 Z^2}{h^3}\left(\frac{1}{n_1^2} - \frac{1}{n_2^2}\right) = RcZ^2\left(\frac{1}{n_1^2} - \frac{1}{n_2^2}\right). \qquad (2.53)$$

This may be written in the form

$$\bar\nu = RcZ^2\left(\frac{(n_2 - n_1)(n_1 + n_2)}{n_1^2 n_2^2}\right). \qquad (2.54)$$

[1] For a more complete treatment of Bohr's correspondence theorem see Van Vleck, "Quantum Principles and Line Spectra," *Nat. Research Council, Bull.*, 1926.

If we now consider transitions where $\Delta n = n_2 - n_1 = 1$, and where n_1 is very large, we get, asymptotically,

$$\bar{\nu} = \frac{2RcZ^2}{n_1^3} = \frac{2RcZ^2}{n_2^3} = f. \tag{2.55}$$

Thus, for very large quantum numbers n, the quantum-theory frequency and the classical orbit frequency become equal, a remarkable and important result.

If we now allow transitions in which $\Delta n > 1$ and $n >> \Delta n$, the frequency $\bar{\nu}$, using Eq. (2.54), is as follows:

$$\bar{\nu} = \frac{2RcZ^2}{n_1^3}\Delta n = \frac{2RcZ^2}{n_2^3}\Delta n = f \cdot \Delta n. \tag{2.56}$$

This general result shows that the quantum-theory frequencies correspond to the fundamental classical frequencies f, or to their harmonics $2f$, $3f$, $4f$, etc.

We shall now derive these same relations in a little different fashion. From Eq. (2.20) we first write down the phase integral for the quantum number n,

$$J = \oint p_\varphi d\varphi = nh. \tag{2.57}$$

It follows from this equation that the difference in J for two states is given by

$$\Delta J = \Delta n \cdot h. \tag{2.58}$$

Since, from Eq. (2.24), $h\bar{\nu} = W_2 - W_1 = \Delta W$, the quantum frequency

$$\bar{\nu} = \frac{\Delta W}{\Delta J}\Delta n. \tag{2.59}$$

Moreover, with $W = -RcZ^2h/n^2$, the classical frequency from Eq. (2.52) becomes, in differential form,

$$f = \frac{1}{h} \cdot \frac{dW}{dn} = \frac{dW}{dJ}, \tag{2.60}$$

or, from Eq. (2.56),

$$\bar{\nu} = \frac{dW}{dJ}\Delta n. \tag{2.61}$$

Thus the difference between the quantum-theory frequency and the classical frequency is just that between the difference quotient $\Delta W/\Delta J$ and the differential quotient dW/dJ. Graphical representations of these frequencies are shown in Fig. 2.13. The energy levels W of hydrogen are plotted in Fig. 2.13 as a function of the phase integral $J = nh$. The slope of the secant $\Delta W/\Delta J$ represents the frequency of the first line of the Balmer series, whereas the two tangent lines give the slope dW/dJ, the classical frequencies at the end points. As we go to higher and higher n values, the slopes of these lines, and hence the frequencies, become more nearly the same.

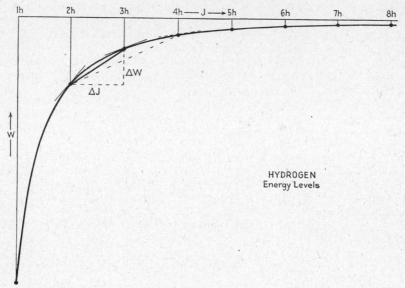

Fig. 2.13.—Graphical representation of Bohr's correspondence theorem.

Using Eqs. (2.52) and (2.53), the classical and quantum-theory frequencies of hydrogen for a few sample cases have been calculated and given in Table 2.3. Just as in Fig. 2.13, the quantum-theory frequency always lies between the initial and final revolution frequencies and at the same time approaches both of the latter asymptotically.

TABLE 2.3.—Asymptotic Approach of the Quantum-theory Frequencies to the Classical Frequency

Initial quantum state	Final quantum state	Initial orbit frequency	Quantum-theory frequency	Final orbit frequency
$n = 2$	$n = 1$	$0.82 \times 10^{15} \text{sec.}^{-1}$	2.47×10^{15}	6.58×10^{15}
6	5	3.04×10^{13}	4.02×10^{13}	5.26×10^{13}
10	9	6.58×10^{12}	7.71×10^{12}	9.02×10^{12}
25	24	4.21×10^{11}	4.48×10^{11}	4.76×10^{11}
101	100	6.383×10^{9}	6.479×10^{9}	6.576×10^{9}
501	500	5.229×10^{7}	5.245×10^{7}	5.261×10^{7}

A comparison of two quantum jumps $\Delta n = 2$ shown by the dotted secant in Fig. 2.13, with the classical orbit frequencies at both end points, may also be made by use of Eqs. (2.52), (2.53), and (2.61). In this case the first harmonic of the classical frequency, *i.e.*, $2f$, is to be compared with the spectral frequency.

Problems

1. As many as 33 members of the Balmer series of hydrogen have been observed in the spectrum of certain stars (see Fig. 1.5). What is the diameter of the hydrogen atom, *i.e.*, the orbit diameter, when the electron is in the orbit $n = 35$?

2. Find the velocity of the electron in Prob. 1.

3. Assuming the nucleus of the hydrogen isotope H^2 to have twice the mass of the chief isotope H^1, compute the wave-length interval between the two lines comprising the second member of the Lyman series.

4. If the measured wave-length of the first Balmer series line of hydrogen is $\lambda_{vac} = 6564.685$ Å, and the first line of the Lyman series in ionized helium is $\lambda_{vac} = 303.797$ Å, what is the average value of the Rydberg constant for infinite mass? Assume the mass of the proton to be 1840 times the mass of the electron.

5. Compute the revolution frequency of the electron in the first 10 orbits of hydrogen, and the quantum-theory frequency for transitions between the same orbits for $\Delta n = 1$. Plot frequency-difference curves $\nu_1 - f$ and $f - \nu_2$ as a function of the quantum number n to show that the quantum frequencies approach the classical revolution frequencies.

6. Using Eqs. (2.22) and (2.23), derive an expression for the period of the electron in its orbit.

CHAPTER III

SOMMERFELD'S ELLIPTIC ORBITS AND SPACE QUANTIZATION

Soon after Bohr put forward his famous theory of the hydrogen atom Sommerfeld[1] extended the model so as to include elliptic orbits. The importance of this extension may be attributed directly to the accuracy with which his resultant equations, with suitable relativity corrections, account for the fine structure of the energy levels and spectrum lines in hydrogen and hydrogen-like atoms.

In order to quantize any proposed atomic system Wilson[2] and Sommerfeld postulated, about the same time and quite independently, that each degree of freedom must be quantized separately. In other words each degree of freedom should be fixed by its own separate quantum number.

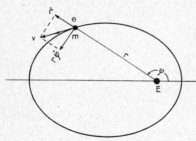

FIG. 3.1.—Elliptic orbit.

3.1. Two Degrees of Freedom.— Following Sommerfeld, the motion of an electron in an elliptic orbit, with the nucleus at one focus, presents a system with two degrees of freedom and hence two quantum conditions. In polar coordinates the position of the electron is given by the azimuth angle φ (see Fig. 3.1) and the electron-nuclear distance r. Assuming that the potential energy is zero when the electron is removed to infinity,

$$V = -\frac{eE}{r} = -\frac{e^2 Z}{r}, \tag{3.1}$$

where e and E are the charges on the electron and nucleus, respectively, and Z is the atomic number. The kinetic energy is given by

$$T = \tfrac{1}{2}mv^2 = \tfrac{1}{2}m(\dot{r}^2 + r^2\dot{\varphi}^2) = \tfrac{1}{2}m\dot{r}^2 + \tfrac{1}{2}mr^2\dot{\varphi}^2. \tag{3.2}$$

These equations involve two displacement coordinates, φ and r, and two momentum coordinates,

$$p_\varphi = mr^2\dot{\varphi} \quad \text{and} \quad p_r = m\dot{r}. \tag{3.3}$$

Corresponding to these two degrees of freedom two phase-space diagrams (see Figs. 2.4 and 3.3) can be drawn in such a way that the

[1] SOMMERFELD, A., *Ann. d. Phys.*, **51**, 1, 1916.
[2] WILSON, W., *Phil. Mag.*, **29**, 795, 1915.

motion of the electron is represented by two graph points, one moving on one diagram and one on the other. Applying the quantum conditions [see Eq. (2.9)] to these two degrees of freedom,

$$\oint p_\varphi d\varphi = kh \qquad (3.4)$$

and

$$\oint p_r dr = rh, \qquad (3.5)$$

where k and r take integral values only and are called the *azimuthal* and *radial quantum numbers*, respectively.

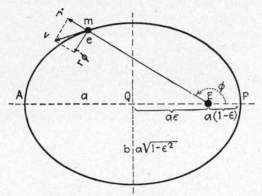

Fig. 3.2.—Elliptic orbit.

According to Kepler's second law of planetary motion the angular momentum p_φ remains constant throughout the motion so that the first integral is readily evaluated. Integrating over a complete cycle,

$$\int_0^{2\pi} p_\varphi d\varphi = 2\pi p_\varphi = 2\pi m r^2 \dot\varphi = kh. \qquad (3.6)$$

This result is identical with Bohr's quantum conditions for circular orbits [Eq. (2.20)]. The quantized angular momentum for elliptic orbits may therefore be represented by a graph point traversing one of the paths in the phase space given for circular orbits in Fig. 2.4.

3.2. The Radial Quantum Number.—In order to quantize the radial motion of the electron the left-hand side of Eq. (3.5) must be evaluated. The object of this section is to present Sommerfeld's method of evaluating this integral. The starting point is the general equation of an ellipse in polar coordinates,

$$\frac{1}{r} = C_1 + C_2 \cos \varphi, \qquad (3.7)$$

where C_1 and C_2 are constants to be determined for every ellipse. If the eccentricity ϵ of an ellipse (see Fig. 3.2) is defined as the ratio EQ/a, where a is the semimajor axis, then

$$EQ = a\epsilon. \qquad (3.8)$$

In terms of the eccentricity ϵ, it is readily shown that the perihelion distance EP, the aphelion distance EA, and the semiminor axis b become:

$$\left.\begin{array}{l} \text{Perihelion } EP = a(1 - \epsilon). \\ \text{Aphelion } EA = a(1 + \epsilon). \\ \text{Semiminor axis } b = a\sqrt{1 - \epsilon^2}. \end{array}\right\} \tag{3.9}$$

With the electron at perihelion, $\varphi = 0$, Eq. (3.7) becomes

$$\frac{1}{a(1 - \epsilon)} = C_1 + C_2 \tag{3.10}$$

while at aphelion, $\varphi = \pi$, Eq. (3.7) becomes

$$\frac{1}{a(1 + \epsilon)} = C_1 - C_2. \tag{3.11}$$

With these two equations, C_1 and C_2 can be evaluated

$$C_1 = \frac{1}{a(1 - \epsilon^2)} \quad \text{and} \quad C_2 = \frac{\epsilon}{a(1 - \epsilon^2)}, \tag{3.12}$$

and the equation of the ellipse written

$$\frac{1}{r} = \frac{1 + \epsilon \cos \varphi}{a(1 - \epsilon^2)}. \tag{3.13}$$

Taking the log of each side of this equation and differentiating, we get

$$\frac{1}{r}\frac{dr}{d\varphi} = \frac{\epsilon \sin \varphi}{1 + \epsilon \cos \varphi}. \tag{3.14}$$

Remembering that $p_\varphi = mr^2\dot{\varphi}$,

$$p_r = m\dot{r} = m\frac{dr}{d\varphi}\dot{\varphi} = \frac{p_\varphi}{r^2}\frac{dr}{d\varphi}. \tag{3.15}$$

Since

$$dr = \frac{dr}{d\varphi}d\varphi, \tag{3.16}$$

one obtains

$$p_r dr = p_\varphi \frac{1}{r^2}\left(\frac{dr}{d\varphi}\right)^2 d\varphi = p_\varphi \epsilon^2 \frac{\sin^2 \varphi}{(1 + \epsilon \cos \varphi)^2}d\varphi. \tag{3.17}$$

The phase integral, Eq. (3.5), now becomes

$$\oint p_r dr = p_\varphi \epsilon^2 \int_0^{2\pi} \frac{\sin^2 \varphi}{(1 + \epsilon \cos \varphi)^2}d\varphi = rh. \tag{3.18}$$

Now, from Eq. (3.6),

$$p_\varphi = \frac{kh}{2\pi}, \tag{3.19}$$

so that

$$\frac{\epsilon^2}{2\pi}\int^{2\pi}\frac{\sin^2\varphi}{(1+\epsilon\cos\varphi)^2}d\varphi = \frac{r}{k}. \qquad (3.20)$$

Integrating by parts, we get

$$\frac{1}{\sqrt{1-\epsilon^2}} - 1 = \frac{r}{k} \qquad (3.21)$$

which upon transposing and squaring becomes, from the definition of the semiminor axis [Eq. (3.9)],

$$1 - \epsilon^2 = \frac{k^2}{(k+r)^2} = \frac{b^2}{a^2}. \qquad (3.22)$$

Since k and r take integral values only, we may write

$$k + r = n, \qquad \text{where } n = 1, 2, 3, \cdots \qquad (3.23)$$

is the so-called *total quantum number.*

In terms of this new quantum number n, Eq. (3.22) leads to the very interesting and simple result that

$$\frac{k}{n} = \frac{b}{a}. \qquad (3.24)$$

Out of all the classically possible ellipses the quantum conditions allow only those for which the ratio of the major and minor axes is that of two integers, *viz.*, the quantum numbers n and k.

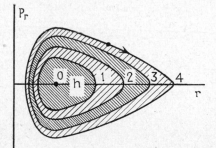

Fig. 3.3.—Phase-space diagram for the radial motion.

The radial motion of the electron may be represented by a graph point traversing one of the curves in the phase space shown in Fig. 3.3.

3.3. The Total Energy W.—The total energy of each stationary state has yet to be calculated. From Eqs. (3.1) and (3.2),

$$W = T + V = \frac{1}{2}m\dot{r}^2 + \frac{1}{2}mr^2\dot{\varphi}^2 - \frac{e^2Z}{r} \qquad (3.25)$$

which in terms of p_r and p_φ [Eqs. (3.3) and (3.15)] gives

$$W = \frac{1}{2m}\left(p_r^2 + \frac{p_\varphi^2}{r^2}\right) - \frac{e^2Z}{r}, \qquad (3.26)$$

$$W = \frac{p_\varphi}{2mr^2}\left[\left(\frac{1}{r}\frac{dr}{d\varphi}\right)^2 + 1\right] - \frac{e^2Z}{r}. \qquad (3.27)$$

By direct substitution of Eqs. (3.13) and (3.14),

$$W = \frac{p_\varphi}{ma^2(1-\epsilon^2)^2}\left(\frac{1+\epsilon^2}{2} + \epsilon\cos\varphi\right) - \frac{e^2Z(1+\epsilon\cos\varphi)}{a(1-\epsilon^2)}. \qquad (3.28)$$

For a conservative system the total energy is constant and is independent of the time and of the angle φ. Since the total energy is constant and $\cos \varphi$ varies, the coefficient of $\epsilon \cos \varphi$ must vanish. Collecting terms in $\epsilon \cos \varphi$ and equating to zero,

$$\epsilon \cos \varphi\left(\frac{p_\varphi}{ma^2(1 - \epsilon^2)^2} - \frac{e^2Z}{a(1 - \epsilon^2)}\right) = 0. \tag{3.29}$$

This gives

$$\frac{p_\varphi}{ma^2(1 - \epsilon^2)^2} = \frac{e^2Z}{a(1 - \epsilon^2)} \tag{3.30}$$

from which

$$a = \frac{p_\varphi}{me^2Z(1 - \epsilon^2)}. \tag{3.31}$$

With the values of p_φ and $1 - \epsilon^2$ from Eqs. (3.6) and (3.22), respectively, the semimajor axis

$$a = \frac{h^2}{4\pi^2me^2Z}(k + r)^2 = a_1\frac{n^2}{Z}, \tag{3.32}$$

and with Eq. (3.9) the semiminor axis

$$b = \frac{h^2}{4\pi^2me^2Z}k(k + r) = a_1\frac{kn}{Z}. \tag{3.33}$$

Here a_1 is the radius of the first Bohr circular orbit [see Eq. (2.33)], and n is the total quantum number.

With the value of a from Eq. (3.31), the total energy [Eq. (3.28)] becomes

$$W = \frac{e^2Z}{a(1 - \epsilon^2)}\left\{\frac{1 + \epsilon^2}{2} - 1\right\} = -\frac{e^2Z}{2a}. \tag{3.34}$$

Substituting a from Eq. 3.32,

$$W = -\frac{2\pi^2me^4Z^2}{h^2(k + r)^2} = -\frac{2\pi^2me^4Z^2}{h^2n^2}, \tag{3.35}$$

This equation is of particular interest in that the energy is exactly the same as that obtained by Bohr for circular orbits [see Eq. (2.23)].

3.4. General Characteristics of Sommerfeld's Elliptic Orbits.—While the introduction of elliptic orbits has thus far introduced no new energy states for the hydrogen atom, the electron may now move in different orbits. For any given value of the energy, corresponding to the *total* quantum number n, there are n different quantized orbits for the electron. If, for example, $n = 5$, the *azimuthal* quantum number k may take on one of the five values 1, 2, 3, 4, or 5, while the *radial* quantum number r takes on the values 4, 3, 2, 1, or 0, respectively. A study of the possibility

of states with $k = 0$ shows that the ellipse reduces to motion along a
straight line with the nucleus at one end.   Sommerfeld therefore excluded
such states on the grounds that the electron would collide with the
nucleus.   As the quantum mechanics leads to a model of hydrogen-like
atoms which possess features that can be described in terms of elliptic
orbits, the size and shape of Sommerfeld's electron orbits are of interest
and will be given here in somewhat more detail.

From Eqs. (3.32) and (3.33) it is seen that the semimajor axis a
is proportional to n^2, and to $1/Z$, and the semiminor axis b is proportional

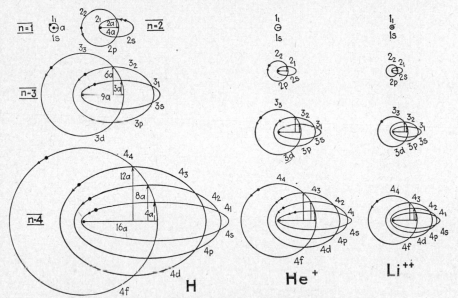

FIG. 3.4.—Relative dimensions of the Sommerfeld elliptic orbits.

to nk, and to $1/Z$.   Starting with the smallest orbits of hydrogen with
$Z = 1$, ionized helium with $Z = 2$, doubly ionized lithium with $Z = 3$,
etc., we place $n = 1$, $k = 1$ and $r = 0$.   These are circles of radius
a_1, $a_1/2$, $a_1/3$, etc., shown at the top of Fig. 3.4, and are exactly the same
as Bohr's circular orbits.   With $n = 2$ there are two possibilities for
each atom, $k = 2$, $r = 0$ and $k = 1$, $r = 1$.   The first set of quantum
numbers gives Bohr's circular orbits of radius $4a_1$, $4a_1/2$, $4a_1/3$, etc.,
and the second set gives elliptic orbits with semimajor axes the same
as for the circles, $4a_1$, $4a_1/2$, $4a_1/3$, etc., and semiminor axes $2a_1$, $2a_1/2$,
$2a_1/3$, etc.

For the next higher states of H, He II, Li III, etc., with $n = 3$, there
are three types of orbits possible, $k = 3$, $r = 0$; $k = 2$, $r = 1$; and $k = 1$,
$r = 2$.   The first set gives Bohr's circular orbits of radius $9a_1$, $9a_1/2$,
$9a_1/3$, etc.   The second set ($k = 2$, $r = 1$) gives elliptic orbits with
semimajor axes the same as for the circles and semiminor axes two-thirds

as large.   The third set ($k = 1$, $r = 2$) gives elliptic orbits with semi-major axes the same as for the circles but with semiminor axes one-third as large.   In general, a and b vary as the reciprocal of the atomic number Z, *i.e.*, as $1/Z$, so that by reducing the hydrogen orbits (Fig. 3.4) to one-half and one-third their dimensions they become identical with the orbits of He II and Li III, respectively.

According to the relation $n = k + r$, each quantized orbit is determined by two out of the three quantum numbers n, k, and r.   It is customary to define each quantized state by giving the total quantum number n and the azimuthal quantum number k.   As will be seen in the following chapters, the radial quantum number is generally not used. In the literature two systems of notation for n and k are found to be in general use.   According to the one system, the numerical value of k is given as a subscript of the numerical value of n.   For example, the state $n = 3$, $k = 2$ is written 3_2.   A later and now more widely used notation is one in which the numerical value of n is followed by one of the letters s, p, d, f, g, h, etc., representing the azimuthal quantum numbers 1, 2, 3, 4, 5, 6, etc., respectively.   The state $n = 4$, $k = 2$, for example, is designated $4p$ (see Table 3.1).

TABLE 3.1.—ELECTRON-ORBIT NOTATION

	$n = 1$	$n = 2$	$n = 3$	$n = 4$
n_k	1_1	2_1 2_2	3_1 3_2 3_3	4_1 4_2 4_3 4_4
nk	$1s$	$2s$ $2p$	$3s$ $3p$ $3d$	$4s$ $4p$ $4d$ $4f$

The origin of the letters s, p, d, and f goes back to the discovery of *sharp, principal, diffuse,* and *fundamental* series, in the alkali spectra, and to the designation of such series by Rydberg formulas.   These have been treated at some length in Chap. I.

It is convenient to remember that, for a given n it is the s orbit which comes closest to, and recedes farthest from, the nucleus, *i.e.*, it is the most elliptic of any family of orbits having the same major axis.   Next in eccentricity come the p electron orbits with $k = 2$, followed by d electrons with $k = 3$, f electrons with $k = 4$, etc.

3.5. Space Quantization.—Up to this point the motion of a single electron of a hydrogen-like atom has been confined to two degrees of freedom.   In this special case an electron orbit or energy state is determined by two of the three quantum numbers n, k, and r.   As a more general case, however, the motion of the electron is three-dimensional. With three degrees of freedom the Wilson-Sommerfeld quantum conditions require three quantum numbers to describe each energy state in place of two.   It should be pointed out at the outset, however, that the introduction of a third quantum number does not change the size or shape of the Bohr-Sommerfeld orbits but simply determines their orientation with respect to some direction in space.

In order to set up a fixed axis in space we first imagine the atom placed in a uniform magnetic field H. Let the vertical axis in Fig. 3.5 be the direction of the applied field, and let α be the angle between this axis and the normal to the plane of the orbit. As a result of the applied field the plane of the orbit precesses about H, just as a mechanical top precesses in a gravitational field and p_ψ, the orbital angular momentum vector, generates a cone about the vertical axis. The quantum conditions imply that the orbit is space-quantized, *i.e.*, that α takes on certain discrete values only. It will be shown in the following section, how, for any given orbit, the precession frequency depends upon H. If now the field H is gradually reduced to zero, the angle α remains constant (α is independent of H), while the rate at which p_ψ precesses about H decreases to zero. In this rather indirect way the atom is left with the plane of the electron orbit, or the orbit angular momentum p_ψ, in one of a discrete set of orienta-

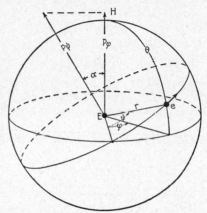

FIG. 3.5.—The motion of the electron with three degrees of freedom.

tions in space, but the energy is identical with that obtained by quantizing the field-free atom.

Now in the two-dimensional problem, treated in the preceding sections, the kinetic energy in terms of the coordinates r and φ is (φ is now replaced by ψ) (see Fig. 3.5)

$$T = \tfrac{1}{2}m\dot{r}^2 + \tfrac{1}{2}mr^2\dot{\psi}^2 = \tfrac{1}{2}(p_r\dot{r} + p_\psi\dot{\psi}) \qquad (3.36)$$

and is subject to the quantum conditions that

$$\oint p_\psi d\psi = kh \text{ and } \oint p_r dr = rh, \qquad (3.37)$$

where the radial quantum number $r = 0, 1, 2, 3, \cdots$ and the azimuthal quantum number $k = 1, 2, 3, 4, \cdots$. The potential energy is given by

$$V = -\frac{e^2 Z}{r}. \qquad (3.38)$$

In the three-dimensional problem, let the position of the electron be given by the polar coordinates r, θ, and φ. With the potential energy exactly the same as it is in the two-dimensional problem, we need only write down the kinetic energy.   In terms of the corresponding momenta, the kinetic energy T is

$$T = \tfrac{1}{2}(p_r \dot{r} + p_\theta \dot{\theta} + p_\varphi \dot{\varphi}).$$ (3.39)

The quantum conditions in terms of the phase integrals are

$$\oint p_r dr = rh, \qquad \oint p_\theta d\theta = th, \qquad \oint p_\varphi d\varphi = mh,$$ (3.40)

where the quantum numbers r, t, and m take integral values only.

Since the total energy $W = T + V$ in the r, ψ coordinates is just the same as in the r, θ, φ coordinates, it follows from Eqs. (3.36) and (3.39) that

$$p_r \dot{r} + p_\psi \dot{\psi} = p_r \dot{r} + p_\varphi \dot{\varphi} + p_\theta \dot{\theta}$$ (3.41)

from which

$$p_\psi d\psi = p_\varphi d\varphi + p_\theta d\theta$$ (3.42)

or

$$\oint p_\psi d\psi = \oint p_\varphi d\varphi + \oint p_\theta d\theta.$$ (3.43)

The quantum conditions for each of the phase integrals are most easily expressed in terms of their corresponding quantum numbers k, m, and t, respectively.   It follows that

$$k = t + m.$$ (3.44)

Since the total angular momentum of the electron p_ψ is constant, p_φ, its projection on the φ axis, is also constant, so that

$$p_\varphi = p_\psi \cos \alpha.$$ (3.45)

The angle between p_φ and p_ψ is therefore determined by the quantum numbers m and k,

$$\cos \alpha = \frac{p_\varphi}{p_\psi} = \frac{m}{k},$$ (3.46)

where the *magnetic* quantum number

$$m = \pm 1, \pm 2, \pm 3, \pm 4, \cdots \pm k$$ (3.47)

and the *azimuthal* quantum number

$$k = 1, 2, 3, 4, \cdots n.$$ (3.48)

It is customary to represent the space quantization of an electron orbit by means of the orbit normal and to treat this as a vector.   Equation (3.47) shows that the number of possible m values is limited by the value of k.   In Fig. 3.6, the space diagram for s electrons (*i.e.*, $k = 1$) shows two possible orientations of p_φ.   Similar diagrams for p and d electrons show four and six possible orientations, respectively.   By drawing the oriented vector of length $k = 2\pi p_\varphi / h$ in place of p_φ, the projection will always be just the magnetic quantum number m. The state $m = 0$ in this early work was always excluded on the ground that the application of an electric field would cause the electron to collide with the nucleus. We shall see later that on the quantum mechanics the states $m = 0$ are allowed. Experimental proof of the space quanti-

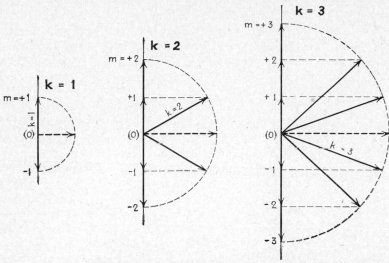

FIG. 3.6.—Space-quantization diagrams for Bohr-Sommerfeld orbits with $k = 1, 2,$ and 3.

zation of atoms in a magnetic field is to be found in the admirable experiments of Stern and Gerlach.[1]

3.6. Larmor's Theorem.—Just as a mechanical top precesses in a gravitational field, so an electron in an orbit would be expected classically to precess in a magnetic field. This precession is called the *Larmor precession* and the relation expressing the frequency of precession is called *Larmor's theorem*. This theorem, derived on the classical theory of electrodynamics, states that to a first approximation the change in the motion of an electron about a nucleus produced by the introduction of a magnetic field of intensity H is a precession of the orbit about the field direction with uniform angular velocity

$$\omega_L = H \cdot \frac{e}{2mc} \tag{3.49}$$

or with a uniform frequency

$$\nu_L = H \cdot \frac{e}{4\pi mc}. \tag{3.50}$$

[1] STERN, O., *Zeits. f. Phys.*, **7**, 249, 1921; GERLACH, W., and O. STERN, *Zeits. f. Phys.*, **8**, 110, 1921; **9**, 349, 1922; STERN, O., *Zeits. f. Phys.*, **41**, 563, 1927.

This theorem is of considerable importance in atomic structure as it enables an easy calculation of energy levels in the presence of an external magnetic field. The classical theory shows that, as the magnetic field starts from zero and gradually increases, there is no change in the size or shape of the electron orbit.[1] The picture formed therefore is the one shown in Fig. 3.7. As the orbit precesses with angular velocity ω_L, the orbit normal describes a cone about the field direction H.

The quantum conditions presented in the previous section show that, if we represent the orbital angular momentum $p_\psi = kh/2\pi$ by a vector of length k, the projection of k on the field direction H must be integral-valued, i.e.,

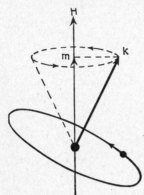

$$m = \pm 1, \pm 2, \pm 3, \cdots \pm k. \qquad (3.51)$$

3.7. Magnetic Moment and the Bohr Magneton.

—It will here be shown classically that, in terms of electron orbits, the ratio between the magnetic moment μ and the orbital angular momentum p is given by

$$\frac{\mu}{p} = \frac{e}{2mc}. \qquad (3.52)$$

Fig. 3.7.—Larmor precession of an electron orbit in an external magnetic field, H.

Hereafter we shall frequently refer to the orbital angular momentum p as the *mechanical moment*. An elementary principle in electrodynamics states that the magnetic moment μ (in electromagnetic units) of a current in a single loop or circuit is equal to the area of the circuit A, times the current I (in electrostatic units) divided by the velocity of light c:

$$\mu = \frac{\text{area} \cdot I}{c}. \qquad (3.53)$$

In terms of the moving charge e and its period of revolution T, the current I is given by

$$I = \frac{e}{T}. \qquad (3.54)$$

Now the area of a Kepler ellipse in terms of the mass of the electron m, its mechanical moment p, and the period T is

$$\text{Area} = \frac{T}{2m}p = \frac{T}{2m} \cdot k \cdot \frac{h}{2\pi} \qquad (3.55)$$

[1] It is not difficult to show from classical electrodynamics that, when a field is applied normal to the plane of a circular electron orbit, the electron speeds up without a change in the radius of the orbit. This unexpected result is due to the balance between the increased centrifugal force and the radial force on the electron due to the magnetic field H. Since the radius remains unchanged, the moment of inertia $I = mr^2$ remains constant.

giving for the magnetic moment, just as stated above in Eq. (3.52),

$$\mu = k \cdot \frac{h}{2\pi} \cdot \frac{e}{2mc} = k\frac{eh}{4\pi mc}. \tag{3.56}$$

According to this result the magnetic moment of a hydrogen atom should always be equal to an integral number of units:

$$\frac{eh}{4\pi mc} \cdot \frac{\text{ergs}}{\text{gauss}}. \tag{3.57}$$

This unit of magnetic moment is called the *Bohr magneton* and is equal to 0.918×10^{-20} erg gauss^{-1}. Returning to Larmor's theorem [Eq. (3.49)], we see that the angular velocity of the Larmor precession is equal to the field strength H, times the ratio between the magnetic and mechanical moments:

$$\omega_L = H \cdot \frac{\mu}{p} = H \cdot \frac{e}{2mc}. \tag{3.58}$$

Similarly the precession frequency

$$\nu_L = \frac{H}{2\pi} \cdot \frac{\mu}{p} = H \cdot \frac{e}{4\pi mc}. \tag{3.59}$$

It is interesting to note in passing that the frequency of precession is independent of the orientation angle between the orbit normal and the field direction (see Fig. 3.7).

Problems

1. Derive a general expression for the period of the electron in any of the Bohr-Sommerfeld orbits. Compare this formula with the one obtained in Chap. II, Prob. 6, for the Bohr circular orbits.

2. From the definition of the eccentricity as given by Eq. (3.8), show that the perihelion, aphelion, and semiminor axis are given by the relations in Eq. (3.9).

CHAPTER IV

QUANTUM MECHANICS AND THE SCHRÖDINGER WAVE EQUATION

While the quantum theory of Planck, as extended to atomic structure by Bohr, Sommerfeld, and others, has proved to be of inestimable value in the analysis of atomic spectra, other methods of representing atomic processes have been developed which are in still better agreement with the experimental facts.

In the year 1923 de Broglie[1] put forward a new theory of quantum dynamics which at the outset met with little success. In the hands of Schrödinger, however, the theory was greatly improved and extended. At about the same time Heisenberg[2] put forward an independent theory of *quantum dynamics* or *matrix mechanics* which was so successful in its general applications that it attracted wide attention. While both of these theories are different in their mathematical formulation Schrödinger[3] was able to show that they lead to the same result and that the two theories are in reality the same.

While quantum mechanics has proved to be so successful in its mathematical formulations of atomic processes that it replaces the older quantum theory, we can still, for want of an atomic model, make some use of the orbital picture of the atom.

4.1. De Broglie's Corpuscular Wave Equation.—De Broglie's outstanding contribution to the new mechanics may be summed up in the very simple but fundamental equation

$$\lambda = \frac{h}{mv}. \qquad (4.1)$$

In this equation h is Planck's constant of action, m is the mass of a particle moving with velocity v, and λ is a wave-length to be associated with the moving particle. Just as light waves are known to have corpuscular properties, so moving particles are now known to have wave properties given by de Broglie's equation. Electrons, protons, atoms, and molecules, for example, may under suitable conditions be diffracted in much the same manner as sound and light. With this

---

[1] DE BROGLIE, L., *Phil. Mag.*, **47**, 446, 1924; *Ann. de phys.*, **3**, 22, 1925.

[2] HEISENBERG, W., *Zeits. f. Phys.*, **33**, 879, 1925.

[3] SCHRÖDINGER, E., *Ann. d. Phys.*, **79**, 361, 489, and 734, 1926; *Phys. Rev.*, **28**, 1049, 1926.

54

brief introduction de Broglie's equation,[1] which indicates that the wave-length associated with any moving particle is inversely proportional to the momentum mv, will serve as a starting point in the quantum mechanics of hydrogen, the simplest of all atomic systems.

4.2. The Schrödinger Wave Equation.—In order to show that, with the coming of the quantum mechanics, we need not lose entirely the Bohr-Sommerfeld orbital picture of the atom, we shall consider in some detail the Schrödinger wave equation as it applies to hydrogen. A very brief and simple derivation of the Schrödinger wave equation will be given here by starting with de Broglie's equation, (4.1), and the well-known equation for the propagation of elastic waves. This latter equation in its very simplest form is written

$$\nabla^2 \Psi = \frac{1}{c^2} \cdot \frac{\partial^2 \Psi}{\partial t^2}, \tag{4.2}$$

where $\nabla^2 \Psi$ stands for the Laplacian of Ψ, which in Cartesian coordinates x, y, and z is given by

$$\nabla^2 \Psi = \frac{\partial^2 \Psi}{\partial x^2} + \frac{\partial^2 \Psi}{\partial y^2} + \frac{\partial^2 \Psi}{\partial z^2}. \tag{4.3}$$

Here Ψ represents the displacement of the waves and c their velocity of propagation. In looking for a solution of Eq. (4.2) we might expect the displacement Ψ to be some periodic function of the time

$$\Psi = \psi e^{i\omega t}. \tag{4.4}$$

In this trial solution, ψ, the amplitude, is some function of the coordinates x, y, and z but not of time; and ω is equal to 2π times the frequency ν.

Taking second derivatives of the displacement

$$\frac{\partial^2 \Psi}{\partial t^2} = -\omega^2 \psi e^{i\omega t}, \qquad \frac{\partial^2 \Psi}{\partial x^2} = \frac{\partial^2 \psi}{\partial x^2} e^{i\omega t}, \text{ etc.,} \tag{4.5}$$

and substituting in the wave equation, (4.2),

$$\nabla^2 \psi + \frac{\omega^2}{c^2} \psi = 0. \tag{4.6}$$

In terms of the wave-length

$$\lambda = \frac{c}{\nu} = \frac{2\pi c}{\omega}, \tag{4.7}$$

the equation may be written

$$\nabla^2 \psi + \frac{4\pi^2}{\lambda^2} \psi = 0. \tag{4.8}$$

---

[1] For an elementary treatment of de Broglie's fundamental equation [Eq. (4.1)], see Arthur Haas, "Wave Mechanics and the New Quantum Theory."

Introducing the de Broglie wave-length for a moving particle [Eq. (4.1)],

$$\nabla^2\psi + \frac{4\pi^2 m^2 v^2}{h^2}\psi = 0. \tag{4.9}$$

With this introduction of the de Broglie wave-length, ψ is interpreted as the amplitude of a wave associated with a particle moving with a velocity v.

In terms of the kinetic energy $T = \frac{1}{2}mv^2$, the potential energy V, and the total energy

$$W = \frac{1}{2}mv^2 + V, \tag{4.10}$$

the equation becomes

$$\nabla^2\psi + \frac{8\pi^2 m}{h^2}(W - V)\psi = 0. \tag{4.11}$$

This is Schrödinger's so-called *wave equation*.

4.3. Schrödinger's Wave Equation Applied to Hydrogen.—The Bohr-Sommerfeld orbital picture of the hydrogen atom is now to be replaced by one in which the probability of the presence of the electron in an element of volume dv is given by the function $\psi\psi^* dv$. Here ψ^* denotes the complex conjugate of ψ, *i.e.*, the function obtained if all imaginary factors $i = \sqrt{-1}$ in ψ, if there be any, are replaced by $-i$. With suitable values of the total energy W, and the potential energy V, and with reasonable boundary conditions imposed upon ψ, the allowed solutions of the wave equation [Eq. (4.11)] belong to a discrete set of solutions, each one of which represents an energy state of the atom. In the older quantum theory the discreteness of the energy states was introduced quite artificially, whereas they will now be shown briefly to appear quite naturally as solutions of Schrödinger's equation. Later in this chapter these solutions will be taken up in detail.

The only successful attempts to find solutions of the wave equation have been those in which the electron position is given in polar or parabolic coordinates. In polar coordinates Eq. (4.11) becomes

$$\frac{1}{r^2}\frac{\partial}{\partial r}\left(r^2\frac{\partial\psi}{\partial r}\right) + \frac{1}{r^2\sin^2\theta}\frac{\partial^2\psi}{\partial\varphi^2} + \frac{1}{r^2\sin\theta}\frac{\partial}{\partial\theta}\left(\sin\theta\frac{\partial\psi}{\partial\theta}\right) + \frac{8\pi^2\mu}{h^2}$$
$$(W - V)\psi = 0, \quad (4.12)$$

where r, θ, and φ are the polar coordinates of the electron with respect to the nucleus as origin (see Fig. 4.1). For an electron of mass m and charge e, moving in the central force field of a nucleus of mass M and charge E, the potential energy is given by

$$V = -\frac{eE}{r} = -\frac{e^2 Z}{r}, \tag{4.13}$$

and the reduced mass of the electron is given by $\mu = \dfrac{mM}{m + M}$. The boundary conditions imposed upon ψ are that it and its first derivative are everywhere continuous, single-valued, and finite. Solutions which satisfy these conditions are called *eigenfunctions*.

The wave equation in this form may be solved by separating it into three total differential equations. This is accomplished by replacing

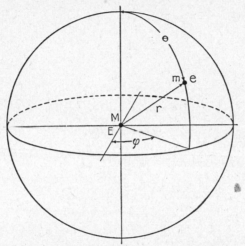

FIG. 4.1.—Position coordinates of the electron.

ψ by a product of a function of φ alone, one of θ alone, and one of r alone, *i.e.*, by

$$\psi = \Phi \cdot \Theta \cdot R. \tag{4.14}$$

Taking first and second derivatives of ψ and substituting in Eq. (4.12),

$$\frac{\partial}{\partial r}\left(r^2\frac{\partial R}{\partial r}\right)\frac{1}{R} + \frac{1}{\sin^2\theta}\frac{\partial^2\Phi}{\partial\varphi^2}\frac{1}{\Phi} + \frac{1}{\sin\theta}\frac{\partial}{\partial\theta}\left(\sin\theta\frac{\partial\Theta}{\partial\theta}\right)\frac{1}{\Theta} + \frac{8\pi^2\mu}{h^2}$$
$$(W - V)r^2 = 0. \tag{4.15}$$

We first separate out the factors involving φ only and set them equal to a constant C_1, since they, as a whole, must be independent of φ, being by Eq. (4.15) equal to a function of θ and r only:

$$\frac{\partial^2\Phi}{\partial\varphi^2}\frac{1}{\Phi} = C_1 \tag{4.16}$$

Since the angle φ goes from 0 to 2π, the solutions of this equation, in order to be single-valued, must have a period 2π. This limitation confines the admissible solutions to functions of the form

$$\Phi = A \cdot e^{im\varphi}, \tag{4.17}$$

where m is any whole number, positive, negative, or zero, and A is any constant. Taking first and second derivatives, Eq. (4.16) becomes

$$\frac{\partial^2 \Phi}{\partial \varphi^2} \frac{1}{\Phi} = -m^2. \tag{4.18}$$

This m is to be associated with the magnetic quantum number of the orbital model treated in Chap. III. Replacing $\frac{\partial^2 \Phi}{\partial \varphi^2} \frac{1}{\Phi}$ of the original equation, (4.15), by $-m^2$, the second equation to be taken is one involving θ alone:

$$\frac{1}{\Theta} \frac{1}{\sin \theta} \frac{\partial}{\partial \theta} \left(\sin \theta \frac{\partial \Theta}{\partial \theta} \right) - \frac{m^2}{\sin^2 \theta} = C_2. \tag{4.19}$$

This equation involving θ as the only variable will be shown in Sec. 4.6 to have solutions when

$$C_2 = -l(l + 1) \tag{4.20}$$

where l takes positive whole number values $\geq |m|$ only. l is here to be associated with the azimuthal quantum number k of the Bohr-Sommerfeld orbits.

Substituting $-l(l + 1)$ for the left-hand side of Eq. (4.19) in Eq. (4.15), the third and last differential equation to be solved becomes

$$\frac{1}{r^2} \frac{\partial}{\partial r} \left(r^2 \frac{\partial R}{\partial r} \right) - \frac{l(l + 1)}{r^2} R + \frac{8\pi^2 \mu}{h^2} (W - V)R = 0. \tag{4.21}$$

This equation has solutions for *all positive values of W*, and for *negative values of W* given by the relation

$$W = -\frac{2\pi^2 \mu e^4 Z^2}{n^2 h^2}, \tag{4.22}$$

where n takes whole integral values only. This n is to be associated with the total quantum number of the Bohr-Sommerfeld orbits. Thus out of Schrödinger's equation the quantum states, first calculated by Bohr and Sommerfeld, and the quantum numbers m, l, and n appear quite naturally as characteristic solutions of the wave equation, a distinct contrast with the quite artificially obtained quantum states and quantum numbers m, k, and n of the older quantum theory.

In the new theory the three quantum numbers have values as follows:

$$\begin{aligned} m &= 0, \pm 1, \pm 2, \pm 3, \cdots \pm l. \\ l &= 0, 1, 2, 3, 4, \cdots n - 1. \\ n &= 1, 2, 3, 4, 5, \cdots \infty. \end{aligned} \tag{4.23}$$

The various electron states of the hydrogen atom in the new theory are designated as shown in Table 4.1.

TABLE 4.1.—DESIGNATION OF THE ELECTRON STATES IN HYDROGEN

	$l = 0$ s	$l = 1$ p	$l = 2$ d	$l = 3$ f	$l = 4$ g	$l = 5$ h
$n = 1$	$1s$					
$n = 2$	$2s$	$2p$				
$n = 3$	$3s$	$3p$	$3d$			
$n = 4$	$4s$	$4p$	$4d$	$4f$		
$n = 5$	$5s$	$5p$	$5d$	$5f$	$5g$	
$n = 6$	$6s$	$6p$	$6d$	$6f$	$6g$	$6h$

For each of these states l there are $2l + 1$ magnetic states m.

4.4. Eigenfunctions.—For any given set of quantum numbers m, l, and n, the eigenfunction ψ, which satisfies the wave equation [Eq. (4.12)], is of the form [see Eq. (4.14)].

$$\psi = \Phi_m \cdot \Theta_{m,l} \cdot R_{l,n}. \tag{4.24}$$

As has been noted before, the theory was found to predict observed phenomena correctly, if the product of ψ with its complex conjugate ψ^* and the volume element dv was interpreted as the probability that the electron would be found in a certain element of volume of extent dv. The product $\psi\psi^*$ may hence be called the *probability density* for the electron. As an example, $\psi\psi^* r^2 \sin\theta\, dr d\theta d\varphi$ is the probability that the single electron will be found in a small element of volume of size $r^2 \sin\theta dr d\theta d\varphi$ specified by given values of the coordinates r, θ, and φ. When this probability is summed up over all space, the result should be unity, *i.e.*, we must find only one electron. This is accomplished by suitable adjustment of the constants occurring in the solutions and the process of adjustment is called *normalization*.

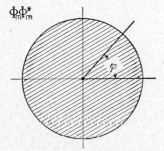

FIG. 4.2.—$\Phi\Phi^*$, the probability-density distribution $\psi\psi^*$ as a function of the angle φ.

It is found that the behavior of the hydrogen atom can be accounted for in most respects if the electron is thought of as being spread out over all space in such a manner that $\psi\psi^*$ gives the *charge density* at any point. It is important, therefore, that we determine just how this charge density is distributed. In attempting to do this, one observes from Eq. (4.14) that

$$\psi\psi^* = \Phi\Phi^* \cdot \Theta\Theta^* \cdot RR^*. \tag{4.25}$$

Expressed in this way $\Phi\Phi^*$ gives the probability density $\psi\psi^*$ as a function of the angle φ alone (see Fig. 4.2), $\Theta\Theta^*$ gives the probability density as a function of the angle θ alone, and finally RR^* gives the probability density as a function of r alone. In the following sections of this chapter each of these three factors will be treated separately in some detail and then compared with the Bohr-Sommerfeld orbits. The three will then be brought together to form the quantum-mechanical model of the atom.

4.5. The φ Factor Φ_m of the Eigenfunction ψ.—The first factor Φ_m of the eigenfunction ψ is obtained as a solution of Eq. (4.16) and is written

$$\Phi_m = A \cdot e^{im\varphi}. \tag{4.26}$$

By setting $m = 0, \pm 1, \pm 2, \pm 3, \cdots$, a complete set of solutions is obtained that are orthogonal and may be normalized. Since A is any constant whatever, this orthogonal set can be normalized to unity:

$$\int_0^{2\pi} \Phi_m \Phi_{m'}^* d\varphi = 1, \qquad \text{where } \Phi_{m'}^* = A \cdot e^{-im'\varphi}. \tag{4.27}$$

This gives

$$A^2 \int^{2\pi} e^{i(m-m')\varphi} d\varphi = A^2 \begin{Bmatrix} 0 \text{ for } m \neq m' \\ 2\pi \text{ for } m = m' \end{Bmatrix}, \tag{4.28}$$

from which the constant

$$A = \frac{1}{\sqrt{2\pi}}. \tag{4.29}$$

Thus normalized

$$\Phi_m = \frac{1}{\sqrt{2\pi}} e^{im\varphi}. \tag{4.30}$$

4.6. The θ Factor $\Theta_{m,l}$ of the Eigenfunction ψ.—The second factor $\Theta_{m,l}$ of the eigenfunction [Eq. (4.24)] is obtained from Eq. (4.19). The solutions of this differential equation obeying the conditions imposed on the eigenfunctions contain as factors the so-called *associated Legendre polynomials*, and are of the form

$$\Theta_{m,l} = B \sin^m \theta \cdot P_l^m (\cos \theta), \tag{4.31}$$

where $m = |m|$ and $P_l^m (\cos \theta)$ is a polynomial in $\cos \theta$. Since these functions vanish except for $|m| \leq l$, m may take on integral values from $+l$ to $-l$. There are therefore $2l + 1$ angular factors Φ_m to be associated with each given value of l. The associated Legendre polynomials form a complete orthogonal set of solutions, for

$$\int_0^{2\pi} \Theta_{m,l} \Theta_{m,l'} \sin \theta d\theta = B^2 \begin{Bmatrix} 0, & \text{for } l \neq l', \\ \dfrac{2 \cdot (l + m)!}{(2l + 1)(l - m)!}, & \text{for } l = l'. \end{Bmatrix} \tag{4.32}$$

They may therefore be normalized to unity by making the constant

$$B = \sqrt{\frac{(2l + 1) \cdot (l - m)!}{2(l + m)!}}. \tag{4.33}$$

As a result,

$$\Theta_{m,l} = \sqrt{\frac{(2l+1)(l-m)!}{2(l+m)!}} \, \sin^m \theta P_l^m(\cos \theta). \qquad (4.34)$$

Expressions for the associated Legendre polynomials are listed in Table 4.2 for values of m and l, corresponding to the various electron types s, p, d, etc.

TABLE 4.2.—VALUES OF THE ASSOCIATED LEGENDRE POLYNOMIALS

Electron	l	m	$P_l^m(\cos \theta)$
s	0	0	1
p	1	1	1
	1	0	$\cos \theta$
d	2	2	3
	2	1	$3 \cos \theta$
	2	0	$\frac{1}{2}(\cos^2 \theta - 1)$
f	3	3	15
	3	2	$15 \cos \theta$
	3	1	$\frac{3}{2}(5 \cos^2 \theta - 1)$
	3	0	$\frac{1}{2}(5 \cos^3 \theta - 3 \cos \theta)$
g	4	4	105
	4	3	$105 \cos \theta$
	4	2	$\frac{15}{2}(7 \cos^2 \theta - 1)$
	4	1	$\frac{5}{3}(7 \cos^3 \theta - 3 \cos \theta)$
	4	0	$\frac{1}{8}(35 \cos^4 \theta - 30 \cos^2 \theta + 3)$

4.7. Correlation of $\Phi_m \Phi_m^*$ and $\Theta_{m,l}\Theta_{m,l}^*$ with the Bohr-Sommerfeld Orbits.—In order to compare the angular factors Φ_m and $\Theta_{m,l}$ of the quantum mechanics with the classical orbits of the quantum theory, it will be necessary to express them in the somewhat classical form of a probability (see Sec. 4.4). This is accomplished by interpreting the product $\Phi_m \Phi_m^* \cdot d\varphi$ as the probability of finding the electron between the angle φ and $\varphi + d\varphi$, and $\Theta_{m,l}\Theta_{m,l}^* \cdot \sin \theta d\theta$ as the probability of finding the electron between θ and $\theta + d\theta$. Using Eq. (4.34), and the values of the associated Legendre polynomials in Table 4.2, values of $\Theta_{m,l}\Theta_{m,l}^* = (\Theta_{m,l})^2$ are computed for Table 4.3.

With a given value of m for any electron, $\Phi_m \Phi_m^* = 1/2\pi$, a constant independent of the angle φ. This means that the probability of an electron being found in a small element of angle $d\varphi_1$ is the same as for any other equal angle $d\varphi_2$. Equal probability in all directions φ, from 0 to 2π, may be represented graphically by a circle as shown in Fig. 4.2.

For an s electron, $l = 0$ and $(\Theta_{m,l})^2 = \frac{1}{2}$, a constant independent of the angle θ. Equal probability in all directions θ, between 0 and π, would be represented graphically by a half circle. Taking φ and θ together, this half circle rotated through 2π radians, the range of φ, results in a sphere the cross section of which is shown at the top and left in Fig. 4.3. Thus for an s electron the charge density is spherically symmetrical about the nucleus. In terms of the classical orbital model this may be taken to mean that there is no motion in a direction of changing φ or θ.

TABLE 4.3.—THE PROBABILITY DENSITY FACTOR $(\Theta_{m,l})^2$

Electron	l	m	$(\Theta_{m,l})^2$	$\displaystyle\sum_{m=-1}^{m=+1} (\Theta_{m,l})^2$
s	0	0	$\frac{1}{2}$	$\frac{1}{2}$
p	1	+1	$\frac{3}{4} \sin^2 \theta$	$\frac{3}{2}$
	1	0	$\frac{3}{2} \cos^2 \theta$	
d	2	+2	$\frac{15}{16} \sin^4 \theta$	$\frac{5}{2}$
	2	+1	$\frac{15}{4} \sin^2 \theta \cos^2 \theta$	
	2	0	$\frac{10}{16}(9 \cos^4 \theta - 6 \cos^2 \theta + 1)$	
f	3	+3	$\frac{35}{32} \sin^6 \theta$	$\frac{7}{2}$
	3	+2	$\frac{105}{16} \sin^4 \theta \cos^2 \theta$	
	3	+1	$\frac{21}{32} \sin^2 \theta(25 \cos^4 \theta - 10 \cos^2 \theta + 1)$	
	3	0	$\frac{7}{8}(25 \cos^6 \theta - 30 \cos^4 \theta + 9 \cos^2 \theta)$	
g	4	+4	$\frac{315}{256} \sin^8 \theta$	$\frac{9}{2}$
	4	+3	$\frac{315}{32} \sin^6 \theta \cos^2 \theta$	
	4	+2	$\frac{225}{320} \sin^4 \theta(49 \cos^4 \theta - 14 \cos^2 \theta + 1)$	
	4	+1	$\frac{225}{160} \sin^2 \theta(49 \cos^6 \theta - 42 \cos^4 \theta + 9 \cos^2 \theta)$	
	4	0	$\frac{9}{128}(1225 \cos^8 \theta - 2100 \cos^6 \theta + 1110 \cos^4 \theta - 180 \cos^2 \theta + 9)$	

For a p electron with $l = 1$, m may take one of the three values 1, 0, and -1. For these three states, $(\Theta_{m,l})^2$ gives the charge distributions shown at the right and top in Fig. 4.3. Each curve is shown plotted symmetrically on each side of the vertical axis in order to represent a cross section of the three-dimensional plot. Three-dimensional curves are obtained by rotating each figure about its vertical axis. It should be pointed out that the electron is not confined to the shaded areas in each figure. The magnitude of a straight line joining the center and any point on a given curve is a measure of the electron's probability of being found in the direction of that line.

For d electrons with $l = 2$, there are five possible states $m = 2, 1, 0, -1$, and -2. Figures for each of these five states are shown in the third row of Fig. 4.3, followed by corresponding figures for f, g, and h electrons. These figures indicate that for all $m = 0$ states, with the exception of s

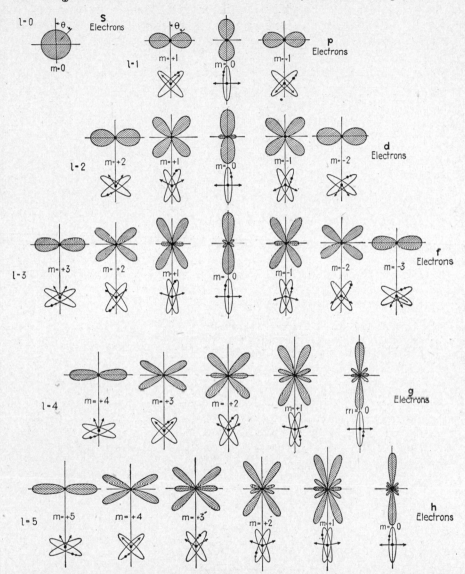

FIG. 4.3.—The probability-density distribution factor $(\theta_{m,l})^2$ plotted as a function of the angle θ for s, p, d, f, g, and h electrons. For states $m = 0$ the scale is approximately $1/(l + 1)$ times that of the other states having the same value. The classical oriented orbit for each state is given below each figure, tilted slightly out of the normal plane to show an orbit rather than a straight line.

electrons, the charge density is greatest in the direction of the poles, *i.e.*, in the direction $\theta = 0$ and π. The exponent of $e^{im\varphi}$ being zero implies that there is no motion in the φ coordinate and that the motion of the electron, *i.e.*, the plane of the orbit, is in some one meridian plane through the φ axis, all meridian planes being equally probable. This corresponds remarkably well with the orientation of the classical orbits shown below each figure (see Fig. 4.3). The orbital angular momentum for these classical orbits is taken to be $\sqrt{l(l+1)} \cdot h/2\pi$ and its projection on the φ axis is taken to be $mh/2\pi$. It will be shown in the succeeding chapters that better agreement between the Bohr-Sommerfeld orbital model and the quantum-mechanical model is obtained when the orbital angular momentum $kh/2\pi$ is replaced by $\sqrt{l(l+1)} \cdot h/2\pi$, where $l = k - 1$.

With $m = +l$ or $-l$, $(\Theta_{m,l})^2$ takes on its largest values in the direction of the equatorial plane. This corresponds to the two classical orbits nearest the equatorial plane, and the opposite signs in the exponents of the φ factors $e^{il\varphi}$ and $e^{-il\varphi}$ correspond to the opposite directions of rotation in the orbit.[1]

The interesting cases for d, f, and g, and h electrons occur when m is not equal to 0, $+l$, or $-l$. Here $(\Theta_{m,l})^2$ takes on its largest values in definite oriented directions which correspond closely with the oriented classical orbits. The opposite signs in the exponents $e^{im\varphi}$ and $e^{-im\varphi}$ correspond to the opposite directions of the electron's rotation in the orbit, and the symmetry about the φ axis corresponds to the orbit normal occupying some one meridian plane with all meridian planes equally probable.

4.8. The Radial Factor $R_{n,l}$ of the Eigenfunction ψ.—The third factor $R_{n,l}$ of the eigenfunction $\psi = \Phi_m \Theta_{m,l} R_{n,l}$ gives, when multiplied by $R_{n,l}^*$, the so-called *probability-density distribution* $\psi\psi^*$ as a function of the nuclear-electron distance r. The radial equation to be solved is

$$\frac{1}{r^2}\frac{\partial}{\partial r}\left(r^2\frac{\partial R}{\partial r}\right) - \frac{l(l+1)}{r^2}R + \frac{8\pi^2\mu}{h^2}(W - V)R = 0, \qquad (4.35)$$

where the potential energy

$$V = \frac{e^2 Z}{r}. \qquad (4.36)$$

The boundary conditions to be imposed are that R shall be everywhere continuous and finite. For any stationary states to be found R should certainly be small for large r and approach zero as $r \rightarrow \infty$.

The radial equation may be simplified by making the substitution

$$R = \frac{1}{r}R' \qquad (4.37)$$

giving

$$\frac{\partial^2 R'}{\partial r^2} + \left(\frac{8\pi^2\mu}{h^2}W + \frac{8\pi^2\mu e^2 Z}{h^2 r} - \frac{l(l+1)}{r^2}\right)R' = 0. \qquad (4.38)$$

[1] See Condon, E. U., and P. M. Morse, "Quantum Mechanics."

This equation is still further simplified by introducing two new variables n and x in place of the total energy W and the radius r.

Let

$$W = \pm \frac{2\pi^2 \mu e^4 Z^2}{n^2 h^2} \quad \text{and} \quad r = \frac{nh^2}{8\pi^2 \mu e^2 Z} x. \tag{4.39}$$

Making these substitutions,

$$\frac{\partial^2 R'}{\partial x^2} + \left(\pm \frac{1}{4} + \frac{n}{x} - \frac{l(l+1)}{x^2} \right) R' = 0. \tag{4.40}$$

In terms of a_1, the radius of the Bohr first circular orbit of hydrogen [see Eq. (2.33)],

$$a_1 = \frac{h^2}{4\pi^2 \mu e^2} = 0.53 \times 10^{-8} \text{cm}, \tag{4.41}$$

the new variable x may be abbreviated

$$x = \frac{2rZ}{na_1}. \tag{4.42}$$

The solutions of the radial equation must satisfy the boundary conditions at $x = 0$ and $x = \infty$. As $x \to \infty$, the terms n/x and $-l(l+1)/x^2$ become negligibly small compared with $\frac{1}{4}$ and Eq. (4.40) becomes

$$\frac{\partial^2 R'}{\partial x^2} \pm \frac{R'}{4} = 0 \tag{4.43}$$

Taking the positive sign, the solutions of this equation are

$$A \sin \frac{x}{2} \quad \text{and} \quad A \cos \frac{x}{2}, \tag{4.44}$$

both of which are finite as $x \to \infty$. These expressions correspond to the continuum of energy states above the series limit in hydrogen. This continuum corresponds to the continuum of the hyperbolic orbits of the classical theory, and the finite value of R' for large x signifies a finite probability for the electron leaving or returning to the atom with a definite velocity.

Taking the negative sign, the solutions of Eq. (4.43) are

$$A e^{+\frac{x}{2}} \quad \text{and} \quad A e^{-\frac{x}{2}}. \tag{4.45}$$

Only the second of these is finite for large x. $R_{n,l}$ will therefore contain a factor $e^{-x/2}$ to make it fit the boundary conditions at $r = \infty$.

In trying for a solution of Eq. (4.40) near the nucleus, *i.e.*, for small x, a power-series development reveals two possible solutions of the form

$$A x^{+l} \quad \text{and} \quad A x^{-l-1}. \tag{4.46}$$

Only the first of these satisfies the boundary conditions and vanishes at $x = 0$. $R_{n,l}$ will therefore contain x^{+l} as a factor.

If we then write the solution as a product of x^{+l}, $e^{-x/2}$, and a third factor in the form of a power series in x, whose coefficients we adjust so as to satisfy the differential equation, (4.40), it is found that this third factor degenerates to a polynomial for integral values of n and that in this case only the total solution satisfies the boundary conditions for $r = \infty$ as well as $r = 0$. These represent the negative energy states [Eq. (4.22)] obtained first by Bohr from the orbital model [Eq. (2.23)].

A further investigation of the radial equation shows that the polynomials above referred to are derivatives of the Laguerre polynomials, an orthogonal system of functions, abbreviated $L_{n+l}^{2l+1}(x)$; see Table 4.4. The solution now takes on the form

$$R_{n,l} = Cx^{+l} \cdot e^{-\frac{x}{2}} \cdot L_{n+l}^{2l+1}(x), \qquad (4.47)$$

where the constant C is yet to be determined as a normalizing factor. This radial normalizing factor is obtained in much the same way as the φ and θ normalizing factors of Secs. 4.5 and 4.6 were obtained:

$$C = \sqrt{\frac{4(n - l - 1)! \, Z^3}{[(n + l)!]^3 n^4 a_1^3}}. \qquad (4.48)$$

Inserting the values of x from Eq. (4.42), the radial function finally becomes[1]

$$R_{n,l} = \sqrt{\frac{4(n - l - 1)! \, Z^3}{[(n + l)!]^3 n^4 a_1^3}} \left(\frac{2Zr}{na_1}\right)^l \cdot e^{-\frac{Zr}{na_1}} \cdot L_{n+l}^{2l+1}\left(\frac{2Zr}{na_1}\right). \qquad (4.49)$$

4.9. Correlation of $R_{n,l}R_{n,l}^*$ with the Bohr-Sommerfeld Orbits.—It is of some interest at this point to examine some of the eigenfunction values for the various types of electron states. To do this we shall make use of Table 4.4 of Laguerre polynomials, where x is written for $2Zr/na_1$ [see Eqs. (4.49) and (4.42)].

The dependence of $R_{n,l}$ upon r is shown in Fig. 4.4 for several states of the hydrogen atom $Z = 1$. The electron-nuclear distance r is given in units of the radius of the first Bohr circular orbit $a_1 = 0.53$Å. The dotted curves represent the radial factor $R_{n,l}R_{n,l}^* = (R_{n,l})^2$ of the probability density $\psi\psi^*$.

If for each value of r the corresponding value of $(R_{n,l})^2$ is multiplied by $4\pi r^2$, the area of a sphere of radius r, curves of the type shown in Fig. 4.5b are obtained. This new function $D = 4\pi r^2(R_{n,l})^2$ is called the *probability-density function* and represents the probability of finding the

---

[1] For a fuller account of the solutions of the radial equation see E. U. Condon and P. M. Morse, "Quantum Mechanics." Also A. Sommerfeld "Wave Mechanics."

TABLE 4.4.—DERIVATIVES OF THE LAGUERRE POLYNOMIALS[1]

Electron	n	l	$L_{n+l}^{2l+1}(x)$
$1s$	1	0	$-1!$
$2p$	2	1	$-3!$
$3d$	3	2	$-5!$
$4f$	4	3	$-7!$
$2s$	2	0	$2x - 4$
$3p$	3	1	$24x - 96$
$4d$	4	2	$720x - 5760$
$3s$	3	0	$-3x^2 + 18x - 18$
$4p$	4	1	$-60x^2 + 600x - 1200$
$4s$	4	0	$4x^3 - 48x^2 + 144x - 96$

[1] Recursion formulas for calculating other polynomials than those tabulated here are given by E. U. Condon and P. M. Morse, "Quantum Mechanics."

electron between two spheres of radius r and $r + dr$. It should be noted, in the particular case chosen, that the principal maximum of D comes at about $5a_1$. This means that a $2s$ electron has a greater prob-

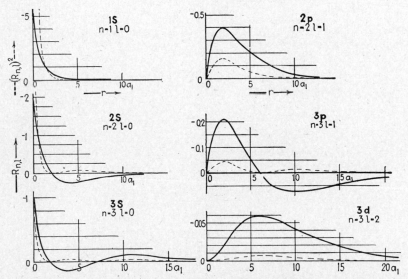

FIG. 4.4.—The radial function $R_{n,l}$ and $(R_{n,l})^2$ plotted as a function of the electron-nuclear distance r for six states in hydrogen, $Z = 1$.

ability of being found at a distance of about $5a_1$ than at any other distance. Other points of particular interest are those at which D comes to zero, $r = 0$, $r = 2a_1$, and $r = \infty$. Although nothing better could be wished for than zero at the end points, it is difficult to imagine how a $2s$

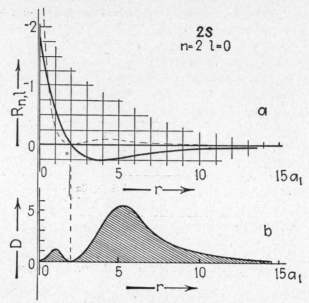

FIG. 4.5.—Plots of the radial factors $R_{n,l}$ and $(R_{n,l})^2$ and the probability-density function $D = 4\pi r^2 (R_{n,l})^2$, for a 2s electron.

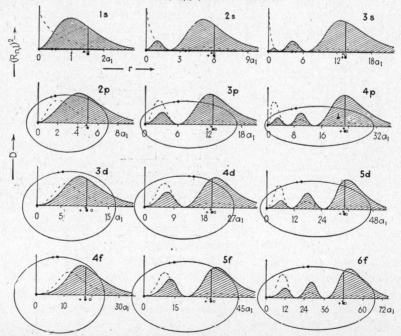

FIG. 4.6.—The probability-density factor $(R_{n,l})^2$ plotted as a function of the electron-nuclear distance r (r is given in units $a_1 = 0.53$ Å, the radius of the first Bohr circular orbit). The density distribution curves $D = 4\pi r^2 (R_{n,l})^2$, the shaded areas, are to be compared with the electron-nuclear distance of the classical electron orbits, where the orbital angular momentum is taken to be $\sqrt{l(l+1)} \cdot h/2\pi$.

electron can sometimes be found on one side of $2a_1$ and sometimes on the other but never in between. In Chap. IX we shall see how, with the introduction of the spinning electron, this difficulty vanishes.

In Fig. 4.6, the probability distribution function D is shown for 12 of the lowest quantum states in hydrogen, $Z = 1$. Corresponding to each of these states an electron orbit is drawn to the same r scale. In each orbit the angular momentum is taken as $\sqrt{l(l + 1)} \cdot h/2\pi$, where $l = 0, 1, 2, 3, \cdots$ for $s, p, d, f, \cdots$ electrons. The major axis of each orbit is given by the total quantum number n and is the same as for the Bohr-Sommerfeld orbits. This model will be discussed, along with three others, at the end of this chapter (see Sec. 4.11).

In each distribution curve it is observed that D differs greatly from zero only within the electron-nuclear distance of the corresponding orbits. It should be mentioned that while the $1s$, $2p$, $3d$, and $4f$ states show single maxima at $r = a_1$, $4a_1$, $9a_1$, and $16a_1$, which are exactly the radii of the corresponding Bohr circular orbits, a better general agreement is obtained with the orbits shown.

A still more striking comparison of the older quantum theory with the quantum mechanics can be made by comparing the average value of r computed for each theory. The method of evaluating $\bar{r}$ from the quantum mechanics has been given by Waller.[1] His formulas along with several others are given below.

Quantum Mechanics:[1]
Probability-density Distribution

Quantum Theory:
Bohr-Sommerfield Orbits

$$\bar{r} - \frac{a_1 n^2}{Z}\left\{1 + \frac{1}{2}\left(1 - \frac{l(l+1)}{n^2}\right)\right\}, \qquad \bar{r} = \frac{a_1 n^2}{Z}\left\{1 + \frac{1}{2}\left(1 - \frac{k^2}{n^2}\right)\right\}, \tag{4.50}$$

$$\overline{r^2} = \frac{a_1^2 n^4}{Z^2}\left\{1 + \frac{3}{2}\left(1 - \frac{l(l+1) - \frac{1}{3}}{n^2}\right)\right\}, \ \overline{r^2} = \frac{a_1^2 n^2}{Z^2}\left\{1 + \frac{3}{2}\left(1 - \frac{k^2}{n^2}\right)\right\}, \tag{4.51}$$

$$\overline{\frac{1}{r^3}} = \frac{Z^3}{a_1^3 n^3 l(l + \frac{1}{2})(l + 1)}, \qquad\qquad \overline{\frac{1}{r^3}} = \frac{Z^3}{a_1^3 n^3 k^3}. \tag{4.52}$$

It should be noted that the time average value of r on the quantum theory becomes identical with the quantum-mechanics expression when k^2 is replaced by $l(l + 1)$. The vertical line on each of the curves in Fig. 4.6 represents the time average distance $\bar{r}$, for the density curves as well as the orbits shown. A further discussion of the above given formulas and the different atomic models will be continued in Sec. 4.11 of this chapter.

4.10. A General Interpretation of the Eigenfunction ψ.—With given values of the quantum numbers m, l, and n, the three factors of the

[1] Waller, I., *Zeits. f. Phys.*, **38**, 635, 1926.

eigenfunction ψ may be brought together to form a general quantum-mechanical model of the atom:

$$\psi_{m,l,n} = \Phi_m \cdot \Theta_{m,l} \cdot R_{n,l}. \tag{4.53}$$

In finding the solutions of Schrödinger's wave equation, each of these three factors has been normalized to unity (see Secs. 4.5, 4.6, and 4.8), so that, if we now integrate $\psi\psi^*$ throughout the whole of the φ, θ, r coordinate space, we must get 1.

$$\int \psi_{m,l,n}\psi^*_{m',l',n'}dv = \begin{cases} 1 \text{ for } m = m', \, l = l', \, n = n', \\ 0 \text{ otherwise.} \end{cases} \tag{4.54}$$

There being but one electron, $\psi_{m,l,n}$ has been normalized to unity. The complex conjugate $\psi^*_{m,l,n}$ differs from $\psi_{m,l,n}$ only in the sign of the exponents $\pm im\varphi$ of the φ factor.

From Eqs. (4.30), (4.34), and (4.49) we may now write for the complete eigenfunction,

$$\psi_{m,l,n} = \frac{e^{im\varphi}}{\sqrt{2\pi}}\sqrt{\frac{(2l+1)(l-m)!}{2(l+m)!}} \, \sin^m \theta P_l^m(\cos\theta)$$

$$\times \sqrt{\frac{4(n-l-1)!Z^3}{[(n+l)!]^3 n^4 a_1^3}}\left(\frac{2Zr}{na_1}\right)^l \cdot e^{\frac{-Zr}{na_1}}L_{n+l}^{2l+1}\left(\frac{2Zr}{na_1}\right). \tag{4.55}$$

Attempts to bring together the probability-density factors $\Phi_m\Phi^*_m$, $(\Theta_{m,l})^2$, and $(R_{n,l})^2$ into one single picture for $\psi\psi^*$, if we may call it a picture, have been somewhat successful. Langer and Walker,[1] using a method which is as yet unpublished, have produced probability-density photographs which represent the spherically symmetrical s states and the $2p$ states $m = +1$ and 0. Using a rather simple mechanical device the author has made photographs of a spinning model which represent time exposures of the hydrogen atom in many other stationary states.[2] A number of these photographs are reproduced in Fig. 4.7. Each figure in three-dimensional space is symmetrical about a vertical axis. Photographs for the states with negative m are identical with those of positive m. The visual or photographic impression of any cloud distribution viewed from the equatorial plane is almost the same as a cross section. A smoke ring, for example, when looked at edge on appears more dense at the ends than in the middle. The circular patterns representing s states are to be pictured as concentric shells, whereas the $2p$ states $m = +1$ and $m = -1$ look more like smoke rings. The $3d$, $m = \pm 1$ states look like two cones with their apices touching each other at the nucleus. The $4d$, $m = \pm 2$ states look like two concentric rings; etc.

[1] See RUARK, A. E., and H. C. UREY, "Atoms, Molecules and Quanta," p. 565, McGraw-Hill Book Company, Inc.; also SLATER, J. C., Phys. Rev., 37, 482, 1931.
[2] WHITE, H. E., Phys. Rev., 37, 1416, 1931.

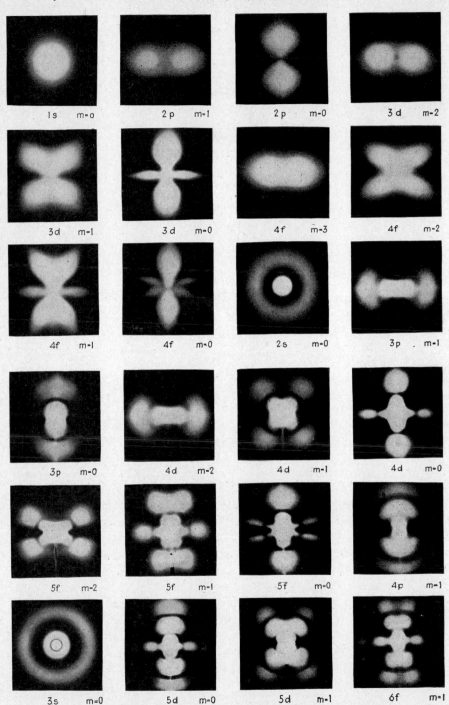

Fig. 4.7.—Photographs of the electron cloud for various states of the hydrogen atom as made from a spinning mechanical model. The probability-density distribution $\psi\psi^*$ is symmetrical about the φ-axis, which is vertical and in the plane of the paper. The scale for each figure may be obtained from Fig. 4.6.

4.11. Useful Atomic Models.—On the older quantum theory the total quantum number n and the azimuthal quantum number k determined the size and shape of the electron orbits, and the magnetic quantum number m determined their orientation in space (see Fig. 3.6). In Sommerfeld's development of the three-dimensional problem, Chap. III, we have seen how the orientation of each orbit may be represented by a vector of magnitude k, or $kh/2\pi$, oriented at such an angle that its projection on the Z axis is m, or $mh/2\pi$. With the introduction of the quantum mechanics the azimuthal quantum number k is replaced by l (see Table 4.1).

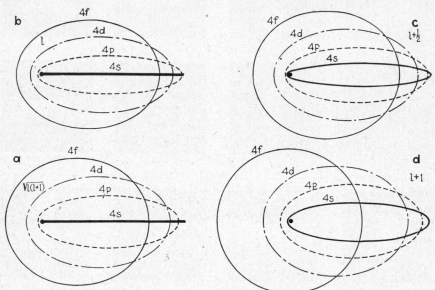

Fig. 4.8.—Four different orbit models proposed by various early investigators.

In setting up an orbital model which will be in harmony with the quantum-mechanical model (Fig. 4.6), we are led by Eq. (4.50) to replace k^2 by $l(l + 1)$, and by Eq. (4.52) to replace k^3 by $l(l + 1)(l + \frac{1}{2})$. This leads, on the one hand, to a model in which k is replaced by $\sqrt{l(l + 1)}$ $= l^*$ and, on the other hand, to two models, one in which k is replaced by $l + \frac{1}{2}$, and the other in which k is replaced by l. The answer to the question as to which of these models is to be preferred is to be found in Weyl's[1] quantum-mechanical proof that values of any angular momentum vector $1^* \dfrac{h}{2\pi}$ and its component along a given axis $\mathbf{m}\dfrac{h}{2\pi}$ are $\sqrt{l(l + 1)} \cdot \dfrac{h}{2\pi}$ and $mh/2\pi$, respectively. Four vector models, which have been used by different investigators, are shown in Fig. 4.8. In each of these

[1] Weyl, "Gruppentheorie und Quantenmechanik," Secs. 12 and 35; see also Condon, E. U., and P. M. Morse, "Quantum Mechanics," Sec. 64.

four models, drawn for $n = 4$ states, the total quantum number is the same. Values of the azimuthal quantum number are given in the following table for each of these models.

TABLE 4.5.—VALUES OF THE AZIMUTHAL QUANTUM NUMBER ACCORDING TO FOUR DIFFERENT ORBIT MODELS

Electron	Quantum-mechanics model a $\sqrt{l(l+1)} = l^*$	Sommerfeld model b $k - 1 = l$	Landé model c $l + \frac{1}{2}$	Bohr-Sommerfeld model d k
s	0	0	$\frac{1}{2}$	1
p	$\sqrt{2}$	1	$\frac{3}{2}$	2
d	$\sqrt{6}$	2	$\frac{5}{2}$	3
f	$\sqrt{12}$	3	$\frac{7}{2}$	4
g	$\sqrt{20}$	4	$\frac{9}{2}$	5

Before the coming of the quantum mechanics, model c was used quite extensively by Back and Landé[1] and model b was used by Sommerfeld.

The commendable features of models a and b are that they give the correct number of magnetic levels. This will become apparent when we come to deal with the Zeeman effect in Chap. X. Space-quantization diagrams for p, d, and f electrons are shown in Fig. 4.9. This is a vector representation of model a showing the various oriented positions of the

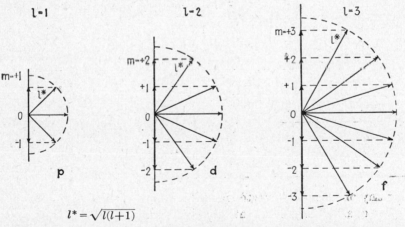

FIG. 4.9.—Vector diagrams of the space quantization of p, d, and f electrons according to model a.

angular momentum vector with respect to a vanishing magnetic field previously set up (see Sec. 3.5) and as such is called a *vector model*.

In describing certain atomic processes it is sometimes convenient to think in terms of the original Bohr-Sommerfeld orbits, model d, or in

[1] See BACK, E., and A. LANDÉ, "Zeemaneffekt."

terms of Landé's model c. Of these two the latter is perhaps to be preferred in that the square of $l + \frac{1}{2}$, i.e., $l(l + 1) + \frac{1}{4}$, is more nearly the quantum-mechanical value $l(l + 1)$.

The average values of the electron-nuclear distance r, calculated for models a, b, c, and d, from Eq. (4.50), are given in the following table for comparison purposes. The same values of $\bar{r}$ are indicated on the r axis of each curve in Fig. 4.6 by ●, ○, ▲ and +, respectively.

As orbital models, c and d are found to be very useful; but as vector models they are objectionable in that they require too many restrictions.[1] Models a and b are useful as vector models but are objectionable as orbital models in that they give zero angular momentum for all s states, orbits originally forbidden by Sommerfeld. Taking all things into consideration one finds that certain difficulties are encountered in attempting to represent the quantum-mechanical formulation of the hydrogen-like atom in terms of any *one* classical model. We are justified, therefore, in

TABLE 4.6.—AVERAGE VALUES OF THE ELECTRON-NUCLEAR DISTANCE r AS CALCULATED FROM EQ. (4.50), IN UNITS OF a_1/Z

Electron	n	l	Model a	Model b	Model c	Model d
1s	1	0	$1\frac{1}{2}$	$1\frac{1}{2}$	$1\frac{3}{8}$	1
2s	2	0	6	6	$5\frac{7}{8}$	$5\frac{1}{2}$
3s	3	0	$13\frac{1}{2}$	$13\frac{1}{2}$	$13\frac{3}{8}$	13
2p	2	1	5	$5\frac{1}{2}$	$4\frac{7}{8}$	4
3p	3	1	$12\frac{1}{2}$	13	$12\frac{3}{8}$	$11\frac{1}{2}$
4p	4	1	23	$23\frac{1}{2}$	$22\frac{7}{8}$	22
3d	3	2	$10\frac{1}{2}$	$11\frac{1}{2}$	$10\frac{3}{8}$	9
4d	4	2	21	22	$20\frac{7}{8}$	$19\frac{1}{2}$
5d	5	2	$34\frac{1}{2}$	$35\frac{1}{2}$	$34\frac{3}{8}$	33
4f	4	3	18	$19\frac{1}{2}$	$17\frac{7}{8}$	16
5f	5	3	$31\frac{1}{2}$	33	$31\frac{3}{8}$	$29\frac{1}{2}$
6f	6	3	48	$49\frac{1}{2}$	$47\frac{7}{8}$	46

using any one orbital or vector model in so far as, when properly set up, it gives qualitatively or quantitatively the quantum-mechanical result. This does not in any way imply that the quantum mechanics always leads to the correct result but that in most cases it does agree with experimental observations. Because of the simplicity of the vector model and its general application to complex spectra, even to some of the finest details, model a will be used extensively in the following chapters. We shall try, however, to think, in so far as seems advisable in this

[1] See BACK, E., and A. LANDÉ, "Zeemaneffekt."

elementary treatment, in terms of the quantum-mechanics electron clouds, *i.e.*, the probability-density distribution.

4.12. Spherical Symmetry.—In Sec. 4.7 we have seen that all s states are spherically symmetrical about the nucleus, *i.e.*, the probability-density or charge distribution is independent of the angles φ and θ. For any given value of l, Unsöld[1] has shown that the charge distribution summed over the states $m = +l$ to $m = -l$ presents spherical symmetry.

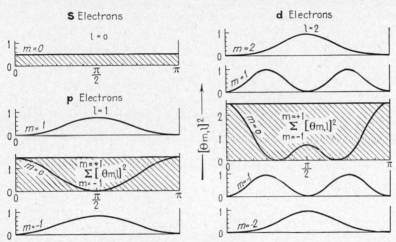

Fig. 4.10.—The probability-density factor $(\Theta_{m,l})^2$ plotted vertically, as a function of the angle θ plotted horizontally, for s, p, and d electrons. The straight lines and the shaded areas represent spherical symmetry, the result of the summation of the curves $m = -l$ to $m = +l$.

Since the charge distribution is symmetrical around the φ axis for all electrons, one has only to show that

$$\sum_{m=-l}^{m=+l} (\Theta_{m,l})^2 = \text{constant.} \tag{4.56}$$

The constancy of this sum may be seen from the values given in Table 4.3 and from the curves in Fig. 4.10. In these curves, $(\Theta_{m,l})^2$ is plotted as a function of the angle θ. The sum of the three curves for the three p states $m = 1, 0$, and -1 gives the straight line indicated by the shaded area in the figure. Similarly the five possible states for a d electron, $m = 2, 1, 0, -1$, and -2, give a straight line. This, it will be shown later, plays an important part in the building up of the elements in the periodic table and leads to the so-called *Pauli exclusion principle*.

Problems

1. For a $2p$ electron of hydrogen in the $m = 0$ state, show that Eq. (4.34) is a solution of Eq. (4.19).

[1] Unsöld, A., *Ann. d. Phys.*, **82**, 379, 1927.

2. For a $2p$ electron of hydrogen, show that Eq. (4.47) is a solution of the radial Eq. (4.35).

3. Using the values of the associated Legendre polynomials in Table 4.2, calculate by means of Eq. (4.34) the probability-density curve $(\Theta_{m,l})^2$ for an f electron, $l = 3$, $m = 1$ (see Fig. 4.3).

4. As in Prob. 3, plot the probability-density curve $(\Theta_{m,l})^2$ for a g electron, $l = 4$, $m = 0$ (see Fig. 4.3).   Tabulate values of $(\Theta_{m,l})^2$ and the corresponding values of θ.

5. From the values of $(\Theta_{m,l})^2$ in Table 4.3, show that the sum of the five d states $m = 2, 1, 0, -1,$ and -2 gives $\frac{5}{2}$.

6. Using Eq. (4.49) and the values of the Laguerre polynomials in Table 4.4, plot, as in Fig. 4.5, the radial curves $R_{n,l}$, $(R_{n,l})^2$, and $4\pi r^2(R_{n,l})^2$ for a $3p$ electron.   Tabulate all values computed.

CHAPTER V

THE ALKALI METALS AND THE PERIODIC TABLE

With the coming of the quantum theory the energy level diagram of hydrogen and its extension to all other atomic systems, with certain modifications, is perhaps the most far-reaching and important discovery

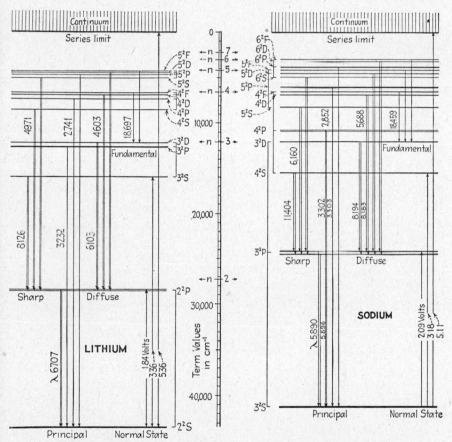

Fig. 5.1.—Energy level diagrams of neutral lithium and sodium atoms.

that has been made in atomic structure. Whether any proposed atomic model is correct or not, it now appears that energy levels and energy level diagrams will always remain with us.

5.1. Energy Level Diagrams.—From a historical standpoint it is of interest to note how nearly the energy level diagram came to being discovered before the advent of the quantum theory. Returning to the frequency plot of the four chief series of spectrum lines of sodium (Fig. 1.7), the Rydberg-Schuster law makes it possible to construct an energy level diagram by turning the figure sideways and raising each series until the limits fall together. Each spectrum line now becomes an energy level and the diagram takes the form shown at the right in Fig. 5.1. The lowest level is a sharp or S level, followed by a principal or P level, then another sharp level S, a diffuse level D, etc. Thus the energy level diagram of sodium consists of a series of sharp, a series of principal, a series of diffuse and a series of fundamental energy levels approaching a common limit.

The diagram at the left in Fig. 5.1 may be obtained in exactly the same way from the four chief series of spectrum lines observed in lithium. The superscript in the level notation indicates that the level in question belongs to a doublet system and that it has certain doublet characteristics.[1]

Just as in hydrogen these energy levels represent certain possible energy states of an electron, and transitions between them represent spectrum lines. The energy levels $n = 1, 2, 3, \cdots$ of hydrogen are given, for comparison, on the term-value scale in the center of the figure. The words *term* or *term value*, often used in place of energy level or state, have been retained from the early use of the terms in the Rydberg and Ritz formulas treated in Chap. I. The fixed term of these series formulas [see Eqs. (1.4) and (1.37)] corresponds to a final or lower energy level common to a given series, and the running terms correspond to the different initial levels, from which the series gets its name, *sharp, principal, diffuse*, or *fundamental*. The first member of the principal series of lithium, for example, is one in which the final state is the lowest level ^2S with a term value [see Eq. (1.10)] of 43487.7 cm^{-1}, and the initial state, neglecting the fine structure, is the first excited level ^2P with a term value of 28582.5 cm^{-1}.

Just as the energy level diagrams of Fig. 5.1, may be obtained directly from the observed series of spectrum lines as shown in Fig. 1.7, so may energy level diagrams for the alkaline earths be obtained from the observed series of lines as given for calcium, for example, in Fig. 1.8. Turning this figure sideways and raising each series until the limits fall together, an energy level diagram is obtained with a singlet sharp level at the bottom. These more complicated diagrams will be taken up in a later chapter. With this brief introduction to energy level diagrams we shall now turn to Bohr's *Aufbauprinzip*.

---

[1] The doublet fine structure of certain of the energy levels and spectrum lines is attributed to the spinning of the electron. This fine structure will be neglected in this chapter but will be taken up in detail in Chap. VIII.

5.2. The Bohr-Stoner Scheme of the Building Up of the Elements.—

Before taking up in detail the well-known spectra of the alkali metals it is important that we first consider the Bohr-Stoner scheme of the building up of the elements in the periodic table.   The periodic table, as it is now frequently formulated, is given in Table 5.1.

The number above each element gives the atomic number Z, and the symbols below give the lowest energy level for that atom.   Referring to Fig. 5.1, for example, the lowest level of lithium and sodium is a sharp level designated as ^2S.   The meaning of the superscripts and the subscripts will be given in detail later.

TABLE 5.1

PERIODIC TABLE

Period	IA	IIA	IIIA	IVA	VA	VIA	VIIA	VIII			IB	IIB	IIIB	IVB	VB	VIB	VIIB	
First Period	1 H $^2S_{1/2}$																	2 He $^1S_0$
Second Period	3 Li $^2S_{1/2}$	4 Be $^1S_0$											5 B $^2P_{1/2}$	6 C $^3P_0$	7 N $^4S_{3/2}$	8 O $^3P_2$	9 F $^2P_{3/2}$	10 Ne $^1S_0$
Third Period	11 Na $^2S_{1/2}$	12 Mg $^1S_0$											13 Al $^2P_{1/2}$	14 Si $^3P_0$	15 P $^4S_{3/2}$	16 S $^3P_2$	17 Cl $^2P_{3/2}$	18 A $^1S_0$
Fourth Period	19 K $^2S_{1/2}$	20 Ca $^1S_0$	21 Sc $^2D_{3/2}$	22 Ti $^3F_2$	23 V $^4F_{3/2}$	24 Cr $^7S_3$	25 Mn $^6S_{5/2}$	26 Fe $^5D_4$	27 Co $^4F_{9/2}$	28 Ni $^3F_4$	29 Cu $^2S_{1/2}$	30 Zn $^1S_0$	31 Ga $^2P_{1/2}$	32 Ge $^3P_0$	33 As $^4S_{3/2}$	34 Se $^3P_2$	35 Br $^2P_{3/2}$	36 Kr $^1S_0$
Fifth Period	37 Rb $^2S_{1/2}$	38 Sr $^1S_0$	39 Y $^2D_{3/2}$	40 Zr $^3F_2$	41 Cb $^6D_{1/2}$	42 Mo $^7S_3$	43 Ma $^6S_{5/2}$	44 Ru $^5F_5$	45 Rh $^4F_{9/2}$	46 Pd $^1S_0$	47 Ag $^2S_{1/2}$	48 Cd $^1S_0$	49 In $^2P_{1/2}$	50 Sn $^3P_0$	51 Sb $^4S_{3/2}$	52 Te $^3P_2$	53 I $^2P_{3/2}$	54 Xe $^1S_0$
Sixth Period	55 Cs $^2S_{1/2}$	56 Ba $^1S_0$	57 La→Hf $^2D_{3/2}$	72 $^3F_2$	73 Ta $^4F_{3/2}$	74 W $^5D_0$	75 Re $^6S_{5/2}$	76 Os $^5F_5$	77 Ir $^2D_{5/2}$	78 Pt $^1S_0$	79 Au $^2S_{1/2}$	80 Hg $^1S_0$	81 Tl $^2P_{1/2}$	82 Pb $^3P_0$	83 Bi $^4S_{3/2}$	84 Po $^3P_2$	85 $^2P_{3/2}$	86 Rn $^1S_0$
Seventh Period	87 Cm $^2S_{1/2}$	88 Ra $^1S_0$	89 Ac	90 Th	91 Pa	92 U												

58 Ce $^3H_4$	59 Pr $^4K_{11/2}$	60 Nd $^5L_6$	61 Il $^6L_{11/2}$	62 Sm $^7K_4$	63 Eu $^8H_{3/2}$	64 Gd $^9D_2$	65 Tb $^8H_{17/2}$	66 Dy $^7K_{10}$	67 Ho $^6L_{21/2}$	68 Er $^5L_{10}$	69 Tu $^4K_{17/2}$	70 Yb $^3H_6$	71 Lu $^2D_{3/2}$

Making the assumption that the number of electrons around the nucleus of a neutral atom is equal to the atomic number Z, and that each of these electrons takes on a definite quantized state, Bohr put forward his *Aufbauprinzip* of building up of the elements.   With quantum numbers assigned to each electron each atom Z in the periodic table is, so far as the extranuclear electrons are concerned, formed by adding one more electron to the atom $Z - 1$.   The quantum numbers to be assigned to this last bound electron are such that the electron in this state is in the most tightly bound state possible.   With such a scheme the atom will have the least amount of energy possible.

Rydberg was the first to show that the atomic numbers of the inert gases He, Ne, A, Kr, Xe, and Rn, which are given in the last column of Table 5.1, are given by the following formula:

$$\begin{array}{cccccc} \text{He} & \text{Ne} & \text{A} & \text{Kr} & \text{Xe} & \text{Rn} \end{array}$$
$$Z = 2(1^2 + 2^2 + 2^2 + 3^2 + 3^2 + 4^2) \qquad (5.1)$$
$$\begin{array}{cccccc} 2 & 10 & 18 & 36 & 54 & 86 \end{array}$$

With relations of this kind already known Bohr's assignments of electrons to the different elements are readily made. The various electrons are classified under so-called *shells* of electrons. *All electrons belonging to the same shell are characterized by the same total quantum number n.* The first shell $n = 1$, the second shell $n = 2$, the third shell $n = 3$, etc., is filled, or completed, when it contains 2, 8, 18, 32, etc., electrons, respectively. These numbers are given by the formula

$$N = 2n^2.$$

The shells $n = 1, 2, 3, 4, \cdots$ are sometimes called (from x-ray spectra) the $K, L, M, N, \ldots$ shells, respectively.

The electrons in any shell n are further divided into *subshells* so that *electrons belonging to the same subshell have the same azimuthal quantum number l.* Electrons for which $l = 0, 1, 2, 3, \cdots$ are called $s, p, d, f, \ldots$ electrons, respectively, where $l = k - 1$ (see Chap. IV). k is the azimuthal quantum number of the Bohr-Sommerfeld orbits (see Chap. III).

Bohr divided the number of electrons in each shell equally among the subshells. Stoner,[1] on the other hand, divided them in the manner shown in Table 5.2.

TABLE 5.2

Subshell	K $n = 1$	L $n = 2$		M $n = 3$			N $n = 4$				System
	$1s$	$2s$	$2p$	$3s$	$3p$	$3d$	$4s$	$4p$	$4d$	$4f$	
Number of electrons.............	2	4	4	6	6	6	8	8	8	8	Bohr
Number of electrons.............	2	2	6	2	6	10	2	6	10	14	Stoner

Stoner's division, as we shall see later, follows directly from Pauli's exclusion principle and is in complete agreement with experimental observations.

5.3. The First Period.—The one electron bound to hydrogen in its normal state is a $1s$ electron with an energy of binding of 109677 cm^{-1}. The energy level is designated $^2S_{\frac{1}{2}}$. Helium in its normal state contains two electrons both of which are bound to the atom in $1s$ states. The energy level of the system is designated as $^1S_0$. The electron configura-

[1] STONER, E. C., *Phil. Mag.*, **48**, 719, 1924.

tions and the corresponding states for normal H and He atoms are therefore written:

$$H,\ 1s,\ ^2S_{\frac{1}{2}}$$
$$He,\ 1s^2,\ ^1S_0$$

5.4. The Second Period.—With the K shell completed in helium the third electron bound to the third element lithium, in its normal S state (see Fig. 5.1), is a $2s$ electron. The fourth electron bound to the fourth element beryllium, $Z = 4$, is also a $2s$ electron to complete the $2s$ subshell. The normal state of the fifth element boron, $Z = 5$, is known from spectroscopic data to be a P state. On the Bohr-Stoner scheme the first electron added should be one with quantum numbers $n = 2$ and $l = 1$. Such an electron is called a $2p$ electron. This, as well as other examples to follow, indicates the origin of our present electron nomenclature s, p, d, etc. The known spectra of the remaining elements in the second period, carbon, nitrogen, oxygen, fluorine, and neon, show that $2p$ electrons are added one after the other to complete not only the $2p$ subshell but also the main L shell, $n = 2$. The electron configurations and the corresponding states for elements in the second period are designated as follows:

Li , $1s^2 2s$	, $^2S_{\frac{1}{2}}$		N , $1s^2 2s^2 2p^3$, $^4S_{\frac{3}{2}}$	
Be, $1s^2 2s^2$	, $^1S_0$		O , $1s^2 2s^2 2p^4$, $^3P_2$	
B , $1s^2 2s^2 2p$,	$^2P_{\frac{1}{2}}$		F , $1s^2 2s^2 2p^5$, $^2P_{\frac{3}{2}}$	
C , $1s^2 2s^2 2p^2$,	$^3P_0$		Ne, $1s^2 2s^2 2p^6$, $^1S_0$	

5.5. The Third Period.—The building up of the eight elements in the third period of the periodic table is similar to that of the eight elements in the second period. The normal level of the well-known sodium diagram (see Fig. 5.1) is an S state, so that the eleventh electron to be bound to sodium must be a $3s$ electron. Following sodium the elements magnesium, aluminum, silicon, phosphorus, sulphur, chlorine, and argon are built up by adding successively one more $3s$ electron and then six $3p$ electrons. The normal states of the atoms and the corresponding configurations of the electrons are;

Na, $1s^2 2s^2 2p^6 3s$	, $^2S_{\frac{1}{2}}$		P , $1s^2 2s^2 2p^6 3s^2 3p^3$, $^4S_{\frac{3}{2}}$	
Mg, $1s^2 2s^2 2p^6 3s^2$	, $^1S_0$		S , $1s^2 2s^2 2p^6 3s^2 3p^4$ $^3P_2$	
Al , $1s^2 2s^2 2p^6 3s^2 3p$,	$^2P_{\frac{1}{2}}$		Cl, $1s^2 2s^2 2p^6 3s^2 3p^5$ $^2P_{\frac{3}{2}}$	
Si , $1s^2 2s^2 2p^6 3s^2 3p^2$,	$^3P_0$		A , $1s^2 2s^2 2p^6 3s^2 3p^6$ $^1S_0$	

For brevity the first 10 electrons of these configurations are often omitted, $e.g.$, the configuration for Al would be written $3s^2 3p$. The chief reason for this is that only the last bound electrons are responsible for the so-called optical spectra. In dealing with x-rays, however, the inner electrons are involved in the process of emission or absorption and should when necessary be given (see Chap. XVI).

5.6. The Fourth Period or First Long Period.—The first long period of elements, starting with potassium $Z = 19$, and ending with krypton $Z = 36$, contains 18 elements. Since the subshells $3s$ and $3p$ have been filled in argon $Z = 18$, and the $3d$ subshell is next in line, one might well expect the normal state of potassium, $Z = 19$, to be a D state, *i.e.*, one given by a $3d$ electron, $n = 3$, $l = 2$. The well-known spectrum of potassium, on the other hand, is like that of sodium with an S state at the bottom of the energy level diagram. It is therefore evident that an s electron, and necessarily a $4s$ electron, must have been added in place of the expected $3d$ electron, and this in turn must be due to the fact that the $4s$ electron is more tightly bound than the $3d$ electron.

Table 5.3.—The Electron Configurations of the 92 Elements in Their Normal Atomic States

Shell	K $n = 1$	L $n = 2$		M $n = 3$			N $n = 4$				Normal state
Subshell	$l = 0$	$l = 0$	$l = 1$	$l = 0$	$l = 1$	$l = 2$	$l = 0$	$l = 1$	$l = 2$	$l = 3$	
1 H	$1s$										$^2S_{\frac{1}{2}}$
2 He	$1s^2$										$^1S_0$
3 Li	$1s^2$	$2s$									$^2S_{\frac{1}{2}}$
4 Be	"	$2s^2$									$^1S_0$
5 B	$1s^2$	$2s^2$	$2p$								$^2P_{\frac{1}{2}}$
6 C	"	"	$2p^2$								$^3P_0$
7 N	"	"	$2p^3$								$^4S_{\frac{3}{2}}$
8 O	"	"	$2p^4$								$^3P_2$
9 F	"	"	$2p^5$								$^2P_{\frac{3}{2}}$
10 Ne	"	"	$2p^6$								$^1S_0$
11 Na	$1s^2$	$2s^2$	$2p^6$	$3s$							$^2S_{\frac{1}{2}}$
12 Mg	"	"	"	$3s^2$							$^1S_0$
13 Al	$1s^2$	$2s^2$	$2p^6$	$3s^2$	$3p$						$^2P_{\frac{1}{2}}$
14 Si	"	"	"	"	$3p^2$						$^3P_0$
15 P	"	"	"	"	$3p^3$						$^4S_{\frac{3}{2}}$
16 S	"	"	"	"	$3p^4$						$^3P_2$
17 Cl	"	"	"	"	$3p^5$						$^2P_{\frac{3}{2}}$
18 A	"	"	"	"	$3p^6$						$^1S_0$
19 K	$1s^2$	$2s^2$	$2p^6$	$3s^2$	$3p^6$		$4s$				$^2S_{\frac{1}{2}}$
20 Ca	"	"	"	"	"		$4s^2$				$^1S_0$
21 Sc	$1s^2$	$2s^2$	$2p^6$	$3s^2$	$3p^6$	$3d$	$4s^2$				$^2D_{\frac{3}{2}}$
22 Ti	"	"	"	"	"	$3d^2$	$4s^2$				$^3F_2$
23 V	"	"	"	"	"	$3d^3$	$4s^2$				$^4F_{\frac{3}{2}}$
24 Cr	"	"	"	"	"	$3d^5$	$4s$				$^7S_3$
25 Mn	"	"	"	"	"	$3d^5$	$4s^2$				$^6S_{\frac{5}{2}}$
26 Fe	"	"	"	"	"	$3d^6$	$4s^2$				$^5D_4$
27 Co	"	"	"	"	"	$3d^7$	$4s^2$				$^4F_{\frac{9}{2}}$
28 Ni	"	"	"	"	"	$3d^8$	$4s^2$				$^3F_4$
29 Cu	"	"	"	"	"	$3d^{10}$	$4s$				$^2S_{\frac{1}{2}}$
30 Zn	"	"	"	"	"	$3d^{10}$	$4s^2$				$^1S_0$

TABLE 5.3.—THE ELECTRON CONFIGURATIONS OF THE 92 ELEMENTS IN THEIR NORMAL ATOMIC STATES.—(*Continued*)

Shell	K $n=1$	L $n=2$		M $n=3$			N $n=4$				O $n=5$			P $n=6$			Q $n=7$	Normal state
Subshell	$l=0$	$l=0$	$l=1$	$l=0$	$l=1$	$l=2$	$l=0$	$l=1$	$l=2$	$l=3$	$l=0$	$l=1$	$l=2$	$l=0$	$l=1$	$l=2$	$l=0$	
31 Ga	$1s^2$	$2s^2$	$2p^6$	$3s^2$	$3p^6$	$3d^{10}$	$4s^2$	$4p$										$^2P_{\frac{1}{2}}$
32 Ge	"	"	"	"	"	"	"	$4p^2$										$^3P_0$
33 As	"	"	"	"	"	"	"	$4p^3$										$^4S_{\frac{1}{2}}$
34 Se	"	"	"	"	"	"	"	$4p^4$										$^3P_2$
35 Br	"	"	"	"	"	"	"	$4p^5$										$^2P_{\frac{3}{2}}$
36 Kr	"	"	"	"	"	"	"	$4p^6$										$^1S_0$
37 Rb	$1s^2$	$2s^2$	$2p^6$	$3s^2$	$3p^6$	$3d^{10}$	$4s^2$	$4p^6$			$5s$							$^2S_{\frac{1}{2}}$
38 Sr	"	"	"	"	"	"	"	"			$5s^2$							$^1S_0$
39 Y	$1s^2$	$2s^2$	$2p^6$	$3s^2$	$3p^6$	$3d^{10}$	$4s^2$	$4p^6$	$4d$		$5s^2$							$^2D_{\frac{3}{2}}$
40 Zr	"	"	"	"	"	"	"	"	$4d^2$		$5s^2$							$^3F_2$
41 Cb	"	"	"	"	"	"	"	"	$4d^4$		$5s$							$^6D_{\frac{1}{2}}$
42 Mo	"	"	"	"	"	"	"	"	$4d^5$		$5s$							$^7S_3$
43 Ma	"	"	"	"	"	"	"	"	$4d^5$		$5s^2$							$^6S_{2\frac{1}{2}}?$
44 Ru	"	"	"	"	"	"	"	"	$4d^7$		$5s$							$^5F_5$
45 Rh	"	"	"	"	"	"	"	"	$4d^8$		$5s$							$^4F_{\frac{9}{2}}$
46 Pd	"	"	"	"	"	"	"	"	$4d^{10}$									$^1S_0$
47 Ag	"	"	"	"	"	"	"	"	$4d^{10}$		$5s$							$^2S_{\frac{1}{2}}$
48 Cd	"	"	"	"	"	"	"	"	$4d^{10}$		$5s^2$							$^1S_0$
49 In	$1s^2$	$2s^2$	$2p^6$	$3s^2$	$3p^6$	$3d^{10}$	$4s^2$	$4p^6$	$4d^{10}$		$5s^2$	$5p$						$^2P_{\frac{1}{2}}$
50 Sn	"	"	"	"	"	"	"	"	"		"	$5p^2$						$^3P_0$
51 Sb	"	"	"	"	"	"	"	"	"		"	$5p^3$						$^4S_{\frac{3}{2}}$
52 Te	"	"	"	"	"	"	"	"	"		"	$5p^4$						$^3P_2$
53 I	"	"	"	"	"	"	"	"	"		"	$5p^5$						$^2P_{\frac{3}{2}}$
54 Xe	"	"	"	"	"	"	"	"	"		"	$5p^6$						$^1S_0$
55 Cs	$1s^2$	$2s^2$	$2p^6$	$3s^2$	$3p^6$	$3d^{10}$	$4s^2$	$4p^6$	$4d^{10}$		$5s^2$	$5p^6$		$6s$				$^2S_{\frac{1}{2}}$
56 Ba	"	"	"	"	"	"	"	"	"		"	"		$6s^2$				$^1S_0$
57 La	"	"	"	"	"	"	"	"	"		"	"	$5d$	$6s^2$				$^2D_{\frac{3}{2}}$
58 Ce	"	"	"	"	"	"	"	"	"	$4f$	"	"	$5d$	$6s^2$				$^3H_4?$
59 Pr	"	"	"	"	"	"	"	"	"	$4f^2$	"	"	$5d$	$6s^2$				$^4K_{1\frac{1}{2}}?$
60 Nd	"	"	"	"	"	"	"	"	"	$4f^3$	"	"	$5d$	$6s^2$				$^5L_6?$
61 Il	"	"	"	"	"	"	"	"	"	$4f^4$	"	"	$5d$	$6s^2$				$^6L_{1\frac{1}{2}}?$
62 Sm	"	"	"	"	"	"	"	"	"	$4f^5$	"	"	$5d$	$6s^2$				$^7K_4?$
63 Eu	"	"	"	"	"	"	"	"	"	$4f^6$	"	"	$5d$	$6s^2$				$^8H_{3\frac{1}{2}}?$
64 Gd	"	"	"	"	"	"	"	"	"	$4f^7$	"	"	$5d$	$6s^2$				$^9D_2?$
65 Tb	"	"	"	"	"	"	"	"	"	$4f^8$	"	"	$5d$	$6s^2$				$^8H_{1\frac{1}{2}}?$
66 Dy	"	"	"	"	"	"	"	"	"	$4f^9$	"	"	$5d$	$6s^2$				$^7K_{10}?$
67 Ho	"	"	"	"	"	"	"	"	"	$4f^{10}$	"	"	$5d$	$6s^2$				$^6L_{2\frac{1}{2}}?$
68 Er	"	"	"	"	"	"	"	"	"	$4f^{11}$	"	"	$5d$	$6s^2$				$^5L_{10}?$
69 Tm	"	"	"	"	"	"	"	"	"	$4f^{12}$	"	"	$5d$	$6s^2$				$^4K_{1\frac{1}{2}}?$
70 Yb	"	"	"	"	"	"	"	"	"	$4f^{13}$	"	"	$5d$	$6s^2$				$^3H_6?$
71 Lu	"	"	"	"	"	"	"	"	"	$4f^{14}$	"	"	$5d$	$6s^2$				$^2D_{\frac{3}{2}}$
72 Hf	$1s^2$	$2s^2$	$2p^6$	$3s^2$	$3p^6$	$3d^{10}$	$4s^2$	$4p^6$	$4d^{10}$	$4f^{14}$	$5s^2$	$5p^6$	$5d^2$	$6s^2$				$^3F_2$
73 Ta	"	"	"	"	"	"	"	"	"	"	"	"	$5d^3$	$6s^2$				$^4F_{\frac{3}{2}}?$
74 W	"	"	"	"	"	"	"	"	"	"	"	"	$5d^4$	$6s^2$				$^5D_0$
75 Re	"	"	"	"	"	"	"	"	"	"	"	"	$5d^5$	$6s^2$				$^6S_{2\frac{1}{2}}?$
76 Os	"	"	"	"	"	"	"	"	"	"	"	"	$5d^7$	$6s$				$^5F_5?$

TABLE 5.3.—THE ELECTRON CONFIGURATIONS OF THE 92 ELEMENTS IN THEIR NORMAL ATOMIC STATES.—(*Concluded*)

Shell	K $n=1$	L $n=2$		M $n=3$			N $n=4$				O $n=5$			P $n=6$			Q $n=7$	Normal state
Subshell	$l=0$	$l=0$	$l=1$	$l=0$	$l=1$	$l=2$	$l=0$	$l=1$	$l=2$	$l=3$	$l=0$	$l=1$	$l=2$	$l=0$	$l=1$	$l=2$	$l=0$	
77 Ir	$1s^2$	$2s^2$	$2p^6$	$3s^2$	$3p^6$	$3d^{10}$	$4s^2$	$4p^6$	$4d^{10}$	$4f^{14}$	$5s^2$	$5p^6$	$5d^9$					$^2D_{\frac{5}{2}}$
78 Pt	"	"	"	"	"	"	"	"	"	"	"	"	$5d^{10}$					$^1S_0$
79 Au	"	"	"	"	"	"	"	"	"	"	"	"	$5d^{10}$	$6s$				$^2S_{\frac{1}{2}}$
80 Hg	"	"	"	"	"	"	"	"	"	"	"	"	$5d^{10}$	$6s^2$				$^1S_0$
81 Tl	$1s^2$	$2s^2$	$2p^6$	$3s^2$	$3p^6$	$3d^{10}$	$4s^2$	$4p^6$	$4d^{10}$	$4f^{14}$	$5s^2$	$5p^6$	$5d^{10}$	$6s^2$	$6p$			$^2P_{\frac{1}{2}}$
82 Pb	"	"	"	"	"	"	"	"	"	"	"	"	"	"	$6p^2$			$^3P_0$
83 Bi	"	"	"	"	"	"	"	"	"	"	"	"	"	"	$6p^3$			$^4S_{\frac{3}{2}}$
84 Po	"	"	"	"	"	"	"	"	"	"	"	"	"	"	$6p^4$			$^3P_2$
85 —	"	"	"	"	"	"	"	"	"	"	"	"	"	"	$6p^5$			$^2P_{\frac{3}{2}}$?
86 Rn	"	"	"	"	"	"	"	"	"	"	"	"	"	"	$6p^6$			$^1S_0$
87 —	$1s^2$	$2s^2$	$2p^6$	$3s^2$	$3p^6$	$3d^{10}$	$4s^2$	$4p^6$	$4d^{10}$	$4f^{14}$	$5s^2$	$5p^6$	$5d^{10}$	$6s^2$	$6p6$		$7s$	$^2S_{\frac{1}{2}}$?
88 Ra	"	"	"	"	"	"	"	"	"	"	"	"	"	"	"		$7s^2$	$^1S_0$
89 Ac	$1s^2$	$2s^2$	$2p^6$	$3s^2$	$3p^6$	$3d^{10}$	$4s^2$	$4p^6$	$4d^{10}$	$4f^{14}$	$5s^2$	$5p^6$	$5d^{13}$	$6s^2$	$6p^6$	$6d$	$7s^2$	$^2D_{\frac{3}{2}}$?
90 Th	"	"	"	"	"	"	"	"	"	"	"	"	"	"	"	$6d^2$	$7s^2$	$^3F_2$?
91 Pa	"	"	"	"	"	"	"	"	"	"	"	"	"	"	"	$6d^3$	$7s^2$	$^4F_{\frac{3}{2}}$?
92 U	"	"	"	"	"	"	"	"	"	"	"	"	"	"	"	$6d^4$	$7s^2$	$^5D_0$?

NOTE.—Electron configurations not confirmed by experimental observations are indicated by question marks after the predicted normal states of the atoms.

This anomaly will be discussed in Sec. 5.10. In calcium another $4s$ electron is added to complete the $4s$ subshell. Following calcium the next 10 elements, scandium, titanium, vanadium, chromium, manganese, iron, cobalt, nickel, copper, and zinc, are built up by the addition of $3d$ electrons. The normal state of zinc has the complete electron configuration

$$\text{Zn, } 1s^2 2s^2 2p^6 3s^2 3p^6 3d^{10} 4s^2, \, {}^1S_0.$$

The following six elements, $Z = 31$ to $Z = 36$, gallium, germanium, arsenic, selenium, bromide, and krypton, are built up by the successive addition of six $4p$ electrons and mark the end of the first long period. The complete electron configuration for krypton in its normal state is written

$$\text{Kr, } 1s^2 2s^2 2p^6 3s^2 3p^6 3d^{10} 4s^2 4p^6, \, {}^1S_0.$$

The building up of the entire periodic table may be given at this point.

5.7. The Fifth Period or Second Long Period.—The second long period, like the first, contains 18 elements starting with an alkali metal and ending with an inert gas. Although the $4d$ and $4f$ subshells are yet to be filled, the thirty-seventh electron bound to rubidium, $Z = 37$, is a

5s electron.   Another electron in a 5s state, added to form strontium, $Z = 38$, completes the 5s subshell.   In the next 10 elements, yttrium, zirconium, columbium, molybdenum, masurium, ruthenium, rhodium, palladium, silver, and cadmium, 10 4d electrons are added as shown in Table 5.3 to complete the 4d subshell.   The irregular way in which these 4d electrons are added is indicative of an attempt to build up one of the inner N subshells more quickly at the expense of one of the already completed O subshells.   Although these irregularities, which are derived from experimental observations, were not predicted, they are now well understood and will be treated in the following chapters.

With the next six elements, indium, tin, antimony, tellurium, iodine, and xenon, six 5p electrons are added successively to complete the 5p subshell.   The normal state of xenon $Z = 54$, an S state, is given by the complete electron configuration

$$\text{Xe, } 1s^2 2s^2 2p^6 3s^2 3p^6 3d^{10} 4s^2 4p^6 4d^{10} 5s^2 5p^6, {}^1S_0$$

5.8. The Sixth Period or Third Long Period.—The third long period, like the first and second, starts with an alkali metal and ends with an inert gas.   This period is unique, however, in that it is interrupted at one point to allow the introduction of the 14 rare-earth elements.   Including these the period contains 32 elements.   In the first two elements, caesium and barium, 6s electrons are added to complete the 6s subshell.   With the addition of one 5d electron in lanthanum, $Z = 57$, a break occurs to allow the successive addition of 14 4f electrons characteristic of the 14 rare-earth elements.   The last element, Lu 71, marks the completion of the N shell, $n = 4$.   With the next element, Hf 72, the addition of 5d electrons is resumed until the subshell is completed.   The building on of six 6p electrons in the next six elements, thallium 81

TABLE 5.4

S-ELECTRONS												p-ELECTRONS					
$1s^1$	$1s^2$																
H	He																
$2s^1$	$2s^2$		**PERIODIC TABLE**									$2p^1$	$2p^2$	$2p^3$	$2p^4$	$2p^5$	$2p^6$
Li	Be		NORMAL STATE ELECTRON									B	C	N	O	F	Ne
$3s^1$	$3s^2$		CONFIGURATIONS									$3p^1$	$3p^2$	$3p^3$	$3p^4$	$3p^5$	$3p^6$
Na	Mg					d-ELECTRONS						Al	Si	P	S	Cl	A

$4s^1$	$4s^2$	$4s^2 3d^1$	$4s^2 3d^2$	$4s^2 3d^3$	$4s^1 3d^5$	$4s^2 3d^5$	$4s^2 3d^6$	$4s^2 3d^7$	$4s^2 3d^8$	$4s 3d^{10}$	$4s^2 3d^{10}$	$4p^1$	$4p^2$	$4p^3$	$4p^4$	$4p^5$	$4p^6$
K	Ca	Sc	Ti	V	Cr	Mn	Fe	Co	Ni	Cu	Zn	Ga	Ge	As	Se	Br	Kr
$5s^1$	$5s^2$	$5s^2 4d^1$	$5s^1 4d^2$	$5s 4d^4$	$5s 4d^5$	$5s^2 4d^5$	$5s 4d^7$	$5s 4d^7$	$4d^{10}$	$5s 4d^{10}$	$5s^2 4d^{10}$	$5p^1$	$5p^2$	$5p^3$	$5p^4$	$5p^5$	$5p^6$
Rb	Sr	Y	Zr	Cb	Mo	Ma	Ru	Rh	Pd	Ag	Cd	In	Sn	Sb	Te	I	Xe
$6s^1$	$6s^2$	$6s^2 5d$	$6s^2 5d^2$		$6s 5d^4 6s^2 5d^5$	$6s^2 5d^5$	$5d^9$	$5d^{10} 6s 5d^{10}$	$6s^2 5d^9$	$6p^1$	$6p^2$	$6p^3$	$6p^4$	$6p^5$	$6p^6$		
Cs	Ba	La	Hf	Ta	W	Re	Os	Ir	Pt	Au	Hg	Tl	Pb	Bi	Po		Rn

$7s^1$	$7s^2$										
	Ra	Ac	Th	Pa	U						

f-ELECTRONS

$5d 4f$	$5d 4f^2$	$5d 4f^3$	$5d 4f^4$	$5d 4f^5$	$5d 4f^6$	$5d 4f^7$	$5d 4f^8$	$5d 4f^9$	$5d 4f^{10}$	$5d 4f^{11}$	$5d 4f^{12}$	$5d 4f^{13}$	$5d 4f^{14}$
Ce	Pr	Nd	Il	Sm	Eu	Gd	Tb	Dy	Ho	Er	Tm	Yb	Lu

to radon 86, completes the third long period. The normal S state of radon is given by the complete electron configuration

$$\text{Rn, } 1s^2 2s^2 2p^6 3s^2 3p^6 3d^{10} 4s^2 4p^6 4d^{10} 4f^{14} 5s^2 5p^6 5d^{10} 6s^2 6p^6, \; {}^1S_0.$$

5.9. The Seventh and Last Period.—The seventh period, like all but the first period, starts with an alkali metal, cornellium, followed by radium, actinium, thorium, uranium X, and uranium. Though the spectroscopic analysis for these elements is very meager, this period very probably starts in just the same way as the first and second long periods.

A very convenient and informing way of representing the addition of the various electrons to the elements of the periodic table is shown in Table 5.4. This arrangement not only retains most of the spectroscopic and chemical relations between elements and groups of elements but also places corresponding electron configurations and subshells together in individual columns.

5.10. Energy Levels of the Alkali Metals.—Many attempts have been made to calculate the energy levels arising from other than hydrogen-like atoms. While calculations of the energy levels for the two and three body problems, hydrogen, and helium have been reasonably successful, many body problems still remain unsolved. In a few special cases, however, some headway has been made with the more complex atoms.

Next to hydrogen the alkali metals Li, Na, K, Rb, and Cs have the simplest of the known spectra. Each alkali atom contains, in addition to the completed subshells of electrons, one single electron in an outer shell (see Table 5.3). The complete configurations are written out in Table 5.5.

TABLE 5.5.—NORMAL CONFIGURATIONS FOR THE ALKALI METALS

Shell	K	L		M			N		O		P
Li	$1s^2$	2s									
Na	$1s^2$	$2s^2$	$2p^6$	3s							
K	$1s^2$	$2s^2$	$2p^6$	$3s^2$	$3p^6$		4s				
Rb	$1s^2$	$2s^2$	$2p^6$	$3s^2$	$3p^6$	$3d^{10}$	$4s^2$	$4p^6$	5s		
Cs	$1s^2$	$2s^2$	$2p^6$	$3s^2$	$3p^6$	$3d^{10}$	$4s^2$	$4p^6$ $4d^{10}$	$5s^2$	$5p^6$	6s

It is the single unbalanced electron that is responsible for the positive valence of one of the alkali metals and also for the quite simple spectrum.

Referring to the simple hydrogen spectrum, the Lyman, Balmer, Paschen, Brackett, and Pfund series are given by Balmer's formula

$$\nu = R_H \left(\frac{1}{n_1^2} - \frac{1}{n_2^2} \right). \tag{5.2}$$

R_H is the Rydberg constant for hydrogen, and n_1 and n_2 are integers. The success of Bohr's theory of the hydrogen atom lay in the fact that he was able for the first time to obtain from theoretical considerations the fundamental Rydberg constant and to show that n_1 and n_2 are the necessary quantum numbers to be associated with each quantized state of the atom. Neglecting small relativity and spin corrections, to be treated in Chaps. VIII and IX, there is no difference in energy between the Bohr circular orbits of hydrogen and the Sommerfeld elliptic orbits with the same total quantum number n.

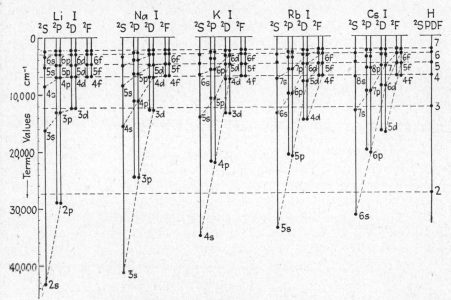

FIG. 5.2.—Energy level diagrams of the alkali metals, lithium, sodium, potassium, rubidium, and caesium, and hydrogen.

In complex atoms, on the other hand, there is a considerable energy difference between the levels arising from s, p, d, and f electrons of the same total quantum number. This difference in energy is attributed to the various amounts of penetration of the different electron orbits into the electron subshells.

Returning to the energy level diagram of lithium in Fig. 5.1, the normal state $2\,{}^2S$ arises from the electron configuration $1s^2 2s$. If now the atom is to be excited, the last bound and most easily moved electron $2s$ has the possibility of going to any of the higher virtual states, *i.e.*, to $2p$, $3s$, $3p$, $3d$, $4s$, $4p$, etc. When in one of these stationary states, the energy level is designated, as in the diagram, by $2\,{}^2P$, $3\,{}^2S$, $3\,{}^2P$, $3\,{}^2D$, $4\,{}^2S$, $4\,{}^2P$, etc. If the excited electron is in the $3d$ state, for example, the complete electron configuration of the atom is designated as $1s^2 3d$ and the energy level as $3\,{}^2D$.

This same designation scheme leads to the level assignments shown for sodium in Fig. 5.1. The K and L shells already being filled, the various possible excited states for the last bound electron 3s are 3p, 3d, 4s, 4p, etc. If the excited electron is in a 4p state, the complete electron configuration is designated $1s^2 2s^2 2p^6 4p$ and the energy level[1] as 4^2P. To save time and space this configuration is abbreviated 4p.

Energy-level diagrams of the five alkali metals are given in Fig. 5.2. In this type of diagram the levels are shown as dots in place of straight horizontal lines. The electron configuration of each level is given in each case by the excited electron only. The energy levels of hydrogen are given at the right in the figure for comparison.

Term values[2] for the first five or six energy levels in each of the four chief series of lithium and sodium are given in Tables 5.6 and 5.7. For comparison purposes the hydrogen values are also given.

TABLE 5.6.—TERM VALUES OF LITHIUM
(*After Paschen and Goetze*)

Term	Electron	$n = 2$	$n = 3$	$n = 4$	$n = 5$	$n = 6$	$n = 7$
^2S	$s, l = 0$	43484.4	16280.5	8474.1	5186.9	3499.6	2535.3
^2P	$p, l = 1$	28581.4	12559.9	7017.0	4472.8	3094.4	2268.9
^2D	$d, l = 2$		12202.5	6862.5	4389.2	3046.9	2239.4
^2F	$f, l = 3$			6855.5	4381.2	3031.0	
Hydrogen		27419.4	12186.4	6854.8	4387.1	3046.6	2238.3

TABLE 5.7.—TERM VALUES OF SODIUM
(*After Paschen and Goetze*)

Term	Electron	$n = 3$	$n = 4$	$n = 5$	$n = 6$	$n = 7$	$n = 8$
^2S	$s, l = 0$	41444.9	15706.5	8245.8	5073.7	3434.9	2481.9
^2P	$p, l = 1$	24492.7	11181.9	6408.9	4152.9	2908.9	2150.7
^2D	$d, l = 2$	12274.4	6897.5	4411.6	3059.8	2245.0	1720.1
^2F	$f, l = 3$		6858.6	4388.6	3039.7	2231.0	1708.2
Hydrogen		12186.4	6854.8	4387.1	3046.6	2238.3	1713.7

5.11. The Effective Quantum Number and the Quantum Defect.—It has already been pointed out in Chap. I that the principal series of sodium has been observed as far as the forty-seventh member (see Fig. 1.11). Although the different series belonging to the other alkali metals have not been observed to quite as many members, the series limits and term

[1] The figure 4 refers to the total quantum number of the electron and is only used in one-electron systems as an abbreviation of the more explicit notation where the electron configuration is given first, followed by the term type, i.e., 4p, ^2P.

[2] The terms, energy level, energy state, state, and term, are to be considered more or less synonymous and are often used indiscriminately.

values of the sharp, principal, diffuse, and fundamental series are known with very great precision. We have also seen in Chap. I that the frequency of a spectrum line is given by the difference between two terms, and that a series of lines is given by the difference between a fixed term and a series of running terms,

$$\nu = \frac{R}{(n_1 + \mu_1)^2} - \frac{R}{(n_2 + \mu_2)^2}, \tag{5.3}$$

where R is the Rydberg constant, n_1 and n_2 are integers, and μ_1 and μ_2 are small constants.

With somewhat definite knowledge concerning the quantum number n of the valence electron in the alkali metals, the integers n_1 and n_2 in Rydberg's formula may be replaced by the total quantum numbers of the electron energy states. Since the quantum number n is in general greater than Rydberg's denominator $n + \mu$, the formula for a spectrum line or series may, changing the sign of μ_1 and μ_2, be written

$$\nu = \frac{R}{(n_1 - \mu_1)^2} - \frac{R}{(n_2 - \mu_2)^2} \tag{5.4}$$

and a spectral term by

$$T = \frac{R}{(n - \mu)^2} = \frac{R}{n_{\text{eff}}^2} \tag{5.5}$$

where n is now the total quantum number. The factor $n - \mu$ is still called the *Rydberg denominator*. μ is the *quantum defect*, and n_{eff} is the so-called *effective quantum number*.

The bracketing together in Fig. 5.1 of the energy levels having the same total quantum number reveals a number of interesting and important relations. One important result is that in each group of levels the S level lies deepest and is followed by P, D, and F levels in this order. A second relation indicates that in going from the more elliptic s orbits (S states) to the more nearly circular p, d, and f orbits (P, D, and F states) the term values approach those of hydrogen. Using the Eq. (5.5), the effective quantum numbers n_{eff} for the term values of lithium and sodium (see Tables 5.6 and 5.7) are calculated and given in Tables 5.8 and 5.9.

TABLE 5.8.—VALUES OF THE EFFECTIVE QUANTUM NUMBER n_{eff} FOR LITHIUM
($R_{\text{Li}} = 109729$ cm^{-1})

Term	Electron	$n = 2$	$n = 3$	$n = 4$	$n = 5$	$n = 6$	$n = 7$
^2S	$s, l = 0$	1.589	2.596	3.598	4.599	5.599	6.579
^2P	$p, l = 1$	1.960	2.956	3.954	4.954	5.955	6.954
^2D	$d, l = 2$		2.999	3.999	5.000	6.001	7.000
^2F	$f, l = 3$			4.000	5.004		

TABLE 5.9.—VALUES OF THE EFFECTIVE QUANTUM NUMBER n_{eff} FOR SODIUM
(R_{Na} = 109734 cm^{-1})

Term	Electron	$n = 3$	$n = 4$	$n = 5$	$n = 6$	$n = 7$	$n = 8$
^2S	$s, l = 0$	1.627	2.643	3.648	4.651	5.652	6.649
^2P	$p, l = 1$	2.117	3.133	4.138	5.141	6.142	7.143
^2D	$d, l = 2$	2.990	3.989	4.987	5.989	6.991	7.987
^2F	$f, l = 3$		4.000	5.001	6.008	7.012	8.015

A correlation of n and n_{eff} shows that μ is greatest for the S states, and that, as we shall see in Chap. VII, it is a measure of the penetration of the valence electron into the subshells of electrons. The picture formed is that of a nucleus of charge Ze closely surrounded by a core of $Z - 1$ electrons outside of which at some distance a single electron is moving in a hydrogen-like state. The effect of the net core-nucleus charge e is such as to make the system hydrogen-like, *i.e.*, a singly charged nucleus and one electron. For the s states the electron penetrates down into the core where the effective nuclear charge is greater and hence the binding is greater.

5.12. The Selection Principle.—Under ordinary conditions spectrum lines corresponding to the transition of an electron from any one state to another are not observed. In emission or absorption spectra a *selection rule* is found to be in operation. In short, this selection rule, which may be derived from Bohr's correspondence principle as well as the quantum mechanics, may be stated as follows: *In any single electron transition the quantum number l must change by $+1$ or -1, i.e.,*

$$\Delta l = \pm 1. \tag{5.6}$$

In terms of the orbital model the orbital angular momentum must change by one unit of $h/2\pi$ only. With the law of the conservation of angular momentum in mind this can only be interpreted to mean that every photon $h\nu$ has associated with it an angular momentum of $h/2\pi$.

In any transition the total quantum number n is not restricted in any way and may change by any integral value, including zero. Let us consider several examples.

If the sodium atom (see Fig. 5.1) is excited by some means or other so that the single-valence electron is raised to one of the excited states 3^2P, 4^2S, 3^2D, 4^2P, . . . , the electron may return to the normal state 3^2S by making only certain selected jumps. According to the selection principle an electron in a 3^2D state must return to the normal state 3^2S in two separate jumps 3^2D to 3^2P with the emission of the first line of the diffuse series, written 3^2P-3^2D; then 3^2P to 3^2S with the emission of the first line of the principal series, written 3^2S-3^2P. If the electron is in a 4^2P state, on the other hand, it has three possible routes open along which it may return to the normal state: first, by the direct transition 4^2P to 3^2S; second, by the three transitions 4^2P to 3^2D to 3^2P to 3^2S; or third, by the three transitions 4^2P to 4^2S to 3^2P to 3^2S. There are some exceptions to the selection rule for the quantum number l, but the forbidden transitions occur so seldom that the resultant spectrum lines are exceedingly faint. These exceptions are found experimentally and should occur theoretically when high external fields are present (see Chaps. X and XIII).

It should be pointed out in passing that the quantum numbers assigned to any electron really belong to the atomic system as a whole. It is only because we can approximate a complex atom by a set of independent one-electron systems with given values for the quantum numbers n and l, that we can associate the latter with the individual electrons.

Problems

1. If the valence electron in sodium is excited to the 4^2D state, what are the different routes open for the electron in returning to the normal state?

2. Calculate the Rydberg denominators for the first five term values of the sharp, principal, diffuse, and fundamental series of potassium (see Fowler, "Series in Line Spectra"). Where the fine structure is known, use the larger of the two values, $R = 109736$ cm^{-1}.

3. From the values of the effective quantum number calculated in Prob. 2, compute the quantum defect μ.

4. The first five members of a certain series have wave-lengths as follows: $\lambda_{air} = 7800.29, 4201.82, 3587.08, 3348.72,$ and 3228.05 Å. Using Eq. (5.4), compute at least four values of μ_2 and from their average determine μ_1 and the term value of the fixed term. With the fixed term known, determine the five running terms. Assume $R = 109737$ cm^{-1}, and $n_1 = 5$ and $n_2 = 5, 6, 7, 8,$ and 9.

5. It will be found very useful to memorize the order of the elements in the periodic table and the corresponding electron configurations of the normal state. This task is greatly facilitated by taking one period at a time and writing them in the form shown in Table 5.4.

CHAPTER VI

EXCITATION POTENTIALS, IONIZATION POTENTIALS, AND THE SPECTRA OF IONIZED ATOMS

One of the most direct proofs of the existence of discrete energy states within an atom was first found in the experiments of Lenard,[1] Franck and Hertz,[2] and others, on critical potentials. The collision of a neutral atom with a fast-moving atom, molecule, or electron will under suitable conditions result in the excitation or ionization of the atom. If in collision the energy exchange between, say, an electron and atom is all energy of translation, the atom is not excited and the

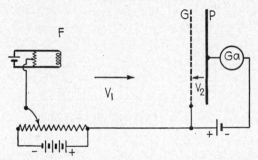

FIG. 6.1.—Schematic diagram of Franck and Hertz' critical potentials experiment.

collision is said to be *elastic*. If, on the other hand, the velocity of the electron is sufficiently high, the collision may be *inelastic*. In this case the electron gives up all or part of its energy in giving potential energy to the atom, or, as we say, *in exciting the atom*. Inelastic collisions between atoms, molecules, or electrons, which by virtue of translational motion result in the excitation or ionization of one of the atoms or molecules, are called *collisions of the first kind*. An excited atom may in turn by collision with another atom, molecule, or electron, return to the normal state without the emission of a radiated frequency. The potential energy of the excited atom is in this case transformed into energy of translation and the collision is called a *collision of the second kind*.

6.1. Critical Potentials.—In the Franck and Hertz experiments on critical potentials a vapor like sodium or mercury is bombarded with

[1] LENARD, *Ann. d. Phys.*, **8**, 149, 1902.

[2] FRANCK, J., and G. HERTZ, *Verh. d. Deutsch. Phys. Ges.*, **16**, 12, 1914; *Phys. Zeits.*, **17**, 409, 1916.

electrons of known velocity.   A diagram of the apparatus in its simplest schematic form is given in Fig. 6.1.   Electrons from a filament F are accelerated toward a grid G by applying a potential V_1 between them. An opposing potential V_2, much smaller than V_1, is applied between the grid G and the plate P.   The vapor pressure in the tube and the distances between *filament, grid,* and *plate* are so adjusted that the *mean free path* is considerably smaller than the filament-grid distance FG and somewhat greater than the grid-plate distance GP.

If an electron starts from rest at the filament and reaches the grid G without an encounter, its velocity v is given by the energy relation

$$Ve = \tfrac{1}{2}mv^2, \tag{6.1}$$

where e is the charge on the electron, m is its mass, and V is the accelerating potential in electrostatic units.   Expressing V in volts V_1 the energy becomes[1]

$$\frac{V_1}{300}e = \tfrac{1}{2}mv^2. \tag{6.2}$$

In order for an electron to collide inelastically with an atom, it must give up sufficient energy $\tfrac{1}{2}mv^2$ to raise the valence electron from its normal state to the first excited state.   In the case of a sodium atom (see Fig. 5.1) this amounts to raising the valence electron from the 3^2S to the 3^2P state, an energy given by

$$W_{3^2P} - W_{3^2S} = h\bar{\nu} = hvc, \tag{6.3}$$

where h is Planck's constant, c the velocity of light, and ν the frequency in wave numbers of the first member of the principal series $3^2S - 3^2P$. In this example the kinetic energy given up by the bombarding electron must be

$$hc \cdot 16956 \text{ ergs.} \tag{6.4}$$

It is customary to express the kinetic energy of an electron in terms of volts.   The general relation between electron velocity expressed in volts and the excitation energy of the atom expressed in wave numbers is, from Eqs. (6.2) and (6.3), given by the expression

$$\frac{300hc}{e}\nu \cong V_1 = \frac{c^2h}{10^8e}\nu = 1.2336 \times 10^{-4} \times \nu. \tag{6.5}$$

An electron starting from rest must therefore fall through a difference of potential $V_1 = 1.2336 \times 10^{-4} \times 16956 = 2.1$ volts in order that upon collision with a sodium atom at rest the valence electron will be raised to the 3^2P state.

---

[1] For a treatment of the early work on critical potentials see K. T. Compton and F. L. Mohler, "Critical Potentials," *Nat. Research Council, Bull.,* Vol. 9, Pt. I, No. 48, 1924.

Characteristic of the early work on critical potentials are the experiments of Tate and Foote[1] on sodium vapor in which an experimental set-up similar to that of Franck and Hertz (Fig. 6.1) was used. The curve reproduced in Fig. 6.2, showing the variation in plate current with accelerating potential V_1, is characteristic of their results and may be explained as follows. Initially, with $V_1 = 0$, very few electrons leave the filament with sufficient velocity to reach the plate against the small retarding field V_2, maintained in this case at about 0.8 volt. As V_1 is gradually increased, the speed and number of electrons reaching

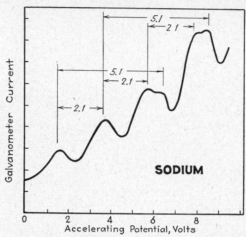

FIG. 6.2.—Critical potential curve of sodium.   (*After Tate and Foote.*)

the grid increase and the plate current rises. When the velocity has increased sufficiently to excite sodium atoms, inelastic collisions occur. With a further increase in V_1 more electrons reach the critical velocity, are stopped by inelastic collision, and not being able to reach the plate cause a temporary drop in galvanometer current. This drop in current continues until the critical speed is attained far enough in front of the grid to collide inelastically and again reach the plate P. The current therefore rises again and continues to rise until the electrons after one inelastic collision attain the critical speed and make a second inelastic collision. Except for the doubling of the third and fourth maxima, this process and explanation repeats itself with each major rise and fall of the curve. ·

The double peaks in Fig. 6.2 show that not only have collisions occurred in which the valence electron has been excited but also collisions in which the valence electron has been completely removed from the atom, *i.e.*, the atom has been ionized. Complete ejection of the electron from sodium would, from Eq. (6.5), require an equivalent electron velocity of $1.2336 \times 41444.9 = 5.1$ volts. In view of the initial electron

[1] TATE, J. T., and P. D. FOOTE, *Jour. Wash. Acad. Sci.*, **7**, 517, 1917.

velocity at the filament the first ionization should occur at about $V_1 = 4.5$ volts. With ionization taking place at this potential, it is to be expected that the electrons starting from rest at this point will collide inelastically at 2.1 volts further on, as observed.

Improved experimental technique on critical potentials has made it possible to obtain not only one excitation potential for a given atom

TABLE 6.1.—CRITICAL POTENTIALS OF THE ALKALI METALS

Element	First excitation potential		Ionization potential	
	Observed	Computed from spectra	Observed	Computed from spectra
Li 3	....	1.84	....	5.37
Na 11	2.12	2.09	5.13	5.12
K 19	1.55	1.60	4.1	4.32
Rb 37	1.6	1.55	4.1	4.16
Cs 55	1.48	1.38	3.9	3.88

but many. The additional critical potentials correspond to the raising of the valence electron to excited states other than the first one discussed above. Although in every element investigated the critical potentials are in excellent agreement with the values calculated from spectral terms, it should be mentioned that an occasional potential is found which is difficult to explain. The first excitation potential and the ionization potential of each of the alkali metals are given in Table 6.1.

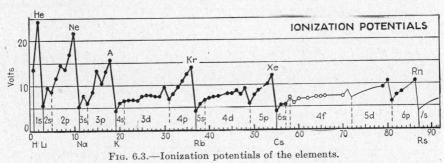

FIG. 6.3.—Ionization potentials of the elements.

These experimental determinations of critical potentials confirm the values computed from spectroscopic data. With the physical constants e, h, and c known with considerable accuracy, spectroscopic data furnish the most accurate means of determining excitation as well as ionization potentials.

Known ionization potentials for the elements in the periodic table are given in Fig. 6.3. The various electron subshells being built up are indicated between the vertical lines. These symbols also indicate the type of electron removed in ionization. It is to be noted that the inert gases show the largest ionization potentials and the alkali metals the smallest.

6.2. The Spectra of Ionized Atoms.—The elements beryllium, magnesium, calcium, strontium, and barium contain, in addition to the closed shells of electrons of the preceding inert gases, two rather loosely bound s electrons (see Tables 5.3 and 5.4). The positive valence two, which is characteristic of the chemical behavior of the alkaline earths, is attributed to these two outermost, but deeply penetrating, electrons. The electron configurations of these elements, excluding the inert gas cores, are

Be I	Mg I	Ca I	Sr I	Ba I
$2s^2$	$3s^2$	$4s^2$	$5s^2$	$6s^2$

If by some excitation process each of these atoms loses one of its valence electrons, *i.e.*, it becomes ionized, the electron configurations, so far as the remaining electrons are concerned, become identical with those of the preceding alkali metals:

Li I	Na I	K I	Rb I	Cs I
Be II	Mg II	Ca II	Sr II	Ba II
$2s$	$3s$	$4s$	$5s$	$6s$

While the process of excitation and emission of radiation from ionized atoms is similar to that for neutral atoms, the energies involved are considerably greater. If the excitation is brought about by an encounter between a fast-moving electron and a neutral calcium atom, then, at impact, the interchange of energy must be sufficient to remove completely one valence electron from the atom and to raise the other to an excited state.

An energy level diagram of singly ionized calcium is given in Fig. 6.4. The normal state of the atom is given by 4^2S and corresponds to the valence electron in a $4s$ orbit. Unlike the alkali metals the first excited state is a diffuse level rather than a principal level, however. Owing to the fact that the electron in a 3^2D level cannot return to the normal level 4^2S, without violating the selection rule ($\Delta l = \pm 1$ only), this 3^2D level is called a *metastable state*. Once the electron is in this metastable state, it will remain there for some time and may return to the normal state only by collision with another particle and the liberation of its energy without radiation. Next following the metastable state comes the first member of the principal series 4^2P, the second member of the sharp series 5^2S, the second member of the diffuse series 4^2D, etc. States having the same total quantum number n are bracketed together. While the strong lines of the alkali metals (see Fig. 5.1) are to be found in the visible and near infra-red spectral region, the corresponding lines in the ionized alkaline earths are to be found in the visible and near ultra-violet region.   In potassium, for example, the first member of the principal series is in the far red between 7000 and 8000 Å, whereas the first line of the principal series of ionized calcium is in the

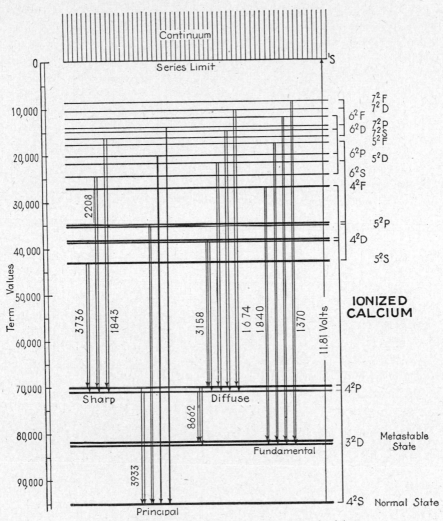

Fig. 6.4.—Energy level diagram of singly ionized calcium.

violet just below 4000 Å.   Photographs of these lines are given in Fig. 17.1.

The atomic picture that may be formed of an alkaline-earth atom after it is ionized is that of a nucleus of charge Ze closely surrounded by a cloud, or core, of $Z-2$ electrons and, outside this, one valence electron. The net core-nucleus charge $2e$ is such as to make the system similar to that of ionized helium where the term values, according to Bohr's theory, are given by

$$T = \frac{Z^2 R}{n^2} = \frac{4R}{n^2}, \qquad n = 1, 2, 3, \cdots \quad \text{(see Chap. II)} \qquad (6.6)$$

By analogy with the formulas of hydrogen and ionized helium it follows that for ionized atoms like those under discussion the expression for term values may be written

$$T = \frac{4R}{n_{\text{eff}}^2} = \frac{4R}{(n - \mu)^2}, \qquad (6.7)$$

where n is the total quantum number of the electron and μ the quantum defect. The well-known enhanced series of the alkaline-earth elements are represented therefore [see Sec. 1.16 and Eq. (1.41)] by the formula

$$\nu = \frac{4R}{(n_1 - \mu_1)^2} - \frac{4R}{(n_2 - \mu_2)^2}. \qquad (6.8)$$

Energy level diagrams for each of the ionized alkaline-earth elements are given in Fig. 6.5. The term-value scale is one-fourth that of the

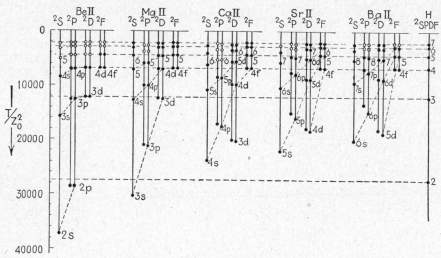

FIG. 6.5.—Energy level diagrams of singly ionized beryllium, magnesium, calcium, strontium, and barium, and hydrogen.

hydrogen scale shown at the right. With the relatively large energy values for the different states, electron transitions between states will in general be large. The difference between each term value and the hydrogen term values of the same n, shown by horizontal lines, is a measure of the quantum defect μ. A comparison of these diagrams with those of Fig. 5.2 brings out a number of interesting relations. The relatively large quantum defect of s electrons in Li I and Be II, of s

and p electrons in Na I and Mg II, and of s, p, and d electrons in K I, Ca II, Rb I, Sr II, Cs I, and Ba II, which is a measure of the penetration of the valence electron into the subshells of electrons, is of particular interest and will be considered in detail in Chap. VII.

One outstanding difference between the diagrams is the relative order of binding of s, p, and d electrons in the third, fourth, and fifth elements.   In potassium, for example, the order is $4s$, $4p$, $5s$, $3d$, $5p$, etc., whereas in Ca II it is $4s$, $3d$, $4p$, $5s$, $4d$, etc.   Noting this shift of the $3d$ electron from fourth place in K I to second place in Ca II, Bohr predicted that in doubly ionized scandium, Sc III, the 3^2D state should lie deepest.   Later investigations, as will be shown in Chap. XVII, confirm this.

Although spectra of many singly ionized atoms are well known, the examples of the alkaline earths as treated here will serve as an introduction to the general subject of the spectra of ionized atoms. This subject will be resumed in Chap. XVII where multiply-ionized atoms will also be treated.

CHAPTER VII

PENETRATING AND NONPENETRATING ORBITS IN THE ALKALI METALS

We shall now turn our attention to the formulation of an atomic model which treats the interaction of a single valence electron with the nucleus when it is screened by an intervening core of electrons, *i.e.*, by inner completed subshells of electrons. This must be done if

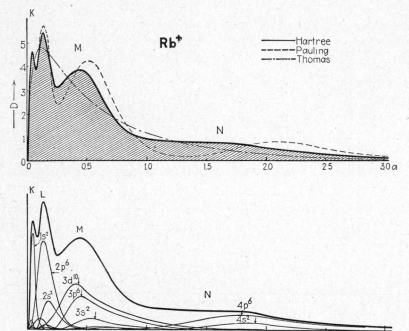

Fig. 7.1.—Probability-density-distribution curves for the rubidium-atom core of 36 electrons. (*After Hartree.*)

we are to calculate from theoretical considerations the energy levels of the alkali metals. On the classical picture of the atom the nucleus is surrounded by various shells and subshells of electrons in orbits resembling the various possible states of the Bohr-Sommerfeld hydrogen atom. The quantum-mechanical picture, on the other hand, appears in the form of a probability-density distribution for the same electrons.

7.1. The Quantum-mechanical Model of the Alkali Metals.—By means of successive approximations to the so-called *self-consistent field*,

100

Hartree[1] has calculated the radial density distributions of each core electron for the different alkali metals. Although a treatment of the methods by which these calculations are made is out of place here, the calculations are not difficult but are long and tedious. It will suffice

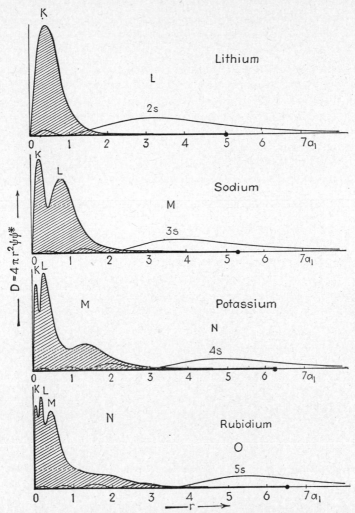

Fig. 7.2.—Probability-density distribution curves for the neutral alkali atoms, lithium, sodium, potassium, and rubidium. In each case the core is shown by one curve and the valence electron by another.

to say, however, that the resultant electric field obtained for any atom is such that the solutions of Schrödinger's wave equation for all of the core electrons in this field give a distribution of electrons which reproduces the field.

[1] HARTREE, D. R., *Proc. Camb. Phil. Soc.*, **24**, 89, 111, 1928.

As an example of Hartree's results, probability-density-distribution curves for the rubidium core are shown in Fig. 7.1. The radial curve for each subshell is shown in the lower half of the figure. The heavy curve represents the sum of all of the 36 core electrons. The four loops, or humps, in the latter are taken to represent the K, L, M, and N shells, even though every electron contributes something to each shell. The dotted curves shown above for comparison purposes have been calculated from hydrogen wave functions by Pauling[1] by using approximation methods and by Thomas[2] from statistical considerations. In comparing these curves with the corresponding hydrogen-like functions shown in Fig. 4.6, it is observed that each density curve, due to a very large nuclear charge, has been drawn in toward the nucleus by a considerable amount.

Probability-density-distribution curves for lithium, sodium, potassium, and rubidium are given together in Fig. 7.2. In each case the core charge is shown by a shaded curve and the valence electron in its normal state by another curve. Radially it should be noted that the major shells in each atom lie well inside the first Bohr circular orbit of hydrogen $r = a_1$, and that the valence electron lies well inside the corresponding hydrogen state. In hydrogen, for example, the density distribution D for a $5s$ electron is appreciably large as far out as $50a_1$, whereas in rubidium the nodes and loops have been pulled in to about one-tenth of this.

The dots on the r axis represent the extremities of the classical orbits based on model a (see Fig. 4.8). In these s states the kinetic energy of the electron at the end of the orbit is zero, and the total energy is all potential,

$$W = \text{P. E.} = -\frac{e^2}{r} = -eV, \tag{7.1}$$

where r is in centimeters. Expressing V in volts and r in Ångströms,

$$V = \frac{300e}{r \times 10^{-8}} = \frac{300 \times 4.77 \times 10^{-10}}{r \times 10^{-8}} = \frac{14.31}{r}. \tag{7.2}$$

Expressing r in units of a_1 ($a_1 = 0.528$ Å),

$$r_{\text{max}} = \frac{27.1}{V} = \frac{27.1}{\text{ionization potential in volts}}. \tag{7.3}$$

From the ionization potentials of the alkali metals given in Table 6.1 the following values of the orbital extremities are obtained:

	Li	Na	K	Rb	Cs
$r_{\text{max}} =$	$5.0a_1$	$5.3a_1$	$6.3a_1$	$6.5a_1$	$7.0a_1$

[1] PAULING, L., *Proc. Roy. Soc.*, **A, 114**, 181, 1927.

[2] THOMAS, L. H., *Proc. Camb. Phil. Soc.*, **23**, 542, 1927; see also GAUNT, *Proc. Camb. Phil. Soc.*, **24**, 328, 1928; and FERMI, *Zeits. f. Phys.*, **48**, 73, 1928.

The above derivation is only a close approximation, for we have assumed a rigid core of unit charge.

7.2. Penetrating and Nonpenetrating Orbits.—The quantum-mechanical model of the sodium atom is shown in Fig. 7.3. In addition to the shaded curve for the 10 core electrons the three lowest possible states for the one and only valence electron are also shown. The corre-

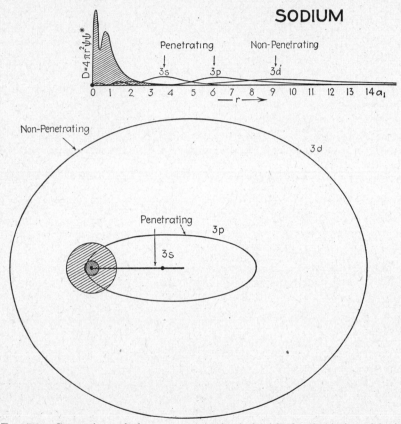

Fig. 7.3.—Comparison of the quantum-mechanical with the classical model of the neutral sodium atom. Three of the lowest possible states for the single valence electron are also shown.

sponding 3s, 3p, and 3d classical orbits based on model b (see Fig. 4.8), are shown in the lower part of the figure. A comparison of these orbits with the corresponding hydrogen orbits shows that, due to penetration into the core, 3s and 3p are greatly reduced in size radially. The 3d orbit, on the other hand, remains well outside the main part of the core and is hydrogen-like. Corresponding to the penetration of the 3s and 3p orbits the probability-density-distribution curves (above) have small loops close to the nucleus.

Consider now the classical picture of a valence electron describing any one of various types of orbits about the spherically symmetrical sodium-atom core. In Fig. 7.4 six different orbits are shown representing valence-electron states with the same total quantum number n (the same major axis) but slightly different azimuthal quantum number l (different minor axes). With a core-density distribution of charge always finite but approaching zero as $r \to \infty$, all valence-electron orbits will be more or less penetrating.

In Fig. 7.4a the electron moves in a path well outside the major part of the core. Since the field in this outside region does not deviate

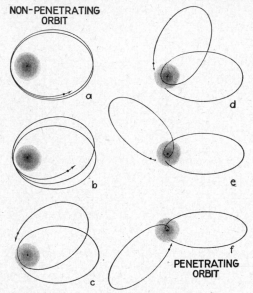

FIG. 7.4.—Showing the change in electron orbits with increasing penetration.

greatly from a Coulomb field, the orbit will be a Kepler ellipse precessing slowly (due to small deviations from a Coulomb field) about the atom center. In the remaining figures increased penetration is shown accompanied by an increase in the precession at each turn of the orbit. As the electron goes from aphelion (r_{max}) to perihelion (r_{min}), it leaves behind it more and more of the core charge. With the steady increase in force field the electron is drawn from its original path into a more and more eccentric path, with the result that at its closest approach to the nucleus the electron has turned through somewhat more than 180 deg. Upon reaching r_{max} again, there has been an advance, i.e., a precession, of the aphelion. The increased force of attraction between nucleus and electron at penetration increases the binding energy, the kinetic energy, and the term values but decreases the total energy of the atomic system [see Eq. (2.15)].

7.3. Nonpenetrating Orbits.—Nonpenetrating orbits are defined as those orbits for which the observed energies are very nearly equal to those of the corresponding hydrogen-like orbits. Such orbits on either the classical or quantum-mechanical model do not appreciably penetrate the atom core and are those states for which the azimuthal quantum number l is more nearly equal to the total quantum number n. The f orbits in all of the alkali metals are good examples of nonpenetrating orbits. Term values for the $4f$, $5f$, and $6f$ states given in Table 7.1 will illustrate this.

TABLE 7.1.—Term Values of Nonpenetrating f Orbits in the Alkali Metals Compared with Those of Hydrogen

| Electron designation....... | $4f$ | $5f$ | $6f$ |
Term designation...........	4^2F	5^2F	6^2F
Hydrogen	6854.85	4387.11	3046.60
Li	6855.5	4381.2	3031.0
Na	6858.6	4388.6	3039.7
K	6879.2	4404.8	3057.6
Rb	6893.1	4413.7	3063.9
Cs	6935.2	4435.2	3076.9

With the exception of caesium the observed values are hydrogen-like to 1 per cent or better.

Term values plotted as they are in Fig. 5.2 show, in general, that p, d, and f orbits in lithium, d and f orbits in sodium and potassium, and f orbits in rubidium and caesium are nearly hydrogen-like. In the enhanced spectra of the ionized alkaline earths the term values are to be compared with those of ionized helium, or they are to be divided by 4 (*i.e.*, by Z^2) and compared with hydrogen as in Fig. 6.5. In these energy level diagrams it is observed that p, d, and f orbits in Be II, d and f orbits in Mg II, and f orbits in Ca II, Sr II, and

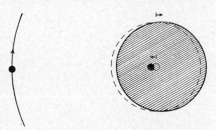

Fig. 7.5.—Schematic representation of the polarization of the atom core by an external electron.

Ba II are hydrogen-like and therefore correspond to nonpenetrating orbits.

Although nearly hydrogen-like, the term values of nonpenetrating orbits (see Table 7.1), in general, are greater than those of hydrogen. Born and Heisenberg[1] attributed these small differences to a polarization of the core by the valence electron (see Fig. 7.5). In the field of the

[1] Born, M., and W. Heisenberg, *Zeits. f. Phys.*, **23**, 388, 1924.

valence electron the atom core is pushed away and the nucleus is pulled toward the electron by virtue of the repulsion and attraction of like and unlike charges, respectively. The effect of this polarization is to decrease the total energy of the system. On an energy diagram this means a lowering of the level, *i.e.*, an increase in the term value. Theoretical values of the polarization energy calculated for the alkali metals with the aid of the quantum mechanics are found to account for the major part of these very small deviations from hydrogen-like terms.[1]

7.4. Penetrating Orbits on the Classical Model.—Although no sharp line of demarkation can be drawn between penetrating and nonpenetrating orbits, the former may be defined as those orbits for which the term values are appreciably different from those of hydrogen. Referring to Fig. 5.2, the *s* orbits of Li, the *s* and *p* orbits of Na and K, and the *s*, *p*, and *d* orbits of Rb and Cs come under this rough classification. Certainly on the quantum-mechanical model all orbits are penetrating.

To effect a calculation of the term values for penetrating orbits on the classical theory, one is led by necessity to simplify somewhat the atom-core model given in Fig. 7.4. A suitable idealized model was first put forward

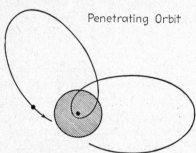

Penetrating Orbit

by Schrödinger[2] in which the core electrons were thought of as being distributed uniformly over the surface of one or more concentric spheres. This same model has been treated by Wentzel,[3] Sommerfeld,[4] Van Urk,[5] Pauling and Goudsmit,[6] and others. Since the classical treatment of penetrating orbits is so closely analogous to the quantum-mechanical treatment of the same orbits, to be taken up in the next section, Schrödinger's simplified model will be considered here in some detail.

Fig. 7.6.—Valence electron penetrating an ideal core where the core electrons are distributed uniformly over the surface of a sphere.

Consider the very simplest model in which the core electrons are distributed uniformly over the surface of a sphere of radius ρ (see Fig. 7.6). Let $Z_i e$ represent the effective nuclear charge inside the charge shell and $Z_o e$ the effective nuclear charge outside the shell. Usually Z_o is 1 for the alkali metals, 2 for the alkaline earths, etc. The potential energy

---

[1] For the quantum-mechanics formula giving the polarization energy see L. Pauling and S. Goudsmit, "Structure of Line Spectra," p. 45, 1930; and also J. H. Van Vleck and N. G. Whitelaw, *Phys. Rev.*, **44**, 551, 1933.

[2] Schrödinger, E., *Zeits. f. Phys.*, **4**, 347, 1921.

[3] Wentzel, G., *Zeits. f. Phys.*, **19**, 53, 1923.

[4] Sommerfeld, A., "Atombau," 5th German ed., p. 422, 1931.

[5] Van Urk, A. T., *Zeits. f. Phys.*, **13**, 268, 1923.

[6] Pauling, L., and S. Goudsmit, "Structure of Line Spectra," p. 40, 1930.

of the valence electron when outside the thin spherical shell of charge $(Z_i - Z_o)e$ will be

$$V_o = -\frac{Z_o e^2}{r} \tag{7.4}$$

while inside it becomes

$$V_i = -\frac{Z_i e^2}{r} + \frac{Z_i e^2}{\rho} - \frac{Z_o e^2}{\rho}. \tag{7.5}$$

The total energy for an elliptic orbit, in polar coordinates r and φ, is given by Eq. (3.26) as

$$W = T + V = \frac{1}{2m}\left(p_r^2 + \frac{p_\varphi^2}{r^2}\right) + V, \tag{7.6}$$

where p_r and p_φ are the radial and angular momenta, respectively. From the results obtained in Chap. III it is seen that outside the charged shell the motion will be that of an electron in a Coulomb field of charge $Z_o e$, and inside the shell the motion will be that of an electron in a Coulomb field of charge $Z_i e$.

Applying the quantum conditions to the orbital angular momentum p_φ, which must be constant at all times throughout the motion,

$$\int_0^{2\pi} p_\varphi d\varphi = kh, \qquad p_\varphi = k\frac{h}{2\pi}. \tag{7.7}$$

That part of the electron path which is outside the shell is a segment of an ellipse determined by the azimuthal quantum number k and the radial quantum number r_o, whereas the path inside the shell is a segment of an ellipse determined by the same azimuthal k ($p_\varphi = $ constant) but a different radial quantum number, r_i. Substituting successively the potential energies of Eqs. (7.4) and (7.5) in the total energy [Eq. (7.6)] and solving for p_r, the radial quantum conditions can be written down as

$$\oint\left\{2m\left(W + \frac{Z_o e^2}{r}\right) - \frac{p_\varphi^2}{r^2}\right\}^{\frac{1}{2}} dr = \oint R_o dr = r_o h, \tag{7.8}$$

$$\oint\left\{2m\left(W + \frac{Z_i e^2}{r} - \frac{(Z_i - Z_o)e^2}{\rho}\right) - \frac{p_\varphi^2}{r^2}\right\}^{\frac{1}{2}} dr = \oint R_i dr = r_i h. \tag{7.9}$$

The total quantum numbers to be associated with r_o and r_i will, as usual, be given by

$$n_o = k + r_o \qquad \text{and} \qquad n_i = k + r_i. \tag{7.10}$$

Since the electron does not complete either of the two ellipses in one cycle, the integrals of Eqs. (7.8) and (7.9) are not to be evaluated over a complete cycle as indicated but over only that part of the ellipse actually traversed. The radial quantum number r for the actual path traversed is therefore given by the sum of the two integrals

$$\int_{\text{outside}} R_o dr + \int_{\text{inside}} R_i dr = rh. \tag{7.11}$$

The total energy in the *outside* region by Eqs. (2.14), (2.15), (2.30), (2.33), and (7.4) is

$$W = -T = \frac{V}{2} = -\frac{Z_o e^2}{2r} = -\frac{Z_o^2 e^2}{2 a_1 n_o^2} \tag{7.12}$$

where a_1 is the radius of the first Bohr circular orbit. The total energy *inside* is

$$W = -T = \frac{V}{2} = -\frac{Z_i^2 e^2}{2 a_1 n_i^2} + \frac{(Z_i - Z_o)e^2}{\rho}. \tag{7.13}$$

Since the energy inside and outside must be the same,

$$-\frac{Z_o^2 e^2}{2 a_1 n_o^2} = -\frac{Z_i^2 e^2}{2 a_1 n_i^2} + \frac{(Z_i - Z_o)e^2}{\rho}. \tag{7.14}$$

Consider now the special case shown in Fig. 7.7, in which the two partial Kepler ellipses are almost complete.[1] If the outside orbit were a complete Kepler ellipse the electron would never penetrate the shell, whereas if the inner orbit were complete the electron would always remain inside. As the outer ellipse is made less and less penetrating, the two ellipses become more and more complete and the integrals of Eq. (7.11) approach those of Eqs. (7.8) and (7.9). Expressing this in terms of the radial quantum numbers,

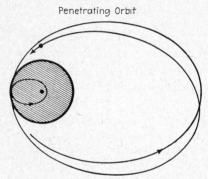

Penetrating Orbit

FIG. 7.7.—Special case where inner and outer ellipses are almost complete. Core charge distributed uniformly over the surface of a sphere.

$$r = r_o + r_i. \tag{7.15}$$

In a similar fashion the perihelion distance of the *outer* orbit $a_o(1 - \epsilon_o)$ approaches the aphelion of the *inner* ellipse $a_i(1 + \epsilon_i)$, both approaching at the same time the radius of the spherical shell ρ. We write, therefore,

$$a_o(1 - \epsilon_o) = a_i(1 + \epsilon_i) = \rho, \qquad \epsilon_i = \frac{\rho}{a_i} - 1. \tag{7.16}$$

In terms of the quantum numbers [Eqs. (3.23), (7.10), and (7.15)]

$$n - n_o = n_i - k = \mu. \tag{7.17}$$

This difference $n - n_o$ is the so-called *quantum defect* and n_o is the Rydberg denominator n_{eff}. The semimajor axis and eccentricity of the

[1] See VAN URK, A. T., *Zeits. f. Phys.*, **13**, 268, 1923.

inner ellipse are by Eqs. (3.32) and (3.22), respectively,

$$a_i = a_1 \frac{n_i^2}{Z_i} \text{ and } \epsilon_i^2 = 1 - \frac{k^2}{n_i^2}. \tag{7.18}$$

Substituting a_i in Eq. (7.16) and squaring, there results

$$\epsilon_i^2 = \left(\frac{\rho Z_i}{n_i^2 a_1} - 1 \right)^2 = 1 - \frac{k^2}{n_i^2}, \tag{7.19}$$

from which

$$n_i = \rho Z_i (2\rho a_1 Z_i - a_1^2 k^2)^{-\frac{1}{2}}. \tag{7.20}$$

Replacing k^2 and k by the corresponding quantum-mechanical values $l(l + 1)$ and $l + \frac{1}{2}$, respectively [see Eq. (4.52)], and substituting in Eq. (7.17), the quantum defect becomes

$$\mu = \rho Z_i \{ 2\rho a_1 Z_i - a_1^2 l(l + 1) \}^{-\frac{1}{2}} - (l + \frac{1}{2}). \tag{7.21}$$

This expresses the experimental result, well known before the quantum mechanics, that for a given atom the quantum defect μ is a function of the azimuthal quantum number and is independent of the total quantum number (see Table 7.2).

Table 7.2.—Experimental Values of the Quantum Defect $n - n_o = \mu$ for Penetrating Orbits in Lithium and Sodium

Element	Term	Electron	$n = 2$	$n = 3$	$n = 4$	$n = 5$	$n = 6$	$n = 7$
Li	^2S	$s, l = 0$	0.41	0.40	0.35	0.35	0.35	0.35
Na	^2S	$s, l = 0$	....	1.37	1.36	1.35	1.35	1.35
	^2P	$p, l = 1$	....	0.88	0.87	0.86	0.86	0.86

In order to calculate quantum defects from Eq. (7.21), it is necessary to determine values for the electron-nuclear distance ρ. Successful attempts to calculate suitable values of ρ from quantum-mechanical density-distribution curves similar to those shown in Figs. 7.1 and 7.2 have been made by Pauling.[1] In the case of Na, Pauling obtains the average value of the electron-nuclear distance ρ_K for the two K electrons as $0.132a_1$, and for the eight L electrons $\rho_L = 0.77a_1$. Assuming that the valence electron penetrates only the outermost shell of eight electrons, the effective nuclear charge $Z_i e$ will be $9e$. Substituting Z_i and ρ_L in Eq. (7.21), the values of $\mu = 1.36$ and $\mu = 0.85$ are obtained for the s and p orbits of sodium, in very good agreement with the observed values given in Table 7.2. For lithium with $Z_i = 3$ and $\rho_K = 0.53a_1$ the value

[1] Pauling, L., *Proc. Roy. Soc.*, A, **114**, 181, 1927.

$\mu = 0.39$ is computed for the s orbits, also in good agreement with experiment.

7.5. Quantum-mechanical Model for Penetrating Orbits.—The solutions of the Schrödinger wave equation for hydrogen-like atoms and for the normal state of the helium-like and lithium-like atoms have been carried out to a high degree of accuracy. The calculations for lithium-like atoms are of particular interest in that they appear to give the quantum-mechanical analogue of the inner and outer orbit segments, so well known on the classical theory and treated in the last section.

Numerous attempts have been made to calculate the energy of the lithium atom in its normal state ^2S. Perhaps the most recent and accurate calculations are those made by Wilson.[1] In previous determinations single-electron wave functions of the hydrogen type were used instead of a wave function for the atom as a whole. The rather brief treatment to be given here is that of Wilson based upon a principle previously introduced by Slater.[2]

Slater has shown that a wave function representing an atom containing many electrons may be properly constructed by expressing it in the form of a determinant the elements of which are built up out of the Schrödinger wave equation. In the case of lithium, for example, the wave function is written

$$\psi = \frac{1}{\sqrt{6}}\begin{vmatrix} A_1 & A_2 & A_3 \\ \bar{A}_1 & \bar{A}_2 & \bar{A}_3 \\ B_1 & B_2 & B_3 \end{vmatrix}, \tag{7.22}$$

where the A's and $\bar{A}$'s are $1s$ hydrogen-like wave functions for the two K electrons and the B's are $2s$ wave functions for the L electron.

From Eq. (4.55) the solutions of the wave equation for $1s$ and $2s$ electrons are

$$A = \psi_{1s} = N_1 e^{-Zr}, \tag{7.23}$$

$$B = \psi_{2s} = N_2 \left\{ \frac{Z}{2}re^{-\frac{Zr}{2}} - e^{-\frac{Zr}{2}} \right\}, \tag{7.24}$$

where $N_1 = -(Z^3/\pi)^{\frac{1}{2}}$, $N_2 = (Z^3/8\pi)^{\frac{1}{2}}$, Z is the atomic number, and a_1, the radius of the first Bohr circular orbit, has been chosen as unit of length. Now the $2s$ function [Eq. (7.24)] for the valence electron is orthogonal to the $1s$ functions [Eq. (7.23)] for the K electrons. This would no longer be so, if different values for Z should be substituted in Eqs. (7.23) and (7.24). For this case Slater[3] has shown that the two functions may be orthogonalized by adding a fraction of one of the

[1] Wilson, E. B., *Jour. Chem. Phys.*, **1**, 210, 1933. For other references see this paper.

[2] Slater, J. C., *Phys. Rev.*, **34**, 1293, 1928.

[3] Slater, J. C., *Phys. Rev.*, **42**, 33, 1932.

1s functions to the 2s function. Now a determinant possesses the property that when any row is multiplied by any factor and added to any other row the determinant remains unchanged in value. Wilson's normalized wave function for the lithium atom therefore takes the form

$$\psi = \frac{1}{\sqrt{6}} \begin{vmatrix} A_1 & A_2 & A_3 \\ \bar{A}_1 & \bar{A}_2 & \bar{A}_3 \\ B_1 + bA_1 & B_2 + bA_2 & B_3 + bA_3 \end{vmatrix}, \qquad (7.25)$$

where the A's and B's now represent the simple hydrogen-like wave functions with modified values for Z.

When determinants involving hydrogen-like functions with Z put equal to the atomic number are used to calculate the energy, the result

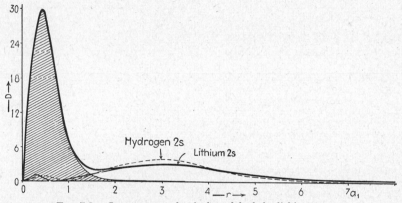

Fig. 7.8.—Quantum-mechanical model of the lithium atom.

is not so good as might be expected. Much better agreement is obtained by considering the Z's as parameters and adjusting them, by variation methods, until a minimum energy is obtained. Wilson found the lowest energy value with the wave functions and their parameters as follows:

$$A_i = \psi_{1s} = N_1 e^{-(Z-\sigma_1)r_i}, \qquad (7.26)$$

$$B_i + bA_i = N_2 \left\{ \frac{Z - \sigma_1}{2} r_i e^{\frac{-(Z-\sigma_2)r_i}{2}} - e^{\frac{-(Z-\sigma_3)r_i}{2}} + be^{-(Z-\sigma_1)r_i} \right\}, \qquad (7.27)$$

where $\sigma_1 = 0.31$, $\sigma_2 = 1.67$, $\sigma_3 = 0$, and N_1 and N_2 are normalizing factors. The probability-density-distribution curve obtained by plotting $4\pi r^2 \psi^2$ against the electron-nuclear distance r is shown by the heavy curve in Fig. 7.8. The dotted curve for the hydrogen 2s state does not rightly belong here but is shown as a comparison with the 2s state of lithium. The latter curve is obtained by plotting $4\pi r^2 \psi_{2s}^2$.

The pulling in of the inner loop of the Li 2s curve over the inner loop of the hydrogen 2s curve is due to the lack of screening by the 1s electrons of the core and is to be compared with the deeper penetration and speeding up of the electron in the *inner* part of the classical orbit. The $2s$ electron, since it is most of the time well *outside* the core, is screened from the nucleus by the two core electrons. This average screening is well represented by the screening constant $\sigma_2 = 1.67$. The screening of each $1s$ electron from the nucleus by the other $1s$ electron should lie between 0 and 1. The value $\sigma_1 = 0.31$ is in good agreement with this. When the $2s$ electron is inside the core (*i.e.*, the smaller loop), the screening by the outer $1s$ electrons is practically negligible. The value $\sigma_3 = 0$ is in good agreement with this. This same analogy between the quantum-mechanical model and the orbital model should extend to all elements.

The accuracy with which Eq. (7.25) represents the normal states of lithium and singly ionized beryllium (see Figs. 5.2 and 6.5) is shown by the following values:

	Spectroscopic	Calculated
Li I, $2s$	$T = 43484$ cm^{-1}	43089 cm^{-1}
Be II, $2s$	$T = 146880$	145984

Calculations of the quantum defect for the alkali metals from a purely theoretical standpoint have also been made by Hartree.[1] Hartree, employing his *self-consistent field* theory (see Sec. 7.1), has determined the quantum defects and energy levels for a number of states in several of the alkalis. After determining a probability-density-distribution curve for the core of the atom, as in Fig. 7.1, the energy of the valence electron moving in this field can be calculated. In rubidium, for example, he obtained the following values of μ:

TABLE 7.3.—OBSERVED AND CALCULATED VALUES OF THE QUANTUM DEFECT
μ FOR RUBIDIUM
(*After Hartree*)

Electron term	μ (obs.)	μ (calc.)	Diff.
$5s$ 5^2S	3.195	3.008	0.187
$6s$ 6^2S	3.153	2.987	0.166
$7s$ 7^2S	3.146	2.983	0.163
$5p$ 5^2P	2.71	2.54	0.17
$6p$ 6^2P	2.68	2.51	0.17
$4d$ 4^2D	0.233	0.028	0.205

Since the quantum defect is a measure of the penetration of the valence electron into the atom core, the orbital model as well as the quantum-mechanical model would be expected to show that the pene-

---

[1] HARTREE, D. R., *Proc. Camb. Phil. Soc.*, **24**, 89, 111, 1928.

tration is not greatly different for all states of the same series. The first seven of a series of d states, $l = 2$, for example, are shown in Fig. 7.9. The orbits given above are drawn according to model a; and beneath them are drawn the hydrogen probability-density-distribution curves of the same quantum numbers.

On the orbital model the perihelion distances are very nearly the same. On the quantum-mechanical model the lengths of the first

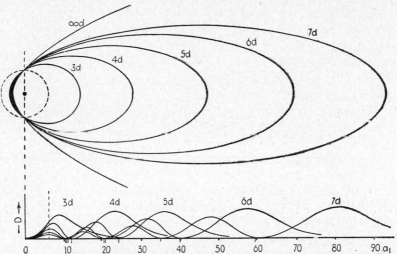

FIG. 7.9.—Series of d orbits illustrating nearly equal penetration for all orbits with the same l on either the classical or the quantum-mechanical model.

loop (indicated by the first nodal points), with the exception of $3d$, are nearly the same. Figure 7.9 brings out better than any other, perhaps, the close analogies that may be drawn between the orbits of the early quantum theory and the probability-density-distribution curves of the newer quantum mechanics. This is one of the reasons why the terms *orbit, penetrating orbit, nonpenetrating orbit*, etc., are still used in discussing quantum-mechanical processes.

Problems

1. Assuming that the s and p orbits in potassium penetrate only the shell of eight M electrons, compute the value of ρ_M from Eq. (7.21). Compare these values of ρ with the density-distribution curve in Fig. 7.2. If the values of the quantum defect are not known from Prob. 2, Chap. V, they are readily calculated from the term values directly.

2. Compute, on the classical theory, model a, the maximum electron-nuclear distances attained by the valence electron of sodium in the first 10 s orbits. Compare these values with the corresponding s orbits of hydrogen by plotting a graph. Plot r_{max} against n for hydrogen and n_{eff} for sodium.

CHAPTER VIII

DOUBLET FINE STRUCTURE AND THE SPINNING ELECTRON

From the very earliest observations of spectral series it has been known that each member of certain general types of series shows fine structure while those of others do not. Each member of some of the series in the alkali metals, for example, is a close doublet (see Fig. 1.9), whereas in the alkaline earths it is a close triplet (see Fig. 1.10). So far as energy levels are concerned, term analyses of so-called *doublet spectra* show that $P, D, F, G, \ldots$ levels are probably double, whereas S levels are always single (see Figs. 5.1, 5.2, 6.4, and 6.5). It is with this fine structure that we are concerned in this chapter, for in its explanation we are led to a new concept, the spinning electron.

8.1. Observed Doublet Fine Structure in the Alkali Metals and the Boron Group of Elements.—Before taking up the question of the origin of fine structure, it is important that we become more or less familiar with the doublet spectra of the alkalies and another group of elements not yet considered. These are the elements in the third group of the periodic table (Table 5.1), boron, aluminum, gallium, indium, and thallium. Like the alkali metals each of these atoms gives rise to four chief series of spectrum lines: sharp, principal, diffuse, and fundamental. From these observed series, energy level diagrams are finally constructed as shown in Fig. 8.1. The chief difference between the alkali metals and what we shall hereafter call the *boron group of elements* is best described in terms of the energy levels rather than in terms of the spectrum lines.

In the alkali metals a ^2S term lies deepest, followed by a ^2P term as the first excited state (see Fig. 5.2); whereas, in the boron group a ^2P term lies deepest, followed by ^2S. This observed experimental fact is the basis, in the Bohr-Stoner scheme of the building up of the elements, for the addition of p electrons in these elements (see Table 5.1). The complete electron configurations for the boron group are written as follows:

B   5, $1s^2\ 2s^2\ \mathbf{2p}$
Al 13, $1s^2\ 2s^2\ 2p^6\ 3s^2\ \mathbf{3p}$
Ga 31, $1s^2\ 2s^2\ 2p^6\ 3s^2\ 3p^6\ 3d^{10}\ 4s^2\ \mathbf{4p}$
In 49, $1s^2\ 2s^2\ 2p^6\ 3s^2\ 3p^6\ 3d^{10}\ 4s^2\ 4p^6\ 4d^{10}\ \ \ \ \ \ 5s^2\ \mathbf{5p}$
Tl 81, $1s^2\ 2s^2\ 2p^6\ 3s^2\ 3p^6\ 3d^{10}\ 4s^2\ 4p^6\ 4d^{10}\ 4f^{14}\ 5s^2\ 5p^6\ 5d^{10}\ 6s^2\ \mathbf{6p}$

All other subshells being complete, it is the single unbalanced p electron which, when the atom is excited, takes on the various possible energy

114

states shown in Fig. 8.1.   In boron, for example, the first excited ^2S state finds the electron in a $3s$ orbit, the $1s$ and $2s$ subshell being already filled.   There being no d electrons in boron and no virtual d orbits with a total quantum number n lower than 3, the excitation of the valence electron to the first ^2D state places the electron into a $3d$ orbit.

Neglecting for the moment the doublet nature of the different levels, it should be noted that the ^2F terms in all five elements, just as in the alkali metals, are nearly hydrogen-like, indicating nonpenetrating

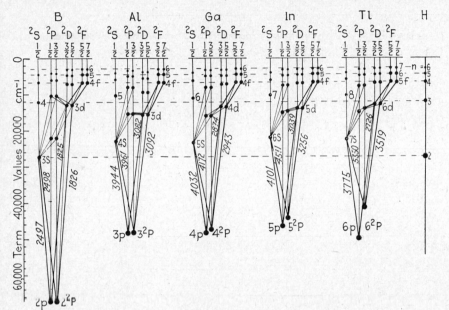

FIG. 8.1.—Energy level diagrams of the boron group of elements.

orbits.   It is to be noted too that for a given total quantum number n the order of binding, which is also the order of increasing penetration, is ^2F, ^2D, ^2P, and ^2S.

The largest fine-structure separations in each element of the boron group are to be found in the normal states ^2P.   The very narrow $^2P_{\frac{1}{2}}$–$^2P_{\frac{3}{2}}$ interval in boron widens with each succeeding element until in thallium it has become almost as large as the gross-structure interval 6^2P–7^2S. The first sharp series doublets given in Table 8.1 indicate the enormous spreading out of the first ^2P terms in going to higher atomic numbers.   One line of the thallium doublet is in the visible green region of the spectrum and the other member is in the ultra-violet over 1500 Å away.

Exactly this same spreading out of the fine structure is observed in the alkali metals in going from lithium to caesium.   This may be seen directly from the principal series as they are plotted in Fig. 8.2.   The sodium doublets are relatively much narrower than shown.   The fine-

TABLE 8.1.—DOUBLET SEPARATIONS FOR THE FIRST MEMBERS OF THE SHARP SERIES

	$^2P_{\frac{3}{2}}-^2S_{\frac{1}{2}}$ λ	$^2P_{\frac{1}{2}}-^2S_{\frac{1}{2}}$ λ	$\Delta\lambda$ $\overset{\circ}{A}$	$\Delta\nu$ cm^{-1}
B	2497.82	2496.87	0.95	5.20
Al	3961.68	3944.16	17.52	112.07
Ga	4172.22	4033.18	139.04	826.10
In	4511.44	4101.87	409.57	2212.63
Tl	5350.65	3775.87	1574.78	7792.42

structure intervals for the first member of the principal series in each of the alkalies and ionized alkaline earths are observed as follows:

Li I	Na I	K I	Rb I	Cs I
0.338	17.2	57.9	237.7	554.0 cm⁻¹

Be II	Mg II	Ca II	Sr II	Ba II
6.61	91.5	223.0	800.0	1691.0 cm⁻¹

In lithium the 2^2S-2^2P interval (see Fig. 5.1) is over 4000 times the fine-structure interval 0.338 cm⁻¹, whereas in caesium the corresponding interval is only 20 times larger.

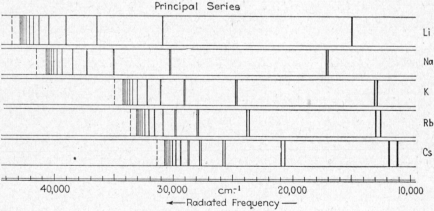

FIG. 8.2.—Illustrating fine structure in the principal series of the alkali metals. (Sodium and potassium doublets are narrower than shown.)

A general survey of the energy level diagrams (Figs. 5.1, 5.2, 6.4, and 6.5) will enable certain general conclusions concerning fine-structure intervals to be drawn: First, corresponding doublet separations increase with atomic number. Second, doublet separations in the ionized alkaline earths are larger than the corresponding doublets in the alkali metals. Third, within each element doublet separations decrease in going to higher members of a series. Fourth, within each element

P doublets are wider than *D* doublets of the same *n*, and *D* doublets are wider than *F* doublets of the same *n*. The last two statements are illustrated schematically in Fig. 8.3 by giving the four lowest members of the three chief term series. It should be mentioned in passing that exceptions to these rules are well known. These exceptions, however, are fully accounted for and will be treated as special cases in Chap. XIX.

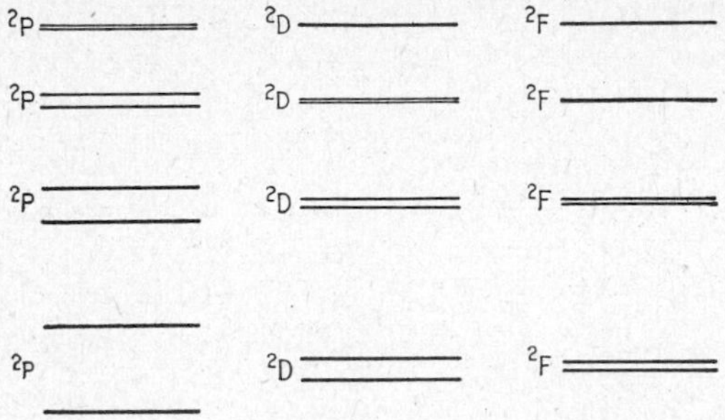

Fig. 8.3.—Schematic representation of relative term separations in the different series.

8.2. Selection Rules for Doublets.—In the doublet spectra of atomic systems containing but one valence electron the small letters s, p, d, f, . . . , for the different electron orbits are replaced by the corresponding capitals S, P, D, F, . . . , for the terms. The small superscript 2 in front of each term indicates that the level in question, including S levels, has doublet properties and belongs to a doublet system. Although all S levels are single, their doublet nature will later be seen to reveal itself when the atom is placed in a magnetic field. In order to distinguish between two fine-structure levels having the same n and l values, the cumbrous but theoretically important half-integral subscripts are used. This subscript to each term, first called the *inner quantum number* by Sommerfeld, is of importance in atomic structure, for it gives the total angular momentum of all the extranuclear electrons (see Sec. 8.4). The *inner quantum number* is frequently referred to as the electron quantum number j or the term quantum number J.

Observation shows that, for the transition of an electron from one energy state to another, definite selection rules are in operation. This is illustrated schematically in Fig. 8.4 by six different sets of combinations. From these diagrams, which are based upon experimental observations, selection rules for doublets may be summarized as follows: In any electron transition[1]

$$l \text{ changes by } +1, \text{ or } -1 \text{ only,}$$

and

$$j \text{ changes by } 0, +1, \text{ or } -1 \text{ only.}$$

---

[1] Violations of either of these selection rules are attributed to the presence of an external electric or magnetic field (see Chaps. X and XX) or to quadripole radiation.

The total quantum number n has no restrictions and may change by any integral amount. The relative intensities of the radiated spectrum lines are illustrated by the heights of the lines directly below each transition arrow at the bottom of the figure. Combinations between ^2P and ^2S always give rise to a fine-structure doublet, whereas all other combinations give rise to a doublet and one satellite. In some doublet spectra, ^2G and ^2H terms are known. In designating any spectrum line like $\lambda5890$ of sodium (see Fig. 5.1), the lower state is written first followed by the higher state thus, $3^2S_{\frac{1}{2}}-3^2P_{\frac{3}{2}}$. The reason for this order goes back to the very earliest work in atomic spectra (see Chap. I). Spectrum lines in absorption are written in the same way, the lowest level first.

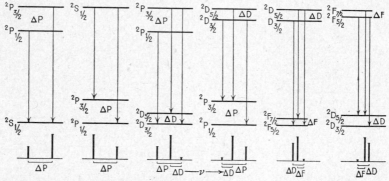

Fig. 8.4.—Illustrating selection and intensity rules for doublet combinations.

8.3. Intensity Rules for Fine-structure Doublets.

—General observations of line intensities in doublet spectra show that certain intensity rules may be formulated. These intensity rules are best stated in terms of the quantum numbers of the electron in the initial and final energy states involved. The strongest lines in any doublet arise from transitions in which j and l change in the same way. When there is more than one such line in the same doublet, the line involving the largest j values is strongest. For example, in the first principal-series doublet of Fig. 8.4. the line $^2S_{\frac{1}{2}}-^2P_{\frac{3}{2}}$ is stronger than $^2S_{\frac{1}{2}}-^2P_{\frac{1}{2}}$ since in the former l changes by -1 ($l = 1$ to $l = 0$) and j changes by -1 ($j = \frac{3}{2}$ to $j = \frac{1}{2}$). As a second example, consider a member of the diffuse series in which there are two strong lines and one satellite. For the two strong lines $^2P_{\frac{3}{2}}-^2D_{\frac{5}{2}}$ .and $^2P_{\frac{1}{2}}-^2D_{\frac{3}{2}}$, j and l both change by -1. The stronger of the two lines $^2P_{\frac{3}{2}}-^2D_{\frac{5}{2}}$ involves the larger j values. For the faint satellite $^2P_{\frac{3}{2}}-^2D_{\frac{3}{2}}$, $\Delta l = -1$ and $\Delta j = 0$.

Quantitative rules for the relative intensities of spectrum lines were discovered by Burger, Dorgelo, and Ornstein.[1] While these rules

[1] BURGER, H. C., and H. B. DORGELO, Zeits. f. Phys., 23, 258, 1924; ORNSTEIN, L. S., and H. C. BURGER, Zeits. f. Phys., 24, 41, 1924; 22, 170, 1924.

apply to all spectra in general, they will be stated here for doublets only. (a) The sum of the intensities of those lines of a doublet which come from a common initial level is proportional to the quantum weight

TABLE 8.2.—INTENSITY MEASUREMENTS IN THE PRINCIPAL SERIES OF THE ALKALI
METALS
(After Sambursky)

Element	Combination	Wave-lengths	Ratio
Na	3^2S-3^2P	5890 : 5896	2 : 1
	3^2S-4^2P	3302 : 3303	2 : 1
	3^2S-5^2P	2852 : 2853	2 : 1
K	4^2S-4^2P	7665 : 7699	2 : 1
	4^2S-5^2P	4044 : 4047	2.2 : 1
	4^2S-6^2P	3446 : 3447	2.3 : 1
	4^2S-7^2P	3217 : 3218	2.5 : 1
Rb	5^2S-5^2P	7800 : 7947	2 : 1
	5^2S-6^2P	4201 : 4215	2.7 : 1
	5^2S-7^2P	3587 : 3591	3.5 : 1
	5^2S-8^2P	3348 : 3351	4.3 : 1
	5^2S-9^2P	3228 : 3229	5 : 1
	5^2S-10^2P	3157 : 3158	3 : 1
Cs	6^2S-6^2P	8521 : 8943	2 : 1
	6^2S-7^2P	4555 : 4593	5 : 1
	6^2S-8^2P	3876 : 3888	10 : 1
	6^2S-9^2P	3611 : 3617	15.5 : 1
	6^2S-10^2P	3476 : 3480	25.0 : 1
	6^2S-11^2P	3398 : 3400	15.8 : 1
	6^2S-12^2P	3347 : 3348	5.7 : 1
	6^2S-13^2P	3313 : 3314	4.5 : 1

of that level.   (b) The sum of the intensities of those lines of a doublet which end on a common level is proportional to the quantum weight of that level.   The quantum weight of a level is given by $2j + 1$.   This, it will be seen in Chap. X, is the number of Zeeman levels into which a level j is split when the atom is placed in a magnetic field.

In applying these intensity rules, consider again the simple case of a principal-series doublet.   Here there are two lines starting from the upper levels $^2P_{\frac{1}{2}}$ and $^2P_{\frac{3}{2}}$ and ending on the common lower level $^2S_{\frac{1}{2}}$.   The quantum weights of the ^2P levels are $2(\frac{3}{2}) + 1$ and $2(\frac{1}{2}) + 1$, giving as the intensity ratio 2:1.   The same ratio results when the ^2S level is above and the ^2P level below.

Quantitative measurements of line intensities in some of the alkali spectra are given in Table 8.2.[1]

The particular investigations of Sambursky on the principal series of Na, K, Rb, and Cs show that, while the first members have, in agreement with observations made by others, the theoretical ratio 2:1, higher members do not. This is expecially true in caesium where the observations have been extended to the eighth member. In caesium the intensity ratio starts with 2 and rises to a maximum of 25 in the fifth member, then drops quite abruptly to $4\frac{1}{2}$ in the eighth member.[2] Consider next the diffuse-series doublets which involve three spectrum lines. The following combination scheme is found to be particularly useful in representing all of the transitions between initial and final states. A diffuse-series doublet is written

$$
\begin{array}{c|cc}
 & {}^{2}P_{\frac{3}{2}} & {}^{2}P_{\frac{1}{2}} \\
 & 4 & 2 \\
\hline
{}^{2}D_{\frac{5}{2}}6 & X & 0 \\
{}^{2}D_{\frac{3}{2}}4 & Y & Z \\
\end{array}
$$

The numbers directly below and to the right of the term symbols are the quantum weights $2j + 1$. Let X, Y, and Z represent the unknown intensities of the three allowed transitions and zero the forbidden transition. From the summation rules (a) and (b) the following relations are set up: The sum of the lines starting from ${}^{2}D_{\frac{3}{2}}$ is to the sum starting from ${}^{2}D_{\frac{3}{2}}$ as 6 to 4, i.e., $\dfrac{X}{Y+Z} = \dfrac{6}{4}$; and, similarly, the sum of the lines ending on ${}^{2}P_{\frac{3}{2}}$ is to the sum ending on ${}^{2}P_{\frac{1}{2}}$ as 4 is to 2, i.e., $\dfrac{X+Y}{Z} = \dfrac{4}{2}$. The smallest whole numbers which satisfy these equations are $X = 9$, $Y = 1$, and $Z = 5$. If the ${}^{2}D$ terms are very close together so that the observed lines do not resolve the satellite from the main line, as is usually the case, the two lines observed will have the intensity ratio $9+1:5$ or $2:1$, the same as the principal-series or sharp-series doublets. Intensity measurements of the diffuse series of the alkali metals by Dorgelo[3] confirm this.

A favorable spectrum in which the satellite of a diffuse-series doublet can be easily resolved, with ordinary instruments, is that of caesium. The first three members of this series are in the infra-red and are not readily accessible to photography. The fourth member of the series, composed of the three lines $\lambda\lambda$ 6213, 6011, and 6218 has been observed

---

[1] SAMBURSKY, S., Zeits. f. Phys., 49, 731, 1928.

[2] The anomalous intensities observed in caesium have been given a satisfactory explanation by E. Fermi, Zeits. f. Phys., 59, 680, 1930.

[3] DORGELO, H. B., Zeits. f. Phys., 22, 170, 1924.

Table 8.3.—Intensity Measurements in the Diffuse Series of the Alkali Metals

(After Dorgelo)

Element	Combination	Wave-lengths	Ratio
Na	$3^2P{-}4^2D$	5688 : 5682	100 : 50
	$3^2P{-}5^2D$	4982 : 4978	100 : 50
K	$4^2P{-}5^2D$	5832 : 5812	100 : 51
	$4^2P{-}6^2D$	5359 : 5342	100 : 50
Rb	$5^2P{-}6^2D$	6298 : 6206	100 : 51
	$5^2P{-}7^2D$	5724 : 5648	100 : 52
	$5^2P{-}8^2D$	5431 : 5362	100 : 52

to have the intensity ratios $9:5.05:1.17$. Theoretical intensities for the combination $^2D{-}^2F$ are given by the following formulations:

$$
\begin{array}{c|cc}
 & {}^2D_{\frac{5}{2}} & {}^2D_{\frac{3}{2}} \\
 & 6 & 4 \\ \hline
{}^2F_{\frac{7}{2}}\ 8 & X & 0 \\
{}^2F_{\frac{5}{2}}\ 6 & Y & Z
\end{array}
\qquad
\begin{aligned}
\frac{X}{Y+Z} &= \frac{8}{6} \\[4pt]
\frac{X+Y}{Z} &= \frac{6}{4}
\end{aligned}
\qquad
\begin{array}{c|cc}
 & {}^2D_{\frac{5}{2}} & {}^2D_{\frac{3}{2}} \\
 & 6 & 4 \\ \hline
{}^2F_{\frac{7}{2}}\ 8 & 20 & 0 \\
{}^2F_{\frac{5}{2}}\ 6 & 1 & 14
\end{array}
$$

The smallest whole numbers satisfying the equations in the center are $X = 20$, and $Z = 14$. The results given in Table 8.2 show that one cannot always expect the intensity rules to hold. The theoretical intensities are extremely useful, however, in making identifications in spectra not yet analyzed.

8.4. The Spinning Electron and the Vector Model.—With the co-development of complex spectrum analysis and the Landé vector model, it became necessary to ascribe to each atom an angular momentum in addition to the orbital angular momentum of the valence electrons. At first this new angular momentum was ascribed to the atom core and assigned various values suitable for the proper explanation of the various types of spectral lines: singlets, doublets, triplets, quartets, quintets, etc. Due to the insight of two Dutch physicists, Uhlenbeck and Goudsmit,[1] and independently Bichowsky and Urey,[2] this new angular momentum was assigned to the valence electrons. In order to account for doublet fine structure in the alkali metals, it is sufficient to ascribe to the single valence electron a spin s of only one-half a quantum unit of angular momentum, $s\dfrac{h}{2\pi} = \dfrac{1}{2} \cdot \dfrac{h}{2\pi}$. This half-integral spin is not to be taken as a quantum number that takes different values like n

---

[1] Uhlenbeck, G. E., and S. Goudsmit, *Naturwissenschaften*, **13**, 953, 1925; *Nature*, **117**, 264, 1926.

[2] Bichowsky, F. R., and H. C. Urey, *Proc. Nat. Acad. Sci.*, **12**, 80, 1926.

and l but as an inherent and fixed property of the electron.   The total angular momentum contributed to any atom by a single valence electron is therefore made up of two parts: one due to the motion of the center

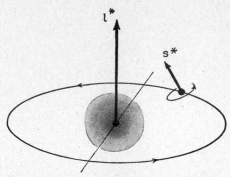

Fig. 8.5.—Spin and orbital motion of the electron on the classical theory.

of mass of the electron around the nucleus in an orbit, and the other due to the spin motion of the electron about an axis through its center of mass (see Fig. 8.5).   Disregarding nuclear spin the atom core, as we shall see later, contributes nothing to the total angular momentum of the atom.

By analogy with the quantum-mechanical developments in Chap. IV, we return now to the orbital models a, b, c, and d (Fig. 4.8) to find a suitable method for combining these two angular momenta.   For this

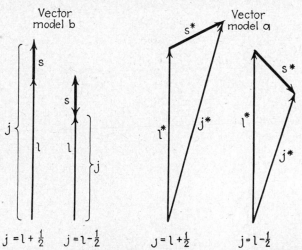

Fig. 8.6.—Vector models a and b for the composition of the electron spin and orbit.

purpose models a and b are both frequently used   Of these models, a is generally preferred since it gives in many cases, but not always, the more accurate quantum-mechanical results.   Models c and d have been rejected because of the many fortuitous rules necessarily introduced to fit the experimental data, and they are of historical interest only.

Vector diagrams for the composition of orbit and spin, on models a and b, are given in Fig. 8.6 for the two possible states of the d electron.

On model b the spin angular momentum $s \cdot h/2\pi$ is added vectorially to the orbital angular momentum $l \cdot h/2\pi$ to form the resultant $j \cdot h/2\pi$, where $j = l \pm s$. On model a the spin angular momentum $s^* \cdot h/2\pi$ is added vectorially to the orbital angular momentum $l^* \cdot h/2\pi$ to form the resultant $j^* \cdot h/2\pi$, where $s^* = \sqrt{s(s + 1)}$, $l^* = \sqrt{l(l + 1)}$, $j^* = \sqrt{j(j + 1)}$, and $j = l + s$. It should be noted that two is the maximum number of j values, differing from each other by unity, that are possible on either model and that for s electrons there is but one possibility.[1] For s, p, d, f, . . . orbits $l = 0$, 1, 2, 3, $\cdots$. The quantum conditions are that j shall take all possible half-integral values only, $i.e.$, $j = \frac{1}{2}, \frac{3}{2}, \frac{5}{2}, \frac{7}{2}, \cdots$. For a d electron $l = 2$, $s = \frac{1}{2}$, $l^* = \sqrt{6}$, and $s^* = \frac{1}{2}\sqrt{3}$. The only possible orientations for l and s, or for l^* and s^*, are such that $j = \frac{5}{2}$ and $\frac{3}{2}$, and $j^* = \frac{1}{2}\sqrt{35}$ and $\frac{1}{2}\sqrt{15}$. For a p electron $l = 1$, $s = \frac{1}{2}$, $l^* = \sqrt{2}$, and $s^* = \frac{1}{2}\sqrt{3}$. The only possible orientations for l and s, or for l^* and s^*, are such that $j = \frac{3}{2}$ and $\frac{1}{2}$, and $j^* = \frac{1}{2}\sqrt{15}$ and $\frac{1}{2}\sqrt{3}$. For an s electron $l = 0$, $s = \frac{1}{2}$, $l^* = 0$, and $s^* = \frac{1}{2}\sqrt{3}$. The only possible value for j is $\frac{1}{2}$, and $j^* = \frac{1}{2}\sqrt{3}$.

8.5. The Normal Order of Fine-structure Doublets.—In the doublet energy levels of atomic systems containing but one valence electron it is generally, but not always, observed that the fine-structure level $j = l - \frac{1}{2}$ lies deeper than the corresponding level $j = l + \frac{1}{2}$. For example, in the case of p and d electrons, ${}^2P_{\frac{1}{2}}$ lies deeper than ${}^2P_{\frac{3}{2}}$ and ${}^2D_{\frac{3}{2}}$ lies deeper than ${}^2D_{\frac{5}{2}}$. This result is to be expected on the classical theory of a spinning electron and on the quantum mechanics. Classically we may think of the electron as having an orbital angular momentum and a spin angular momentum. Due to the charge on the electron each of these two motions produces magnetic fields.

Due to the orbital motion of the electron, of charge e, in the radial electric field of the nucleus E, there will be a magnetic field H at the electron normal to the plane of the orbit.[2] That this field is in the direction of the orbital mechanical moment l may readily be seen by imagining the electron at rest and the positively charged nucleus moving in an orbit around it. In this field the more stable state of a given doublet will then be the one in which the spinning electron, thought of as a small magnet of moment μ_s, lines up in the direction of H. In Fig. 8.7 the electron spin moment μ_s is seen to be parallel to H in the state $j = l - \frac{1}{2}$, and antiparallel to H in the state $j = l + \frac{1}{2}$. Of the two

---

[1] The small letter s used for electron spin must not be confused with the small letter for s electrons.

[2] This field is not apparent to an observer at rest with the nucleus but would be experienced by an observer on the electron.

possible orientations the one $j = l - \frac{1}{2}$ is classically then the more stable and therefore lies deeper on an energy level diagram. On the vector model a (see Fig. 8.6) the same conclusion is reached and we can say that of the two states the one for which the spin moment μ_s is more nearly parallel to H lies deeper.

Although most of the doublet spectra of one-electron systems are in agreement with this, there are a few exceptions to the rule. In caesium, for example, the ^2P and ^2D terms are normal, and the first ^2F term is inverted. By inverted is meant that the term $j = l + \frac{1}{2}$ lies deepest on an energy level diagram. In rubidium the ^2P terms are normal, and the ^2D and ^2F terms are inverted. In sodium and potassium

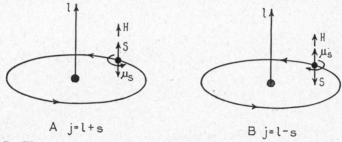

FIG. 8.7.—Illustrating the mechanical and magnetic moments of the spinning electron for the two fine-structure states $j = l + \frac{1}{2}$ and $j = l - \frac{1}{2}$. The vectors are drawn according to the classical model (b).

the ^2P terms are normal, and the ^2D, and very probably the ^2F, terms are inverted. For a possible explanation of the inversions see Sec. 19.6. It can be shown quantum mechanically that, neglecting disturbing influences, doublet levels arising from a single valence electron will be normal. Where resolved, all of the observed doublets of the boron group of elements, the ionized alkaline earths, and the more highly ionized atoms of the same type are in agreement with this.

8.6. Electron Spin-orbit Interaction.—The problem which next presents itself is that of calculating the magnitude of the doublet separations. Experimentally we have seen that doublet-term separations, in general, vary from element to element, from series to series, and from member to member. Any expression for these separations will therefore involve the atomic number Z, the quantum number l, and the quantum number n.

A calculation of the interaction energy due to the addition of an electron spin to the atom model has been made on the quantum mechanics by Pauli,[1] Darwin,[2] Dirac,[3] Gordon,[4] and others. By use of the vector

[1] PAULI, W., *Zeits. f. Phys.*, **43**, 601, 1927.

[2] DARWIN, C. G., *Proc. Roy. Soc.*, A, **116**, 227, 1927; A, **118**, 654, 1928.

[3] DIRAC, P. A. M., *Proc. Roy. Soc.*, A, **117**, 610, 1927; A, **118**, 351, 1928.

[4] GORDON, W., *Zeits. f. Phys.*, **48**, 11, 1929.

model a semiclassical calculation of the interaction energy may also be made which leads to the same result. Because of its simplicity this treatment will be given here. Dirac's quantum-mechanical treatment of the electron will be given in the next chapter.

On the classical model of hydrogen-like atoms the single electron moves in a central force field with an orbital angular momentum

$$l^* \frac{h}{2\pi} = m\mathbf{r} \times \mathbf{v} \tag{8.1}$$

where $l^* = \sqrt{l(l+1)}$, m is the mass of the electron, $\mathbf{v}$ its velocity, and $\mathbf{r}$ the radius vector. According to classical electromagnetic theory, a charge Ze on the nucleus gives rise to an electric field E at the electron given by

$$\mathbf{E} = \frac{Ze}{r^3}\mathbf{r}. \tag{8.2}$$

Moving in this field the electron experiences a magnetic field given by

$$H = \frac{\mathbf{E} \times \mathbf{v}}{c}. \tag{8.3}$$

From these two equations,

$$H = \frac{Ze}{cr^3}\mathbf{r} \times \mathbf{v}. \tag{8.4}$$

Applying Bohr's quantum assumption [Eq. (2.20)]

$$2\pi m\mathbf{r} \times \mathbf{v} = l^* h, \tag{8.5}$$

the field becomes

$$H = l^* \frac{h}{2\pi} \cdot \frac{Ze}{mc} \cdot \frac{1}{r^3}. \tag{8.6}$$

In this field the spinning electron, like a small magnetic top, undergoes a Larmor precession around the field direction. From Larmor's theorem [Eq. (3.58)] the angular velocity of this precession should be given by the product of the field strength H and the ratio between the magnetic and mechanical moment of the spinning electron:[1]

$$\omega_L = H \cdot 2\frac{e}{2mc} = l^* \frac{h}{2\pi} \cdot \frac{Ze}{mc} \cdot \frac{1}{r^3} \cdot 2\frac{e}{2mc}. \tag{8.7}$$

This is just twice the ordinary Larmor precession, given in Eq. (3.58)

---

[1] The ratio between the magnetic and mechanical moment of a spinning electron is just twice the corresponding ratio for the electron's orbital motion. This is in agreement with results obtained on the quantum mechanics and accounts for the anomalous Zeeman effect to be treated in Chap. X.

A relativistic treatment of this problem by Thomas[1] has revealed, in addition to the Larmor precession ω_L, a relativity precession ω_T, one-half as great and in the opposite direction. The resultant precession of the spinning electron is therefore one-half ω_L, *i.e.*, just equal to the ordinary Larmor precession:

$$\omega' = \omega_L + \omega_T = \frac{1}{2}l^*\frac{h}{2\pi} \cdot \frac{Ze^2}{m^2c^2} \cdot \frac{1}{r^3}. \tag{8.8}$$

Now, the interaction energy[2] is just the product of the precessional angular velocity ω' and the projection of the spin angular momentum on l^*:

$$\Delta W_{l,s} = \omega' \cdot s^* \frac{h}{2\pi} \cos (l^*s^*). \tag{8.9}$$

With the value of ω' from Eq. (8.8),

$$\Delta W_{l,s} = \frac{Ze^2}{2m^2c^2} \cdot \frac{h^2}{4\pi^2} \cdot \frac{1}{r^3} \cdot l^*s^* \cos (l^*s^*). \tag{8.10}$$

In this equation for the interaction energy the last two factors are still to be evaluated. In general the electron-nuclear distance r is a function of Z, n, and l and changes continually in any given state. Because the interaction energy is small compared with the total energy of the electron's motion the average energy $\overline{\Delta W}_{l,s}$ may be calculated by means of perturbation theory. In doing this, only the average value $\left(\frac{1}{r^3}\right)$ need be calculated. From perturbation theory and the quantum mechanics (see Sec. 4.9),

$$\left(\overline{\frac{1}{r^3}}\right) = \frac{Z^3}{a_1^3 n^3 l(l + \frac{1}{2})(l + 1)}, \tag{8.11}$$

where a_1 is the radius of the first Bohr circular orbit,

$$a_1 = \frac{h^2}{4\pi^2 me^2}. \tag{8.12}$$

For the last factor of Eq. (8.10) we turn to the vector model of the atom. In calculating the precessional frequency of s^* around the field produced by the orbital motion the vector l^* was assumed fixed in space.

[1] THOMAS, L. H., *Nature*, **117**, 514, 1926.
[2] The interaction energy here is just the kinetic energy of the electron's precession around the field H. If $W = \frac{1}{2}I\omega^2$ represents the kinetic energy of the spin of the electron in the absence of the field H, and $W' = \frac{1}{2}I(\omega + \omega')^2$ the kinetic energy in the presence of the field, then the change in energy is just $\Delta W = W' - W = \frac{1}{2}I\omega'^2 + I\omega\omega'$. Since I remains constant and $\omega >> \omega'$, the first term is negligibly small and the energy is given by the product of ω' and the mechanical moment $I\omega = s^*h/2\pi = p_s$.

One might equally well have calculated the precession of the orbit in the field of the spinning electron. It is easily shown that this frequency is just equal to the ordinary Larmor precession and to the precession of the electron around l^*. In field-free space both orbit and spin are free to move so that l^* and s^* will precess around their mechanical resultant j^*. By the law of conservation of angular momentum this resultant j^* and hence the angle between l^* and s^* must remain invariant. The vector model therefore takes the form shown in Fig. 8.8. With the angle fixed the cosine does not need to be averaged and l^*s^* cos (l^*s^*) is calculated by the use of the cosine law

$$j^* = l^{*2} + s^{*2} + 2l^*s^* \cos (l^*s^*) \qquad (8.13)$$

from which

$$l^*s^* \cos (l^*s^*) = \frac{j^{*2} - l^{*2} - s^{*2}}{2}. \qquad (8.14)$$

Substituting Eqs. (8.11) and (8.14) in Eq. (8.10),

$$\overline{\Delta W}_{l,s} = \frac{Ze^2}{2m^2c^2} \cdot \frac{h^2}{4\pi^2} \cdot \frac{Z^3}{a_1^3 n^3 l(l + \frac{1}{2})(l + 1)} \cdot$$
$$\frac{j^{*2} - l^{*2} - s^{*2}}{2} \qquad (8.15)$$

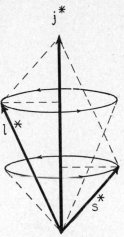

Fig. 8.8.—Classical precession of electron spin s^* and orbit l^* around their mechanical resultant j^*.

Upon substituting the Rydberg constant $R = 2\pi^2me^4/ch^3$ and the square of the fine-structure constant $\alpha^2 = 4\pi^2e^4/c^2h^2$, the energy becomes

$$\overline{\Delta W}_{l,s} = \frac{R\alpha^2 chZ^4}{n^3 l(l + \frac{1}{2})(l + 1)} \cdot \frac{j^{*2} - l^{*2} - s^{*2}}{2} \qquad (8.16)$$

and, dividing by hc, the term shift in wave numbers becomes

$$\overline{\Delta T}_{l,s} = -\frac{R\alpha^2 Z^4}{n^3 l(l + \frac{1}{2})(l + 1)} \cdot \frac{j^{*2} - l^{*2} - s^{*2}}{2} = -\Gamma. \qquad (8.17)$$

This spin-orbit interaction energy, often referred to as the Γ factor, is written in short as

$$\Gamma = a \cdot \frac{(j^{*2} - l^{*2} - s^{*2})}{2} = a \cdot l^*s^* \cos (l^*s^*), \qquad (8.18)$$

where

$$a = \frac{R\alpha^2 Z^4}{n^3 l(l + \frac{1}{2})(l + 1)} \text{ cm}^{-1}. \qquad (8.19)$$

Measured from the series limit down, the term value of any fine-structure level will be given by

$$T = T_0 - \Gamma, \qquad (8.20)$$

where T_0 is a hypothetical term value for the center of gravity of the doublet in question and Γ gives the shift of each fine-structure level from T_0. Γ values for ^2P, ^2D, and ^2F terms are shown in Fig. 8.9. For an s orbit $l = 0$, $j = s$, and $\Delta T = 0$. This is in agreement with observation that *all S states are single*. The two states of a doublet are seen by the figure to be given by the difference between their Γ values. It is to be noted that Z occurs in the numerator of Eq. (8.19), and n and l occur in the denominator. This is in agreement with experimental observations

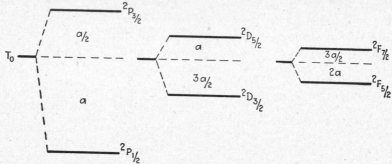

Fig. 8.9.—Illustrating fine-structure separations due to spin-orbit interaction.

that doublet-term separations (1) increase with increasing atomic number, *e.g.*, in going from Na I to K I, or from Na I to Mg II; (2) decrease with increasing n, *i.e.*, in going to higher members of a given series; (3) decrease with increasing l, *i.e.*, in going to different series p, d, f, etc. As the interaction energy gets smaller and smaller in a given series, Γ will approach zero and the levels will gradually come together at their center of gravity T_0.

8.7. Spin-orbit Interaction for Nonpenetrating Orbits.—In applying the spin-orbit-interaction energy formula [Eq. (8.17)], as just derived, to the observed data, it is necessary that we first simplify the expression and substitute the known physical constants. For any given doublet, l and s have the same values whereas $j = l + \frac{1}{2}$ for the upper level and $l - \frac{1}{2}$ for the lower level. The successive substitution of these values for j in the last factor of Eq. (8.17) gives, by subtraction,

$$\Delta\nu = \frac{R\alpha^2 Z^4}{n^3 l(l + \frac{1}{2})(l + 1)}\left(l + \frac{1}{2}\right) = \frac{R\alpha^2 Z^4}{n^3 l(l + 1)} \text{ cm}^{-1}. \tag{8.21}$$

Inserting the value of the Rydberg constant $R = 109737$ cm^{-1} and the fine-structure constant $\alpha^2 = 5.3 \times 10^{-5}$,

$$\Delta\nu = 5.82 \frac{Z^4}{n^3 l(l + 1)} \text{ cm}^{-1}. \tag{8.22}$$

For hydrogen-like systems the effective nuclear charge is given simply by the atomic number Z.

In the previous chapters we have seen how for other atomic systems the deviations of the term values from those of hydrogen-like atoms are attributed to a polarization of the atomic core or generally to a quantum defect [see Eq. (5.4)],

$$T = \frac{RZ^2}{(n - \mu)^2} = \frac{RZ^2}{n_{\text{eff}}^2},$$ (8.23)

where $Z = 1$ for neutral atoms, 2 for singly ionized atoms, etc. Instead of attributing the increased binding of the electron to a defect in the quantum number n, one may argue that it should be attributed to a screening of the valence electron from the nucleus by the intervening core of electrons, and that Z should be replaced by Z_{eff} where $Z_{\text{eff}} = Z - \sigma$, Z is the atomic number, and σ is a screening constant:

$$T = \frac{RZ_{\text{eff}}^2}{n^2} = \frac{R(Z - \sigma)^2}{n^2}.$$ (8.24)

By exactly the same reasoning one may write the fine-structure doublet formula [Eq. (8.22)] as

$$\Delta\nu = \frac{R\alpha^2(Z - s)^4}{n^3 l(l + 1)} = 5.82\frac{(Z - s)^4}{n^3 l(l + 1)}.$$ (8.25)

Most of the doublets to which this formula applies are known only for singly and multiply ionized atoms. Although its general application will be left to Chap. XVII on Isoelectronic Sequences, it should be remarked here that this formula gives doublet intervals in remarkably good agreement with experimental observations.

8.8. Spin-orbit Interaction for Penetrating Orbits.—In the preceding chapter on penetrating and nonpenetrating orbits we have seen how penetrating orbits may be considered as made up of two parts, an *inside* segment of an ellipse and an *outside* segment. In attempting to apply Eq. (8.25) to the doublets of penetrating orbits, much better agreement with the observed values is obtained, especially for the heavier elements, by again considering separately the inner and the outer part of the orbit (see Fig. 7.6). Whatever atomic model is formulated, the electron in a deeply penetrating orbit is by far the greater part of the time in an outer region where the field is nearly hydrogen-like. If the electron remained in an outer orbit like the outer segment, the doublet formula [Eq. (8.21)] would be

$$\Delta\nu_o = \frac{R\alpha^2 Z_o^4}{n_o^3 l(l + 1)},$$ (8.26)

whereas, if it remained in an inner orbit like the inner segment, the formula would be

$$\Delta\nu_i = \frac{R\alpha^2 Z_i^4}{n_i^3 l(l + 1)}.$$ (8.27)

To bring these two formulas together for the actual orbit, the motion in each of these segments is weighted according to the time spent in each. Now the time t required to traverse the whole path is so nearly equal to the time t_o required to traverse a complete outer ellipse that we may write, to a first approximation,

$$t = t_o = \frac{n_o^3 h^3}{4\pi^2 m e^4 Z_o^2}. \tag{8.28}$$

This equation for the period of an electron in a Kepler ellipse was left as an exercise at the end of Chap. III. The time required to traverse a completed inner ellipse is

$$t_i = \frac{n_i^3 h^3}{4\pi^2 m e^4 Z_i^2}. \tag{8.29}$$

Now the resultant frequency separation $\Delta\nu$ for the actual orbit will be $\Delta\nu_o$ times the fractional time t_o/t spent in the outer segment, plus $\Delta\nu_i$ times the fractional time t_i/t spent in the inner segment:

$$\Delta\nu = \Delta\nu_o \frac{t_o}{t} + \Delta\nu_i \frac{t_i}{t}. \tag{8.30}$$

Making the approximation that $t_o = t$ and substituting the values of $\Delta\nu_o$, $\Delta\nu_i$, t, and t_i from Eqs. (8.26), (8.27), (8.28), and (8.29), we get

$$\Delta\nu = \frac{R\alpha^2 Z_o^2}{n_o^3 l(l+1)}(Z_o^2 + Z_i^2) \text{ cm}^{-1}. \tag{8.31}$$

For heavy elements the effective charge $Z_i e$ at deepest penetration is so much greater than the effective charge $Z_o e$ outside, that the formula may be simplified to

$$\Delta\nu = \frac{R\alpha^2 Z_o^2 Z_i^2}{n_o^3 l(l+1)} \text{ cm}^{-1}. \tag{8.32}$$

This equation was derived from the quantum theory and used by Landé[1] before the advent of the spinning electron and the newer quantum mechanics. In calculating Z_i for a number of atoms Landé showed that the penetration in many cases is almost complete, Z_i being almost equal to the atomic number Z (see Table 17.4A). It is to be noted that n_o is the effective quantum number.

Inserting screening constants for each of the Z's, in Eq. (8.32),

$$\Delta\nu = \frac{R\alpha^2 (Z - s_o)^2 (Z - s_i)^2}{n_o^3 l(l+1)} \text{ cm}^{-1}. \tag{8.33}$$

The application of this formula to observed doublets, in general, will be set aside, to be taken up again in treating isoelectronic sequences of atoms in Chap. XVII.

[1] LANDÉ, A., Zeits. f. Phys., **25**, 46, 1924.

Problems

1. Compute doublet-term separations for the nonpenetrating $2p$ states of lithium and singly ionized beryllium. Assume complete screening by the core electrons. Compare the calculated values with the observed values given in Sec. 8.1.

2. Determine theoretical intensity ratios for the doublet transitions $^2F_j-^2G_j$.

3. Construct vector-model diagrams for $^2F_{\frac{5}{2}}$, $^2F_{\frac{7}{2}}$, $^2G_{\frac{7}{2}}$ and $^2G_{\frac{9}{2}}$ states based on model a, Fig. 8.6.

4. Determine the electron spin-orbit precession frequency $\omega/2\pi$ for a $4f$ state in potassium. Assume complete screening by the 18 core electrons.

5. Compute a theoretical doublet separation for the 6^2P state in caesium. Assume complete penetration when the electron is inside the core, *i.e.*, $s_i = 0$, and perfect screening when it is outside, *i.e.*, $s_o = Z - 1$. The effective quantum number n_o can be determined from the observed term values (use the center of gravity of the doublet). All other factors remaining the same, what value of s_i will give the observed doublet separation?

CHAPTER IX

HYDROGEN FINE STRUCTURE AND THE DIRAC ELECTRON

Even the hydrogen spectrum, the simplest of all systems, is observed to have a fine structure. At an early date Michelson studied the Balmer lines with an interferometer and found that both H_α and H_β were close doublets with separations of only 0.14 and 0.08 Å, or 0.32 and 0.33 cm^{-1}, respectively. Many subsequent investigations by others have confirmed these results (see Fig. 9.1).

$$H_\alpha^1 \qquad\qquad H_\alpha^2$$

FIG. 9.1.—Photographs of the H_α line of both of the hydrogen isotopes H[1] and H[2]. (*After Lewis and Spedding.*)

The most informing observations that have been made on hydrogen-like atoms are those of Paschen[1] on the singly ionized helium line λ4686. This line (see Fig. 2.8) corresponds to the first member of the so-called *Paschen series of hydrogen.* Historically Paschen's observations were made and published at a most opportune time, for in the next issue of the *Annalen der Physik* Sommerfeld independently predicted just such a fine structure by an extension of the Bohr atom to include elliptic orbits and the special theory of relativity.[2] While the quantum mechanics gives a more perfect account of the observed fine structure, the development of the orbital model is interesting in that it leads to the same energy levels.

9.1. Sommerfeld Relativity Correction.—The extension of Bohr's atomic model by Sommerfeld to include elliptic orbits adds no new energy levels to the hydrogen atom (see Sec. 3.3). For a given total quantum number n, all elliptic orbits $s, p, d, \ldots$ have just the same

[1] PASCHEN, F., *Ann. d. Phys.*, **50**, 901, 1916.
[2] SOMMERFELD, A., *Ann. d. Phys.*, **51**, 1, 1916.

energy as the Bohr circular orbit with the same n. This energy in wave numbers is

$$\frac{W}{hc} = -\frac{RZ^2}{n^2} = -T, \tag{9.1}$$

where R is the Rydberg constant

$$R = \frac{2\pi^2 m e^4}{ch^3\left(1 + \dfrac{m}{M}\right)}, \tag{9.2}$$

h is Planck's constant, c the velocity of light, m and e the mass and charge of the electron, and M the mass of the nucleus with charge Ze.

Bohr pointed out in his earliest papers that the relativistic change in mass of the orbital electron should be taken into account in computing the energy levels. Introducing elliptic orbits, Sommerfeld applied the special theory of relativity to the electron mass. Due to the different velocity of the electron in orbits of the same n but differing azimuthal quantum number, the mass of the electron and hence the resultant energy levels are all different. If the rest mass of the electron is m_0, its mass when moving with velocity v is given by the special theory of relativity as

$$m = m_0\left(1 - \frac{v^2}{c^2}\right)^{\frac{1}{2}}. \tag{9.3}$$

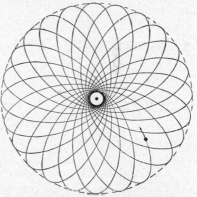

FIG. 9.2.—Schematic representation of the precession of an electron orbit due to the relativity change in mass of the electron with velocity. (*After Sommerfeld.*)

As a result of this change in mass, which is greatest at perihelion and greatest for the most elliptic orbits, there is an advance of the perihelion, or a precession of the electron orbit, similar to that of a penetrating orbit in the alkali metals (see Fig. 7.4), or to that of the planet Mercury moving about the sun. This precession is shown schematically in Fig. 9.2. While the derivation of Sommerfeld's equation for the change in energy due to this precession is out of place here, we shall find use for it in making comparisons with the quantum-mechanical results.[1] According to the Sommerfeld theory the term values of hydrogen-like atoms are given by

$$T = -\frac{W}{hc} = \frac{\mu c}{h}\left\{1 + \frac{\alpha^2 Z^2}{(n - k + \sqrt{k^2 - \alpha^2 Z^2})^2}\right\}^{-\frac{1}{2}} + \frac{\mu c}{h}, \tag{9.4}$$

[1] For a derivation of Sommerfeld's relativistic fine-structure formula see "Atomic Structure and Spectral Lines," p. 467, 1923; also A. E. Ruark and H. C. Urey, "Atoms, Molecules and Quanta," p. 132.

where α is the fine-structure constant

$$\alpha^2 = \frac{4\pi^2 e^4}{h^2 c^2} = 5.30 \times 10^{-5} \tag{9.5}$$

and

$$\mu = \frac{Mm}{M + m}.$$

For convenience of evaluation, Eq. (9.4) has been expanded by Sommerfeld into a converging series,

$$T = -\frac{W}{hc} = \frac{RZ^2}{n^2} + \frac{R\alpha^2 Z^4}{n^4}\left[\frac{n}{k} - \frac{3}{4}\right]$$

$$+ \frac{R\alpha^4 Z^6}{n^6}\left[\frac{1}{4}\left(\frac{n}{k}\right)^3 + \frac{3}{4}\left(\frac{n}{k}\right)^2 - \frac{3}{2}\left(\frac{n}{k}\right) + \frac{5}{8}\right]$$

$$+ \frac{R\alpha^6 Z^8}{n^8}\left[\frac{1}{8}\left(\frac{n}{k}\right)^5 + \frac{3}{8}\left(\frac{n}{k}\right)^4 + \frac{1}{8}\left(\frac{n}{k}\right)^3 - \frac{15}{8}\left(\frac{n}{k}\right)^2\right.$$

$$\left. + \frac{15}{8}\left(\frac{n}{k}\right) - \frac{35}{64}\right]$$

$$+ \cdots \tag{9.6}$$

The first term of this expansion is the same as that derived by Bohr for circular orbits, neglecting relativity, and gives the major part of the energy. With $n = 1, 2, 3, \cdots$, and with $Z = 1$ for hydrogen, $Z = 2$ for ionized helium, and $Z = 3$ for doubly ionized lithium, this term gives the following values:

TABLE 9.1.—TERM VALUES, NEGLECTING FINE-STRUCTURE CORRECTIONS

	Hydrogen (isotope mass 1) R = 109677.76	Hydrogen (isotope mass 2) R = 109707.56	Ionized helium R = 109722.4	Doubly ionized lithium R = 109728.9
For $n = 1$	109677.76	109707.56	438889.6	987560.1
2	27419.4	27426.9	109722.4	246890.0
3	12186.4	12189.7	48765.5	109728.9
4	6854.8	6856.7	27430.6	61722.5
5	4387.1	4388.3	17555.5	39502.4
6	3046.6	3047.4	12191.3	27432.2
7	2238.3	2238.9	8956.9	20154.4

To each of these values corrections from Eq. (9.6) must be added. For small values of Z the first term involving Z^4 and α^2 is the only one of importance and the third and succeeding terms may be neglected. In x-ray spectra, however, Z becomes large for the heavier elements and terms in α^4 and α^6 must be taken into account (see Chap. XVI).

The corrections to be added to each of the above given terms are therefore given by

$$\Delta T = \frac{R\alpha^2 Z^4}{n^4}\left(\frac{n}{k} - \frac{3}{4}\right) = \frac{R\alpha^2 Z^4}{n^3}\left(\frac{1}{k} - \frac{3}{4n}\right), \tag{9.7}$$

where k is Sommerfeld's azimuthal quantum number 1, 2, 3, . . . for $s, p, d, ...$ For all allowed values of n and k the correction is positive and is to be added to the terms in Table 9.1. For either of the two hydrogen isotopes,

$$\Delta T = 5.819\left(\frac{1}{n^3}\right)\left(\frac{1}{k} - \frac{3}{4n}\right). \tag{9.8}$$

These corrections are shown graphically in Fig. 9.3. The straight lines at the top of each of the four diagrams represent the first four terms

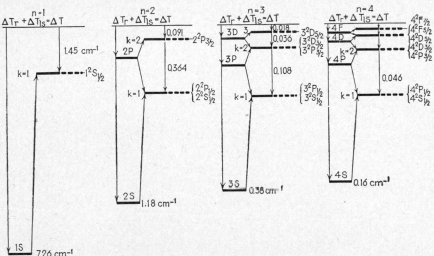

Fig. 9.3.—Fine structure of the hydrogen energy levels. ΔT_r and $\Delta T_{l,s}$ represent the relativity and the spin-orbit corrections respectively. The dashed lines represent Sommerfeld's relativity corrections.

of hydrogen given by Table 9.1. The shifted levels for each value of n and k are shown by the dotted lines with the term value increasing downward. The left-hand side of each diagram has to do with the spinning-electron picture of the atom and will be taken up in the following section. For ionized helium and doubly ionized lithium the intervals given in Fig. 9.3 must be multiplied by 16 and 81, respectively.

9.2. Fine Structure and the Spinning Electron.—With the introduction of the spinning electron and the quantum mechanics another account of the hydrogen fine structure has been given. Heisenberg and Jordan[1]

---

[1] HEISENBERG, W., and P. JORDAN, *Zeits. f. Phys.*, **37**, 263, 1926.

have shown from a quantum-mechanical treatment that Sommerfeld's relativity correction for hydrogen-like atoms should be

$$\Delta T_r = \frac{R\alpha^2 Z^4}{n^3}\left(\frac{1}{l + \frac{1}{2}} - \frac{3}{4n}\right), \tag{9.9}$$

where $l = 0, 1, 2, \cdots$ for $s, p, d, \cdots$ electrons. A general comparison of all classical with quantum-mechanical results for the same phenomenon shows that the classical values k, k^2, and k^3 may usually, but not always, be replaced by $l + \frac{1}{2}$, $l(l + 1)$, and $l(l + \frac{1}{2})(l + 1)$, respectively, to obtain the quantum-mechanical results. Sommerfeld's relativity equation is a good example of this; k in Eq. (9.7) replaced by $l + \frac{1}{2}$ gives Eq. (9.9).

To the quantum-mechanical relativity correction [Eq. (9.9)] a second term due to the spin-orbit interaction must be added. This interaction energy has already been calculated in Sec. 8.6 and shown to be given by Eq. (8.17):[1]

$$\Delta T_{l,s} = -\frac{R\alpha^2 Z^4}{n^3 l(l + \frac{1}{2})(l + 1)} \cdot \frac{j^{*2} - l^{*2} - s^{*2}}{2}. \tag{9.10}$$

Applying the first correction ΔT_r to the hydrogen terms of Table 9.1, each level n is split into n components as shown at the left of each of the four diagrams in Fig. 9.3. Applying now the spin-orbit interaction $\Delta T_{l,s}$, each of these terms, with the exception of s terms, is split into two parts just as in the alkali metals. In each case the level with $j = l + \frac{1}{2}$ has been shifted up, and the one with $j = l - \frac{1}{2}$ has been shifted down, to the nearest Sommerfeld level. In other words, levels with the same j values come together at the older relativity levels k, where $k = j + \frac{1}{2}$. The remarkable fact that Sommerfeld's formula derived from the relativity theory alone should give the same result as the newer theory, where both relativity and spin are taken into account, is a good example of how two incorrect assumptions can lead to the correct result. While the number of numerically different energy levels is the same on both theories, there is an experimental method for showing that the first theory is not correct and that the latter very probably is correct. This will become apparent in Sec. 9.4.

Since the newer theory leads to Sommerfeld's equation, the sum of Eqs. (9.9) and (9.10) should reduce to Eq. (9.7). Since j takes on values $l + \frac{1}{2}$ or $l - \frac{1}{2}$ only, Eq. (9.10) is split into two equations:

$$\Delta T_{l,s} = -\frac{R\alpha^2 Z^4}{n^3 2(l + \frac{1}{2})(l + 1)} \quad \text{for} \quad j = l + \frac{1}{2}, \tag{9.11}$$

$$\Delta T_{l,s} = +\frac{R\alpha^2 Z}{n^3 2l(l + \frac{1}{2})} \quad \text{for} \quad j = l - \frac{1}{2}. \tag{9.12}$$

---

[1] Equation (9.10) was first derived on the quantum mechanics by W. Heisenberg and P. Jordan, *loc. cit.*

The sign in front of the right-hand side of each of these equations has been changed to conform with Eq. (9.9), where a positive sign means an increase in the term value, or a decrease in the energy. Adding Eq. (9.9) to each of Eqs. (9.11) and (9.12),

$$\Delta T = \Delta T_{l,s} + \Delta T_r = \frac{R\alpha^2 Z^4}{n^3}\left(\frac{1}{l+1} - \frac{3}{4n}\right) \quad \text{for} \quad j = l + \frac{1}{2},$$

$$\Delta T = \Delta T_{l,s} + \Delta T_r = \frac{R\alpha^2 Z^4}{n^3}\left(\frac{1}{l} - \frac{3}{4n}\right) \quad \text{for} \quad j = l - \frac{1}{2}.$$

(9.13)

If k in Sommerfeld's equation is replaced by l and $l + 1$, respectively, these equations will result. If again k is replaced by $j + \frac{1}{2}$, which is just

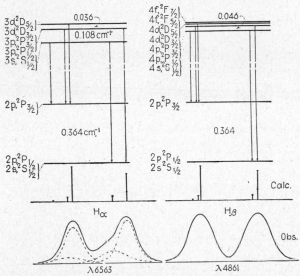

FIG. 9.4.—Schematic diagrams of the lines $H\alpha$ and $H\beta$, in the Balmer series of hydrogen.

the same as replacing $l + 1$ and l of Eq. (9.13) by $j + \frac{1}{2}$, we obtain the single equation

$$\Delta T = \frac{R\alpha^2 Z^4}{n^3}\left(\frac{1}{j + \frac{1}{2}} - \frac{3}{4n}\right).$$

(9.14)

9.3. Observed Hydrogen Fine Structure.—Schematic diagrams of the theoretical fine structure of the first two lines of the Balmer series of hydrogen are shown in Fig. 9.4. Applying selection and intensity rules, both H_α and H_β should be composed of two strong components and three weaker ones. Neither one of these patterns has ever been resolved into more than two components. The best results to date are those of Lewis, Spedding, Shane, and Grace,[1] obtained from H^2, the behavior of

[1] LEWIS, G. N., and F. H. SPEDDING, *Phys. Rev.*, **43**, 964, 1933; also SPEDDING, F. H., C. D. SHANE, and N. S. GRACE, *Phys. Rev.*, **44**, 58, 1933.

the two known hydrogen isotopes. Using Fabry and Perot étalons, photographs similar to the one shown in the center of Fig. 9.5 have been obtained. For this photograph the first order of a 30-ft. grating mounting (of the Littrow type) was used as the auxiliary dispersion instrument. Microphotometer curves of both H^1 and H^2 are reproduced above and below each pattern. It is to be noted that the components of H_α^2 are considerably sharper than H_α^1, and that a third component is beginning to show up. The broadening is due to the Doppler effect and should be greater for the lighter isotope.

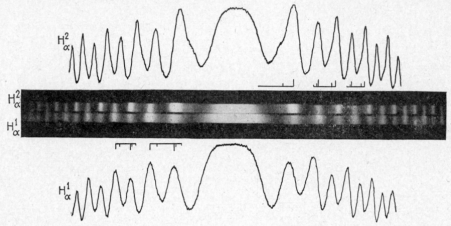

Fig. 9.5.—Fine structure of H_α^1 and H_α^2 from the Balmer series of the two hydrogen isotopes. Microphotometer curves above and below were made from the interference patterns in the center. (*After Spedding, Shane, and Grace.*)

Theoretical intensities for the fine structure of hydrogen were first calculated by Sommerfeld and Unsöld[1] in 1926. Experimentally it is found that the relative intensities of the two main components, the only ones resolved, depend largely upon the conditions of excitation. In some instances the supposedly weaker of the two lines will be the stronger, as it is in Fig. 9.5.

In going to higher members of the Balmer series the separation of the two strong components of each member approaches theoretically and experimentally the separation of the common lower state, 0.364 cm^{-1}. This interval occurs in each doublet between the fainter of the two strong lines and the next to the weakest satellite.

9.4. Fine Structure of the Ionized Helium Line λ4686.—A better detailed agreement between observation and theory has been found in the hydrogen-like spectrum of ionized helium. A microphotometer curve of the line λ4686 is given at the bottom of Fig. 9.6. This line corresponds with the first line of the Paschen series in hydrogen (see Fig. 2.8). With

[1] SOMMERFELD, A., and A. UNSÖLD, *Zeits. f. Phys.*, **36**, 259, 1926; **38**, 237, 1926; see also SCHRÖDINGER, E., *Ann. d. Phys.*, **80**, 437, 1926.

$Z = 2$ the fine-structure separations should be 16 times as great as in hydrogen [see Eqs. (9.13) and (9.14)]. The predicted fine structure shown above in Fig. 9.6 was first given by Sommerfeld and Unsöld. At least four and possibly five of the predicted components may be said to have been resolved by Paschen.[1] The appearance of certain component lines in this pattern, which are not allowed on Sommerfeld's original theory of hydrogen fine structure, are strong points in favor of the newer theory of the coincidence of levels having the same j values.

9.5. The Dirac Electron and the Hydrogen Atom.—On Dirac's[2] theory a single electron in a central force field is specified by a set of four wave functions ψ_1, ψ_2, ψ_3, and ψ_4, in place of just one as in the case of the Schrödinger theory. Each of these functions is a solution of a wave equation. Although the setting up of the equations is out of place here we shall accept the solutions arrived at by Darwin and Gordon[3] and show in what way they correspond to the earlier theories and, at the same time, get some picture of the new atom model.

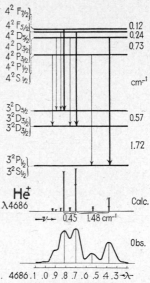

FIG. 9.6.—Diagram of the fine structure of the ionized helium line λ4686. (*After Sommerfeld, Unsöld, and Paschen.*)

With each wave function ψ_1, ψ_2, ψ_3, and ψ_4 properly normalized, the probability density, just as in the case of Schrödinger's theory (see Chap. IV), is given by

$$P = \psi\psi^*, \tag{9.15}$$

where

$$\psi\psi^* = \psi_1\psi_1^* + \psi_2\psi_2^* + \psi_3\psi_3^* + \psi_4\psi_4^*. \tag{9.16}$$

For given values of the azimuthal quantum number l and the magnetic quantum number m ($m = u + \frac{1}{2}$), there are two sets of solutions corresponding to $j = l + \frac{1}{2}$ and $j = l - \frac{1}{2}$, respectively (j equals inner quantum number).

$$j = 1 + \tfrac{1}{2}$$

$$
\begin{aligned}
\psi_1 &= && -iM_\theta P_{l+1}^u \cdot M_r F_l \\
\psi_2 &= && -iM_\theta P_{l+1}^{u+1} \cdot M_r F_l \\
\psi_3 &= (l + u + 1) \cdot M_\theta P_l^u & \cdot M_r G_l \\
\psi_4 &= -(l - u) \cdot M_\theta P_l^{u+1} & \cdot M_r G_l
\end{aligned}
\tag{9.17}
$$

[1] Paschen, F., *Ann. d. Phys.*, **82**, 692, 1926.

[2] Dirac, P. A. M., *Proc. Roy. Soc.*, A, **117**, 610, 1928; A, **118**, 351, 1928; see also Darwin, C. G., *Proc. Roy. Soc.*, A, **118**, 654, 1928.

[3] Gordon, W., *Zeits. f. Phys.*, **48**, 11, 1928.

$$j = 1 - \tfrac{1}{2}$$

$$\begin{aligned}
\psi_1 &= & -i(l + u) \cdot M_\theta P^u_{l-1} \cdot M_r F_{-l-1}. \\
\psi_2 &= i(l - u - 1) \cdot M_\theta P^{u+1}_{l-1} \cdot M_r F_{-l-1}. \\
\psi_3 &= & M_\theta P^u_l \cdot M_r G_{-l-1}. \\
\psi_4 &= & M_\theta P^{u+1}_l \cdot M_r G_{-l-1}.
\end{aligned} \tag{9.18}$$

In this form each wave function in polar coordinates is written as the product of two functions, one of which gives ψ as a function of the angles Φ and θ alone and the other as a function of r alone. M_θ and M_r are the angular and radial normalizing factors, respectively. The spherical harmonics $P^u_l(\varphi, \theta)$ are defined by

$$P^u_l = (-1)^u (l + u)! \sin^{-u}\theta \left(\frac{d}{d\cos\theta}\right)^{l-u} \frac{(\cos^2\theta - 1)^l}{2^l \cdot l!} \cdot e^{iu\varphi}. \tag{9.19}$$

The radial functions F and G are functions of the electron-nuclear distance alone and are given by

$$F^2_l = \frac{N - p - n_r}{N + p + n_r}(\sigma_1 - \sigma_2) \quad \text{and} \quad G^2_l = (\sigma_1 + \sigma_2) \tag{9.20}$$

where

$$\sigma_1 = (N + l + 1) \cdot r^{p-1} \cdot e^{-kr} \cdot {}_1F_1(-n_r, 2p + 1, 2kr), \tag{9.21}$$

$$\sigma_2 = -n_r \cdot r^{p-1} \cdot e^{-kr} \cdot {}_1F_1(-n_r + 1, 2p + 1, 2kr), \tag{9.22}$$

and

$$n_r = n - |l - 1| = \text{radial quantum number}, \tag{9.23}$$

$$p = [(l + 1)^2 - \alpha^2]^{\frac{1}{2}}, \tag{9.24}$$

$$N = [n_r^2 + (l + 1)^2 + 2pn_r]^{\frac{1}{2}}, \tag{9.25}$$

$$k = \frac{1}{a_1 N}, \quad a_1 = 0.528 \text{ Ångströms}, \quad \alpha^2 = 5.30 \times 10^{-5}, \tag{9.26}$$

where a_1 is the radius of the Bohr first circular orbit and α is the fine-structure constant. The functions ${}_1F_1$ are of the form of series

$${}_1F_1(a,b,c) = 1 + \frac{a}{b \cdot 1!}c + \frac{a(a + 1)}{b(b + 1) \cdot 2!}c^2 + \frac{a(a + 1)(a + 2)}{b(b + 1)(b + 2) \cdot 3!}c^3 + \cdots \tag{9.27}$$

which terminate for negative integer values of a.

9.6. The Angular Distribution of the Probability Density P_θ.—With two sets of four wave functions, the solutions and hence the probability density $\psi\psi^*$ must be divided into two parts, one for $j = l + \tfrac{1}{2}$ and one for $j = l - \tfrac{1}{2}$. Corresponding to given n, l, and j, there are $2j + 1$ magnetic states for which the magnetic quantum number m takes values from $m = +j$ to $m = -j$. Hartree[1] has shown that *for given n, l, and j the magnetic states with equal but opposite m have the same probability-density distribution*. He has also shown that *the angular distribution*

---

[1] HARTREE, D. R., *Proc. Camb. Phil. Soc.*, **25**, 225, 1929.

for two electrons with the same n, j, *and* m, *and* $l = j \pm \frac{1}{2}$ *is the same.* As an example of these two theorems, the *angular charge distributions,* as they are called by Hartree, for the magnetic states $m = \pm \frac{3}{2}$ of a $^2P_{\frac{3}{2}}$ term are not only the same but are also identical with the two magnetic states $m = \pm \frac{3}{2}$ of the $^2D_{\frac{3}{2}}$ term. It should be pointed out, however, that the radial charge distributions of the ^2P and ^2D terms are different. With this simplification of the problem the charged distributions need be determined for $j = l + \frac{1}{2}$ and positive m only.

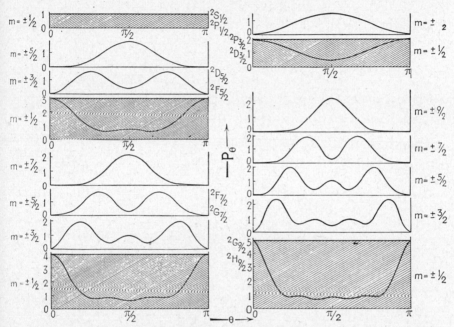

FIG. 9.7.—The angular factor P_θ of the probability density $\psi\psi^*$, plotted as a function of the angle θ. The shaded areas indicate spherical symmetry presented by two or four p electrons, or four or six d electrons.

For $j = l + \frac{1}{2}$ the probability density $\psi\psi^*$ on the Dirac theory is written

$$\psi\psi^* = P_\theta \cdot P_r = M_\theta^2[P_{l+1}^u P_{l+1}^{u*} + P_{l+1}^{u+1} P_{l+1}^{u+1*}] \cdot M_r^2[F_l^2 + G_l^2], \quad (9.28)$$

The first part of the solution is a function of the angles φ and θ alone.

$$P_\theta = M_\theta^2[P_{l+1}^u P_{l+1}^{u*} + P_{l+1}^{u+1} P_{l+1}^{u+1*}], \quad (9.29)$$

where the angular normalizing factor in the form given by Roess[1] is

$$M_\theta^2 = [4\pi(l + u + 1)!(l - u)!]^{-1}. \quad (9.30)$$

From Eqs. (9.19) and (9.29) it may be seen that the angle φ occurs in each polynomial in the form of an exponential $e^{im\varphi}$ and is always

[1] ROESS, L. C., *Phys. Rev.*, **37**, 532, 1931.

to be multiplied by its complex conjugate $e^{-im\varphi}$. This gives a constant for all m values. Exactly the same result is obtained on the Schrödinger theory, which indicates that the probability density is symmetrical about the φ (magnetic) axis for all states. Leaving out the factor $1/4\pi$ in the normalizing factor M_θ^2, the probability density P_θ for a number of states is given in Table 9.2 and is shown graphically in Fig. 9.7.[1]

Hartree has shown that for electrons with the same n, l, and j, the probability density summed over the states $m = +\frac{1}{2}$ to $m = +j$ presents spherical symmetry. In this case spherical symmetry is shown by

$$\sum_{m = +\frac{1}{2}}^{m = +j} P_\theta = \text{constant}, \tag{9.31}$$

given in the last column of Table 9.2 and graphically by the shaded

TABLE 9.2.—THE PROBABILITY DENSITY AS A FUNCTION OF THE ANGLE θ

Energy states	j	m	P_θ	$\displaystyle\sum_{m = +\frac{1}{2}}^{m = +j} P_\theta$
$^2S_{\frac{1}{2}}$ or $^2P_{\frac{1}{2}}$	$\frac{1}{2}$	$\frac{1}{2}$	1	1
$^2P_{\frac{3}{2}}$ or $^2D_{\frac{3}{2}}$	$\frac{3}{2}$	$\frac{3}{2}$ $\frac{1}{2}$	$\frac{3}{2} \sin^2 \theta$ $\frac{1}{2}(3 \cos^2 \theta + 1)$	2
$^2D_{\frac{5}{2}}$ or $^2F_{\frac{5}{2}}$	$\frac{5}{2}$	$\frac{3}{2}$ $\frac{1}{2}$	$\frac{15}{8} \sin^4 \theta$ $\frac{3}{8} \sin^2 \theta(15 \cos^2 \theta + 1)$ $\frac{6}{8}(5 \cos^4 \theta - 2 \cos^2 \theta + 1)$	3
$^2F_{\frac{7}{2}}$ or $^2G_{\frac{7}{2}}$	$\frac{7}{2}$	$\frac{7}{2}$ $\frac{5}{2}$ $\frac{3}{2}$ $\frac{1}{2}$	$\frac{35}{16} \sin^6 \theta$ $\frac{5}{16} \sin^4 \theta(35 \cos^2 \theta + 1)$ $\frac{15}{16} \sin^2 \theta(21 \cos^4 \theta - 6 \cos^2 \theta + 1)$ $\frac{1}{16}(175 \cos^6 \theta - 165 \cos^4 \theta + 45 \cos^2 \theta + 9)$	4

areas under the straight lines in Fig. 9.7. Since the probability density for the negative m states is the same as that for the corresponding positive m states, the sum of the probability densities for all negative m states is also a constant. This means that four electrons in $^2P_{\frac{3}{2}}$ states or two electrons in $^2P_{\frac{1}{2}}$ states will form a spherically symmetrical charge distribution.[2] Another and similar consequence of the Dirac theory is that a single electron in a $^2P_{\frac{1}{2}}$ state is two electrons in a $^2P_{\frac{3}{2}}$ state present spherical symmetry. Not only are all S states, formed from a

[1] WHITE, H. E., Phys. Rev., **38**, 513, 1931.
[2] These correspond to the jj-coupling states $(\frac{3}{2}\frac{3}{2}\frac{3}{2}\frac{3}{2})_0$ and $(\frac{1}{2}\frac{1}{2})_0$ in Fig. 14.21.

single *s* electron or from a completed subshell of any type of electrons, spherically symmetrical, as on the Schrödinger theory, but, also, all

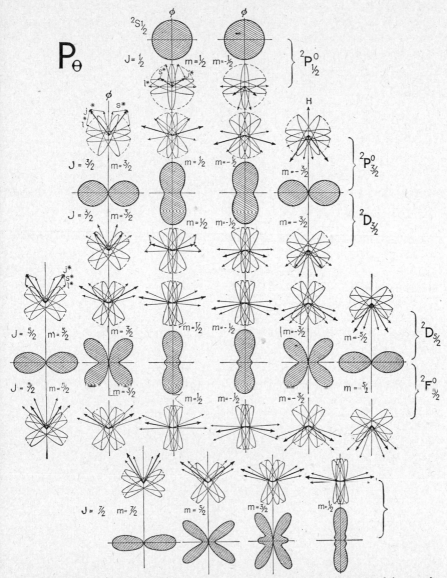

Fig. 9.8.—The angular factor P_θ of the probability density $\psi\psi^*$ plotted in angular coordinates. Above and below the quantum-mechanical electron distributions the corresponding classical electron orbits are shown oriented in each case according to the model l^*, s^*, j^*, and m.

one-electron systems with but one valence electron and that in a $^2P_{\frac{1}{2}}$ state. The normal states of B, Al, Ga, In, and Tl are examples of this.

If angular coordinates are used in plotting P_θ a number of interesting correlations with the classical orbits may be made. Such angular distributions are shown in Fig. 9.8 for s, p, d, and f electrons. Above and below each density figure the corresponding classical orbits are shown oriented in each case according to model a (see Fig. 4.8). On this model the angular momentum vectors $l^* = \sqrt{l(l+1)}$ and $s^* = \sqrt{s(s+1)}$ are combined to form the resultant $j^* = \sqrt{j(j+1)}$, j^* in turn being so oriented that its projection m on the φ axis takes half-integral values $m = \pm\frac{1}{2}, \pm\frac{3}{2}, \pm\frac{5}{2}, \cdots \pm j$. It may be seen from the figures that in the precession of l^* about j^* and the simultaneous precession of j^* about the φ (magnetic) axis the electron orbit fills out a figure in space not greatly unlike that of the quantum mechanics. The density curves are symmetrical about φ. The orbit normal l^* is shown for the four positions it takes when in the same meridian plane (the plane of the paper). In order to illustrate an orbit rather than its straight-line projection, the orbit plane is tipped slightly out of the normal to l^*. While the classical models b, c, and d may also be compared with the probability curves of Fig. 9.8, model a seems to be in the best general agreement. It should be pointed out that the electron is not confined to the shaded areas in each probability curve, but that the magnitude of a line joining the center to any point on the curve is a measure of the probability of the electron being found in the direction of that line. From the physical standpoint it is interesting that P_θ becomes zero for $\theta = 0$ and π only. The electron can pass therefore from any region to another without going through a node of zero probability. This is also true for the radial factor as will be shown.

9.7. The Radial Distribution of the Probability Density P_r.—For $j = l + \frac{1}{2}$ the probability-density factor P_r is [see Eq. (9.28)],

$$P_r = M_r^2(F_l^2 + G_l^2). \tag{9.32}$$

The radial normalizing factors M_r^2 have been given by Roess as

$$M_r^2 = \frac{(N + p + n_r)(2k)^{2p+1}\Gamma(2p + n_r + 1)}{n_r!2N[\Gamma(2p + 1)]^2[(N + l + 1)^2 + n_r(n_r + 2p)]}, \tag{9.33}$$

which from tables of the gamma function are readily evaluated. The radial function F_l^2, as compared with G_l^2, is extremely small and for hydrogen is of the order of magnitude of the square of the fine-structure constant. If α is set equal to zero throughout the radial equations the gamma functions become simple factorials, F_l^2 vanishes, and P_r reduces to the radial factor of the Schrödinger theory $(R_{n,l})^2$ (see Chap. IV).

Since the radial densities on the Schrödinger and Dirac theories are so nearly identical, it is difficult to show their differences graphically.

However, by splitting up $M_r^2(F_l^2 + G_l^2)$ into two parts $M_r^2 F_l^2$ and $M_r^2 G_l^2$, curves may be given for each on different scales.   In Fig. 9.9, for example, curves for the $4p$, $^2P_{\frac{3}{2}}$ state are drawn.   The factors $M_r^2 G_l^2$ and $M_r^2 F_l^2$ are shown by the dotted lines in the top and middle figures, respectively. Multiplying by $4\pi r^2$ the density-distribution curves (shaded areas) are obtained.   The main reason for representing the density distribution in this way is to show that the zero points of each of the two upper

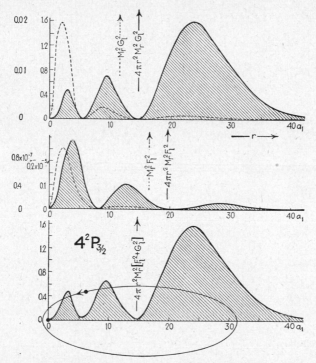

Fig. 9.9.—The radial factor P_r of the probability density $\psi\psi^*$, for the state $4p$,$^2P_{\frac{3}{2}}$. The spin correction (middle figure) added to the Schrödinger distribution (upper figure) gives the Dirac distribution (lower figure).

curves, other than those points at $r = 0$ and $r = \infty$, occur at different values of r.   While the resultant curve $4\pi r^2 M_r^2 (F_l^2 + G_l^2)$ in the lower figure is almost identical with the top figure for $4\pi r^2 M_r^2 G_l^2$, it does not come to zero at the two points near $r = 6$ and $r = 14$.   The difference at these two points only has been exaggerated in the bottom figure.   The slight shift in the probability density, due chiefly to the addition of the F function, produces the fine-structure shift of the hydrogen energy levels.   This will be given in Sec. 9.9.   The classical $4p$ orbit shown in the last figure is drawn according to model a.   As in the case of the Schrödinger theory, the density distribution differs greatly from zero only within the electron-nuclear distance of the corresponding classical orbits.

9.8. The Probability-density Distribution $\psi\psi^*$.—Attempts to bring together the probability factors P_θ and P_r into one single picture for $\psi\psi^*$ have been somewhat successful. With a spinning mechanical model,[1] photographs have been made which represent the Dirac electron cloud for a number of the simpler hydrogen states. The photographs given in Fig. 9.10 were taken from the equatorial plane of the model,

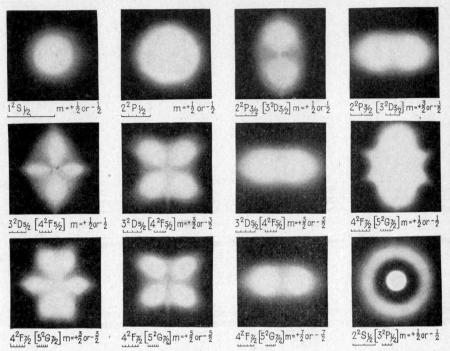

Fig. 9.10.—Photographs representing the Dirac electron cloud for a number of the simpler hydrogen-like states made by means of photographing a mechanical model. The φ (magnetic) axis is vertical and in the plane of the paper. The scale for each state is given below each symbol in Ångström units.

so that the φ (magnetic) axis is vertical and in the plane of the paper. While these photographs were made to represent the electron cloud and not simply cross sections, the latitude lost in photograph copying and printing makes them appear as cross sections. The states represented are given beneath each figure. Since states with negative m values are identical with the corresponding positive m states, only one picture is given for both $+m$ and $-m$. The electron cloud for each state, given in brackets, is so nearly like the figure given for the unbracketed state that the difference is not distinguishable in such a photograph. The scale in Ångström units for each state is given beneath each symbol.

Graphical comparisons of the classical electron orbits, without spin, have shown (see Chap. IV) that the electron path closely follows

[1] WHITE, H. E., *Phys. Rev.*, **38**, 513, 1931.

the probability density $\psi\psi^*$ on Schrödinger's theory. Introducing the electron spin into the classical model, the orbit in a weak field no longer precesses about the magnetic axis but about the spin-orbit resultant j^*; and j^* in turn precesses about φ (or H). Corresponding to this change in space quantization is the change in the θ factor of the probability density $\psi\psi^*$ brought about by introducing the spin through Dirac's theory. Radially, however, little change has occurred in either the orbital or the quantum-mechanical model $\psi\psi^*$. This might have been expected, since the main part of the energy in hydrogen is given by the radial factor in ψ and the introduction of the spin has added only the fine-structure corrections to this energy.

9.9. The Sommerfeld Formula from Dirac's Theory.—Gordon[1] has shown that Sommerfeld's fine-structure formula [Eq. (9.4)] may be derived from Dirac's theory of the hydrogen atom. Gordon obtains for the term values of Eq. (9.4),

$$T = -\frac{\mu c}{h}\left\{1 + \frac{\alpha^2 Z^2}{(n - j - \frac{1}{2} + \sqrt{j'^2 - \alpha^2 Z^2})^2}\right\}^{-\frac{1}{2}} + \frac{\mu c}{h}, \quad (9.34)$$

where j' is a new quantum number given for the various terms by the values given in Table 9.3.

TABLE 9.3.—QUANTUM NUMBERS FOR THE HYDROGEN ATOM ON DIRAC'S THEORY

	$^2S_{\frac{1}{2}}$	$^2P_{\frac{1}{2}}$	$^2P_{\frac{3}{2}}$	$^2D_{\frac{3}{2}}$	$^2D_{\frac{5}{2}}$	$^2F_{\frac{5}{2}}$	$^2F_{\frac{7}{2}}$
l	0	0	1	2	2	3	3
j	$\frac{1}{2}$	$\frac{1}{2}$	$\frac{3}{2}$	$\frac{3}{2}$	$\frac{5}{2}$	$\frac{5}{2}$	$\frac{7}{2}$
j'	-1	$+1$	-2	$+2$	-3	$+3$	-4

Since j' occurs as the square only, the minus sign can be neglected. Due to this fact j'^2 can be replaced by $(j + \frac{1}{2})^2$, and Eq. (9.34) becomes

$$T = -\frac{\mu c}{h}\left\{1 + \frac{\alpha^2 Z^2}{(n - j - \frac{1}{2} + \sqrt{(j + \frac{1}{2})^2 - \alpha^2 Z^2})^2}\right\}^{-\frac{1}{2}} + \frac{\mu c}{h}. \quad (9.35)$$

Expanding, following Sommerfeld's treatment,[2] and dropping all but the first two terms,

$$T = \frac{RZ^2}{n^2} + \frac{R\alpha^2 Z^4}{n^3}\left(\frac{1}{j + \frac{1}{2}} - \frac{3}{4n}\right). \quad (9.36)$$

The first term gives the Balmer terms and the second the corrections given by Eq. (9.14).

---

[1] GORDON, W., *Zeits. f. Phys.*, **48**, 11, 1928.

[2] See SOMMERFELD, A., "Atomic Structure and Line Spectra," p. 477, 1923.

Problems

1. Calculate the fine-structure pattern for the electron transition $n = 3$ to $n = 2$ for ionized helium.   Determine the wave-length at which this line is to be found, and compare the fine-structure intervals in Ångströms with those of H_α in hydrogen.

2. Construct radial-density-distribution curves for a $4d, {}^2D_{\frac{3}{2}}$ and $4d, {}^2D_{\frac{3}{2}}$ states (see Fig. 9.9).

CHAPTER X

ZEEMAN EFFECT AND THE PASCHEN-BACK EFFECT

10.1. Early Discoveries and Developments.—In the year 1896 Zeeman[1] discovered that when a sodium flame is placed between the poles of a powerful electromagnet the two lines of the first principal doublet are considerably broadened. Lorentz pointed out that this phenomenon is in harmony with the electron theory of matter and radiation proposed by himself. He predicted from theoretical considerations that the light from these lines should be polarized by the magnetic field, *circularly polarized* if viewed in a direction *parallel* to the lines of force, and *plane polarized* if viewed at *right angles* to the field. These predictions were later verified by Zeeman by means of Nicol prisms as analyzers.

It has been shown from the simple classical theory of Lorentz that, if a light source be placed in a magnetic field, the motions of the electrons should be modified in such a way as to change their periods of motion. In the simple case of an electron moving in a circular orbit, the plane of which is normal to the field direction H, the electron will be speeded up or slowed down by an amount which depends upon the magnetic field strength H, the mass and charge on the electron, and the velocity of light. A classical treatment of this problem shows that if ν_0 represents the orbital frequency of the electron without field, the frequency in the presence of a field will be given by $\nu_0 \pm \Delta\nu$, where [see Eqs. (3.50) and (3.59)]

$$\Delta\nu = \frac{eH}{4\pi mc}. \tag{10.1}$$

If the field is normal to and up from this page of the book, then electrons moving in a counterclockwise direction in the plane of the paper are speeded up by an amount $\Delta\nu$ and those moving in a clockwise direction are slowed down by the same amount. It will now be shown how these modified motions have been employed in giving a classical explanation of the normal Zeeman effect.

In the following explanation we are concerned with an assembly of electrons moving in orbits oriented at random in space. We start by selecting one of these orbits and resolve the motion into three components along three mutually perpendicular axes (see Fig. 10.1a). The

---

[1] ZEEMAN, P., *Phil. Mag.*, **5**, 43, 226, 1897.

motion of the electron is here pictured as consisting of three simple-harmonic motions, one along the x axis, one along the y axis, and one along the z axis. When this resolution is repeated for all of the electrons, the average amplitude of all the motions along each axis will be the same. If now, in the absence of a field, the electrons are emitting light and we observe the radiation in the x direction, only the light from the y and z motions will be observed. Since these motions are projections from all orientations, this light will be *unpolarized*. Thus, in the absence of a field, the light observed in any direction is unpolarized.

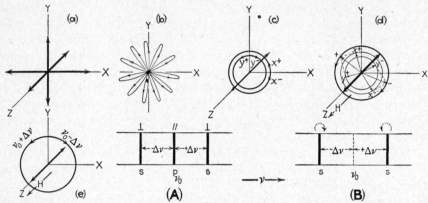

Fig. 10.1.—Schematic diagrams for the classical explanation of the normal Zeeman effect.

If now we return to Fig. 10.1a, which represents the three harmonic components of a single orbital electron, and apply a magnetic field in the direction of the z axis, the x and y motions will be modified and the z motion will remain unchanged. Moving transversely to the field, the x and y motions will take the form of rosettes as shown in Fig. 10.1b.[1] This is the same type of motion as one encounters in the Faraday effect.

These apparently complex motions can be described to better advantage in terms of circular motions somewhat as follows. The simple-harmonic motion given by the y component of Fig. 10.1a, for example, is equivalent to the resultant of two equal but opposite circular motions y^+ and y^- as shown in Fig. 10.1c. Similarly the x component can be represented by two opposite circular motions x^+ and x^-. When the field is applied, the x^+ and y^+ rotations will be speeded up by an amount $\Delta\nu$ [see Eq. (10.1)] and the x^- and y^- rotations will be slowed down by the same amount. (The faster x^+ motion combined with the slower x^- motion results in Fig. 10.1b.) The x^+ and y^+ motions and the x^- and y^-

---

[1] The electrons are here moving at right angles to the field, and they therefore experience a force at right angles to their motion the direction of which depends upon the direction of the field and the direction of the motion.

motions are now combined, as shown in Fig. 10.1*d*, to form plus and minus resultants.   Thus the motion of a single electron in a magnetic field is represented by a linear motion along the field direction with unchanged frequency ν_0 and two circular motions at right angles to this, one with the frequency $\nu_0 + \Delta\nu$ and the other with frequency $\nu_0 - \Delta\nu$.   On summing up such motions for all of the electrons, the result will be the same as if one-third of the electrons are moving with unchanged frequency along the z axis, one-third moving with a counter-clockwise circular motion normal to z of frequency $\nu_0 + \Delta\nu$, and the other third moving with clockwise circular motion normal to z of frequency $\nu_0 - \Delta\nu$ (see Fig. 10.1*e*).

We are now interested in the nature of the light that should classically be radiated from these motions.   When viewed in the direction of the field, only the circular motions are observed and these as right- and left-handed circularly polarized light (Fig. 10.1*B*).   Since light is a transverse wave motion, the z motions will not emit light in the field direction.   When viewed perpendicular to the field, the z motions are observed as plane-polarized light with the electric vector vibrating parallel to the field, and the circular motions, seen edge on, are observed as plane-polarized light with the electric vector at right angles to the field.   A spectrum line viewed normal to H should therefore reveal three plane-polarized components (see Fig. 10.1*A*), a center unshifted line and two other lines equally displaced one on either side.   This is called a *normal triplet*.   The abbreviation *p* stands for a vibration *parallel* to the field and *s* (*senkrecht*) stands for a vibration *normal* to the field.   The experimental agreement with the direction of rotation of the circularly polarized components is proof that the radiation is due to moving negative electric charges.

In Zeeman's early investigations he was not able to split any lines into doublets or triplets, but he did find that they were widened and that their outside edges were polarized as predicted.   He was later able to photograph the two outer components of lines in a number of the elements, Zn, Cu, Cd, and Sn, by cutting out the *p* components with a Nicol prism.   Preston[1] using greater dispersion and resolving power was able to show not only that certain lines were split up into triplets when viewed perpendicular to the field, but that others were split into as many as four and even six components (see Fig. 10.2*a*).   He also pointed out that the pattern of all lines (usually called *Zeeman patterns*) belonging to the same series of spectrum lines was the same and was characteristic of that series.   This is now known as *Preston's law*.   With Preston's law firmly established, the Zeeman effect has been, and still is, a powerful tool in spectrum analysis.

[1] PRESTON, T., *Phil. Mag.*, **45**, 325, 1898.

From Lorentz's classical treatment of the Zeeman effect (Fig. 10.1) the shift $\Delta\nu$ of the s components from the unshifted p component (see Eq. 10.1) is given by

$$\Delta\nu = \frac{He}{4\pi mc^2} = 4.67 \times 10^{-5} \cdot H \text{ cm}^{-1} = L \text{ cm}^{-1}, \qquad (10.1a)$$

where $\Delta\nu$ is in wave numbers, H is the field in gauss, c is the velocity of light, and e is the charge on the electron in electrostatic units. Zee-

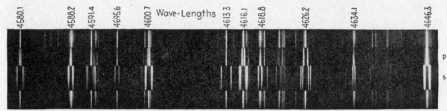

Zeeman Effect in the Chromium Spectrum

FIG. 10.2a.—Anomalous Zeeman effect as observed in the neutral spectrum of chromium. (*After Babcock.*)

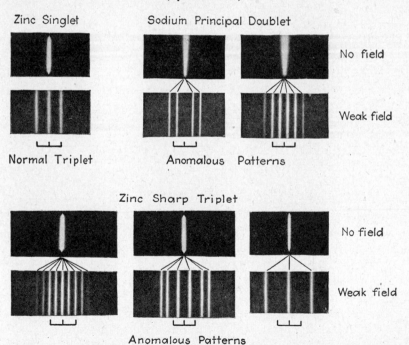

FIG. 10.2b.—Normal and anomalous Zeeman effect. Viewed perpendicular to the magnetic field.

man patterns showing just three lines with exactly these separations are called *normal triplets*. All other line groups, as, for example, the complex patterns observed in the chromium spectrum (see Fig. 10.2a), are said to exhibit the *anomalous Zeeman effect*. One of the most important of the early investigations of the anomalous Zeeman effect was carried out by Paschen and Runge.[1] Each member of the principal series of sodium, copper, and silver was observed to have 10 components as shown in Fig. 10.2b. The sharp-series triplets in mercury are still more complicated, the strongest line in each triplet having nine components, the middle line six, and the weakest line only three. This last line does not form a normal triplet since it has twice the normal separation.

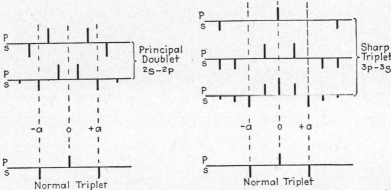

Fig. 10.3.—Schematic representation of anomalous Zeeman patterns viewed perpendicular to the field and showing polarization (*p*-components above and *s*-components below), relative intensities (heights of lines), and intervals (dotted lines).

In 1907 Runge made an important contribution to a theoretical explanation of the anomalous Zeeman effect by announcing that all known patterns could be expressed as rational multiples of the normal-triplet separations. If, for example, L represents the shift of the *s* components from the unshifted line, as given by Lorentz's formula, then the principal- or sharp-series doublets (see Fig. 10.3) may be expressed as

$$^2S_{\frac{1}{2}} - {}^2P_{\frac{1}{2}}, \qquad \pm \tfrac{2}{3}L, \ \pm \tfrac{4}{3}L$$
$$^2S_{\frac{1}{2}} - {}^2P_{\frac{3}{2}}, \qquad \pm \tfrac{1}{3}L, \ \pm \tfrac{3}{3}L, \ \pm \tfrac{5}{3}L$$

and the principal- or sharp-series triplets are expressed as

$$^3S_1 - {}^3P_2, \qquad 0, \ \pm \tfrac{1}{2}L \pm \tfrac{2}{2}L \pm \tfrac{3}{2}L \pm \tfrac{4}{2}L$$
$$^3S_1 - {}^3P_1, \qquad \pm \tfrac{1}{2}L \pm \tfrac{3}{2}L \pm \tfrac{4}{2}L$$
$$^3S_1 - {}^3P_0, \qquad 0, \ \pm \tfrac{4}{2}L.$$

this is now known as *Runge's law*.

10.2. The Vector Model of a One-electron System in a Weak Magnetic Field.—Soon after the discovery of the anomalous Zeeman effect

[1] PASCHEN, F., and C. RUNGE, *Astrophys. Jour.*, **15**, 235, 333, 1902; *Phys. Zeits.*, **3**, 441, 1902.

came the development of the *Landé vector model* of the atom and the calculation of the famous *Landé g factor*. The accuracy with which this model, with its empirical rules, accounted for all observed Zeeman patterns, and predicted others which were later verified, is one of the

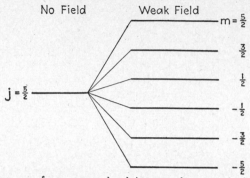

FIG. 10.4.—Splitting up of an energy level in a weak magnetic field. This figure is drawn for the case where $j = \frac{5}{2}$.

marvels of scientific history. With the advent of the spinning electron, and later the quantum mechanics, Landé's vector model gave way to a more satisfactory and, at the same time, a simpler semiclassical model. It is with this simplified model and its adequate account of the Zeeman effect that we are concerned in this chapter.

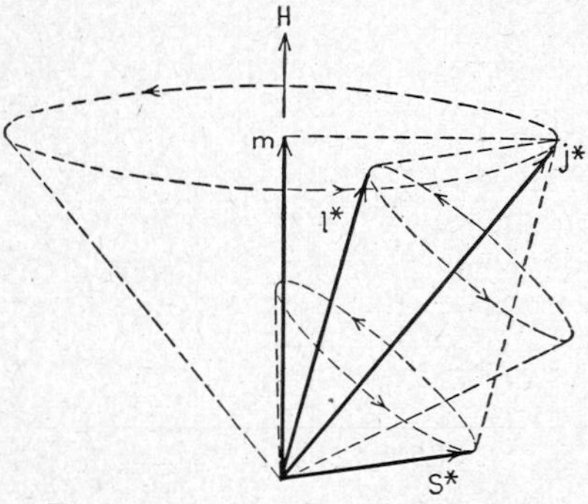

Experimentally it is observed that in a weak field each spectrum line is split up into a number of components forming a symmetrical Zeeman pattern, and that, in general, the width of any given pattern is not greatly different from that of a normal triplet. Theoretically this effect is attributed to a splitting up of the energy levels into a number of predetermined equally spaced levels (see Fig. 10.4).

FIG. 10.5.—Classical precession of a single valence electron around the field direction H.

Transitions between two sets of these levels, subject to certain selection and intensity rules, give rise to the observed spectral frequencies.

Before attempting a calculation of these Zeeman levels it is well that we formulate some picture of the atom in terms of the semiclassical model. In Fig. 8.8, we have seen that the orbital angular-momentum vector l^* and the spin angular-momentum vector s^* precess with uniform speed around their resultant j^*. When the atom is placed in a weak magnetic field, the magnetic moment μ_j associated with the total mechanical moment $p_j = j^* h/2\pi$ causes the atom to precess like a top around the field direction H (see Fig. 10.5). The quantum conditions imposed upon this motion (see Sec. 9.6) are that the projection of the angular momentum $j^*h/2\pi$ on the field direction H will take only those values given by $mh/2\pi$, where $m \pm \frac{1}{2}$, $\pm \frac{3}{2}$, $\pm \frac{5}{2} \cdots$, $\pm j$. In other words the projection of j^* on H takes half-integral values from $+j$ to $-j$ only. The discrete orientations of the atom in space, and the small change in energy due to the precession, give rise to the various discrete Zeeman levels. While the number of these levels is determined by the mechanical moment $j^*h/2\pi$, the magnitude of the separations is determined by the field strength H and the magnetic moment μ. In field-free space an energy level is defined by the three quantum numbers n, l, and j. In a weak magnetic field an additional or fourth quantum number m is necessary to define the state.

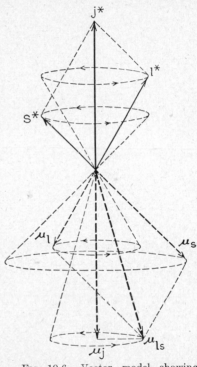

10.3. The Magnetic Moment of a Bound Electron.—To determine the magnitude of the separations between Zeeman levels, it is essential that we first determine the total magnetic moment of the atom. In the simplest case to be considered here the atom core and nucleus will be assumed to have zero magnetic and mechanical moments so that any moments attri buted to the atom must be assigned to a single valence electron. Later it will be shown where these assumptions are justified.

FIG. 10.6.—Vector model showing the magnetic and mechanical moments of a single valence electron.

According to the classical theory, the ratio between the magnetic and mechanical moments of an electron in an orbit [see Eq. (3.52)] is given by

$$\frac{\mu_l}{p_l} = \frac{e}{2mc}. \tag{10.2}$$

Just as observations of the fine structure of spectrum lines show that the mechanical moment of the spinning electron is given by $s^*h/2\pi$, where $s^* = \sqrt{s(s + 1)}$ and $s = \frac{1}{2}$, so the anomalous Zeeman effect shows that the ratio between the magnetic and mechanical moments for the spinning electron is just twice that for the orbital motion, $i.e.$,

$$\frac{\mu_s}{p_s} = 2\frac{e}{2mc}. \tag{10.3}$$

This result has also been derived theoretically on the quantum mechanics (see Chap. IX).

A schematic vector diagram of the magnetic and mechanical moments is shown in Fig. 10.6. Here it is seen that the resultant magnetic moment $\mu_{l,s}$ is not in line with the resultant mechanical moment $j^*h/2\pi$. Since the resultant mechanical moment is invariant, l^*, s^*, μ_l, μ_s, and $\mu_{l,s}$ precess around j^*. As a result of this precession, only the component of $\mu_{l,s}$ parallel to j^* contributes to the magnetic moment of the atom. This may be seen by resolving $\mu_{l,s}$ into two components, one parallel to j^* and the other perpendicular. The perpendicular component, owing to the continual change in direction, will average out to zero. The parallel component μ_j may be evaluated as follows:

By Eqs. (10.2) and (10.3) μ_l and μ_s are given as

$$\mu_l = l^*\frac{h}{2\pi} \cdot \frac{e}{2mc}\frac{\text{ergs}}{\text{gauss}} \text{ and } \mu_s = 2 \cdot s^*\frac{h}{2\pi} \cdot \frac{e}{2mc}\frac{\text{ergs}}{\text{gauss}}; \quad (10.4)$$

and their components along j^* are given as

$$\text{Component } \mu_l = l^*\frac{h}{2\pi} \cdot \frac{e}{2mc} \cos (l^*j^*)$$

$$\text{Component } \mu_s = 2 \cdot s^*\frac{h}{2\pi} \cdot \frac{e}{2mc} \cos (s^*j^*). \quad (10.5)$$

Adding these, we obtain

$$\mu_j = [l^* \cos (l^*j^*) + 2s^* \cos (s^*j^*)]\frac{h}{2\pi} \cdot \frac{e}{2mc}. \quad (10.6)$$

Since the last two factors in this equation are equivalent to one Bohr magneton [see Eq. (3.57)], the quantity determined by the bracket gives the total magnetic moment of the atom in Bohr magnetons. This bracket term is readily evaluated by setting it equal to j^* times a constant g,

$$j^* \cdot g = l^* \cos (l^*j^*) + 2s^* \cos (s^*j^*). \quad (10.7)$$

Making use of the vector model and the cosine law that

$$s^{*2} = l^{*2} + j^{*2} - 2l^*j^* \cos (l^*j^*), \quad (10.8)$$

we obtain

$$l^* \cos (l^*j^*) = \frac{j^{*2} + l^{*2} - s^{*2}}{2j^*}. \quad (10.9)$$

Similarly,

$$s^* \cos (s^*j^*) = \frac{j^{*2} - l^{*2} + s^{*2}}{2j^*}. \quad (10.10)$$

Substituting these two cosines in Eq. (10.7), we get

$$g = 1 + \frac{j^{*2} + s^{*2} - l^{*2}}{2j^{*2}}; \quad (10.11)$$

in terms of the quantum numbers l and j and the spin s,

$$g = 1 + \frac{j(j + 1) + s(s + 1) - l(l + 1)}{2j(j + 1)}. \tag{10.12}$$

The importance of this g factor cannot be overemphasized, for it gives directly the relative separations of the Zeeman levels for the different terms.[1]   We shall now see how this comes about.

10.4. Magnetic Interaction Energy.—By Eqs. (10.6) and (10.7) the ratio between the total magnetic and mechanical moments of the atom, μ_j and p_j, is just

$$\frac{\mu_j}{p_j} = g \cdot \frac{e}{2mc}, \tag{10.13}$$

where $p_j = j^*h/2\pi$.[2]   The precession of j^* around H is the result of a torque acting on both l^* and s^*.   Due to the electron's anomalous spin magnetic moment, s^* tends to precess twice as fast around H as does l^*. If the field is not too strong, the coupling between l^* and s^* is sufficiently strong to maintain a constant j^*, so that this resultant precesses with a compromise angular velocity, by Larmor's theorem [Eq. (3.58)], given by g times the orbital precession angular velocity

$$\omega_L = Hg\frac{e}{2mc}. \tag{10.14}$$

The total energy of the precession is given by the precessional angular velocity ω_L times the component of the resultant mechanical moment $j^*h/2\pi$ on the axis of rotation H:[3]

$$\Delta W = \omega_L j^*\frac{h}{2\pi} \cos (j^*H) = H \cdot g\frac{e}{2mc}j^*\frac{h}{2\pi} \cos (j^*H). \tag{10.15}$$

---

[1] The values of g given by Eq. (10.12) are exactly the same as those given by Landé's model.

[2] In any experiment like the Stern-Gerlach experiment (*Zeits. f. Phys.*, **8**, 110, 1922), performed for the purpose of determining the magnetic and mechanical moment of the atom, the moments μ_j and p_j are oriented at some angle with the field just as in the Zeeman effect (see Fig. 10.7).   What one measures in this experiment is the component μ of the resultant magnetic moment along H.   By theory we say the component of μ_j will be $\mu = \mu_j \cos (j^*H)$, and the component of $j^*h/2\pi$ along H will be $mh/2\pi$, where m takes values differing from each other by unity from $m = +j$ to $m = -j$.

[3] The magnetic energy can be considered as the energy of a permanent magnet of moment μ, at an angle θ, in the field H, or as the added kinetic energy of the electron's orbital motion.   If, in the case of a circular orbit normal to the field, E represents the kinetic energy before the field is applied, and $E' = \frac{1}{2}I(\omega + \omega_L)^2$ the kinetic energy after, then the change in energy is just $\Delta E = E' - E = \frac{1}{2}I\omega_L^2 + I\omega\omega_L$.   Since the added field does not change the size of the orbit, I remains constant.   With $\omega >> \omega_L$, the first term is negligibly small and the energy change is given by the product of the mechanical moment, $I\omega = j^*h/2\pi$, and ω_L.

In terms of the magnetic quantum number m, $j^*h/2\pi \cdot \cos(j^*H)$ is just equal to $mh/2\pi$, so that[1]

$$\Delta W = H \cdot g\frac{e}{2mc} \cdot m \cdot \frac{h}{2\pi} = m \cdot g \cdot H\frac{eh}{4\pi mc}. \tag{10.16}$$

Dividing by hc, the interaction energy in wave numbers becomes

$$\frac{\Delta W}{hc} = -\Delta T = m \cdot g \cdot \frac{He}{4\pi mc^2} \text{ cm}^{-1}. \tag{10.17}$$

With $g = 1$ this equation reduces to Lorentz's classical formula [Eq. (10.1)].

Since the field H is the same for all levels of a given atom, it is convenient to express the Zeeman splitting in terms of what may be called the *Lorentz unit*, $\mathbf{L} = He/4\pi mc^2$, and write simply

$$-\Delta T = m \cdot g \cdot \mathbf{L} \text{ cm}^{-1}. \tag{10.18}$$

It should be emphasized that ΔT is the change in energy for each m level from the original level, and that the shift is proportional to the field strength H. With $m = \pm\frac{1}{2}, \pm\frac{3}{2}, \pm\frac{5}{2}, \cdots, \pm j$, the g factor is seen to be of primary importance in the splitting of each level. Values of the g factor for doublets are given in Table 10.1 and, along with them, values of the corresponding splitting factors mg.

TABLE 10.1.—THE LANDÉ g FACTORS AND THE SPLITTING FACTORS mg FOR DOUBLET TERMS

l	Term	g	mg
0	$^2S_{\frac{1}{2}}$	$\frac{2}{1}$	± 1
1	$^2P_{\frac{1}{2}}$	$\frac{2}{3}$	$\pm\frac{1}{3}$
	$^2P_{\frac{3}{2}}$	$\frac{4}{3}$	$\pm\frac{2}{3}, \pm\frac{6}{3}$
2	$^2D_{\frac{3}{2}}$	$\frac{4}{5}$	$\pm\frac{2}{5}, \pm\frac{6}{5}$
	$^2D_{\frac{5}{2}}$	$\frac{6}{5}$	$\pm\frac{3}{5}, \pm\frac{9}{5}, \pm\frac{15}{5}$
3	$^2F_{\frac{5}{2}}$	$\frac{6}{7}$	$\pm\frac{3}{7}, \pm\frac{9}{7}, \pm\frac{15}{7}$
	$^2F_{\frac{7}{2}}$	$\frac{8}{7}$	$\pm\frac{4}{7}, \pm\frac{12}{7}, \pm\frac{20}{7}, \pm\frac{28}{7}$
4	$^2G_{\frac{7}{2}}$	$\frac{8}{9}$	$\pm\frac{4}{9}, \pm\frac{12}{9}, \pm\frac{20}{9}, \pm\frac{28}{9}$
	$^2G_{\frac{9}{2}}$	$\frac{10}{9}$	$\pm\frac{5}{9}, \pm\frac{15}{9}, \pm\frac{25}{9}, \pm\frac{35}{9}, \pm\frac{45}{9}$

Consider, for example, the splitting of a $^2P_{\frac{3}{2}}$ level in a weak magnetic field. With $j = \frac{3}{2}$, there are four magnetic levels $m = \frac{3}{2}, \frac{1}{2}, -\frac{1}{2}$, and $\frac{3}{2}$, shifted from the field-free level by $mg = \frac{6}{3}, \frac{2}{3}, -\frac{2}{3}$, and $-\frac{6}{3}$. A graphical

---

[1] Here m, the magnetic quantum number in the numerator, must not be confused with m, the mass of the electron in the denominator.

representation of this splitting is shown in Fig. 10.7, where the vector j^* is shown in the four allowed positions. Multiplying j^* by g and projecting the product on the H axis, the displacements mg shown at the left are obtained.

Referring now to the spin-orbit interaction energy [Eqs. (8.17) and (8.20)], which gives rise to the doublet fine structure, and to the equation

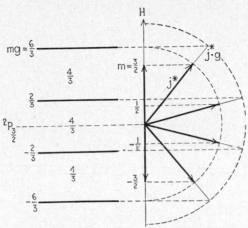

FIG. 10.7.—Schematic orientation diagram of an atom in a $^2P_{\frac{3}{2}}$ state showing the resultant Zeeman levels in a weak magnetic field.

just derived from the Zeeman splitting, the complete term value T of any magnetic level may be written

$$T = T_0 - \Gamma - mg \cdot \mathbf{L}. \tag{10.19}$$

T_0 is the term value of the hypothetical center of gravity of the field-free doublet, Γ is the fine-structure shift, and $mg \cdot \mathbf{L}$ is the magnetic shift.

10.5. Selection Rules.—As an example of the calculation of Zeeman patterns, consider the simple case of a principal-series doublet like the sodium yellow D lines $\lambda\lambda5890$ and 5896. The g factors for the initial $^2P_{\frac{1}{2}}$ and $^2P_{\frac{3}{2}}$ states and for the final $^2S_{\frac{1}{2}}$ state (see Table 10.1) are $\frac{2}{3}$, $\frac{4}{3}$, and 2, respectively. The splitting of each of these levels is shown schematically in Fig. 10.8, starting with the field-free levels at the left. The dotted lines in each case represent the centers of gravity of the associated levels.

The theoretical selection rules for transitions between levels, in agreement with observations, may be stated as follows: *In any transition the magnetic quantum number m changes by +1, 0, or −1, i.e.,*

$$\Delta m = 0, \pm 1. \tag{10.20}$$

For the stronger of the two field-free lines there are six allowed transitions and two forbidden transitions. For the other line there are four allowed transitions. The observed and calculated patterns are shown at the bottom of the figure.

Polarization rules derived from the classical theory as well as the quantum mechanics are found to hold experimentally. These rules may be stated in the following way:

Viewed $\perp$ to field $\begin{cases}\Delta m = \pm 1; \text{ plane polarized } \perp \text{ to } H; \; s \text{ components} \\ \Delta m = \quad 0; \text{ plane polarized } \parallel \text{ to } H; \; p \text{ components}\end{cases}$

Viewed $\parallel$ to field $\begin{cases}\Delta m = \pm 1; \text{ circularly polarized}; \qquad s \text{ components} \\ \Delta m = \quad 0; \text{ forbidden}; \qquad\qquad\quad\; p \text{ components}\end{cases}$

10.6. Intensity Rules.—The intensity rules for field-free energy levels, first derived from experimental observations by Burger, Dorgelo,

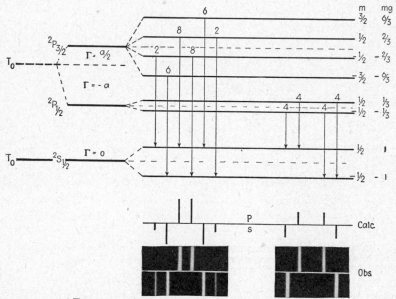

FIG. 10.8.—Zeeman effect of a principal-series doublet.

and Ornstein (see Sec. 8.3) are readily shown to follow directly from the intensity rules for the same levels in a weak magnetic field. In short these rules may be stated as follows:

The sum of all the transitions starting from any initial Zeeman level is equal to the sum of all transitions leaving any other level having the same n and l values. The sum of all transitions arriving at any Zeeman level is equal to the sum of all transitions arriving at any other level having the same n and l values.

For any given field-free spectrum line these rules are better expressed in terms of formulas which have been derived from the classical[1] as well

[1] For a classical derivation of the intensity rules, based on Bohr's correspondence principle, see J. H. Van Vleck, "Quantum Principles and Line Spectra," *Nat. Research Council, Bull.*, Vol. 10, 1926.

as the quantum-mechanical theories.   These formulas may be abbreviated as follows:

Transition $j \to j$ $\begin{cases} m \to m \pm 1, I = A(j \pm m + 1)(j \mp m). \\ m \to m \quad , I = 4Am^2. \end{cases}$ (10.21)

Transition $j \to j + 1$ $\begin{cases} m \to m \pm 1, I = B(j \pm m + 1)(j \pm m + 2). \\ m \to m \quad , I = 4B(j + m + 1)(j - m + 1). \end{cases}$

(10.22)

A and B are constants that need not be determined for relative intensities within each Zeeman pattern.   These formulas take into account the

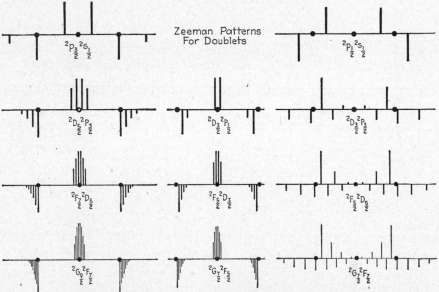

Zeeman Patterns
For Doublets

FIG. 10.9.—Zeeman patterns for all of the commonly observed doublet transitions.   The dots represent normal triplet separations.

fact that, when the radiation is observed perpendicular to the field direction, only half of the light making up the s components of a pattern is observed.   Observations parallel to the field give the other half of the s components' intensity.   The above given rules and formulas applied to the principal doublet in Fig. 10.8 give the relative intensities shown at the top of the arrows.   The same values are indicated by the heights of the lines shown at the bottom of the figure.   The sum of all transitions starting from any level in the figure is 12, and the sum arriving at either of the lower levels is 36.   (In obtaining these values the s components must be multiplied by 2.)   Experimentally, the p or s components may be photographed separately by inserting a Nicol prism in the path of the light coming from the source between the poles of an electromagnet.

Zeeman patterns for a number of doublet transitions are given in Fig. 10.9. These calculated patterns are in excellent agreement with all experimental observations. It is particularly interesting to see how closely the different lines group themselves around the normal-triplet separations, which are indicated in the figure by dots. Normal Zeeman triplets, as will be seen later, arise in special cases and in particular for all lines belonging to a singlet series, where the g factor for both the initial and final states is unity.

A method frequently employed for a rapid calculation of Zeeman patterns will be given briefly as follows. The separation factors mg, for both the initial and final states, are first written down in two rows with equal values of m directly below or above each other. For a $^2D_{\frac{3}{2}}-^2P_{\frac{3}{2}}$ transition they are:

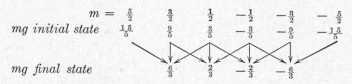

$$m = \tfrac{5}{2} \quad \tfrac{3}{2} \quad \tfrac{1}{2} \quad -\tfrac{1}{2} \quad -\tfrac{3}{2} \quad -\tfrac{5}{2}$$

In this array, the vertical arrows indicate the p components, $\Delta m = 0$, and the diagonal arrows the s components, $\Delta m = \pm 1$. The differences expressed with a least common denominator are as follows:

Vertical Differences   Diagonal Differences
  p Components s Components
$+\tfrac{3}{15}, +\tfrac{1}{15}, -\tfrac{1}{15}, -\tfrac{3}{15}$ $\pm\tfrac{15}{15}, \pm\tfrac{17}{15}, \pm\tfrac{19}{15}, \pm\tfrac{21}{15}$

In short these may be abbreviated,

$$\Delta\nu = \frac{(\pm 1), (\pm 3), \pm 15, \pm 17, \pm 19, \pm 21}{15} L \text{ cm}^{-1},$$

the four p components being set in parentheses, followed by the eight s components (see Fig. 10.9).

A simple qualitative rule for the intensities has been given by Kiess and Meggers as follows: If the j values of the two combining terms are equal, the vertical differences at the end of the scheme, and the diagonal differences at the center, give the strongest p and s components, respectively. If the j values are not equal, as in the case shown above, the vertical differences in the middle of the scheme and the diagonal differences at the ends give the strongest p and s components, respectively.

10.7. The Paschen-Back Effect.—In deriving the interaction energy between an atom containing one single valence electron and an external magnetic field, it was assumed that the field was weak as compared with the internal fields due to the spin and orbital motion of the electron. When the external field becomes greater than these internal fields the internal motions are greatly perturbed and the atom gives rise to the so-called *Paschen-Back effect.*

Just as the doublet fine-structure separations are a measure of the classical frequency with which l^* and s^* precess around their resultant j^* (see Sec. 10.4), so the Zeeman separations of the same energy states in a weak magnetic field are a measure of the frequency with which j^* precesses around H. In calculating the Zeeman separations in Sec. 10.4, it was tacitly assumed that the precession of l^* and s^* around j^* was much faster than that of j^* around H. This was necessary in order that the components of l^* and s^* normal to j^* average to zero and do not appreciably perturb the other precession. If now the field H is increased until the two precessions are of the same order of magnitude, then the Zeeman levels of the doublet will begin to overlap, there will be no averaging to zero, and Eqs. (10.17) and (10.19) will not hold.   Under these conditions the coupling between l^* and s^* will be partially broken down, the classical motions of l^* and s^* will become complicated, and j^* will no longer be fixed in magnitude. As the field H is still further increased, l^* and s^* will soon become

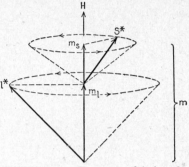

Fig. 10.10.—Vector model for the Paschen-Back effect where the field is so strong that l^* and s^* precess independently around the field direction H.

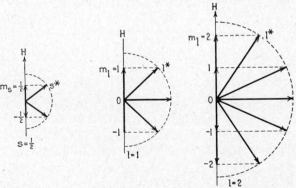

Fig. 10.11.—Space-quantization diagrams for p and d electrons in a strong magnetic field, Paschen-Back effect.

quantized separately and precess more or less independently around H (see Fig. 10.10).   This is the Paschen-Back effect.[1]

The quantum conditions in a strong Paschen-Back field are: (1) The projection of l^* on H takes integral values from $m_l = +l$ to $m_l = -l$. (2) The projection of s^* on H takes one of the two values $m_s = +\frac{1}{2}$, or

[1] Paschen, F., and E. Back, *Ann. d. Phys.*, **39**, 897, 1912; **40**, 960, 1913.

$-\frac{1}{2}$. For a p electron with $l = 1$, $s = \frac{1}{2}$, there are six possible states $m_l = 1$, 0, and -1, when $m_s = \frac{1}{2}$ or $-\frac{1}{2}$. Space-quantization diagrams of these cases are given in Fig. 10.11. Since for every electron there are two values of m_s and $2l + 1$ values of m_l, there are $2(2l + 1)$ combinations of the quantum numbers corresponding to $2(2l + 1)$ different states of the atom. As might be expected, this is exactly the number of weak-field levels.

The total energy of the atom in a field strong enough to give the Paschen-Back effect is made up of the three parts: (1) *the energy due to the precession of l^* around H;* (2) *the energy due to the precession of s^* around H;* (3) *the interaction energy between l^* and s^*.* By Larmor's theorem [Eq. (3.58)], the precessional angular velocities are given by H times the ratio between the magnetic and mechanical moments:

$$\omega_{l^*} = H\frac{e}{2mc} \text{ and } \omega_{s^*} = 2H\frac{e}{2mc}. \tag{10.23}$$

Since the ratio between the magnetic and mechanical moment for the spin of the electron is twice the orbital ratio, s^* should, on the classical picture, precess twice as fast as l^*. Multiplying each of these angular velocities by the projection of the angular momentum on H [see Eq. (10.15)], one gets the first two terms of the energy:

$$\Delta W_{l,H} = H\frac{e}{2mc}l^*\frac{h}{2\pi} \cos (l^*H) = H\frac{e}{2mc}m_l\frac{h}{2\pi}, \tag{10.24}$$

$$\Delta W_{s,H} = 2H\frac{e}{2mc}s^*\frac{h}{2\pi} \cos (s^*H) = 2H\frac{e}{2mc}m_s\frac{h}{2\pi}. \tag{10.25}$$

The sum of these two energies accounts for the main energy shift from the unperturbed energy level and is

$$\Delta W_H = (m_l + 2m_s)H\frac{eh}{4\pi mc}. \tag{10.26}$$

Dividing by hc, the term shift in wave numbers becomes

$$-\Delta T_H = (m_l + 2m_s)\frac{He}{4\pi mc^2} \text{ cm}^{-1}, \tag{10.27}$$

or in Lorentz units of $He/4\pi mc^2$,

$$-\Delta T_H = (m_l + 2m_s)\mathbf{L} \text{ cm}^{-1}. \tag{10.28}$$

To this magnetic energy the small correction term due to the interaction between l^* and s^* must be added. Although these two vectors precess independently around H, each motion still produces a magnetic field at the electron which perturbs the motion of the other. This interaction energy, though small as compared with that due to the external field, is of the same order of magnitude as the fine-structure doublet separations in field-free space, which by Eqs. (8.14), (8.18), and (8.19) are given by the Γ factor,

$$\Gamma = -\Delta T_{l,s} = al^*s^* \cos (l^*s^*), \tag{10.29}$$

where

$$a = \frac{R\alpha^2 Z^4}{n^3 l(l + \frac{1}{2})(l + 1)} \text{ cm}^{-1}. \tag{10.30}$$

In field-free space, the angle between l^* and s^* is constant and the cosine term cos (l^*s^*) is easily evaluated. In the present case, however, the angle is continually changing, so that an average value of the cosine must be calculated. From a well-known theorem in trigonometry it may be shown that with s^* and l^* precessing independently with fixed angles around a third direction H,

$$\overline{\cos (l^*s^*)} = \cos (l^*H) \cdot \cos (s^*H). \tag{10.31}$$

Making this substitution in (10.29),

$$\Gamma = -\Delta T_{l,s} = al^* \cos (l^*H)s^* \cos (s^*H). \tag{10.32}$$

These are just the projections of l^* and s^* on H, so that

$$-\Delta T_{l,s} = am_l m_s = \Gamma. \tag{10.33}$$

Adding this term to Eq. (10.28), the total energy shift becomes

$$-\Delta T_{cm^{-1}} = (m_l + 2m_s)\mathbf{L} + am_l m_s. \tag{10.34}$$

We may now write down a general relation for the term value of any strong field level,

$$T_{cm^{-1}} = T_0 - (m_l + 2m_s)\mathbf{L} - am_l m_s, \tag{10.35}$$

where T_0 is the term value of the hypothetical center of gravity of the fine-structure doublet.

10.8. Paschen-Back Effect of a Principal-series Doublet.—As an example of the Paschen-Back effect, consider first the calculation of terms and term separations involved in a principal-series doublet $^2S_{\frac{1}{2}}-^2P_{\frac{1}{2},\frac{3}{2}}$. The fine-structure separations due to the interaction of l^* and s^* in field-free space are given in Col. 2, Table 10.2 (see Fig. 8.9). In the next three columns the weak-field energies are calculated (see Fig. 10.8). In the last five columns the strong-field energies are calculated, using Eq. (10.34).

The values tabulated are shown schematically in Fig. 10.12. At the left the undisturbed fine-structure levels and the observed transitions are shown. The weak-field Zeeman levels are next shown with the observed Zeeman patterns below. In the strong field the Paschen-Back levels are shown with, and without, the small l^*s^* coupling correction

$am_l m_s$. The allowed transitions and the calculated pattern are shown below.

In deriving the above equations for the Zeeman and Paschen-Back effects, the atomic system was assumed to be in one of two ideal situations. In the first case the field was assumed so weak that j^*, the resultant of l^* and s^*, was invariant as regards magnitude and inclination to the field axis. In the second case the field was assumed so strong that l^* and s^* precess independently around H. The question of intermediate

TABLE 10.2.—WEAK- AND STRONG-FIELD ENERGIES FOR A PRINCIPAL-SERIES DOUBLET

No field		Weak field (Zeeman effect)			Strong field (Paschen-Back effect)				
Term	Γ	m	g	mg	m_l	m_s	$m = m_l + m_s$	$m_l + 2m_s$	$am_l m_s$
$^2P_{\frac{3}{2}}$	$+a/2$	$+\frac{3}{2}$	$\frac{4}{3}$	$+\frac{6}{3}$	$+1$	$+\frac{1}{2}$	$+\frac{3}{2}$	$+2$	$+a/2$
		$+\frac{1}{2}$		$+\frac{2}{3}$	0	$+\frac{1}{2}$	$+\frac{1}{2}$	$+1$	0
		$-\frac{1}{2}$		$-\frac{2}{3}$	-1	$+\frac{1}{2}$	$-\frac{1}{2}$	0	$-a/2$
		$-\frac{3}{2}$		$-\frac{6}{3}$	$+1$	$-\frac{1}{2}$	$+\frac{1}{2}$	0	$-a/2$
$^2P_{\frac{1}{2}}$	$-a$	$+\frac{1}{2}$	$\frac{2}{3}$	$+\frac{1}{3}$	0	$-\frac{1}{2}$	$-\frac{1}{2}$	-1	0
		$-\frac{1}{2}$		$-\frac{1}{3}$	-1	$-\frac{1}{2}$	$-\frac{3}{2}$	-2	$+a/2$
$^2S_{\frac{1}{2}}$	0	$+\frac{1}{2}$	2	$+1$	0	$+\frac{1}{2}$	$+\frac{1}{2}$	$+1$	0
		$-\frac{1}{2}$		-1	0	$-\frac{1}{2}$	$-\frac{1}{2}$	-1	0

fields, therefore, arises, and one asks, how does each weak-field level go over to a corresponding strong-field level? Darwin's treatment of this problem, which will not be given here, answers this question in a very simple manner.[1] According to the classical law of the conservation of angular momentum, the sum of the projections on H of the various angular-momentum vectors must remain the same for all field strengths. Since in weak field this sum is given by m and in strong field by $m_l + m_s$, we may write, as part of the correlation rule, $m = m_l + m_s$. This alone is not sufficient to correlate all weak- and strong-field levels, since in most instances there will be more than one level with the same m value. The more specific rule, in keeping with the quantum mechanics, may be stated as follows: *Levels with the same m never cross.*

An ingenious method for obtaining the same correlation has been given by Breit.[2] An array of weak- and strong-field quantum numbers

[1] DARWIN, C. G., *Proc. Roy. Soc.*, A, **115**, 1, 1927.
[2] BREIT, G., *Phys. Rev.*, **28**, 334, 1926.

is written down as follows (see Fig. 10.13).   Values of m_l are written down in their regular order in a horizontal row and values of m_s in a vertical column.   The array is next filled in with all possible sums of

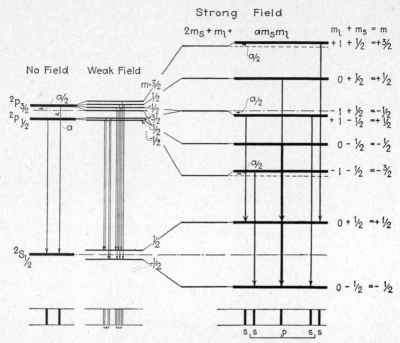

FIG. 10.12.—Energy levels for a principal-series doublet starting with no field at the left and ending with a strong field (Paschen-Back effect) at the right.   Allowed transitions are shown below.

m_l and m_s.   These sums are the weak-field quantum numbers, divided into two parts by the dotted lines.   Each weak-field level m is to be correlated with the strong-field level given by the value of m_l directly above, and the value of m_s directly to the right of the m value.   The $^2P_{\frac{3}{2}}$, $m = \frac{3}{2}$ state, for example, goes to the state $m_l = 1$, and $m_s = \frac{1}{2}$.

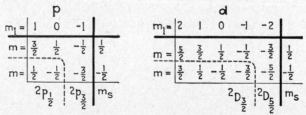

FIG. 10.13.—Correlation of weak- and strong-field quantum numbers and energy levels.
(*After Breit.*)

It is obvious that there are two ways of drawing the L-shaped dotted line.   Of the two ways only the one shown will give the correct correlation for doublets from a single electron.

10.9. Selection Rules for the Paschen-Back Effect.—Selection rules for the Paschen-Back effect, derived from the classical theory may be stated as follows: In any transition

$$\Delta m_l = 0, \pm 1 \text{ and } \Delta m_s = 0. \tag{10.36}$$

When these rules are applied to a given doublet they are found to lead, in a very strong field, to a pattern closely resembling a normal Zeeman triplet. The radiated frequencies of the principal-series doublet considered above are assembled again in Fig. 10.14. The restriction $\Delta m_s = 0$ implies the necessary condition that the polarization of any given line be retained throughout all field strengths. The p and s components

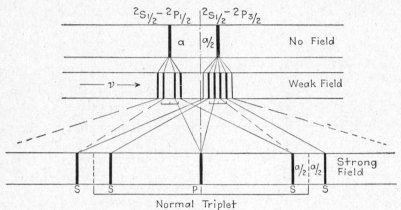

FIG. 10.14.—Principal-series doublet in various magnetic field strengths. Paschen-Back effect.

in weak field become p and s components, respectively, in the strong field or else disappear as forbidden lines. For the s components, the fine-structure separation is just two-thirds that of the field-free doublet.

It should be made clear that as the field strength increases and the quantum number j disappears, and, as j and its projection m are replaced by m_l and m_s, the selection rules for j can no longer be expected to hold. This is in agreement with observations made by Paschen and Back[1] who were the first to observe experimentally the so-called *normal triplet* of a principal-series doublet in a very strong field. Since the strong-field levels must be widely separated as compared with the fine structure, only the very narrow fine-structure doublets may be expected to be carried over to the Paschen-Back normal triplet with the ordinarily obtained field strengths. Using the principal-series doublet of lithium, with only a separation of 0.34 wave numbers, Paschen and Back required the very strong field of 43000 gauss to observe it as a magnetic triplet.

10.10. The Zeeman Effect, and Paschen-Back Effect, in Hydrogen.— Although the hydrogen atom is the simplest of all atomic systems, the

[1] PASCHEN, F., and E. BACK, *Physica*, **1**, 261, 1921.

Zeeman effect in hydrogen is not very simple. In Sec. 9.3 we have seen how each of the Balmer terms contains a fine structure which is made up of doublets ^2S, ^2P, ^2D, etc. When placed in a weak magnetic field each of these doublet levels, as in sodium, should undergo an anomalous splitting (see Fig. 10.8). As a result of this splitting each fine-structure component of a line like H_α, λ6563, should reveal an anomalous but symmetrical Zeeman pattern (see Fig. 10.9). With H_α made up of seven different transitions, there would be, in this case, seven patterns of the type shown in Fig. 10.9, all lying within an interval of about half a wave number (see Fig. 9.4). It is now easy to see why the Zeeman effect of hydrogen has not been observed.

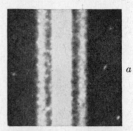

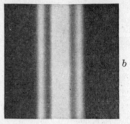

In a strong magnetic field, the magnetic levels of each doublet begin to overlap each other, until in a field strength of several thousand gauss the Paschen-Back effect sets in. Under these conditions each doublet level, combining with another doublet level, gives rise to approximately a *normal triplet* like the one shown in Fig. 10.12. The H_α line, for example, will be made up of three normal triplets ^2S–^2P, ^2P–^2S, and ^2P–^2D, superimposed almost on top of each other. In a field of 32000 gauss, Paschen and Back[1] observed just that; a well-resolved triplet with practically the classical separation. In such a field the pattern is some six times as wide as the field-free line. A photographic reproduction of this triplet is given in Fig. 10.15. Normal triplets have also been observed by Paschen and Back for H_β and H_γ.

FIG. 10.15.—Paschen-Back effect of hydrogen H_α, λ6563. (*a*) Enlarged from photograph in the published paper of Paschen and Back. (*b*) Same as *a* with photographic paper moved parallel to lines during enlargement.

10.11. A Quantum-mechanical Model of the Atom in a Strong Magnetic Field.—In this chapter the Zeeman effect, as well as the Paschen-Back effect, has been treated chiefly from the standpoint of the semi-classical vector model. Quantum-mechanical treatments of the same problems have been made by different investigators and found to lead to exactly the same formula. Chronologically, the more accurate quantum mechanics led the way to a simpler formulation of Landé's vector model. We have seen in Chaps. IV and IX how, in field-free space, this model is surprisingly similar to the quantum-mechanical model of probability-density distributions for the electron. As would be expected from energy relations, the weak- and strong-field distributions for the electron on any model should be little different from each other

[1] PASCHEN, F., and E. BACK, *Ann. d. Phys.*, **39**, 897, 1912. The photograph in Fig. 10.15 is a copy of the photograph given in Plate VIII of *Ann. d. Phys.*, Vol. 39, 1912.

radially. Angularly, as shown by the vector model, they should change considerably.

Space-quantized to a vanishing magnetic field the field-free states, oriented as shown in Fig. 9.8, may be taken to represent the weak-field states, the Zeeman effect, of the atom. Assuming separate angular distribution curves for the spin of the electron, similar to the orbital curves in Fig. 4.3, pictures analogous to the independent precession of l^* and s^* around the field direction H may be formulated for strong fields, *i.e.*, the Paschen-Back effect.

In passing, it should be mentioned that a given state of the atom in a weak field is specified by the quantum numbers n, l, j, and m, and in a strong field by n, l, m_l, and m_s. For intermediate fields either set may be used, although, to use an expression introduced by Mulliken, j, m_l, and m_s are *not good quantum numbers*.

Problems

1. Compute the Zeeman pattern (separations and intensities) for the doublet transition $^2G_{\frac{9}{2}}-^2H_{\frac{11}{2}}$.

2. Find the total width in wave numbers of the Zeeman pattern of Prob. 1 in a weak field of 5000 gauss.

3. Compute the weak- and strong-field energies for a diffuse-series doublet, and tabulate them as in Table 10.2. Plot the initial and final states, as shown in Fig. 10.12, and indicate the allowed transitions by arrows.

4. Plot, as in Fig. 10.14, the field-free lines, the weak-field lines, and the strong-field lines of the above example. [NOTE:—Certain components of the forbidden transition $^2P_{\frac{1}{2}}-^2D_{\frac{3}{2}}$ appear in strong fields and should be indicated (see Fig. 13.14)].

5. What field strength would be required to carry the first member of the principal series of sodium over to the Paschen-Back effect where the separation of the resultant normal triplet (see Fig. 10.14) is four times the fine-structure separation of the field-free doublet?

CHAPTER XI

SINGLET AND TRIPLET SERIES OF TWO-VALENCE-ELECTRON SYSTEMS

In the preceding chapters only the simplest of the known atomic systems have been treated in any detail. The simplest of elements, classified as one-electron systems, always give rise to doublet energy levels, transitions between which account for their observed doublet series of spectrum lines. It is now well known that atoms like beryllium, magnesium, zinc, cadmium, mercury, calcium, strontium, and barium, in groups IIA and IIB of the periodic table, contain two valence electrons and give rise to series of singlet and triplet energy levels and spectrum lines. Some of these series were briefly introduced in Chap. I. Before taking up any quantum-mechanical or vector-model treatment of two-electron systems, it is important that we first become familiar with the observed series, the derived energy level diagrams, and the associated types of electron orbits.

11.1. General Series Relations.—Like the doublet spectra of the alkali metals, the singlet and triplet series of the elements Be, Mg, Zn, Cd, Hg, Ca, Sr, and Ba may be grouped into four chief classes: sharp, principal, diffuse, and fundamental. In each of these atoms, however, there are four chief series of singlets as well as four chief series of triplets. If the chief series for each element are plotted to a frequency scale, as in Fig. 1.8, a number of important relations are brought out. In calcium, as well as in most spectra, the fine structure is very small as compared with the other structure and for such a diagram can be neglected. The schematic plot in the lower half of the figure brings out the following relations: (1) The ^3S and ^3D series have one common limit and the ^1S and ^1D series another. (2) The frequency difference between the common limit of the ^3S and ^3D series and the ^3P series limit X_1 is equal to the frequency of the first member of the ^3S series. This is the Rydberg-Schuster law. (3) The frequency difference between the common limit of the ^3S and ^3D series and the ^3F series limit X_2 is equal to the frequency of the first member of the triplet diffuse series. This is the Runge law. (4) The above relations are also observed to hold when the fine structure is taken into account. (5) Relations (1), (2), and (3) hold for the respective singlet series.

Taking into account the fine structure of the triplets in general it is observed (see Fig. 1.10) that (1) all members of the sharp series are

171

composed of three lines with the same separations and approach a triple
limit; (2) all members of the principal series are composed of three lines
with decreasing separations and approach a single limit; (3) all members
of the diffuse and fundamental series contain six lines, three strong lines
and three satellites, and approach triple limits.

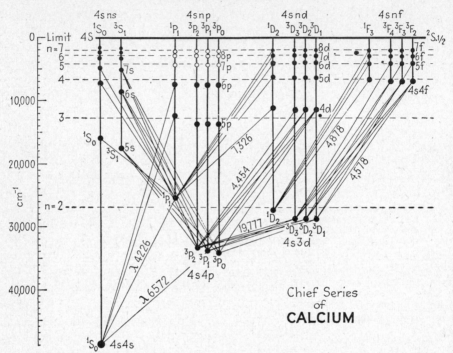

FIG. 11.1.—Energy level diagram for the four chief singlet and triplet series of the neutral
calcium atom.   For complete diagram, see Fig. 11.9.

As in the doublet series of the alkali metals nearly all of the observed
singlet or triplet series are closely represented by the general series
formula

$$\nu_n = \frac{R}{(n_1 - \mu_1)^2} - \frac{R}{(n_2 - \mu_2)^2},$$ (11.1)

where ν_n is the radiated frequency of a line in wave numbers, R is the
Rydberg constant ($= 109737$ cm^{-1}), and μ_1 and μ_2 are constants.   Thus
each spectrum series, or each fine-structure component of a series, is
given by the difference between a fixed term T_1 and a running term T_n;

$$T_1 = \frac{R}{(n_1 - \mu_1)^2}, \qquad T_n = \frac{R}{(n_2 - \mu_2)^2},$$ (11.2)

where n_1 is an integer and n_2 takes successive integral values.   With
these relations known to hold for each series, and the relations summarized above, term diagrams for each element may be constructed.

Such a diagram is given for calcium in Fig. 11.1.   This same energy level diagram may be arrived at in another way.

If all of the limits of the eight chief series of calcium (Fig. 1.8) are brought together into one common limit, the spectrum lines, including

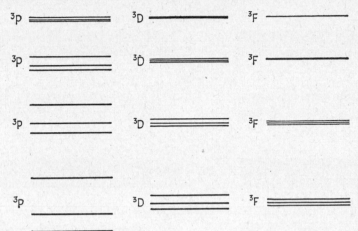

FIG. 11.2.—Schematic representation of the triplet fine structure of the first four members of the three chief ^3P, ^3D, and ^3F term series.

the ones plotted as negative, become the energy levels of Fig. 11.1. Taking into account the fine structure of the triplet series, shown in Fig. 1.10, this process transforms the triplet sharp-series lines into single levels and the three remaining triplet series into series of con-

TABLE 11.1.—TERM VALUES OF THE CHIEF SERIES IN CALCIUM

Terms	Electron configuration	$n = 3$	$n = 4$	$n = 5$	$n = 6$	$n = 7$	$n = 8$
$^3S_1$	$4s\ ns$			17765	8830	5324	3566
$^3P_2$	$4s\ np$		33989	12730	6778	4343	
$^3D_3$	$4s\ nd$	28933	11547	6557	4252	2998	2259
$^3F_4$	$4s\ nf$		7134	4541	3140	2298	1754
^1S_c	$4s\ ns$		49305	15988	7518	5028	3417
$^1P_1$	$4s\ np$		25652	12573	7626	5371	3880
$^1D_2$	$4s\ nd$	27455	12006	6385	4315	2995	
$^1F_3$	$4s\ nf$		6961	4500	3122	2290	1750
Hydrogen..........		12186	6855	4387	3047	2238	1714

verging triple levels (see Fig. 11.2).   Although the so-called ^3S levels are single, their triplet nature will be brought out when the atom is placed in a magnetic field (see Chap. XIII).   The assignment of the total quantum numbers n to the valence electrons in the different levels will be taken up in Sec. 11.3. The integral subscripts, used to distinguish between levels, are the *inner quantum numbers*. Term values of the singlet series and the upper fine-structure component of the triplet series of calcium are given in Table 11.1.

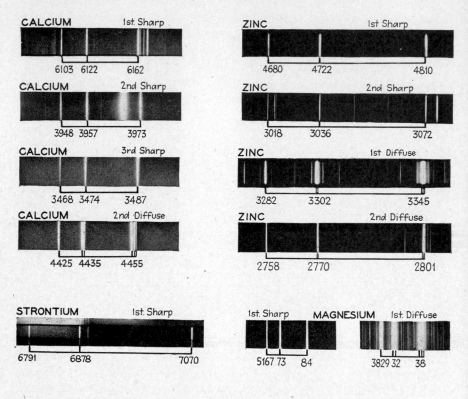

FIG. 11.3.—Photographs of triplets taken from original spectrograms kindly loaned to the author by Dr. A. S. King.

11.2. Triplet Fine Structure.—Photographs showing a number of triplets are given in Fig. 11.3. Lines having the same frequency separations are enlarged to the same frequency scale. The sharp triplets, all with the same separations, arise from transitions starting from the series of ^3S levels and ending on the lowest ^3P levels. Similar transitions from the series of ^3D levels into the lowest ^3P levels give rise to the observed diffuse triplets with satellites. Transitions from the series of ^1P terms into the normal state ^1S give rise to principal-series singlets, etc. In some spectra, lines arising from transitions between levels higher up on the energy level diagram are observed. These lines do not belong to the chief series and are called *combination lines*. Occasionally transitions between singlet and triplet levels are also observed. Such lines are called *intercombination lines*.

Observations on the fine structure of triplets in general enable one to formulate certain qualitative rules concerning triplet term intervals: (1) In each series the triplet fine structures converge rapidly as they approach a single common limit. (2) ^3P intervals are wider than the corresponding ^3D intervals. (3) ^3D intervals are wider than the corresponding ^3F intervals. (4) Corresponding triplet intervals in corresponding elements increase with atomic number. This latter rule is illustrated by the values given in Table 11.2.

TABLE 11.2.—TRIPLET FINE-STRUCTURE INTERVALS
(First member of the principal and diffuse series showing increase in wave-number separation with atomic number)

Element	Z	$^3P_1$–$^3P_2$	$^3P_0$–$^3P_1$	$^3D_2$–$^3D_3$	$^3D_1$–$^3D_2$
Be	4	2.36	0.69	Unresolved	
Mg	12	40.92	19.89	Unresolved	
Zn	30	388.90	189.8	5.5	3.4
Cd	48	1171.00	541.8	18.2	11.7
Hg	80	4630.60	1767.3	35.1	60.0
Ca	20	105.9	52.30	21.7	13.9
Sr	38	394.4	187.1	100.3	60.0
Ba	56	878.2	370.6	381.1	181.5

A brief study of the diffuse and fundamental triplets will show the reader that certain general selection rules are in operation. These rules are most easily stated in terms of the quantum numbers or quantum values of the different energy states. For various types of levels the capital letter L is almost universally used and assigned the following quantum values:

$$L = 0, 1, 2, 3, 4, 5, \cdots$$
$$\text{for } S, P, D, F, G, H, \ldots \text{ terms.}$$

The subscripts to the right of each term are the inner quantum numbers J and always take the following values:

$^1S_0$	$^1P_1$	$^1D_2$	$^1F_3$	$^1G_4$	$^1H_5$
$^3S_1$	$^3P_0\,^3P_1\,^3P_2$	$^3D_1\,^3D_2\,^3D_3$	$^3F_2\,^3F_3\,^3F_4$	$^3G_3\,^3G_4\,^3G_5$	$^3H_4\,^3H_5\,^3H_6$

The selection rules for triplet-triplet transitions or for singlet-singlet transitions are[1]

$$\Delta L = \pm 1 \text{ and } \Delta J = 0, \pm 1.$$

[1] Under certain conditions in complex spectra the transitions $\Delta L = 0$ are allowed, but not for the chief series being here discussed.

The allowed transitions for a number of triplets are shown in Fig. 11.4. Relative separations and intensities are shown directly below the arrows by the respective separations and heights of the lines. Qualitatively the following rules for the intensities are found to hold experimentally: The stronger lines arise where ΔL changes in the same direction as ΔJ.

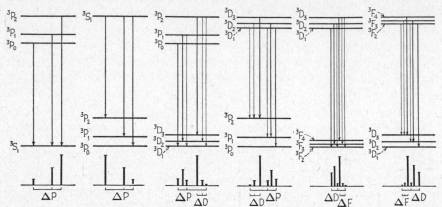

FIG. 11.4.—Triplet-triplet transitions showing selection rules and relative intensities.

These are shown by the heavier arrows. Of these the strongest line arises from the transition involving the largest values of L and J. These two well-known rules should be memorized, for they are quite generally applicable in complex spectra. It should be pointed out in passing that small letters s, l, and j are used for the quantum values of individual electrons, whereas capital letters S, L, and J are used to designate terms in all atomic systems where there are one or more valence electrons.

11.3. The Quantum Numbers n and l of Both Valence Electrons.—In order to correlate energy levels with the various types of electron orbits we return to the Bohr-Stoner scheme of the building up of the elements and the normal states of the atom. According to Table 5.2, the complete normal electron configurations for the neutral atoms of Groups IIA and IIB (Table 5.1) are as follows:

TABLE 11.3.—ELECTRON CONFIGURATIONS

4	Be,	$1s^2$	$2s^2$								
12	Mg,	$1s^2$	$2s^2$	$2p^6$	$3s^2$						
20	Ca,	$1s^2$	$2s^2$	$2p^6$	$3s^2$	$3p^6$	$4s^2$				
30	Zn,	$1s^2$	$2s^2$	$2p^6$	$3s^2$	$3p^6$	$3d^{10}$	$4s^2$			
38	Sr,	$1s^2$	$2s^2$	$2p^6$	$3s^2$	$3p^6$	$3d^{10}$	$4s^2$	$4p^6$	$5s^2$	
48	Cd,	$1s^2$	$2s^2$	$2p^6$	$3s^2$	$3p^6$	$3d^{10}$	$4s^2$	$4p^6$	$4d^{10}$	$5s^2$
56	Ba,	$1s^2$	$2s^2$	$2p^6$	$3s^2$	$3p^6$	$3d^{10}$	$4s^2$	$4p^6$	$4d^{10}$	$5s^2$ $5p^6$ $6s^2$
80	Hg,	$1s^2$	$2s^2$	$2p^6$	$3s^2$	$3p^6$	$3d^{10}$	$4s^2$	$4p^6$	$4d^{10}$	$4f^{14}$ $5s^2$ $5p^6$ $5d^{10}$ $6s^2$

It is the last two *equivalent* electrons in each of these configurations (**set in heavy type**) that are responsible for the chemical valence of two and are chiefly responsible for the general characteristics of their optical spectra.

Just as in the alkali metals we may think of all but the last subshell of electrons as comprising a core of completed subshells around which the valence electrons move in various types of orbits, some penetrating the core and coming close to the nucleus and others remaining well outside the core. Thus in calcium, on the Bohr-Stoner scheme, there are in the normal state two equivalent electrons in $4s$ orbits. If now the calcium atom is excited, by some means or other, either or both of these electrons may be excited to higher energy levels. It turns out that all eight of the chief series of spectrum lines and energy levels result from the excitation of only one of the valence electrons.[1]

Noting what subshells of electrons are already filled in calcium, one can predict with reasonable certainty that the first excited states of the atom should be D or P states, corresponding to the excited electron being in a $3d$ or a $4p$ orbit, respectively. Experiment confirms this, the levels ^3D, ^1D, ^3P, and ^1P coming almost together (see Fig. 11.1). The first ^3P along with the ^1P close by is therefore attributed to one of the valence electrons being in a $4s$ orbit and the other in a $4p$ orbit. The abbreviated electron configuration for these states is written $4s\,4p$. Similarly the first ^3D and ^1D are attributed to the electron configuration $4s\,3d$. By the same process the second ^3P and ^1P are assigned the configuration $4s\,5p$. It is to be noted that close by each triplet a singlet level with the same L value is found. In agreement with theory, the single exception to this observed rule is the normal state $4s4s,{}^1S_0$, where no $^3S_1$ term has ever been found. Exceptions of this kind always occur where the electrons are equivalent, *i.e.*, have the same n and l values.

This rule of finding a singlet and triplet close together fits in with the theory of the spinning electron and will be treated in the next chapter. Continuing the assignments of the observed energy levels, successive members of the ^3P and ^1P series in calcium have the electron configurations $4s4p$, $4s5p$, $4s6p$, . . . , $4s\infty p$, or in short $4snp$, where $n = 4$, 5, 6, . . . , ∞ (see Table 11.1). When n becomes infinite the p electron is removed from the atom and the atom is said to be ionized. The diffuse term series ^3D and ^1D are represented by the configurations $4snd$, where $n = 3, 4, 5, \cdots , \infty$, and the fundamental series by $4snf$, where $n = 4$, 5, 6, . . . ∞. Regardless of the series of orbits through which we may imagine the electron to be carried in ionizing the atom, we are finally left with one valence electron in a $4s$ state. This is as it should be, for all eight term series approach a common limit. Hereafter the universally adopted notation will be used in which the designation of all of the valence electrons is given preceding the term symbols $4s5p,{}^3P_2$; $4s3d$,

---

[1] When both electrons are raised to excited states the atom gives rise to a complex system of energy levels. These will be treated in the next chapter.

$^3D_1$; $4s4f, ^1F_3$; etc. When a certain term is to be given frequently, the configuration is written down the first time and subsequently omitted.

11.4. Penetrating and Nonpenetrating Electrons for Two-electron Systems.—A quantum-mechanical picture of the neutral calcium atom is shown in Fig. 11.5, with the corresponding classical model below. Above, the probability-density distribution $4\pi r^2\psi\psi^*$ is plotted as a function of r, the electron-nuclear distance in units of the radius of the first Bohr circular orbit ($a_1 = 0.528$ Å.) (see Chaps. IV and IX). The

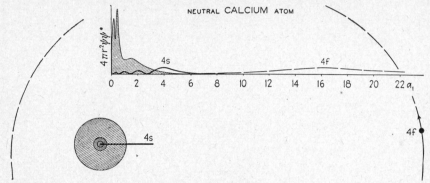

FIG. 11.5.—Quantum-mechanical model and the corresponding orbital model of the neutral calcium atom. The two valence electrons are shown separately, one in a penetrating $4s$ orbit and the other in a nonpenetrating $4f$ orbit.

shaded area represents the calcium core of 18 electrons. The two valence electrons are shown separately, one in a penetrating $4s$ orbit and the other in a nonpenetrating $4f$ orbit. On the classical model the orbits are drawn according to model a (see Fig. 4.8).

As in the one-electron systems the penetrating of the various possible electron orbits into the atom core is measured by the deviation of the term values from those of hydrogen. From the energy level diagram of calcium in Fig. 11.1, or from the term values in Table 11.1, it is observed (1) that only the levels involving f electrons are hydrogen-like, and (2) that the order of penetration is f, d, p, and s, e.g., for the total quantum number $n = 5$ the order is $4s5f$, $4s5d$, $4s5p$, and $4s5s$.

Two methods have already been given by which this penetration can be measured, one by modifying the nuclear charge in the hydrogen formula $T = RZ^2/n^2$, and the other in modifying the total quantum number. On the one hand there is the general *term* formula

$$T = \frac{R(Z - \sigma)^2}{n^2}, \tag{11.3}$$

where Z is the atomic number and σ is a screening constant, and on the other hand the Rydberg formula

$$T = \frac{Z_o^2}{(n - \mu)^2} \tag{11.4}$$

where Z_o is the effective nuclear charge when the electron is well outside the core, n is the total quantum number of the excited electron, and μ is the quantum defect. Values of $Z - \sigma$ and of μ, calculated from the above Eqs. (11.3) and (11.4), and Table 11.1, are given in Table 11.4, for calcium. For nonpenetrating orbits, and hydrogen, $Z - \sigma = 1$ and $\mu = 0$. The values of $Z - \sigma$ for the $4snf$ terms clearly show that the f electron orbits lie, for the most part, well outside the core of 18 electrons as well as outside the orbit of the $4s$ electron and that they move in a field which is nearly hydrogen-like. All of the other orbit types are penetrating.

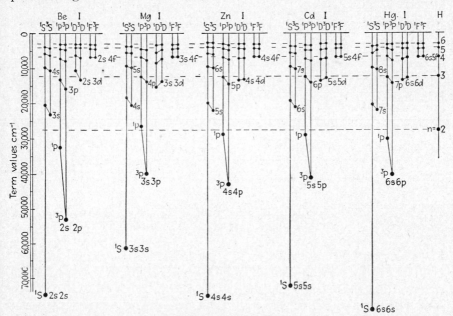

FIG. 11.6.—Energy level diagrams of beryllium, magnesium, zinc, cadmium, and mercury. (Hydrogen comparison.)

Energy level diagrams of a complete group of elements are given in Fig. 11.6. These diagrams show throughout that s orbits are penetrating and f orbits are nonpenetrating.

11.5. The Excitation of Both Valence Electrons.—Not all of the prominent lines in the spectra of the alkaline earths, calcium, strontium, and barium, can be attributed to the four chief series of singlets and triplets: sharp, principal, diffuse, and fundamental. Through the identification and classification of these additional lines into what are called *multiplets*, Russell and Saunders,[1] in 1925, were led to the key to complex spectra. There are in the spectra of Ca, Sr, and Ba three prominent groups of lines now recognized as forming a triad of *triplet*

[1] RUSSELL, H. N., and F. A. SAUNDERS, *Astrophys. Jour.*, **61**, 38, 1925.

multiplets. These three great triplet multiplets, photographs of which are given in Fig. 11.7, for calcium, arise from transitions which start

TABLE 11.4.—PENETRATING AND NONPENETRATING ORBITS IN CALCIUM

[Values of the effective nuclear charge $Z-\sigma$ (in **heavy type**) and values of the quantum defect μ (in *italics*)]

Configuration	Term	$n = 3$	$n = 4$	$n = 5$	$n = 6$	$n = 7$	Orbit
$4s\ ns$	$^1S_1$	......	**2.6** *2.5*	**1.9** *2.4*	**1.6** *2.2*	**1.5** *2.3*	Penetrating
	$^3S_0$	......	......	**2.0** *2.5*	**1.7** *2.5*	**1.5** *2.5*	
$4s\ np$	$^1P_1$	......	**1.9** *1.9*	**1.7** *2.0*	**1.6** *2.2*	**1.5** *2.5*	Penetrating
	$^3P_2$	......	**2.2** *2.2*	**1.7** *2.1*	**1.5** *2.0*	**1.4** *2.0*	
$4s\ nd$	$^1D_2$	**1.5** *1.0*	**1.3** *1.0*	**1.2** *0.9*	**1.2** *1.0*	**1.2** *1.0*	Penetrating
	$^3D_3$	**1.5** *1.1*	**1.3** *0.9*	**1.2** *0.9*	**1.2** *0.9*	**1.2** *1.0*	
$4s\ nf$	$^1F_3$	......	**1.0** *0.0*	**1.0** *0.1*	**1.0** *0.1*	**1.0** *0.1*	Nonpenetrating
	$^3F_4$	......	**1.0** *0.1*	**1.0** *0.1*	**1.0** *0.1*	**1.0** *0.1*	
Hydrogen..		**1.0** *0.0*	**1.0** *0.0*	**1.0** *0.0*	**1.0** *0.0*	**1.0** *0.0*	

from three triplet terms which have no place in the ordinary chief series of terms and end on the lowest $^3D_{1,2,3}$ of the diffuse series. The ^3D intervals, common to all three multiplets, are shown by brackets in the frequency plot. It is to be noted that each multiplet is composed of

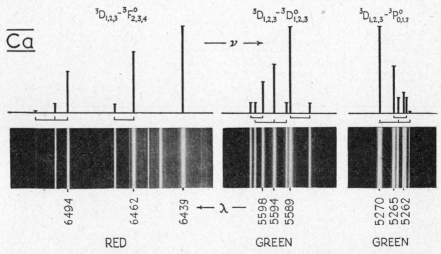

FIG. 11.7.— Photographs and frequency plot of the great calcium triad of triplet multiplets, one in the red region of the spectrum and the other two in the green.

three relatively strong lines and three or four fainter lines. The observed intensities indicate that the inner quantum numbers of the upper triad of triplet levels are those of $^3P_{0,1,2}$, $^3D_{1,2,3}$, and $^3F_{2,3,4}$ terms. The wavelengths, frequencies, and estimated relative intensities are given in multiplet form in Table 11.5.

TABLE 11.5.—RELATIVE INTENSITIES, WAVE-LENGTHS, AND FREQUENCIES OF THE GREAT CALCIUM TRIAD
(Given in multiplet form)

	$^3D_3$	21.77	$^3D_2$	13.89	$^3D_1$
$^3F_4$	150 6439.09 *15525.87*				
78.15					
$^3F_3$	40 6471.66 *15447.72*		125 6462.58 *15469.44*		
88.28					
$^3F_2$	1 6508.84 *15359.40*		30 6499.65 *15381.20*		80 6493.79 *15395.08*
$^3D_3$	80 5588.74 *17888.15*		25 5581.97 *17909.85*		
40.01					
$^3D_2$	30 5601.28 *17848.11*		60 5594.46 *17869.87*		20 5590.11 *17883.79*
26.73					
$^3D_1$			20 5002.83 *17843.18*		50 5508.48 *17857.03*
$^3P_2$	60 5270.27 *18969.08*		20 5264.24 *18990.89*		2 5260.38 *19004.77*
4.80					
$^3P_1$			40 5265.56 *18986.07*		20 5261.70 *18999.99*
1.94					
$^3P_0$					25 5262.24 *18998.05*

In addition to this triad Russell and Saunders identified, in calcium, a series of anomalous multiplets in the ultra-violet spectrum. At the time of discovery this series was peculiarly different from the ordinary series, for the upper terms combine like $^3P_{0,1,2}$ terms with the low $4s4p$, $^3P_{0,1,2}$ terms of the principal series. One of the five members of this series is shown schematically in Fig. 11.8.   The significance of this series of multiplets is due to the fact that the running terms have a negative series limit, *i.e.*, a limit which lies above the limit of the chief S, P, D, and F series.   The last three members of the series have negative term values.   In such negative states the atom contains more than enough energy to ionize it, yet it cannot be doubted that the atom is still neutral in the sense that it still contains all of its electrons.   As shown by Russell and Saunders this is the clue to anomalous multiplets and to complex spectra. A complete energy level diagram of calcium, as it is now known, is given in Fig. 11.9.

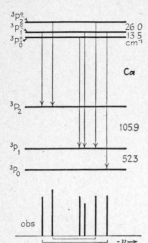

Fig. 11.8.—A $^3P^o - {}^3P$ multiplet observed in calcium.

If more than enough energy to ionize an atom be put into the atom, and ionization does not occur, the energy must be divided between two electrons, each one of which is excited to a higher energy state.[1]   The series of ^3P terms found by Russell and Saunders to

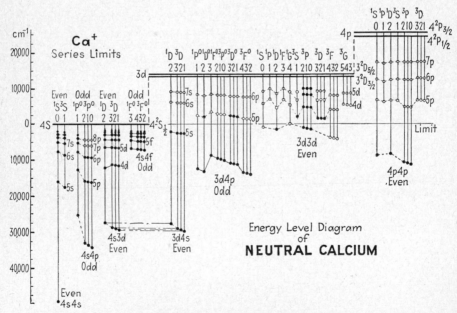

Fig. 11.9.—Complete energy level diagram of calcium.

approach a negative limit corresponds to a set of energy states in which

---

[1] The suggestion that two electrons are excited to higher energy states was first made by Bohr and Wentzel, *Phys. Zeits.*, **24**, 106, 1923, to account for wide separations in the anomalous spectral terms in calcium and strontium.

one of the two valence electrons is in a $3d$ orbit, while the other occupies successively the states $3d$, $4d$, $5d$, $6d$, etc. With one of the electrons taking on larger and larger n values $(n \rightarrow \infty)$, the atom will finally be left ionized with one electron in a $3d$ state. The series limit of the anomalous ^3P terms therefore becomes an excited state of the first spark spectrum, Ca II, and lies above the common limit of the chief series.

Returning to the energy level diagram of Ca II (Fig. 6.4), the normal state is seen to be in the new notation $4s,^2S$, followed by $3d,^2D$ and $4p,^2P$. The first excited state (the metastable state ^2D) lies 13711 cm^{-1} above the normal state ^2S. The series limit of the anomalous ^3P terms is calculated by Russell and Saunders to be 13961 cm^{-1} above ^2S. The agreement is so remarkable that there is little doubt that the two are one and the same.

The question now arises as to how two electrons in d orbits give rise to ^3P terms, or how one electron in a $4p$ orbit and the other in a $3d$ orbit give rise to a triad of triplets like the ones given above. The answer to this question will serve as a starting point for the next chapter.

Problems

1. With the term values of the chief series in strontium given, plot an energy level diagram similar to the one shown in Fig. 11.1. Indicate the hydrogen levels with dotted lines. For term values see Bacher and Goudsmit, "Atomic Energy States."

2. Compute values of $Z - \sigma$ and the quantum defect μ for the first four members of the chief term series in strontium. Show which terms indicate penetrating and nonpenetrating orbits (see Table 11.4).

CHAPTER XII

THE ATOM MODEL FOR TWO VALENCE ELECTRONS

In the early development of spectrum analysis it was well known to all spectroscopists that the elements in the center of the periodic table gave rise to large numbers of spectrum lines yet revealed no apparent series. While equal wave-number differences and other regularities were occasionally found in the spectra of these elements, complex spectrum analysis undoubtedly had its beginning with the analysis of the manganese spectrum by Catalan[1] in 1922. Catalan was able to classify large groups of spectrum lines into what are now called *multiplets* (see Fig. 14.15). By 1923 the theory of atomic structure had developed to such an extent that Landé, by an extension of a theory proposed by Sommerfeld and Heisenberg, was able to account for the relative fine-structure separations of the lines within these multiplets and to predict the anomalous Zeeman pattern of each identified line.[2]

According to Landé's model a multiple term was thought to be due to the space quantization of a single valence electron with the atom core (or the atom *rumpf* as it is sometimes called). To be more specific the angular momentum of the single valence electron $Kh/2\pi$, was assumed to take only certain quantized angular positions with respect to the core angular momentum $Rh/2\pi$. While this model, with suitable restrictions, can be brought into excellent agreement with most experimental observations, we now attribute the angular momentum $Kh/2\pi$, and the *rumpf* angular momentum $Rh/2\pi$, to the resultant orbital angular momentum $L^*h/2\pi$, and the resultant electron-spin momentum $S^*h/2\pi$, of all the extranuclear electrons, respectively.

We have already seen in the preceding chapters that in addition to the orbital angular momentum $l^*h/2\pi$, where $l^* = \sqrt{l(l+1)}$, and

$$l = 0, 1, 2, 3, 4, 5, 6, \cdots$$

for $s, p, d, f, g, h, i, \ldots$ electrons, respectively,[3]

each electron is assigned a spin angular momentum $s^*h/2\pi$, where

---

[1] CATALAN, M. A., *Trans. Roy. Soc.*, **A, 223**, 127, 1922.

[2] For a complete account of the Landé vector model, see E. Back and A. Landé, "Zeemaneffekt."

[3] In complex spectra small letters $s, p, d, \ldots$, and s, l, j, and m, are used for individual electrons and capital letters $S, P, D, \ldots$, and S, L, J, and M, are used for resultant terms.

$s^* = \sqrt{s(s + 1)}$ and $s = \frac{1}{2}$. The angular momentum of any atom containing n extranuclear electrons is therefore the vector sum of $2n$ angular momenta. It will be shown in Sec. 15.6, that all electrons making up completed subshells of electrons are so quantized with respect to each other that their resultant angular momentum vanishes. For this reason, only the electrons in incomplete subshells, in general the valence electrons, contribute to the resultant angular momentum of the atom. In this chapter the problem confronting us is that of accounting for the observed fine structure arising from atomic systems containing two valence electrons.

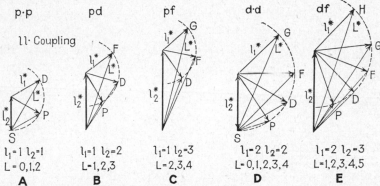

FIG. 12.1.—Vector diagrams of the space quantization of the orbital motions of two valence electrons.

12.1. ll-coupling.—Consider first the orbital motions of two electrons and let l_1 and l_2 represent their respective orbital quantum numbers, and $l_1^* h/2\pi$ and $l_2^* h/2\pi$, or better l_1^* and l_2^*, their respective angular momenta. Following Russell and Saunders' coupling scheme,[1] modified according to the quantum-mechanical ideas, l_1^* and l_2^* are quantized with respect to each other in such a way that they form a resultant L^*, where

$$L^* = \sqrt{L(L + 1)} \text{ and}$$

$L = 0, 1, 2, 3, 4, 5, 6, 7, 8, 9, \cdots$
for $S, P, D, F, G, H, I, K, L, M, \ldots$ terms, respectively.

Consider, for example, one electron in a p orbit and the other in a d orbit (see Fig. 12.1 B). Here the two vectors $l_1^* = \sqrt{2}$ and $l_2^* = \sqrt{6}$ may orient themselves in any one of three positions, $L^* = \sqrt{2}, \sqrt{6}$, and $\sqrt{12}$, corresponding to $L = 1, 2,$ and 3, or to $P, D,$ and F terms, respectively. Vector diagrams of other electron configurations commonly occurring in two-electron systems are also shown in Fig. 12.1.

The following method is very useful in making rapid calculations of terms. With given values of l_1 and l_2, where $l_2 \geqq l_1$, all integral

[1] RUSSELL, H. N., and F. A. SAUNDERS, *Astrophys.*, *Jour.*, **61**, 38, 1925.

values of L from $l_2 - l_1$ to $l_2 + l_1$ are allowed. Making use of this fact the following term table is formulated.

TABLE 12.1.

$s \cdot s,$	S	$ps,$	P	$ds,$	D	$fs,$	F
$sp,$	P	$p \cdot p,$	SPD	$dp,$	PDF	$fp,$	DFG
$sd,$	D	$pd,$	PDF	$d \cdot d,$	$SPDFG$	$fd,$	$PDFGH$
$sf,$	F	$pf,$	DFG	$d \cdot f,$	$PDFGH$	$f \cdot f,$	$SPDFGHI$

The dot between two electrons of the same type indicates that the electrons have different total quantum numbers. If they are alike certain of the terms shown are not allowed. (Such special cases will be treated in Sec. 13.11.) Where $l_2 < l_1$ the rôles of the two electrons are interchanged.

Returning at this point to the discussion of calcium in Sec. 11.5, we observe from Table 12.1 how it comes about that a P term may arise from two electrons in d orbits. It is also observed how with only two valence electrons, one in a p orbit and the other in a d orbit, the atom may be in a ^3P, a ^3D, or a ^3F state. In calcium these three terms, combining with another ^3D term arising from the configuration $4s3d$, give rise to the three great triplet multiplets of Fig. 11.7.

SPIN - SPIN - COUPLING

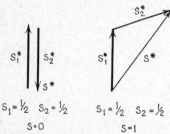

$S_1 = \frac{1}{2}$ $S_2 = \frac{1}{2}$ $S_1 = \frac{1}{2}$ $S_2 = \frac{1}{2}$

$S = 0$ $S = 1$

FIG. 12.2.—Vector diagrams of the space quantization of the spins of two valence electrons.

12.2. Spin-spin-, or ss-coupling.— With two electrons, each having a spin angular momentum of $s^*h/2\pi$, where $s^* = \sqrt{s(s + 1)}$ and $s = \frac{1}{2}$, there are two ways in which a spin resultant $S^*h/2\pi$ may be formed. Let s_1^* and s_2^* represent the respective spin vectors of the two electrons. Quantizing these (see Fig. 12.2), we find, with $s_1^* = \frac{1}{2}\sqrt{3}$ and $s_2^* = \frac{1}{2}\sqrt{3}$, two resultants, one with $S^* = 0$, and the other with $S^* = \sqrt{2}$. These give the resultant quantum values $S = 0$ and $S = 1$. The resultant $S^* = 0$ will now be shown to give rise to singlet terms and $S^* = \sqrt{2}$ to triplet terms.

12.3. LS-, or Russell-Saunders Coupling.—With the orbital motions of two electrons coupled together to give a resultant L^*, and the spins of the same electrons coupled together to form S^*, both L^* and S^* will in turn be coupled together to form J^*, which is a vector representing $J^*h/2\pi$ the total angular momentum of the atom. The quantum conditions imposed upon this coupling are that $J^* = \sqrt{J(J + 1)}$, and that J take non-negative integral values. Consider, as a specific example, the case of one electron in a p orbit and the other in a d orbit. From Secs. 12.1 and 12.2 we have the following possible values to work with; $L = 1,$

2, and 3 and $S = 0$ and 1. Taking first $S = 0$ and $L = 1$, 2, and 3, we construct the vector diagrams at the left in Fig. 12.3. S^* being zero, J^* is just equal to L^*, and $J = 1$, 2, and 3. These correspond to three singlet terms $^1P_1$, $^1D_2$, and $^1F_3$. With $S = 1$ there are three possibilities for each of the three L's. These are shown at the right in Fig. 12.3 and correspond to three triplets

$$^3P_0\,^3P_1\,^3P_2 \qquad ^3D_1\,^3D_2\,^3D_3 \qquad ^3F_2\,^3F_3\,^3F_4.$$

With these term symbols it may now be pointed out that the superscript, which we have already used, expressing the multiplicity of the fine-structure system to which the term belongs, is always $2S + 1$.

Singlets	Doublets	Triplets
$S = 0$	$S = \frac{1}{2}$	$S = 1$

The term type S, P, D, etc., gives the value of L, and the subscript gives the resultant value of J. The following method may conveniently

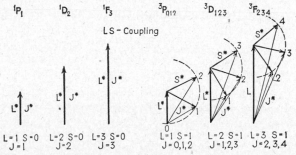

FIG. 12.3. Vector diagrams of two valence electrons in LS- (Russell-Saunders) coupling.

be used for the rapid calculation of J values, when they are not remembered. With given values of L and S, (1) where $L \geqq S$, all integral values of J between $L - S$ and $L + S$ are allowed, or, (2) where $S \geqq L$, all integral values of J between $S - L$ and $S + L$ are allowed. All allowed terms arising from some of the more common electron configurations are given in Table 12.2.

TABLE 12.2.—TERMS ARISING FROM THE INTERACTION OF TWO ELECTRONS IN LS-COUPLING (RUSSELL-SAUNDERS COUPLING)

$s \cdot s$, $^1S_0$ $^3S_1$	$p \cdot p$, $^1S_0\,^1P_1\,^1D_2$	$^3S_1\,^3P_{0,1,2}\,^3D_{1,2,3}$
s p, $^1P_1^{\circ}$ $^3P_{0,1,2}$	p d, $^1P_1^{\circ}\,^1D_2^{\circ}\,^1F_3^{\circ}$	$^3P_{0,1,2}^{\circ}\,^3D_{1,2,3}^{\circ}\,^3F_{2,3,4}^{\circ}$
s d, $^1D_2$ $^3D_{1,2,3}$	p f, $^1D_2\,^1F_3\,^1G_4$	$^3D_{1,2,3}\,^3F_{2,3,4}\,^3G_{3,4,5}$
s f, $^1F_3^{\circ}$ $^3F_{2,3,4}^{\circ}$	$d \cdot d$, $^1S_0\,^1P_1\,^1D_2\,^1F_3\,^1G_4$	$^3S_1\,^3P_{0,1,2}\,^3D_{1,2,3}\,^3F_{2,3,4}\,^3G_{3,4,5}$

Terms for which the sum $l_1 + l_2$ is odd are called *odd terms,* all others are called *even terms.* Odd terms are distinguished by the small superscript "°" to the right of the term symbol S, P, D . . . . Thus we have completed the explanation and meaning of the modern spectroscopic nomenclature. It is to be noted that with $S = 1$ and $L = 0$ there is but one possibility, $J = 1$. This is in agreement with experiment that all S levels are single. In the following chapter it will be shown that in a magnetic field each S level will reveal its true characteristics, i.e., a ^3S level splits up into three components, a ^2S level into two, and a ^1S level remains single.

12.4. The Pauli Exclusion Principle.—If two electrons have the same total quantum number n, and the same azimuthal quantum number l, they are called *equivalent electrons*. Observation shows that when two electrons are equivalent, certain terms are forbidden. For example, the normal state of each alkaline-earth element is given by two equivalent s electrons. Of the two possible terms arising from the schemes developed above, only the $^1S_0$ term is observed. As soon as one of the electrons

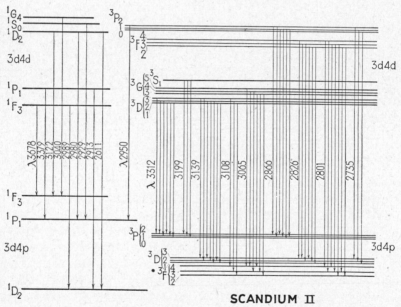

FIG. 12.4.—Singlet and triplet levels observed in ionized scandium, Sc II.

is excited to an s orbit of different n the $^3S_1$ term is also observed (see Fig. 11.1). Simply stated the Pauli exclusion principle is that *no two electrons can have all quantum numbers the same*. Although the calculation of allowed spectral terms for equivalent electrons will be deferred to Sec. 13.11, the results will be given here.

TABLE 12.3.—TERMS ARISING FROM TWO EQUIVALENT ELECTRONS
(Pauli exclusion principle in operation)

s^2,	^1S					
p^2,	^1S	^3P	^1D			
d^2,	^1S	^3P	^1D	^3F	^1G	
f^2,	^1S	^3P	^1D	^3F	^1G	^3H	^1I

The energy-level diagram of calcium (Fig. 11.9) shows two good examples of the exclusion principle. The normal ^1S state is the only term arising from $4s4s$. At the extreme right ^1S, ^3P, and ^1D arise from $4p4p$. Of the terms predicted for $3d3d$, only ^1D and ^3P have been observed. Violations of the Pauli exclusion principle have never been found. Two equivalent electrons are written, for example, $4p^2$, p^2, or $4p4p$.

12.5. Triplet Multiplets in Ionized Scandium, Sc II.—Before going further with theoretical developments let us consider some of the experimental observations confirming what has already been derived. For this purpose a single example will be chosen from the spectrum of singly ionized scandium, atomic number 21. In this spectrum a fairly complete set of singlets and one of triplet multiplets have been photographed in the ultra-violet. From these lines energy levels have been derived which fall into two groups, one a complete group of *initial* states and the other a complete group of *final* states (see Fig. 12.4). The electron configurations that have been assigned these levels (see Table 12.2) are as follows:

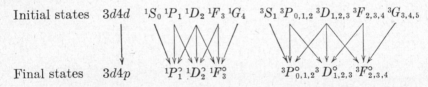

Initial states $3d4d$ $^1S_0\,^1P_1\,^1D_2\,^1F_3\,^1G_4$ $^3S_1\,^3P_{0,1,2}\,^3D_{1,2,3}\,^3F_{2,3,4}\,^3G_{3,4,5}$

Final states $3d4p$ $^1P_1^\circ\,^1D_2^\circ\,^1F_3^\circ$ $^3P_{0,1,2}^\circ\,^3D_{1,2,3}^\circ\,^3F_{2,3,4}^\circ$

The quantum values, *i.e.*, the term types assigned each level are determined by selection rules for complex spectra (see Sec. 12.14). The upper set is composed of a *pentad* of singlet and triplet levels and the lower set of a *triad* of singlet and triplet levels. It should be noted that the selection rule for electrons is obeyed in that one electron goes from a $4d$ to a $4p$ orbit, $\Delta l = 1$, while the other remains in a $3d$ orbit.

12.6. Coupling Schemes for Two Electrons.—Attempts to calculate the fine-structure separations of the various energy levels arising from any given electron configuration have been made by many investigators. Prior to the development of the quantum mechanics, the vector model, qualitatively, accounted for the fine structure of all analyzed spectra. Although quantitative agreement was also found in a few cases, it remained for the quantum mechanics to bring about a more general agreement. It should be pointed out that, even at this time, there is much to be desired especially in the case of the more complex atomic systems. We shall first consider, in detail, the vector model as it applies to atoms containing two electrons and then formulate a quantum-mechanical picture of the same atomic states.

In hydrogen and the alkali metals, the simplest of all atomic systems, the interaction between the electron spin s^* and the orbit l^* of the single valence electron splits each energy level P, D, F, . . . into two fine-structure components. We have already seen in Sec. 8.6, that this interaction energy, *i.e.*, the shift of each fine-structure level from the hypothetical center of gravity, is given by

$$-\Delta T_{l,s} = a \cdot l^*s^* \overline{\cos (l^*s^*)} = a \frac{(j^{*2} - l^{*2} - s^{*2})}{2} = \Gamma, \quad (12.1)$$

where

$$a = \frac{R\alpha^2 Z^4}{n^3 l(l + \frac{1}{2})(l + 1)} \text{ cm}^{-1}. \quad (12.2)$$

In the case of two valence electrons there are four angular momenta l_1^*, l_2^*, s_1^*, and s_2^*, which give rise to the following six possible interactions:

$$s_1^* \text{ with } s_2^*, \quad l_1^* \text{ with } s_1^*, \quad l_1^* \text{ with } s_2^*, \quad (12.3)$$
$$l_1^* \text{ with } l_2^*, \quad l_2^* \text{ with } s_2^*, \quad l_2^* \text{ with } s_1^*.$$

Applying Eq. (12.1) to these six interactions, there will be six energy relations:

$$\Gamma_1 = a_1 s_1^* s_2^* \cos (s_1^* s_2^*), \quad \Gamma_3 = a_3 l_1^* s_1^* \cos (l_1^* s_1^*), \quad \Gamma_5 = a_5 l_1^* s_2^* \cos (l_1^* s_2^*),$$
$$(12.4)$$
$$\Gamma_2 = a_2 l_1^* l_2^* \cos (l_1^* l_2^*), \quad \Gamma_4 = a_4 l_2^* s_2^* \cos (l_2^* s_2^*), \quad \Gamma_6 = a_6 l_2^* s_1^* \cos (l_2^* s_1^*).$$

In terms of the classical model of the precession of vectors, each spin s^*, and each orbit l^*, produces a field around which the others tend to carry out a Larmor precession. In some atomic systems and electron configurations certain of the interactions are large as compared with others, whereas in other systems and configurations different interactions predominate. A predominating interaction between any two vectors may be interpreted to mean that these two vectors precess more rapidly around their mutual field than around any other. With this in mind it is easy to see that any attempt to formulate classical models for all possible coupling schemes would be very difficult. Fortunately, however, two rather simple ideal models have been developed, one or the other of which gives fair agreement with experiment in most cases. These cases are known as *LS*-, or *Russell-Saunders, coupling*, on the one hand, and *jj-coupling*, on the other. A large percentage of all known spectrum lines and energy levels may be classified with one of these coupling schemes, or with some intermediate but closely associated scheme.

In *LS*-coupling, the interaction energies Γ_1 and Γ_2 [Eq. (12.4)] are assumed to predominate over Γ_3 and Γ_4, while Γ_5 and Γ_6 are assumed negligibly small. In *jj*-coupling, Γ_3 and Γ_4 are assumed to predominate over Γ_1 and Γ_2, while Γ_5 and Γ_6 are again assumed negligibly small. Vector diagrams of these two coupling schemes are shown in Fig. 12.5.

With Γ_1 and Γ_2 predominant in Fig. 12.5A, s_1^* and s_2^* precess rapidly around their resultant S^*, and l_1^* and l_2^* precess rapidly around their resultant L^*. Due to the weaker interactions Γ_3 and Γ_4, L^* and S^* precess more slowly around their resultant J^*.

In Fig. 12.5B, with Γ_3 and Γ_4 predominant, l_1^* and s_1^* precess around their resultant j_1^*, and l_2^* and s_2^* precess around their resultant j_2^*. Due to the weaker interactions Γ_1 and Γ_2, j_1^* and j_2^* precess more slowly around their mechanical resultant J^*. We shall now take up these two ideal models separately and consider some of the consequences of each.

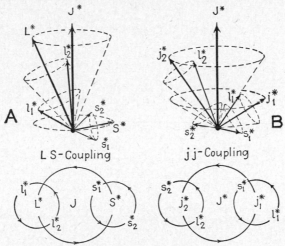

FIG. 12.5.—Ideal vector models for (A) LS-coupling, and (B) jj-coupling. Examples drawn with $l_1 = 1$, $l_2 = 2$, $J = 3$.

12.7. Γ Factors for LS-coupling.

In deriving an expression for fine structure, assuming the ideal case of LS-coupling between the two valence electrons, we have only to evaluate the first four interaction energies

$$\Gamma_1 = a_1 s_1^* s_2^* \cos (s_1^* s_2^*), \qquad \Gamma_3 = a_3 l_1^* s_1^* \cos (l_1^* s_1^*),$$
$$\Gamma_2 = a_2 l_1^* l_2^* \cos (l_1^* l^*), \qquad \Gamma_4 = a_4 l_2^* s_2^* \cos (l_2^* s_2^*). \tag{12.5}$$

Since s_1^* and s_2^* precess, with fixed angles of inclination, around their resultant S^*, which remains invariant in magnitude (see Fig. 12.5A), Γ_1 is readily evaluated by applying the cosine law[1] for triangles, $i.e.$,
$$S^{*2} = s_1^{*2} + s_2^{*2} + 2s_1^* s_2^* \cos (s_1^* s_2^*),$$

$$\Gamma_1 = \tfrac{1}{2} a_1 (S^{*2} - s_1^{*2} - s_2^{*2}). \tag{12.6}$$

With l_1^* and l_2^* precessing around their resultant L^* with fixed angles of inclination, Γ_2 is readily evaluated in the same way,

$$\Gamma_2 = \tfrac{1}{2} a_2 (L^{*2} - l_1^{*2} - l_2^{*2}). \tag{12.7}$$

[1] The cosine law as given above is used a great deal in the calculation of interaction energies and will be referred to hereafter as the $cosine$ law.

Now L^* and S^*, due to their respective fields, precess around their mechanical resultant in just the same way as l^* and s^* of a single electron precess around their resultant j^*. The interaction energy due to this precession is attributed to the coupling between each electron's l^* and its own s^*, Γ_3 and Γ_4. Here the average values of the cosines must be evaluated since the angles between the vectors are continually changing. Due to the constancy of certain angles throughout the various precessions, and a well-known theorem in trigonometry (see Sec. 10.7), this is readily accomplished. For example, the projection of l_1^* on L^*, then L^* on S^*, and finally S^* on s_1^* gives, for the average cosine,

$$\overline{\cos(l_1^* s_1^*)} = \cos(l_1^* L^*) \cdot \cos(L^* S^*) \cdot \cos(S^* s_1^*).$$

Similarly,
$$\overline{\cos(l_2^* s_2^*)} = \cos(l_2^* L^*) \cdot \cos(L^* S^*) \cdot \cos(S^* s_2^*). \qquad (12.8)$$

In these equations it is assumed that the individual precessions of s_1^* and l_1^* are much more rapid than that of L^* and S^* around J^*, so that their components normal to the respective axes of rotation will cancel out.

Adding these two terms together, taking out the common factor $\cos(L^* S^*)$, and employing the cosine law for triangles, we obtain the following interaction energy:

$$\Gamma_3 + \Gamma_4 = (a_3\alpha_3 + a_4\alpha_4)L^* S^* \cos(L^* S^*) = \tfrac{1}{2}(a_3\alpha_3 + a_4\alpha_4)$$
$$(J^{*2} - L^{*2} - S^{*2}), \quad (12.9)$$

where

$$\alpha_3 = \frac{s_1^{*2} - s_2^{*2} + S^{*2}}{2S^{*2}} \cdot \frac{l_1^{*2} - l_2^{*2} + L^{*2}}{2L^{*2}} \cdots \qquad (12.10)$$

and

$$\alpha_4 = \frac{s_2^{*2} - s_1^{*2} + S^{*2}}{2S^{*2}} \cdot \frac{l_2^{*2} - l_1^{*2} + L^{*2}}{2L^{*2}}. \qquad (12.11)$$

For any given triplet s_1^*, s_2^*, l_1^*, l_2^*, S^*, L^*, n_1, and n_2 are fixed in magnitude so that a_3, a_4, α_3, and α_4 are constants. Writing

$$A = a_3\alpha_3 + a_4\alpha_4, \qquad (12.12)$$

Eq. (12.9) becomes

$$\Gamma_3 + \Gamma_4 = A \cdot L^* S^* \cos(L^* S^*) = \tfrac{1}{2}A(J^{*2} - L^{*2} - S^{*2}). \qquad (12.13)$$

In the next section we shall see that this equation yields the Landé interval rule.

We have now to evaluate the a coefficients to obtain complete expressions of the energies. If in each case the interactions are magnetic in character, then formulas of the type shown in Eq. (12.2), can be derived for each coefficient. A comparison of the calculated energies with observed fine structure in general shows that, while spin-orbit interactions are magnetic in character, orbit-orbit and spin-spin interactions may be attributed mainly to electrostatic effects. Due to the general observation that singlet levels lie above the corresponding triplet levels of the same electron configuration, the coefficient a_1 of Γ_1 may be considered *negative*. This has been explained by Heisenberg as being due to an electrostatic resonance-interaction phenomenon and will be considered briefly here, to be taken up again in Sec. 12.17. We shall assume that Eq. (12.6) gives the singlet-triplet intervals in terms of the quantum values s_1, s_2, and S, and a constant a_1 which is *negative*, even though it is questionable just what significance can be attached to this equation.

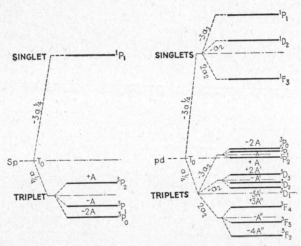

Fig. 12.6.—Schematic representation of the interaction energies between two valence electrons in LS-coupling.

Schematic representations of the fine structure for two different electron configurations are shown in Fig. 12.6. The effect of each interaction Γ_1, Γ_2, Γ_3, and Γ_4 is shown separately, starting at the left with only the energy attributed to the n and l values of the two electrons. With $s_1 = \frac{1}{2}$, $s_2 = \frac{1}{2}$, and $S = 0$ or 1, for singlets or triplets, respectively, we obtain from Eq. (12.6), $\Gamma_1 = -3a_1/4$, or $a_1/4$. This is the first splitting shown.

Second comes Γ_2, the $l_1 l_2$ interaction which gives rise to the various term types S, P, D, . . . (see Sec. 12.3). Classically it may be shown, by the same arguments put forward in considering the spin-orbit interaction of a single electron in Sec. 8.6, that the most stable state for two orbital motions is one in which the two magnetic moments, and hence the mechanical moments, are most nearly parallel to each other. In other words, out of all the terms arising from a given configuration and with given multiplicity the term with the largest L value should lie deepest. This is part of Hund's rule,[1] which applies to LS-coupling only and states that *out of all the terms with the same L value arising from any given electron configuration* (1) *a term with the highest multiplicity, i.e., the highest S value, will lie deepest, and* (2) *of these the term with the highest L value will lie deepest.* As a consequence of these considerations the coefficient a_2 in Eq. (12.7) should be *negative*.

For a pd configuration (Fig. 12.6) with $l_1 = 1$ and $l_2 = 2$, there will be F, D, and P terms with $L = 3$, 2, and 1, respectively. Substituting these values in Eq. (12.7), $\Gamma_2 = 2a_2$, $-a_2$, and $-3a_2$, respectively. For any configuration involving an s electron, $l_1 = 0$ and Γ_2 vanishes.

We have already seen in Sec. 8.6, that the spin-orbit interaction leads to coefficients a_3 and a_4, given by Eq. (12.2), which are *positive*. Substituting the various allowed values of s_1, s_2, l_1, l_2, S, L, and J in Eqs. (12.10), (12.11), (12.12), and (12.13), the last splitting $\Gamma_3 + \Gamma_4$, shown at the right in the figure, is obtained. For singlet terms with $S = 0$, the α's and hence the A's vanish.

We may now write for any fine-structure term value the following formula:

$$T_{cm^{-1}} = T_0 - \Gamma_1 - \Gamma_2 - \Gamma_3 - \Gamma_4 \qquad (12.14)$$

where T_0 is a hypothetical term value for the center of gravity of the entire electron configuration. The horizontal dotted lines in the figure represent centers of gravity. For each triplet they lie at points obtained by assigning each level a weight $2J + 1$. For the triplets, or singlets, they lie at points obtained by assigning each term L a weight $2L + 1$. For the entire configuration in turn the weights $2S + 1$ are assigned the triplets below and the singlets above. The results obtained from the preceding equations will now be compared with observed fine structures.

12.8. The Landé Interval Rule.—Of the equations derived in the previous section, Eq. (12.13) is perhaps the most significant, for it expresses symbolically the well-established Landé interval rule. Introducing the quantum values S, L, and J, this equation becomes

$$\Gamma_3 + \Gamma_4 = \tfrac{1}{2}A\{J(J+1) - L(L+1) - S(S+1)\} \qquad (12.15)$$

and states that for a given triplet, *i.e.*, for given S and L, each fine-structure term difference is proportional to the larger of the two J values associated with it. In the following examples,

$$^3P_0\ ^3P_1\ ^3P_2 \qquad ^3D_1\ ^3D_2\ ^3D_3 \qquad ^3F_2\ ^3F_3\ ^3F_4$$

the ratios are

$$\mathbf{1:2} \qquad\qquad \mathbf{2:3} \qquad\qquad \mathbf{3:4}$$

This result is directly obtained from Eq. (12.15) by taking the difference between one term J and the adjacent term $J + 1$:

[1] See HUND, F., "Linienspektren," p. 124, 1927.

$$-\Delta T = \tfrac{1}{2}A\{(J + 1)(J + 2) - J(J + 1)\} = A(J + 1). \quad (12.16)$$

The intervals are thus proportional to the larger J values.

Observed separations of many triplets in a number of elements are in excellent agreement with the interval rule. Several examples

TABLE 12.4.—TRIPLET SEPARATIONS IN WAVE NUMBERS ILLUSTRATING THE LANDÉ INTERVAL RULE (*LS*-COUPLING)

Theoretical interval ratio **2 : 1**				Theoretical interval ratio **3:2**			
Element Configuration	$^3P_0 - {}^3P_1$	$^3P_1 - {}^3P_2$	Obs. ratio	Element Configuration	$^3D_1 - {}^3D_2$	$^3D_2 - {}^3D_3$	Obs. ratio
Ca, $3d3d$	13.5	26.9	**2.0**	Ca, $3d4s$	13.6	21.7	**1.6**
Ca, $4s4p$	52.3	105.9	**2.0**	Ca, $3d4p$	26.7	40.0	**1.5**
Sr, $5s5p$	187.0	394.6	**2.1**	Zn, $4s4d$	3.4	4.6	**1.4**
Mg, $3s3p$	20.0	40.9	**2.0**	Cd, $5s5d$	11.7	18.2	**1.6**
Zn, $4s4p$	190.0	389.0	**2.0**	Ca, $4s4d$	3.8	5.6	**1.5**

taken from one group of elements in the periodic table are given in Table 12.4.

The agreement with theory clearly justifies the use of the vector model and identifies the electron coupling as Russell-Saunders.

A graphical representation of the Landé interval rule is shown in Fig. 12.7 for a ^3D term. With $S = 1$ and $L = 2$, S^* is shown quantized with respect to L^* in the three allowed positions $J = 1$, 2, and 3. The J vectors are not shown. Projecting S^* on L^*, we obtain S^* cos (L^*S^*). The resultant intervals have the ratio 2:3, and the central dotted line is at the center of gravity.

The chief characteristics by which *LS*-coupling is readily recognized are: (1) The singlet-triplet intervals are large compared with the triplet fine structure. (2) The triplet intervals follow the Landé interval rule. Both of these conditions are observed when the coupling is *LS*.

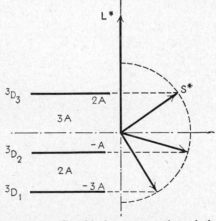

FIG. 12.7.—Graphical representation of the Landé interval rule for a ^3D term.

12.9. jj-Coupling.—We now turn to the ideal case of *jj*-coupling for two electrons. Before calculating general expressions for the interaction energies on such a scheme, let us first determine all of the various spectral terms arising from any given electron configuration in jj-coupling. The spin s_i^* of each electron is quantized with respect to its own l_i^* to form a resultant j_i^*, such that j_i takes half-integral values only. The two j*s are in turn quantized with respect to each other to form a resultant J^*, such that J takes integral values only. Consider, for example, the configuration pd, with $s_1 = \frac{1}{2}$, $l_1 = 1$, $s_2 = \frac{1}{2}$, and $l_2 = 2$. For the p electron, $j_1 = \frac{1}{2}$, or $\frac{3}{2}$; and for the d electron, $j_2 = \frac{3}{2}$, or $\frac{5}{2}$. Combining these four values in all possible ways (see Fig. 12.8), one obtains from $j_1 = \frac{1}{2}$ and $j_2 = \frac{3}{2}$, $J = 1$, and 2; from $j_1 = \frac{3}{2}$ and $j_2 = \frac{3}{2}$, $J = 0, 1, 2$, and 3; from $j_1 = \frac{1}{2}$ and $j_2 = \frac{5}{2}$, $J = 2$, and 3; and from $j_1 = \frac{3}{2}$ and $j_2 = \frac{5}{2}$,

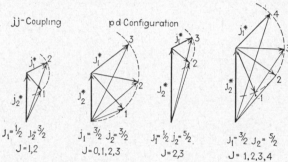

Fig. 12.8.—Vector diagrams of two valence electrons in jj-coupling.

$J = 1, 2, 3$, and 4. This is exactly the same number of terms arrived at on the LS-coupling scheme, and they have exactly the same set of resultant J values.

The question arises as to how each term is to be designated when the coupling is jj, and L and S no longer are constants. Although no scheme has been generally adopted, such terms will here be designated by writing down the two j values in parentheses followed by the resultant J value as a subscript, e.g., $(\frac{3}{2} \frac{5}{2})_4$. When the electron configuration is required, it will precede these values, e.g., $3d4d, (\frac{3}{2} \frac{5}{2})_4$.

In setting up the jj-coupling model in Sec. 12.6, it was assumed that the interaction between the spin of each electron and its own orbit is greater than the interactions between the two spins and the two orbits, respectively. Proceeding in exactly the same way as for LS-coupling the cosine terms in the Γ factors [Eq. (12.5)] must be evaluated. With the angle between s_1^* and l_1^* fixed, and the angle between s_2^* and l_2^* fixed, Γ_3 and Γ_4 are readily calculated from the cosine law for triangles:

$$\Gamma_3 = \tfrac{1}{2}a_3(j_1^{*2} - l_1^{*2} - s_1^{*2}), \tag{12.17}$$
$$\Gamma_4 = \tfrac{1}{2}a_4(j_2^{*2} - l_2^{*2} - s_2^{*2}). \tag{12.18}$$

Since the angle between s_1^* and s_2^* and the angle between l_1^* and l_2^* are continually. changing (see Fig. 12.5B), the cosines in Γ_1 and Γ_2 must be averaged. Projecting s_1^* on j_1^*, then j_1^* on j_2^*, and finally j_2^* on s_2^*,

$$\Gamma_1 = a_1 s_1^* s_2^* \overline{\cos (s_1^* s_2^*)} = a_1 s_1^* s_2^* \cos (s_1^* j_1^*) \cos (j_1^* j_2^*) \cos (j_2^* s_2^*) \quad (12.19)$$

and, similarly,

$$\Gamma_2 = a_1 l_1^* l_2^* \overline{\cos (l_1^* l_2^*)} = a_1 l_1^* l_2^* \cos (l_1^* j_1^*) \cos (j_1^* j_2^*) \cos (j_2^* l_2^*). \quad (12.20)$$

Each of these cosines is constant and readily evaluated with the cosine law:

$$\Gamma_1 + \Gamma_2 = \tfrac{1}{2}(a_1\beta_1 + a_2\beta_2)\{J^{*2} - j_1^{*2} - j_2^{*2}\}, \quad (12.21)$$

where

$$\beta_1 = \frac{s_1^{*2} + j_1^{*2} - l_1^{*2}}{2j_1^{*2}} \cdot \frac{s_2^{*2} + j_2^{*2} - l_2^{*2}}{2j_2^{*2}} \quad (12.22)$$

and

$$\beta_2 = \frac{l_1^{*2} + j_1^{*2} - s_1^{*2}}{2j_1^{*2}} \cdot \frac{l_2^{*2} + j_2^{*2} - s_2^{*2}}{2j_2^{*2}}. \quad (12.23)$$

Writing

$$A = a_1\beta_1 + a_2\beta_2, \quad (12.24)$$

Eq. (12.21) may be written

$$\Gamma_1 + \Gamma_2 = A j_1^* j_2^* \cos (j_1^* j_2^*) = \tfrac{1}{2}A(J^{*2} - j_1^{*2} - j_2^{*2}). \quad (12.25)$$

In applying these equations, consider the configuration ps as an example. Here with $s_1 = \tfrac{1}{2}$, $l_1 = 1$, $s_2 = \tfrac{1}{2}$, and $l_2 = 0$, four values of J

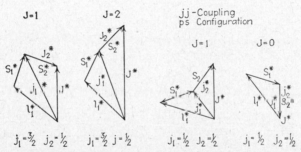

FIG. 12.9.—Vector diagrams for a ps electron configuration in jj-coupling.

are possible. Vector diagrams are shown in Fig. 12.9. Substituting in Eqs. (12.17) and (12.18), $\Gamma_3 = a_3/2$, or $-a_3$, and $\Gamma_4 = 0$. These splittings are shown schematically at the left in Fig. 12.10. Substituting in Eqs. (12.21), (12.22), and (12.23), the values $\Gamma_1 + \Gamma_2 = -5a_1/12$, $+3a_1/12$, $-a_1/12$, and $+3a_1/12$ are calculated for the states $(\tfrac{3}{2}\ \tfrac{1}{2})_1$, $(\tfrac{3}{2}\ \tfrac{1}{2})_2$, $(\tfrac{1}{2}\ \tfrac{1}{2})_1$, and $(\tfrac{1}{2}\ \tfrac{1}{2})_0$, respectively. In jj-coupling the spin-spin interaction is greatly reduced in magnitude (as compared with LS-coupling). The coupling, however is such that the coefficient a_1 is still negative. For this reason the terms have the order shown in the figure.

A good example of a ps configuration revealing jj-coupling is to be found in tin. The observed separations are given at the right in Fig. 12.10. Each observed separation has been divided into two parts to show the magnitude of the different interactions. It is to be noted, as shown by the formulas, that the large interaction is due to Γ_3, the spin-orbit interaction of the p electron; the s electron, with $l_2 = 0$, contributes nothing ($\Gamma_4 = 0$). That this splitting is due to the p electron is evidenced by the $5p, {}^2P_{\frac{1}{2},\frac{3}{2}}$ separation, observed in the ionized spectrum where the $6s$ electron is absent. It is seen that the effect of the addition of a $6s$ electron to Sn II, $5p$, to form Sn I, $5p6s$, is to split each doublet level into two levels as calculated. This smaller interaction is due to the spin-spin coupling Γ_1. If this latter splitting were due to the interaction between l_1 and s_2 [see Eq. (12.4)], the two upper terms would be inverted.

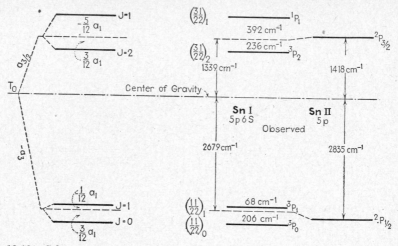

Fig. 12.10.—Schematic representation of the interaction energies between two valence electrons.

12.10. jj-coupling in the Carbon Group of Elements.

—Good examples of atomic systems revealing jj-coupling between two valence electrons are to be found in the carbon group of elements (groups IV and IV B of the periodic table). Energy level diagrams of these elements, carbon, silicon, germanium, tin, and lead, are so nearly alike, generally, that a study of any one of them will illustrate the main features of all. Germanium, atomic number 32, will serve as a typical example (see Fig. 12.11). The normal state of this atom is given by the complete electron configuration (see Table 5.3):

$$\text{Ge, 32,} \qquad 1s^2\, 2s^2\, 2p^6\, 3s^2\, 3p^6\, 3d^{10}\, 4s^2\, 4p^2.$$

All of these electrons, with the exception of the last two *similar p electrons*, form completed subshells. Two similar p electrons (see Table 12.3) give rise to the terms ${}^1S_0$, ${}^3P_{0,1,2}$, ${}^1D_2$. Applying Hund's rule, which is always valid for normal electron configurations, the ${}^3P_{0,1,2}$ terms should lie deepest, followed by ${}^1D_2$ and then ${}^1S_0$, as observed.

Exciting the atom now by raising one electron to the lowest possible available state $5s$, changes the configuration to $4p5s$. From Table 12.2

these two electrons give rise to $^1P_1$ and $^3P_{0,1,2}$ terms. On examining the fine-structure intervals, it is observed that the coupling is not LS but very closely jj. These four terms constitute the first member of a series of terms arising from the series of configurations $4pns$, where

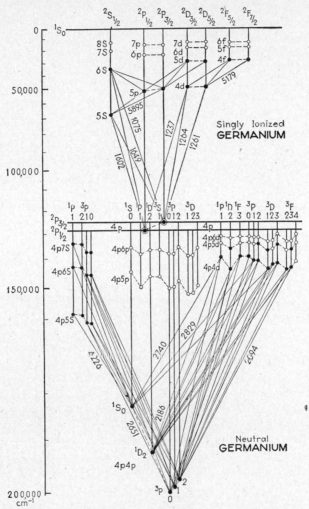

Fig. 12.11.—Energy level diagram of germanium, Ge I below and Ge II above.

$n = 5, 6, 7, \cdots \infty$. When the limit of this series is reached, the atom is ionized with but one $4p$ electron remaining. This is the normal $^3P_{\frac{1}{2},\frac{3}{2}}$ state of the ionized atom.

Starting at the normal state of Ge I again, the excitation of one of the electrons to either a $5p$ or $4d$ state raises the atom to one of the states shown in the figure. The circles represent states not yet identified in germanium but known in other elements in this group. These terms likewise form series, which have as a limit the $4p,^3P_{1,2}$ state of the ionized atom. Subsequent excitation of the ionized atom will raise the one remaining electron to other doublet states, which as series have a single limit, $^1S_0$. When this limit is reached, the atom is doubly ionized and 30 electrons still remain in completed subshells.

In taking up each one of the carbon group of elements in detail, good examples of intermediate coupling between LS- and jj-coupling are found. Consider the first member of the $4pns$ series mentioned above. In carbon this first member, due to the configuration $2p3s$, shows good LS-coupling; the $^3P_0 - {}^3P_1$, $^3P_1 - {}^3P_2$ intervals are 20 and 40 cm^{-1}, with the theoretical ratio $1:2$ and the $^1P_1 - {}^3P_2$ interval 1589 cm^{-1}

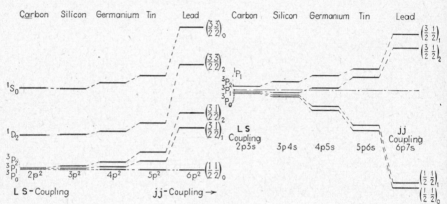

Fig. 12.12.—LS- to jj-coupling as shown by the normal and first excited states in the carbon group of elements.

is correspondingly large. These levels are shown at the left of the right-hand figure in Fig. 12.12. In lead the same four levels have gone over to jj-coupling with two groups of two levels rather far apart. The intermediate elements (Si, Ge, and Sn) furnish transition stages between the two extreme cases. While jj-coupling for similar electrons has not been treated above, the terms making up the normal states of these atoms show LS-coupling in C and relatively good jj-coupling in Pb.

12.11. Term Series and Limits in Two-electron Systems.—The fine structure of two series of singlet and triplet terms is shown graphically in Fig. 12.13. Fine-structure intervals are plotted vertically, and the term values, on a very much smaller scale, horizontally. The cadmium series, it is observed, shows fairly good LS-coupling as far as the series is observed. The silicon series, on the other hand, shows fairly good LS-coupling for the first series member and goes over to good jj-coupling as the series approaches the double limit.

In the cadmium series $5snp$, the $5s$ electron remains in the same tightly bound state while the p electron takes on one of the series of more and more loosely bound states $5p$, $6p$, $7p$, . . . ∞. The limit of this series is consequently $5s,^2S_{\frac{1}{2}}^1$. In silicon the p electron is in a tightly bound $3p$ state and the s electron takes on one of a series of more loosely bound states $4s$, $5s$, $6s$, . . . ∞. The limit of this series is $3p,^2P_{\frac{1}{2},\frac{3}{2}}$. In more complex configuration series like the $4pnd$ series in germanium (Fig. 12.11), jj-coupling is also to be expected near the series limits.

Although a scheme for predicting the terms that go to each limit has been developed by Hund[1] for complex spectra in general, Shenstone[2] has shown that the rules are often incorrect and cannot be relied upon. The very simple rule that levels with the same J values never cross,

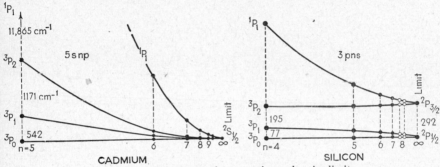

Fig. 12.13.—Two types of term series and series limits.

along with the jj-coupling scheme developed in Fig. 12.8, will show what levels go to each limit.

One interesting result brought out in Fig. 12.13 is that the overall separation of each of the ^3P terms in silicon is approximately the same as that of the ^2P limit. This quite frequent observation occurs when one of the electrons is an s electron. For a ps configuration in LS-coupling (see Fig. 12.6) the $^3P_0 - {}^3P_2$ interval is calculated to be $3A$, or $3a_3/2$. In jj-coupling the same interval (see Fig. 12.10) is again $3a_3/2$. For the ionized atom the $^2P_{\frac{1}{2}} - {}^2P_{\frac{3}{2}}$ interval is given by Eq. (8.18) (see also Fig. 8.9) as $3a/2$. In cases where the s electron does not appreciably change the effective nuclear charge for the p electron, the a's in each case should be nearly the same. These conditions are met in a number of other atoms, and the same phenomenon is observed in the following series, in C I, N II, and O III, $2pns$, ^3P, where $n = 3, 4, 5, . . . \infty$; in Si I and P II, $3pns$, ^3P, where $n = 4, 5, 6, \cdots \infty$; in Sc II, Ti III, V, IV, and Cr V, $3dns$, ^3D, where $n = 4, 5, 6, \cdots \infty$.

12.12. The Great Calcium Triad.—Sufficient preparation has now been made to enable us to return to the energy levels of the well-known calcium triad and to calculate the width of each triplet in the upper set

[1] HUND, F., Zeits. f. Phys., **52**, 601, 1928, and previous papers.
[2] SHENSTONE, A. G., Nature, **121**, 619, 1928; **122**, 727, 1928.

of levels. The relative positions of the ^3P, ^3D, ^3F, ^1P, ^1D, and ^1F terms arising from the electron configuration $3d4p$ may be seen in the energy level diagram of calcium (Fig. 11.9). Assuming LS-coupling for this configuration the triplet intervals may be calculated with a reasonable degree of accuracy. With the treatment of LS-coupling in Sec. 12.7, we have only to determine the values of two coefficients, a_3 and a_4, in the A's at the bottom of Fig. 12.6:

$$^3P, \; A = \frac{-a_3}{4} + \frac{3a_4}{4};$$

$$^3D, \; A' = \frac{a_3}{12} + \frac{5a_4}{12}; \qquad (12.26)$$

$$^3F, \; A'' = \frac{a_3}{6} + \frac{a_4}{3}.$$

Since a_3 and a_4 are both due to the interaction between the spin of each electron and its own orbit, they may be evaluated directly from the electron configurations $4p4s$ and $3d4s$, respectively. Here with one electron in an s orbit the observed triplet separations $4p4s,^3P$ and $3d4s$, ^3D are due to the $4p$ and $3d$ electrons, respectively. The following table gives the observed intervals and the calculated coefficients [see Eq. (12.9)].

TABLE 12.5.—COEFFICIENTS FOR $4p$ AND $3d$ ELECTRONS IN CALCIUM

Configuration	Term	Triplet separations				Coefficients	
$4p4s$	$^3P_{0,1,2}$	52 cm^{-1}	106 cm^{-1}	A	$2A$	$A = \dfrac{a_3}{2}$	$a_3 = 105$ cm^{-1}
$3d4s$	$^3D_{1,2,3}$	14	21	$2A$	$3A$	$A = \dfrac{a_3}{2}$	$a_3 = 14$

Using these values of 105 cm^{-1} and 14 cm^{-1}, for a_3 and a_4, in the preceding Eq. (12.26), the following values for the ^3P, ^3D, and ^3F triad are obtained:

Interval	$^3F_2 - {}^3F_4$	$^3D_1 - {}^3D_3$	$^3P_0 - {}^3P_2$
Observed.............................	166 cm^{-1}	67 cm^{-1}	7 cm^{-1}
Calculated...........................	156	72	-47

Although the intervals throughout this configuration do not indicate ideal LS-coupling, the agreement between observed and calculated intervals is quite good.

12.13. The Branching Rule.—The branching rule is a very simple rule frequently used in the construction of energy level diagrams. Suppose, for example, that the atom of germanium has been doubly ionized. This state of the atom is represented in Fig. 12.11 by the $^1S_0$

term at the top of the diagram.   Now allow one electron to return to the atom and end up in a $4p$ orbit.   This state, $4p,^2P$, of the atom is represented in the middle of the diagram as the lowest doublet state of the singly ionized atom and at the same time the doublet limit of the various series of the neutral atom.   Suppose now that the second electron is allowed to return to the atom in a $5s$, or a $5p$, or a $4d$ orbit. The various possible states of the atom corresponding to these configurations may be written down as follows:

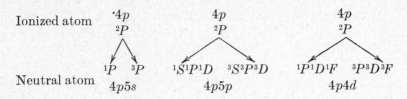

By adding the second electron, the multiplicity goes up one to triplets and down one to singlets.   If the added electron is in an s orbit ($l = 0$), the L value is not changed.   Adding a $5p$ electron ($l = 1$), the L values go up one and down one and include all integral values in between.   Adding a $4d$ electron to a $4p,^2P$ state gives the same resultant terms as adding a $4p$ electron to a $4d,^2D$ state; the multiplicity goes up and down one, and the L values go up and down one from ^2D, the larger of the two, and include all integral values in between.

Consider, as another example, the energy levels of calcium (see Fig. 11.9).   Starting with the ionized atom in a $3d,^2D$ state, let the second electron return to a $4s$, a $4p$, or a $4d$ orbit.   The various possible states arising from these configurations are:

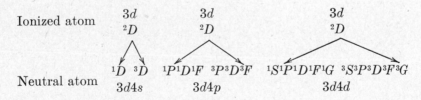

The $4p,^2P$ and $3d,^2D$ terms in these two atoms are known as *parent terms* to the ones below them.   If the L values of a parent term is equal to or greater than the l of the added electron, the allowed terms go from $L - l$ to $L + l$.   If $l > L$, they go from $l - L$ to $l + L$ (see Sec. 12.1 and Fig. 12.1).

12.14. Selection Rules.—An extension of the selection rules of hydrogen and the alkali metals to two-electron systems introduces new sets of rules, of which those for one-electron spectra may be thought of as special cases.   With two electrons taking part in producing the various types of terms, transitions may occur in which two electrons jump simultaneously with the emission of a single radiated frequency. Selection rules for two-electron systems in general may be written as

$$\Delta l_1 = \pm 1 \quad \text{and} \quad \Delta l_2 = 0, \pm 2. \quad (12.27)$$

If a single electron jumps, the l value of one changes by unity, and the other by zero. If a double electron jump occurs, the l value of one changes by unity and the other by zero or by two. There are no restrictions on the total quantum number n of either electron. For the various types of terms arising from all possible electron configurations the further restrictions are divided into two parts.

A. For LS-coupling the further restrictions are:

$$\begin{aligned} \Delta S &= 0 \\ \Delta L &= 0, \pm 1 \\ \Delta J &= 0, \pm 1 \quad (0 \to 0 \text{ excluded}) \end{aligned} \quad (12.28)$$

The singlet and triplet transitions shown for ionized scandium in Fig. 12.4 will serve as good examples of these rules.

B. For jj-coupling the further restrictions are:

$$\left.\begin{aligned} \Delta j_1 &= 0 \\ \Delta j_2 &= 0, \pm 1 \end{aligned}\right\} \text{or vice versa} \quad (12.29)$$
$$\Delta J = 0, \pm 1 \quad (0 \to 0 \text{ excluded})$$

According to these rules transitions are allowed which, under the rules for LS-coupling, are not allowed. Intercombination lines, although weak, are good indications that the coupling in either the initial or final state is not good LS-coupling.

A more convenient way of expressing the selection rules for the individual electrons [Eq. (12.27)] has been brought out by the quantum mechanics. The rules are expressed in terms of the *oddness* or *evenness* of the electron configurations and terms. All spectrum terms arising from an electron configuration for which the sum of the l values is even are called *even* terms. All terms for which the sum is odd are called *odd* terms. Odd terms are designated by small exponents "°." For example we write:

$$3d4d \ (even)\colon {}^1S_0, \ {}^3P_0{}^3P_1{}^3P_2, \ {}^1D_2, \ {}^3F_2{}^3F_3{}^3F_4, \ {}^1G_4$$
$$4s4p \ (odd)\colon {}^1P_1^\circ, \ {}^3P^\circ{}^3P_1^\circ{}^3P^\circ$$

The selection rules for l values are that only even terms can combine with odd terms, and only odd terms with even terms. This rule[1] was discovered empirically by Laporte. The even terms in the above example

---

[1] For a quantum-mechanical proof of this rule see H. Weyl, "The Theory of Groups and Quantum Mechanics," p. 201, 1931.

can combine with the lower set in what is called a *double electron jump*, $4d$ to $4p$ ($\Delta l = 1$), and $3d$ to $4s$ ($\Delta l = 2$), or $3d$ to $4p$ ($\Delta l = 1$), and $4d$ to $4s$ ($\Delta l = 2$). In calcium the $3dnd, {}^3P$ terms combining with $4s4p, {}^3P°$ terms give rise to all but the first member of the anomalous series observed by Russell and Saunders,[1] (see Sec. 11.5). In jj-coupling odd terms will be designated in analogous fashion, *e.g.*, $(\tfrac{1}{2} \ \tfrac{3}{2})^°_1$.

12.15. Intensity Relations.—In calculating relative intensities of spectrum lines in general it is not always sufficient to use the summation rules of Ornstein, Burger, and Dorgelo (see Secs. 8.3 and 10.6). In thermal excitation, for example, the intensity of a line will depend upon the temperature of the source. At low temperature there will be very few atoms in excited states. With an increase in temperature the number in higher states will increase, and hence the possibility of jumping back with the emission of radiation becomes more probable. Just as in the classical theory of the emission of energy from an electric oscillator the intensity of a spectrum line will also depend upon the frequency. The ratio between the intensities of two emitted spectrum lines may be written as

$$\frac{I_{m\to n}}{I_{p\to q}} = \frac{e^{-\frac{h\nu_m}{kT}}}{e^{-\frac{h\nu_p}{kT}}} \cdot \frac{\nu^4_{m\to n}}{\nu^4_{p\to q}} \cdot \frac{P_{m\to n}}{P_{p\to q}}. \tag{12.30}$$

The first term involves the well-known Boltzmann factor containing the effective temperature T of the two initial states m and p and is called the *excitation function* for each state. The second term is called *Einstein's ν^4 correction*. The third term involves the ratios given by the sum rules, which may be stated as follows: (1) *The sum of the intensities of all lines of a multiplet which start from a common initial level is proportional to the quantum weight $(2J + 1)$ of the initial level*, (2) *The sum of the intensities of all lines of a multiplet which end on a common final level is proportional to the quantum weight $(2J + 1)$ of the final level.*[2] These sum rules alone are not sufficient to determine the relative intensities within a multiplet. Before the principles of the quantum mechanics were introduced, correct intensity formulas were derived by Kronig,[3] Russell,[4] and Sommerfeld and Hönl,[5] by means of Bohr's correspondence principle and the classical model of the atom.

---

[1] The first member of the series is now ascribed by Russell to the transition $4p^2$ to $4s4p$.

[2] The quantum weight $(2J + 1)$ gives the number of magnetic levels into which a given fine-structure level J will split when the atom is placed in a magnetic field.

[3] Kronig, R. de L., *Zeits. f. Phys.*, **31**, 885, 1925; **33**, 261, 1925.

[4] Russell, H. N., *Proc. Nat. Acad. Sci.*, **11**, 314, 322, 1925; *Nature*, **115**, 835, 1925.

[5] Sommerfeld, A., and H. Hönl, Sitz-ber., *Berl. Akad. Wiss.*, **9**, 141, 1925.

A Fourier analysis of precessing electron orbits in conjunction with the sum rules leads to the following formulas:

$$\text{For transitions } \mathbf{L} - \mathbf{1} \to \mathbf{L}$$

$$\begin{cases} \mathbf{J} - \mathbf{1} \to \mathbf{J},\, I = \dfrac{B(L + J + S + 1)(L + J + S)(L + J - S)(L + J - S - 1)}{J} \\[2ex] \mathbf{J} \to \mathbf{J}, \quad I = -\dfrac{B(L+J+S+1)(L+J-S)(L-J+S)(L-J-S-1)(2J+1)}{J(J+1)} \\[2ex] \mathbf{J} + \mathbf{1} \to \mathbf{J},\, I = \dfrac{B(L - J + S)(L - J + S - 1)(L - J - S - 1)(L - J - S - 2)}{(J + 1)} \end{cases}$$

$$(12.31)$$

$$\text{For transitions } \mathbf{L} \to \mathbf{L}$$

$$\begin{cases} \mathbf{J} - \mathbf{1} \to \mathbf{J},\, I = -\dfrac{A(L + J + S + 1)(L + J - S)(L - J + S + 1)(L - J - S)}{J} \\[2ex] \mathbf{J} \to \mathbf{J}, \quad I = \dfrac{A[L(L + 1) + J(J + 1) - S(S + 1)]^2(2J + 1)}{J(J + 1)} \\[2ex] \mathbf{J} + \mathbf{1} \to \mathbf{J},\, I = -\dfrac{A(L + J + S + 2)(L + J - S + 1)(L - J + S)(L-J-S-1)}{(J + 1)} \end{cases}$$

$$(12.32)$$

These equations have since been derived on the quantum mechanics by Dirac.[1] If the initial states of a multiplet are close together and the final states are not far apart, the ν^4 and temperature corrections will be very small and the constants A and B need not be determined for the calculation of relative intensities.

Consider, for example, the calculation of the relative intensities for a $^3P - {}^3D$ multiplet. Writing down the terms in an array like the one shown at the left in Table 12.6, and substituting the S, L, and J values in Eq. (12.31), the intensities given in the center of the array are obtained.

TABLE 12.6.—ILLUSTRATING RELATIVE INTENSITIES AND THE SUM RULE FOR A $^3P - {}^3D$ MULTIPLET

	$^3D_3$	$^3D_2$	$^3D_1$				$^3D_3$	$^3D_2$	$^3D_1$		$^3D_3$	$^3D_2$	$^3D_1$
$^3P_2$	168	30	2	200	5	$^3P_2$	100	17.9	1.2	$^3P_2$	100	17.5	1.6
					··								
$^3P_1$		90	30	120	3	$^3P_1$		53.6	17.9	$^3P_1$		54.0	17.5
					··								
$^3P_0$			40	40	1	$^3P_0$			23.8	$^3P_0$			22.2
	168	120	72										
	7	: 5	: 3										

According to the sum rules, the sums of the intensities in the columns have the ratios given by the integers 7:5:3 below and the sums of the intensities in the rows have the ratios given by the integers 5:3:1 at the right in the array. The three strongest lines are those for which L and J change in the same direction and they are called the *diagonal*

[1] DIRAC, P. A. M., *Proc. Roy. Soc.*, **A, 111,** 281, 1926.

lines. Of these lines the one involving the largest L and J is the strongest. The three weaker lines are called *off-diagonal lines*. At times it is convenient to compare the intensities of the lines of each multiplet with the strongest line in the multiplet designated as 100. These reduced intensities are given in the center in Table 12.6. Relative intensities expressed in this way are given in the Appendix for all triplet combinations up to ^3I. The relative intensities of the calcium $^3P - {}^3D$ multiplet (see Fig. 11.7), as measured by Burger and Dorgelo, are given in the third array. Wherever LS-coupling is revealed by the fine structure, the calculated intensities are in good agreement with those observed. Where deviations occur in one they occur as expected in the other. It should be noted that the sum rules make it possible to interchange the rôles of the initial and final states in the above given formulas.

For the relative intensities of lines arising from jj-coupling schemes, Eqs. (12.31) and (12.32) may be employed by replacing S by j_1 and L by j_2. Here j_1 is taken as the quantum value which, in any given transition, does not change. Applying the modified formulas to the intensities of the lines arising from the configurations $sp \rightarrow s \cdot s$, the values shown in the first two arrays in Table 12.7 are obtained:

TABLE 12.7

sp, $(\tfrac{1}{2}\tfrac{1}{2})$

	$J =$	0	1	
$s \cdot s$, $(\tfrac{1}{2}\tfrac{1}{2})$	$J = 0$	3		*1*
	••			
	$J = 1$	3	6	*3*
		1 : 3		

sp, $(\tfrac{1}{2}\tfrac{3}{2})$

	$J =$	1	2	
$s \cdot s$, $(\tfrac{1}{2}\tfrac{1}{2})$	$J = 0$	24		*1*
	••			
	$J = 1$	12	60	*3*
		3 : 5		

sp

	$J =$	0	1	1	2	
$s \cdot s$	$J = 0$	12	24			*1*
	••					
	$J = 1$	12	24	12	60	*3*
		1 : 3		3 : 5		

Assuming that the temperature and the ν^4 corrections are negligibly small, these two sets of three lines each are brought into agreement with the sum rule by multiplying the first array by four. The two are brought together at the right in Table 12.7 and are to be compared with the values obtained for LS-coupling and given in Table 12.8.

TABLE 12.8

	$^1P_1$	$^3P_0$	$^3P_1$	$^3P_2$	
$^1S_0$	36				*1*
					••
$^3S_1$	.	12	36	60	*3*
	3	*1* :	*3* :	*5*	

The relative intensities given in this table, as calculated from Eqs. (12.31), have been multiplied by three.

Although no formulas have been derived for intermediate coupling schemes, the summation rules may be applied in any case. As seen in the above tables the transitions corresponding to $^3S_1 - {}^3P_2$, $^3S_1 - {}^3P_0$, and $^1S_0 - {}^3P_0$ will have the same intensities (60, 12, and 0) in all coupling schemes. For the other transitions it is possible to determine only the sum of the intensities of all transitions starting from, or ending on, levels with the same J values.

12.16. Relative Intensities of Related Multiplets.—Formulas for the relative intensities of multiplets arising from certain types of configurations have been derived by Kronig[1] and checked experimentally in the more complex spectra by Harrison and Engwicht.[2] These formulas have been derived for one-electron jumps where the electron configurations reveal LS-coupling. Consider, for example, the electron configurations $d \cdot d$ and dp, which in Sc II have been observed to give rise to a number of triplet multiplets (see Fig. 12.4).

Let L_0 represent the orbital value of the parent term, *i.e.*, the electron common to both configurations, l the orbital value of the other electron, and L their resultant. These three quantum values are coupled together in just the same fashion as S, L, and J (see Figs. 12.1 and 12.3) and, as shown by Kronig, lead to the same formulas. Making the substitutions of L_0 for S, l for L, and L for J in Eqs. (12.31), and (12.32), formulas for the relative intensities of related multiplets are obtained. It must be remembered that these formulas apply only after the ν^4 and the temperature corrections are made. For multiplets lying close together this is unnecessary.

In the scandium example $d \cdot d \to dp$, given above, $L_0 = 2$, $l = 2$, and $L = 4, 3, 2, 1$, and 0. Substituting these values for S, L, and J in Eqs. (12.31), and (12.32), the intensities shown in Table 12.9 are found.

TABLE 12.9

	^3S	^3P	^3D	^3F	^3G	
$^3P^\circ$	24	54	42			3
$^3D^\circ$		18	70	112		5
$^3F^\circ$			8	56	216	7
	1 :	3 :	5 :	7 :	9	

Although only visual estimates of the lines in all of these multiplets have been made from photographic plates, the general agreement of the observed values with those calculated is quite good. On the basis

[1] Kronig, R. de L., *Zeits. f. Phys.*, **33**, 261, 1925.
[2] Harrison, G. R., and H. Engwicht, *Jour. Opt. Soc. Amer.*, **18**, 287, 1929.

of 100 for the strongest multiplet, the calculated and observed values
are as follows:

TABLE 12.10

	^3S	^3P	^3D	^3F	^3G		^3S	^3P	^3D	^3F	^3G
$^3P°$	11.1	25.0	19.4			$^3P°$	24.0	18.3	14.1		
$^3D°$		8.3	32.4	51.8		$^3D°$		4.2	41.0	35.2	
$^3F°$			3.7	25.9	100	$^3F°$			9.9	22.5	100
			calculated						observed		

Due to nonuniformity in photographic plates the multiplets at
shorter wave-lengths have been underestimated and those at longer
wave-lengths overestimated.   Objective measurements of the lines will
doubtless lead to much better agreement.

12.17. Helium and Helium-like Atoms.—Like that of the alkaline
earths the helium spectrum is composed of four chief series of singlets called
parhelium and four chief series of triplets called *orthohelium*.   That the

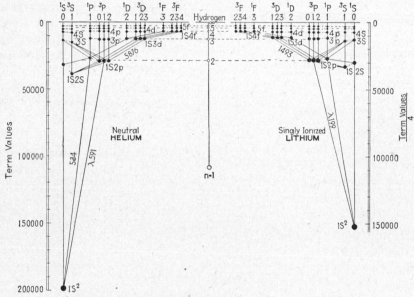

FIG. 12.14.—Energy level diagrams of helium and singly ionized lithium.

fine structure of the very narrow orthohelium series was triplets and
not doublets was first predicted by Slater[1] and verified by Heisenberg.[2]
Similar series have been observed also in ionized lithium.   The two sets
of series in each of the elements may be arranged into two apparently
noncombining sets of energy levels which, in the case of helium, have
come to be known as *parhelium* and *orthohelium levels*.

[1] SLATER, J. C., *Proc. Nat. Acad. Sci.*, **11**, 732, 1925.
[2] HEISENBERG, W., *Zeits. f. Phys.*, **39**, 499, 1926.

Energy level diagrams of helium and singly ionized lithium are shown in Fig. 12.14. The enormous energy shift from the normal $1s^2, {}^1S_0$ state to the first excited states $1s2s, {}^1S_0$ and ${}^3S_1$ is characteristic of all the inert gases and similar atomic systems.

Many attempts to calculate the energy levels of helium, a three-body problem, from a purely theoretical standpoint have been made, and with reasonable success. The normal state of helium, for example, has been calculated by Hylleraas[1] to be 24.470 volts below the series limit, a value differing only 0.003 volt from the spectroscopic value of 24.467 volts. For Li^+ he obtained the value 75.272 volts, in excellent agreement with the observed value 75.279 volts.

Heisenberg has shown that the enormous energy difference between the first two or three triplet levels and their associated singlet levels is due not to the magnetic interactions of the two electrons but to an electrostatic resonance interaction. This phenomenon of resonance, which so frequently arises in the quantum mechanics, is analogous to the resonance between two mechanical oscillators. The analogy has been drawn of two similar pendulums, connected to the same support, and set swinging. If the support is not too rigid the energy of oscillation is found to shift back and forth between one pendulum and the other. At one instant one pendulum is at rest and the second vibrates with a maximum amplitude. Some time later the second pendulum comes to rest and the first vibrates with the maximum amplitude. *It may be said that the two pendulums have changed places.*

For helium-like atoms this resonance phenomenon has been shown to yield fair agreement with experiment by Heisenberg, Dirac, Slater, Gaunt, Unsöld, Breit, Hylleraas, and others. The first attempts to solve the three-body problem of helium on the quantum mechanics led to a wave equation, quite like Schrödinger's equation for hydrogen, and of the form,

$$\nabla_1^2\psi + \nabla_2^2\psi + \frac{8\pi^2\mu}{h^2}\left(W + \frac{Ze^2}{r_1} + \frac{Ze^2}{r_2} - \frac{e^2}{r_{12}}\right)\psi = 0, \qquad (12.33)$$

where the subscripts refer to the two electrons respectively. The first term in parentheses represents the total energy of the system; the second and third terms represent the potential energies of the two electrons, due to their attraction by the nucleus; the last term represents the potential energy due to the mutual repulsion of the two electrons. If it were not for this last term, which accounts for the fine structure we wish to measure, the equation could be solved by analytical methods. Neglecting this term, the solution is of the form of the product of two hydrogen-like functions,

$$\psi = \psi_H(n_a, l_a, m_a; r_1, \theta_1, \phi_1) \cdot \psi_H(n_b, l_b, m_b; r_1, \theta_1, \phi_1), \qquad (12.34)$$

[1] Hylleraas, E. A., *Zeits. f. Phys.*, **54**, 347, 1929; **65**, 209, 1930.

where n, l, and m are the quantum numbers of the two electrons and r, θ, and ϕ their polar coordinates. This solution is degenerate in that the energy of any state of the atom is not altered by interchanging the two electrons, i.e., interchanging the coordinates r, θ, and ϕ:

$$\psi' = \psi_H(n_a, l_a, m_a; r_2, \theta_2, \phi_2) \cdot \psi_H(n_b, l_b, m_b; r_1, \theta_1, \phi_1). \quad (12.35)$$

Treating the e^2/r_{12} term as a perturbation,[1] two solutions may be obtained, one of which is symmetric in the electrons; i.e., when the coordinates are interchanged, the wave function is not altered. The other solution is antisymmetric in that when the coordinates of the two electrons are interchanged, the wave function changes sign. As the interaction is made smaller and tends to zero, the limiting form of the solutions is such that each electron has an equal probability of being found in either of the two states. This is the *austausch* principle which has been interpreted as meaning that the two electrons exchange places regularly as time goes on, i.e., periodically. The rate of this interchange depends upon the magnitude of the interaction and for the lower excited states of atoms like helium is of the same order as the frequency of ordinary light. The total energy is not altered by this interchange, and hence no radiation takes place. Taking into account the spin of the electrons it may be shown that all triplet states realized correspond to wave functions which are antisymmetric in spin and coordinates, i.e., change sign when both electron spins and electron coordinates are interchanged. To the triplet system of terms belong functions antisymmetric in the coordinates and symmetric in the spins. To the singlet system of terms belong functions symmetric in the coordinates and antisymmetric in the spins.

12.18. Quantum-mechanical Model of Helium.—A fairly accurate quantum-mechanical picture of the helium atom in different energy states may be formed by the superposition of hydrogen-like density-distribution curves (see Figs. 4.3 and 4.6). In doing this for the excited states the inner electron, in a $1s$ state, takes on a distribution which is like the $1s$ of ionized helium, i.e., radially it is one-fourth that of hydrogen in the normal state. The outer electron, due to almost perfect screening by the inner electron, is during most of the time in a field not greatly different from that of hydrogen (see Fig. 12.15). The term values of helium and ionized lithium, as shown in Fig. 12.14, indicate quite clearly that the outer electron in all of the excited states is almost hydrogen-like.

It is the overlapping with each other of the dense regions of the distribution curves that makes for a greater electrostatic repulsion, or interaction, i.e., greater singlet-triplet separations. This overlapping

---

[1] For an elementary treatment of this problem the reader is referred to that given by E. U. Condon and P. M. Morse, "Quantum Mechanics," Chap. IV.

decreases rapidly with an increase in the total quantum number of the excited electron.

12.19. Fine Structure of Helium-like Atoms.—Taking into account all of the interactions between two electrons, Heisenberg has calculated the fine-structure triplet separations for helium and helium-like atoms.[1]

For many different electron configurations the energy of the singlet term is very much greater than that of the corresponding triplet (the singlet lies above the triplet). On the vector model the spins s_1^* and s_2^*

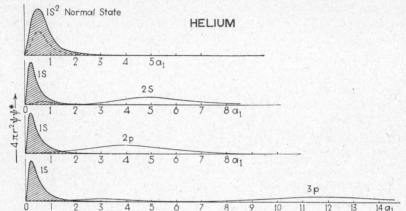

Fig. 12.15.—Probability-density distribution curves for the two electrons of helium in the normal $1s^2, {}^1S_0$ state and several of the excited states.

are oppositely directed for the singlets, $S = 0$, and more nearly in the same direction for the triplets, $S = 1$. It follows that the interaction energy is positive when the angle between s^* and s_2^* is large, and negative when the angle is small (see Sec. 12.7).

According to Heisenberg's results the interaction energy between S and L for the configuration $1s2p$ is given by

$$-\Delta T = a\left\{\frac{Z-3}{4}(J^{*2} - L^{*2} - S^{*2})\right.$$

$$+ 3\frac{(J^{*2} - L^{*2} - S^{*2})^2 - [(J + \tfrac{3}{2})^2 - (L + \tfrac{1}{2})^2][(L + \tfrac{1}{2})^2 - (J - \tfrac{1}{2})^2]}{16L^{*2}}$$

$$\left. - \frac{1}{4}\right\}, \quad (12.36)$$

where a is a constant given by Eq. (8.19) and Z is the atomic number. For the triplet terms ${}^3P_{0,1,2}$ of helium, $Z = 2$; of singly ionized lithium, $Z = 3$; of doubly ionized beryllium, $Z = 4$; etc.:

He I, $-\Delta T = a(\tfrac{18}{8}, -\tfrac{1}{8}, -\tfrac{3}{8})$; Be III, $-\Delta T = a(\tfrac{2}{8}, -\tfrac{9}{8}, +\tfrac{5}{8})$; (12.37)
Li II, $-\Delta T = a(\tfrac{10}{8}, -\tfrac{5}{8}, +\tfrac{1}{8})$; B IV, $-\Delta T = a(-\tfrac{6}{8}, -\tfrac{13}{8}, +\tfrac{9}{8})$.

[1] Heisenberg, W., Zeits. f. Phys., **39**, 499, 1926; see also Breit, G., Phys. Rev., **36**, 383, 1930; **39**, 616, 1932, for later improvements and references.

These intervals are shown in Fig. 12.16.   The dash-dot line represents the center of gravity of each triplet.   As Z becomes large, the second and third terms of Eq. (12.36) become negligibly small compared with the first.   Dropping them we obtain

$$-\Delta T_z = A\frac{J^{*2} - L^{*2} - S^{*2}}{2}. \tag{12.38}$$

This is the Landé interval rule which for $^3P_{0,1,2}$ gives the interval ratio 1:2.   The relative separations of the first two elements, He I and Li II, have been observed to have, quite accurately, the intervals given by

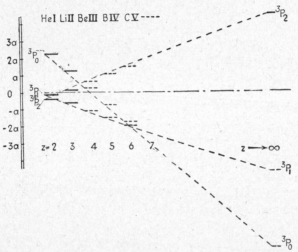

Fig. 12.16.—Relative separations for the $1s2p$, $^3P_{0,1,2}$, states of helium-like atoms.   (*After Heisenberg.*)

Heisenberg's formula, Eq. (12.37).   The fact that the ^3P intervals in He I and Li II are far from the ratio given by the interval rule shows that the interaction between the s electron spin and the p electron orbit is of the same order of magnitude as the spin-orbit interaction of the p electron alone.

Spectrum lines arising from transitions into and out of the $1s2p$, ^3P levels of ionized lithium show that, in addition to the triplet fine structure of the levels, there is a still finer structure known as *hyperfine structure* (see Chap. XVIII).   A discussion of the more recent quantum-mechanical treatments of the interaction of two electrons in complex spectra will be given at the end of Chap. XIV.

Problems

1. Derive all of the terms arising from the electron configuration fg.
2. Graphically represent the Landé interval rule for a ^3P term as in Fig. 12.7.

3. Show for a ds electron configuration that the total ^3D separation is the same in both LS- and jj-coupling. Show also that the d electron alone gives the same ^2D separation (see Sec. 12.11).

4. Using Eqs. (12.31) and (12.32), calculate the relative intensities in each of the three triplets arising from the transition $p \cdot p \rightarrow ps$. Assume LS-coupling.

5. Calculate the relative multiplet intensities for the triad of triplets arising in Prob. 4 (see Sec. 12.16).

6. Repeat Prob. 4 assuming jj-coupling between the electrons. Compare these intensities, as in Tables 12.7 and 12.8, by applying the sum rules.

CHAPTER XIII

ZEEMAN EFFECT, PASCHEN-BACK EFFECT, AND THE PAULI EXCLUSION PRINCIPLE FOR TWO ELECTRONS

One of the outstanding successes of the vector model, developed by Landé before the advent of the quantum mechanics, is the amazing accuracy with which it predicts the observed Zeeman patterns of many spectrum lines. Modified according to the quantum mechanics this model was employed in the last chapter in the treatment of LS- and jj-coupling for two electrons. This treatment will be extended in this chapter to the Zeeman effect, the Paschen-Back effect, and the Pauli exclusion principle.

13.1. The Magnetic Moment of the Atom.—We have already seen, in Chap. X, how the total magnetic moment of the atom and the Landé g factor enter into the development and derivation of expressions for the Zeeman effect. The same principles used in obtaining these two factors for a single valence electron will now be extended to atomic systems containing two valence electrons. With two electrons there will be four individual magnetic moments to be taken into account; these are associated with the mechanical moments s_1^*, s_2^*, l_1^*, and l_2^*. With the magnitude of each of these moments known, their vector sum will depend upon their mutual orientations. If the coupling between the four mechanical moments is LS-coupling (Russell-Saunders coupling), there will be one set of resultant magnetic moments, whereas, if the coupling is jj-coupling, there will be a different set.

The magnetic moments of the spin and orbital motions of an electron have already been given by Eq. (10.4) as

$$\mu_l = 1 \cdot l^* \frac{h}{2\pi} \cdot \frac{e}{2mc} \frac{\text{ergs}}{\text{gauss}}, \qquad \mu_s = 2 \cdot s^* \frac{h}{2\pi} \cdot \frac{e}{2mc} \frac{\text{ergs}}{\text{gauss}} \cdot \quad (13.1)$$

In LS-coupling the two spins are coupled strongly together and are quantized to form a resultant S^* (see Fig. 12.5). Projecting each spin moment on S^* and adding, we obtain the vector sum of the two magnetic moments,

$$\mu_s = [s_1^* \cos (s_1^* S^*) + s_2^* \cos (s_2^* S^*)] \frac{h}{2\pi} \cdot 2 \frac{e}{2mc} = S^* \frac{h}{2\pi} \cdot 2 \frac{e}{2mc} \frac{\text{ergs}}{\text{gauss}} \cdot \quad (13.2)$$

Similarly the two l's are coupled together and quantized to form a resultant L^*. Projecting each orbital moment on L^* and adding,

$$\mu_L = [l_1^* \cos (l_1^* L^*) + l_2^* \cos (l_2^* L^*)]\frac{h}{2\pi} \cdot \frac{e}{2mc} = L^*\frac{h}{2\pi} \cdot \frac{e}{2mc}\frac{\text{ergs}}{\text{gauss}}. \quad (13.3)$$

Just as the spin and orbit of a single electron are coupled together to form a resultant moment j^*, so L^* and S^* are coupled together to form a resultant moment J^* (see Sec. 10.3 and Fig. 10.6). Projecting μ_S and μ_L on J^* and adding, we get for the total magnetic moment of the atom,

$$\mu_J = [L^* \cos (L^* J^*) + 2S^* \cos (S^* J^*)]\frac{h}{2\pi} \cdot \frac{e}{2mc}\frac{\text{ergs}}{\text{gauss}}. \quad (13.4)$$

The terms within the brackets give μ_J in units of the Bohr magneton, $he/4\pi mc$. Replacing these terms in the brackets by g times J^*, *i.e.*,

$$gJ^* = L^* \cos (L^* J^*) + 2S^* \cos (S^* J^*), \quad (13.5)$$

we obtain

$$\mu_J = gJ^* \cdot \frac{he}{4\pi mc}\frac{\text{ergs}}{\text{gauss}}. \quad (13.6)$$

Since the angles between L^*, S^*, and J^* are fixed, in LS-coupling, the cosine terms in Eq. (13.5) are readily evaluated.

$$L^* \cos (L^* J^*) = \frac{J^{*2} + L^{*2} - S^{*2}}{2J^*},$$
$$S^* \cos (S^* J^*) = \frac{J^{*2} + S^{*2} - L^{*2}}{2J^*}. \quad (13.7)$$

Substituting these two cosines in Eq. (13.5), we get for the g factor,

$$g = 1 + \frac{J^{*2} + S^{*2} - L^{*2}}{2J^{*2}}. \quad (13.8)$$

This is the Landé g factor in exactly the same form as Eq. (10.11) for a single electron, except that l^* is here replaced by L^*, s^* by S^*, and j^* by J^*. Values of the g factor calculated from this equation are given in the Appendix.

In jj-coupling the s^* and l^* of each electron are coupled together and quantized to form their own resultant j^*. The magnetic moment of a single electron has already been given in Eqs. (10.6) and (10.7). With two electrons we may write for each one separately,

$$\mu_1 = g_1 j_1^* \frac{he}{4\pi mc}, \qquad \mu_2 = g_2 j_2^* \frac{he}{4\pi mc}. \quad (13.9)$$

With j_1^* and j_2^* in turn coupled together and quantized to form a resultant J^*, these moments are projected on J^* and added to give the total magnetic moment of the atom,

$$\mu_J = g_1 j_1^* \frac{he}{4\pi mc} \cos (j_1^* J^*) + g_2 j_2^* \frac{he}{4\pi mc} \cos (j_2^* J^*) \tag{13.10}$$

$$= [g_1 j_1^* \cos (j_1^* J^*) + g_2 j_2^* \cos (j_2^* J^*)] \frac{he}{4\pi mc} \frac{\text{ergs}}{\text{gauss}}. \tag{13.11}$$

Replacing the terms in the brackets by g times J^*, we get

$$g \cdot J^* = g_1 j_1^* \cos (j_1^* J^*) + g_2 j_2^* \cos (j_2^* J^*). \tag{13.12}$$

Since the angles between j_1^*, j_2^*, and J^* are constant, the cosine formula gives

$$\begin{aligned} j_1^* \cos (j_1^* J^*) &= \frac{J^{*2} + j_1^{*2} - j_2^{*2}}{2J^*}, \\ j_2^* \cos (j_2^* J^*) &= \frac{J^{*2} + j_2^{*2} - j_1^{*2}}{2J^*}. \end{aligned} \tag{13.13}$$

The g factor for jj-coupling now becomes

$$g = g_1 \frac{J^{*2} + j_1^{*2} - j_2^{*2}}{2J^{*2}} + g_2 \frac{J^{*2} + j_2^{*2} - j_1^{*2}}{2J^{*\circ}}. \tag{13.14}$$

A table of g factors for jj-coupling is given in the Appendix.

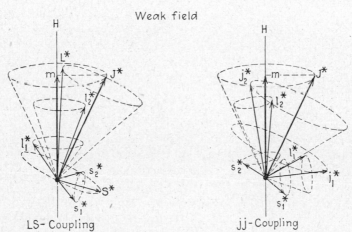

FIG. 13.1.—The vector model for *LS*- and *jj*-coupling in a weak magnetic field (Zeeman effect).

13.2. The Zeeman Effect.

—In a weak magnetic field the atom as a whole is quantized with H in such a fashion that the projection of the angular momentum $J^* h/2\pi$ on H is equal to $Mh/2\pi$, where M takes values differing from each other by unity, from $M = +J$ to $M = -J$.[1] In

---

[1] For a quantum-mechanical proof of this relation see E. U. Condon and P. M. Morse, "Quantum Mechanics," Sec. 64.

terms of the vector model these quantum conditions are expressed as follows:

$$J^* \cos (J^*H) = M, \qquad \text{where} \qquad M = 0, \pm 1, \pm 2 \cdots \pm J \qquad (13.15)$$

for singlets and triplets. On the classical model of a precessing atom (see Fig. 13.1), J^* carries out a Larmor precession around H with an angular velocity given by Eq. (10.4),

$$\omega_L = H \cdot g \cdot \frac{e}{2mc}. \qquad (13.16)$$

Multiplying by the projection of the mechanical moment on H, the energy of this precession (see footnote 3 on page 157)

$$\Delta W = H \cdot g \cdot \frac{e}{2mc} J^* \cdot \frac{h}{2\pi} \cos (J^*H). \qquad (13.17)$$

In terms of the magnetic quantum number [Eq. (13.15)],

$$\Delta W_M = M \cdot g \cdot H \frac{he}{4\pi mc}. \qquad (13.18)$$

Dividing by hc, the energy in wave numbers (see Sec. 10.4) is given by

$$-\Delta T_M = M \cdot g \frac{He}{4\pi mc^2} \text{ cm}^{-1} = M \cdot g \cdot \mathbf{L} \text{ cm}^{-1}. \qquad (13.19)$$

If T represents the term value of a field-free energy level, then in a weak magnetic field the term value of each magnetic level will be given by

$$T_M = T - M \cdot g \frac{He}{4\pi mc^2} \text{ cm}^{-1} = T - M \cdot g \cdot \mathbf{L} \text{ cm}^{-1}. \qquad (13.20)$$

Before going further it should be pointed out just what assumptions were made in deriving the preceding expressions for the g factor and the magnetic interaction energy. On the classical model for LS-coupling it was assumed (1) that s_1^* and s_2^* precess rapidly around S^*, (2) that l_1^* and l_2^* precess rapidly around L^*, (3) that L^* and S^* precess more slowly around J^*, and (4) that J^* in turn precesses still more slowly around H. These assumptions, as well as similar ones for jj-coupling, are necessary in order that the components of the different magnetic moments normal to their respective axes of precession cancel out. The quantum-mechanical analogue of these precessions is to be found in the angular factors of the probability-density distributions (see Sec. 4.3). The formula for the Landé g factor has recently been derived on the quantum mechanics.

As an example of the splitting up of an energy level in a magnetic field, consider the case of a $^3D_3$ level. With $g = \frac{4}{3}$ and $J = 3$, there will be seven equally spaced magnetic levels $M = 3, 2, 1, 0, -1, -2,$ and -3, shifted from the field-free level by $M \cdot g = \tfrac{12}{3}, \tfrac{8}{3}, \tfrac{4}{3}, 0, -\tfrac{4}{3}, -\tfrac{8}{3}, -\tfrac{12}{3}$.

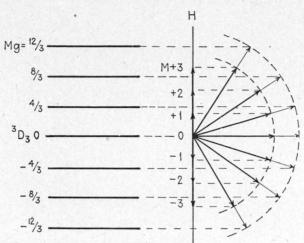

Fig. 13.2.—Graphical representation of the splitting of a $^3D_3$ level in a weak magnetic field.

A graphical representation of this splitting is shown in Fig. 13.2, where the vector J^* is drawn in the seven allowed positions. Multiplying J^* by g and projecting on the H axis, the displacements Mg, shown at the left, are obtained. If numbers in this figure are multiplied by $He/4\pi mc^2$, the level separations are given directly in wave numbers.

From Eq. (13.19) it is observed that the relative separations of the magnetic levels of one term and those of another are determined by the g factor alone. This fact greatly simplifies the calculation of Zeeman patterns. As a simple case consider the diffuse-series singlet $^1P_1 - {}^1D_2$. For each of these levels the g factor is equal to unity, so that the initial and final states with $J = 2$ and $J = 1$ are split into five and three equally spaced levels, respectively (see Fig. 13.3).

The selection rules for the Zeeman effect of two-electron systems are just the same as those for a single electron (Sec. 10.5).

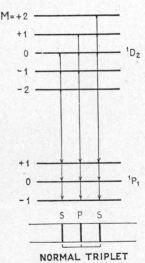

NORMAL TRIPLET

Fig. 13.3.—Zeeman pattern of a diffuse-series singlet, showing equal separations in both the initial and final states of the atom.

$$\text{Viewed} \perp \text{to field} \begin{cases} \Delta M = \pm 1; \text{ plane polarized } \perp \text{ to } H; s \text{ components} \\ \Delta M = 0; \text{ plane polarized } \parallel \text{ to } H; p \text{ components} \end{cases}$$

$$\text{Viewed} \parallel \text{to field} \begin{cases} \Delta M = \pm 1; \text{ circularly polarized}; s \text{ components} \\ \Delta M = 0; \text{ forbidden}; p \text{ components} \end{cases}$$

For the $^1P_1$-$^1D_2$ transition there are nine allowed combinations falling into three equally spaced groups (see Fig. 13.3). Having just the separations given by Lorentz's classical theory of the Zeeman effect [Eq. (10.1)], this pattern is called a *normal triplet*. Since the g factor for all singlet levels is unity, all singlet lines will show a normal-triplet pattern in a magnetic field. For an observed pattern see Fig. 10.2.

Turning now to the triplet levels, let us consider the Zeeman patterns arising from a principal-series triplet $^3S_1 - {}^3P_{0,1,2}$. Assuming LS-coupling,

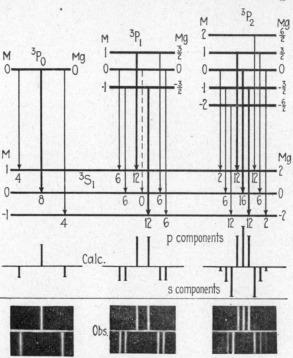

FIG. 13.4.—Calculated and observed Zeeman patterns of a principal-series triplet, $^3S_1 - {}^3P_{0,1,2}$.

the g factors for the initial states $^3P_0$, $^3P_1$, and $^3P_2$, and for the final state $^3S_1$, are $\frac{0}{0}$, $\frac{3}{2}$, $\frac{3}{2}$, and 2, respectively. The resultant magnetic levels are shown schematically in Fig. 13.4. At the bottom of the figure the observed patterns are shown for a zinc triplet. With a g factor of two for the lower state $^3S_1$, the pattern $^3S_1 - {}^3P_0$ has *twice the normal-triplet separation*.

13.3. Intensity Rules for the Zeeman Effect.—Intensity rules for the Zeeman effect of atomic systems containing more than one valence electron are independent of the type of coupling and depend only on the quantum numbers M and J. These rules, first discovered empirically by Ornstein and Burger,[1] may be derived from the sum rules. *The*

---

[1] ORNSTEIN, L. S., and H. C. BURGER, *Zeits. f. Phys.*, **28**, 135, 1924; **29**, 241, 1924.

sum of the intensities of all transitions starting from any initial Zeeman level is equal to the sum starting from any other level. Similarly, the sum of the intensities of all the transitions arriving at any final Zeeman level is equal to the sum arriving at any other level. From the classical model and these rules the following equations have been derived,
Transition $J \rightarrow J$:

$$\begin{cases} M \rightarrow M \pm 1, & I = A(J \pm M + 1)(J \mp M); \\ M \rightarrow M, & I = 4AM^2; \end{cases}$$

Transition $J \rightarrow J + 1$: (13.21)

$$\begin{cases} M \rightarrow M \pm 1, & I = B(J \pm M + 1)(J \pm M + 2); \\ M \rightarrow M, & I = 4B(J + M + 1)(J - M + 1). \end{cases}$$

In deriving these equations account has been taken of the fact that when observed perpendicular to the field only half the intensity of the s components is observed. Observations parallel to the field give the other half of the s components. In any direction the total light emitted is unpolarized just as in field-free space. The constants A and B in the above equations are proportionality constants and are not needed for any given Zeeman pattern. Applying these equations to the principal triplet of Fig. 13.4, the values shown at the arrow tips are obtained. In order that the sum rules hold for all of the levels in the figure the values derived for the first pattern $^3S_1 - {}^3P_0$ have all been multiplied by two and those of the second pattern $^3S_1 - {}^3P_1$ by three. Doubling the s components the sum of the intensities of all transitions starting from any upper level is 24 and the sum ending on any lower level is 72.

13.4. The Calculation of Zeeman Patterns.—A scheme for the rapid calculation of Zeeman patterns has been given by Sommerfeld (see Sec. 10.6). Consider, for example, the complex pattern arising from the transition $^3D_3 - {}^3P_2$. Here the J values are 3 and 2, and the respective g factors, from Eq. (13.8), are $\frac{4}{3}$ and $\frac{3}{2}$. The separation factors Mg for both the initial and final states are first written down in two rows with equal values of M directly below and above each other as follows:

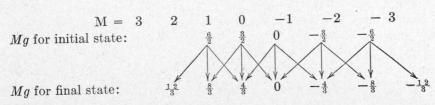

M = 3	2	1	0	−1	−2	− 3

Mg for initial state: $\frac{6}{2}$ $\frac{3}{2}$ 0 $-\frac{3}{2}$ $-\frac{6}{2}$

Mg for final state: $\frac{12}{3}$ $\frac{8}{3}$ $\frac{4}{3}$ 0 $-\frac{4}{3}$ $-\frac{8}{3}$ $-\frac{12}{3}$

In this array the vertical differences $\Delta M = 0$ give the p components $\frac{2}{6}$, $\frac{1}{6}$, 0, $-\frac{1}{6}$, and $\frac{2}{6}$, and the diagonal differences $\Delta M = \pm 1$ give the s components $\pm\frac{6}{6}$, $\pm\frac{7}{6}$, $\pm\frac{8}{6}$, $\pm\frac{9}{6}$, and $\pm\frac{10}{6}$. These may be abbreviated to give the separations (see Fig. 13.5 and Sec. 10.6):

$$-\Delta T_M = \pm \frac{(0),\ (1),\ (2),\ 6,\ 7,\ 8,\ 9,\ 10}{6} \cdot L\ \text{cm}^{-1}. \qquad (13.22)$$

The common denominator is called the *Runge denominator* and is the least common multiple of the two denominators of the Mg factors. This pattern is plotted in Fig. 13.5. The p components are plotted

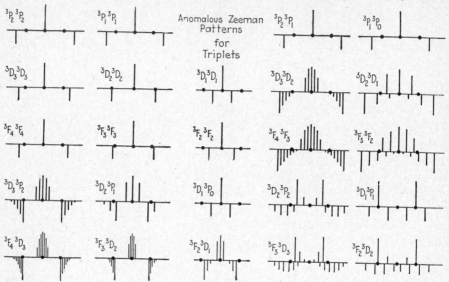

Fig. 13.5.—Anomalous Zeeman patterns for triplet combinations. Dots show normal triplet intervals (LS-coupling).

above the line in the usual way, and the s components are plotted below. The heights of the lines represent the relative intensities as calculated from the equations in Sec. 13.3.

13.5. LS- and jj-coupling and the g Sum Rule.—In classifying a given spectrum line for the first time it is not always known to just what type of coupling scheme the corresponding levels belong. Since the g factors are in many instances different for jj-coupling than they are for LS-coupling, the Zeeman patterns will also be different. For this reason it is sometimes difficult to assign a given pattern to a definite transition. This uncertainty is often alleviated by Pauli's[1] so-called *g sum rule*. This rule states that out of all the states arising from a given electron configuration the sum of the g factors for levels with the same J value is a constant independent of the coupling scheme. As an example, consider the four terms $^3P_{0,1,2}$ and $^1P_1$, arising from the configuration ps. The following table gives the g values of these four

[1] Pauli, W., *Zeits f. Phys.*, **16**, 155, 1923.

levels, calculated for LS-coupling by Eq. (13.8) and for jj-coupling by Eq. (13.14).

TABLE 13.1.—CALCULATED g FACTORS ILLUSTRATING PAULI'S g SUM RULE FOR A ps ELECTRON CONFIGURATION

Terms	$J = 0$	$J = 1$	$J = 2$	Coupling scheme
$^1P_1$	..	$g = 1$	..	LS
$^3P_{0,1,2}$	0	$\frac{3}{2}$	$\frac{3}{2}$	
$j_1 = \frac{1}{2},\ j_2 = \frac{1}{2}$	0	$\frac{4}{3}$	..	jj
$j_1 = \frac{1}{2},\ j_2 = \frac{3}{2}$	..	$\frac{7}{6}$	$\frac{3}{2}$	
Σg	0	$\frac{5}{2}$	$\frac{3}{2}$	

When only one term occurs for a certain J value the g sum rule states that the g factor is the same in all coupling schemes. Observed Zeeman patterns illustrating the g sum rule are to be found for many elements. In Table 13.2 zinc, tin, and lead are given as examples.

TABLE 13.2.—OBSERVED g FACTORS ILLUSTRATING PAULI'S g SUM RULE FOR A ps ELECTRON CONFIGURATION

Element	Terms	$J = 0$	$J = 1$	$J = 2$	Coupling scheme
Zn	$^1P_1$	..	$g = 1.000$		LS
	$^3P_{0,1,2}$	0	1.500	1.500	
Sn*	$^1P_1$	..	1.125		Intermediate
	$^3P_{0,1,2}$	0	1.375	1.500	
Pb†	$^1P_1$	..	1.150		jj
	$^3P_{0,1,2}$	0	1.350	1.500	
	Σg	0	1.500	1.500	

* GREEN, J. B., and R. A. LORING, *Phys. Rev.*, **30**, 574, 1927.
† GOUDSMIT, S., and E. BACK, *Zeits. f. Phys.*, **40**, 530, 1927.

The observed Zeeman patterns of the transition $^3S_1 - {}^3P_1$ in each of these elements are shown in Fig. 13.6.

13.6. Paschen-Back Effect.—In the preceding sections of this chapter we have seen how in a weak magnetic field the atom as a whole is quantized with respect to the field direction. If the magnetic field is continually increased there will come a time when the interaction energy between J^* and H becomes so great that the coupling between S^* and L^* in the case of LS-coupling, or between j_1^* and j_2^* in the case of

jj-coupling, is broken down.   This will occur when the interaction energy, given by Eq. (13.19), exceeds the L^*S^* interaction energy given by Eq. (12.13) or the $j_1^*j_2^*$ interaction energy given by Eq. (12.25).   In other words when the Zeeman levels of the different levels of a multiplet begin to overlap each other, Eq. (13.19) will no longer hold.   As the field

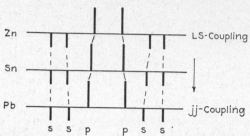

Fig. 13.6.—Observed Zeeman patterns for the transition $^3S_1 - {}^3P_1$ in Zn, Sn, and Pb.

is still further increased, S^* and L^*, or j_1^* and j_2^*, will independently become quantized with the field H.   This is the Paschen-Back effect in terms of the atom model.

The classical vector model of the Paschen-Back state of the atom is shown in Fig. 13.7.   With L^* and S^* precessing independently around the field direction, J^* is no longer constant in magnitude and ceases to be a quantum number.   Similarly with j_1^* and j_2^* precessing inde-

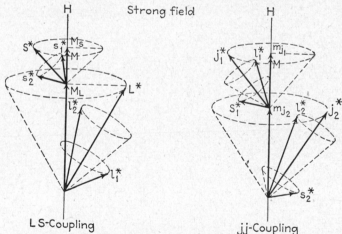

Fig. 13.7.—Classical vector model for LS- and jj-coupling schemes in a strong magnetic field (the Paschen-Back effect).

pendently around H, their resultant J^* ceases to have any meaning.   The two special cases of LS- and jj-coupling will now be treated separately.

13.7. LS-coupling and the Paschen-Back Effect.—The method used in deriving an expression for the interaction energy when the Paschen-Back effect sets in, for original LS-coupling, is exactly the same as that used for a single electron in Sec. 10.7. With L^* and S^* independently quantized with the field H, the quantum conditions are (1) that the projection of $L^*h/2\pi$ on H is equal to $M_Lh/2\pi$, where $M_L = 0, \pm 1, \pm 2, \cdots \pm L$; and (2) that the projection of $S^*h/2\pi$ on H is equal to $M_sh/2\pi$, where $M_S = 0, \pm 1, \pm 2, \cdots \pm S$. For singlets $M_S = 0$, and for triplets $M_S = +1$, 0, and -1. On the classical model the Larmor precessions of L^* and S^* will be given by H times the ratio between the magnetic and mechanical moments,

$$\omega_L = H \cdot \frac{e}{2mc} \quad \text{and} \quad \omega_S = H \cdot 2 \cdot \frac{e}{2mc}. \tag{13.23}$$

Multiplying each of these angular velocities by the corresponding angular-momentum components along H (see footnote 3 on page 157) gives the two interaction energies:

$$\Delta W_{LH} = H \cdot \frac{e}{2mc} L^* \frac{h}{2\pi} \cos (L^*H) = H \cdot \frac{e}{2mc} M_L \frac{h}{2\pi}, \tag{13.24}$$

$$\Delta W_{SH} = 2H \cdot \frac{e}{2mc} S^* \frac{h}{2\pi} \cos (S^*H) = 2H \cdot \frac{e}{2mc} M_S \frac{h}{2\pi}. \tag{13.25}$$

The sum of these two energies gives the main energy shift of each magnetic level from the field-free level from which it sprang:

$$\Delta W_H = (M_L + 2M_S) \cdot H \frac{eh}{4\pi mc}. \tag{13.26}$$

Dividing by hc, the energy in wave numbers becomes

$$-\Delta T_H = (M_L + 2M_S) \cdot \frac{He}{4\pi mc^2} = (M_L + 2M_S) \cdot \text{L cm}^{-1}. \tag{13.27}$$

To this energy a small correction due to the interaction energy between L^* and S^* must be added. By exactly the same treatment as that given for a single electron in Sec. 10.7 this energy is given by

$$-\Delta T_{LS} = A \cdot M_L M_S = \Gamma_{\text{strong}} \tag{13.28}$$

where A is given by Eq. (12.12). Adding this term to Eq. (13.26), the total energy shift becomes

$$-\Delta T_M = (M_L + 2M_S)\text{L} + A \cdot M_S M_L. \tag{13.29}$$

If now T_1 represents the term value of the center of gravity of a multiple term, the term value of each magnetic level (see Fig. 12.6) will be given by

$$T_M = T_1 - (M_L + 2M_S) \cdot \text{L} - AM_L M_S. \tag{13.30}$$

This splitting is shown graphically in Fig. 13.8, for $^3S_1$, $^3P_{0,1,2}$, and $^3D_{1,2,3}$ levels. In each case the field-free levels are shown at the left.

Next come the weak-field Zeeman levels symmetrical about the field-free levels followed by the Paschen-Back levels at the right. The

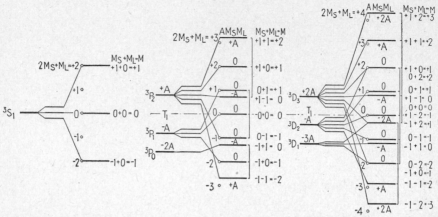

FIG. 13.8.—Strong-field energy levels for ^3S, ^3P, and ^3D terms (Paschen-Back effect, LS-coupling).

equally spaced dots in the strong-field levels represent the two inter-action energies due to the external field. Adding the L^*S^* interaction term divides the $^3D_3$ levels into three groups of five equally spaced levels.

TABLE 13.3.—COMPUTATION OF MAGNETIC ENERGIES FOR LS-COUPLING IN WEAK AND STRONG MAGNETIC FIELDS

Term	Weak field			Strong field					
	Γ_{weak}	M	Mg	M	M_S	M_L	$2M_S$	$2M_S + M_L$	Γ_{strong} $A \cdot M_L M_S$
$^3P_2$	$+A$	$+2$	$+\frac{6}{2}$	$+2$	$+1$	$+1$	$+2$	$+3$	$+A$
		$+1$	$+\frac{3}{2}$	$+1$	$+1$	0	$+2$	$+2$	0
		0	0	0	$+1$	-1	$+2$	$+1$	$-A$
		-1	$-\frac{3}{2}$						
		-2	$-\frac{6}{2}$	$+1$	0	$+1$	0	$+1$	0
$^3P_1$	$-A$			0	0	0	0	0	0
		$+1$	$+\frac{3}{2}$	-1	0	-1	0	-1	0
		0	0	0	-1	$+1$	-2	-1	$-A$
		-1	$-\frac{3}{2}$	-1	-1	0	-2	-2	0
$^3P_0$	$-2A$	0	0	-2	-1	-1	-2	-3	$+A$

As an example of the use of Eq. (13.30) in calculating strong-field levels, consider the triplet terms $^3P_{0,1,2}$. Since $L = 1$ and $S = 1$ the possible values of M_L are 1, 0, and -1, and the possible values of M_S are 1, 0, and -1. A tabulation of all possible combinations of these values is given in Table 13.3.

Corresponding to each of the nine weak-field levels there is a strong-field level with the same M. Actual calculations of the magnetic energy for the stages between weak and strong fields have been made by Darwin.[1] These calculations enable one to determine just what weak-field level goes over to each strong-field level. A general rule for connecting weak- and strong-field levels may be stated as follows: *The sum of the projections*

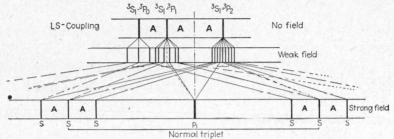

FIG. 13.9.—Paschen-Back pattern of a principal-series triplet.

of the mechanical moments on H does not change. In other words, the weak field M is equal to the strong field $M_L + M_S$:

$$M = M_L + M_S. \tag{13.31}$$

Conservation of angular momentum requires this to be true. In addition to this rule the further restriction is necessary that *no two levels with the same M ever cross.*

As an example of an observed Paschen-Back pattern, consider a principal-series triplet $^3S_1 - {}^3P_{0,1,2}$. The initial and final states for this case are shown at the left in Fig. 13.8. The selection rules for strong field are

$$\Delta M_S = 0,$$

$$\Delta M_L = \begin{cases} 0 \text{ for } p \text{ components,} \\ \pm 1 \text{ for } s \text{ components.} \end{cases} \tag{13.32}$$

Applying these rules the pattern shown at the bottom of Fig. 13.9 is obtained. The bracket shows that, were it not for the small inter-action between L^* and S^*, the pattern would be a normal triplet. Experimental observations of such strong-field patterns are very few, owing to the enormous fields required for producing the effect. A principal-series triplet has been observed by Paschen and Back[2] in oxygen as a

[1] DARWIN, K., *Proc. Roy. Soc.*, A, **118**, 264, 1928.

[2] PASCHEN, F., and E. BACK, *Ann. d. Phys.*, **39**, 897, 1912; **40**, 960, 1913. See figures at end of each article in the *Annalen.*

fairly good normal triplet with the s components unresolved. There is good evidence, however, that with suitably strong fields experiment will check theory in almost every detail.

13.8. jj-coupling and the Paschen-Back Effect.—A calculation of the magnetic energy for jj-coupling in a strong magnetic field is essentially the same as the treatment given for LS-coupling in the previous section. As seen in Fig. 13.7, j_1^* and j_2^* are quantized independently with the field H. The conditions for this quantization are: (1) The projection of $j_1^*h/2\pi$ on H is equal to $m_{j_1}h/2\pi$, where $m_{j_1} = \pm\frac{1}{2},\ \pm\frac{3}{2},\ \cdots\ ,\ \pm j_1$. (2) The projection of $j_2^*h/2\pi$ on H is equal to $m_{j_2}h/2\pi$, where $m_{j_2} = \pm\frac{1}{2},\ \pm\frac{3}{2},\ \cdots\ ,\ \pm j_2$.

The total magnetic energy will be given by the sum of three energies, the interaction energy between (1) j_1^* and H, (2) j_2^* and H, and (3) j_1^* and j_2^*. By Eq. (10.14) the Larmor precessions of j_1^* around H, and j_2^* around H, are given by

$$\omega_{j_1} = H \cdot g_1\frac{e}{2mc} \qquad \text{and} \qquad \omega_{j_2} = H \cdot g_2\frac{e}{2mc}, \qquad (13.33)$$

where g_1 and g_2 are the g factors for the two electrons, respectively. Multiplying each of these angular velocities by the corresponding projections of the angular momenta on H (see footnote 3 on page 157) gives the two energies,

$$\Delta W_{j_1H} = H \cdot g_1\frac{e}{2mc}j_1^*\frac{h}{2\pi} \cos (j_1^*H) = H \cdot g_1\frac{e}{2mc}m_{j_1}\frac{h}{2\pi}, \qquad (13.34)$$

$$\Delta W_{j_2H} = H \cdot g_2\frac{e}{2mc}j_2^*\frac{h}{2\pi} \cos (j_2^*H) = H \cdot g_2\frac{e}{2mc}m_{j_2}\frac{h}{2\pi}. \qquad (13.35)$$

The sum of these energies is

$$\Delta W_H = (g_1m_{j_1} + g_2m_{j_2})H\frac{eh}{4\pi mc}. \qquad (13.36)$$

Dividing by hc, this energy in wave numbers becomes

$$-\Delta T_H = (g_1m_{j_1} + g_2m_{j_2})\frac{He}{4\pi mc^2}\ \text{cm}^{-1} = (g_1m_{j_1} + g_2m_{j_2}) \cdot \text{L cm}^{-1}. \qquad (13.37)$$

To this energy must be added the interaction energy due to the coupling between j_1^* and j_2^*. By analogy with LS-coupling this energy is given by [see Eq. (13.28)]

$$-\Delta T_{jj} = A \cdot m_{j_1}m_{j_2}\ \text{cm}^{-1} = \Gamma_{\text{strong}} \qquad (13.38)$$

where A is given by Eq. (12.24). Adding this small term to Eq. (13.36), the total magnetic energy becomes

$$-\Delta T_M = (g_1m_{j_1} + g_2m_{j_2}) \cdot \text{L} + A \cdot m_{j_1}m_{j_2}. \qquad (13.39)$$

If now we let T_1 represent the term value of the center of gravity of a multiple term (see Fig. 12.10), the term value of each magnetic level will be given by

$$T_M = T_1 - (g_1 m_{j_1} + g_2 m_{j_2}) \cdot L - A \cdot m_{j_1} m_{j_2}). \qquad (13.40)$$

As an example of the calculation of strong-field energy levels, consider the terms arising from part of the electron configuration sp, where

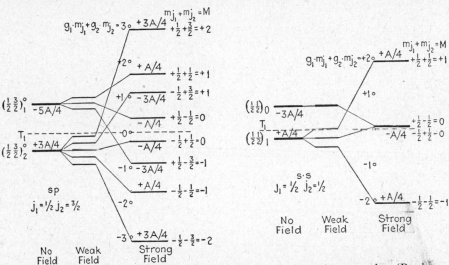

Fig. 13.10.—Strong-field energy levels for the electron configurations sp and $s \cdot s$ (Paschen-Back effect, jj-coupling).

$j_1 = \frac{1}{2}$ and $j_2 = \frac{3}{2}$, and those arising from the configuration $s \cdot s$, where $j_1 = \frac{1}{2}$ and $j_2 = \frac{1}{2}$. A graphical representation of the resultant levels $J = 1$ and 2, and $J = 0$ and 1, is shown in Fig. 13.10. The weak- and

TABLE 13.4.—COMPUTATION OF MAGNETIC ENERGIES FOR jj-COUPLING IN WEAK AND STRONG MAGNETIC FIELDS. CONFIGURATION sp, $j_1 = \frac{1}{2}$ AND $j_2 = \frac{3}{2}$

Weak field				Strong field					
Term	Γ_{weak}	M	Mg	M	m_{j_1}	m_{j_2}	$g_1 m_{j_1}$	$g_2 m_{j_2}$	Γ_{strong}
$(\frac{1}{2} \frac{3}{2})_2$	$+3A/4$	$+2$	$+\frac{6}{2}$	$+2$	$+\frac{1}{2}$	$+\frac{3}{2}$	$+1$	$+\frac{6}{3}$	$+3A/4$
		$+1$	$+\frac{3}{2}$	$+1$	$+\frac{1}{2}$	$+\frac{1}{2}$	$+1$	$+\frac{2}{3}$	$+A/4$
		0	0	0	$+\frac{1}{2}$	$-\frac{1}{2}$	$+1$	$-\frac{2}{3}$	$-A/4$
		-1	$-\frac{3}{2}$	-1	$+\frac{1}{2}$	$-\frac{3}{2}$	$+1$	$-\frac{6}{3}$	$-3A/4$
		-2	$-\frac{6}{2}$						
$(\frac{1}{2} \frac{3}{2})_1$	$-5A/4$			$+1$	$-\frac{1}{2}$	$+\frac{3}{2}$	-1	$+\frac{6}{3}$	$-3A/4$
		$+1$	$+\frac{7}{6}$	0	$-\frac{1}{2}$	$+\frac{1}{2}$	-1	$+\frac{2}{3}$	$-A/4$
		0	0	-1	$-\frac{1}{2}$	$-\frac{1}{2}$	-1	$-\frac{2}{3}$	$+A/4$
		-1	$-\frac{7}{6}$	-2	$-\frac{1}{2}$	$-\frac{3}{2}$	-1	$-\frac{6}{3}$	$+3A/4$

strong-field levels for the two terms at the left are calculated by tabulating the various interaction energies as in Table 13.4.

It is to be noted that for each weak-field level M, there is a strong-field level with the same M value. Just as in the case of LS-coupling the conservation of angular momentum requires that *the sum of the projections of the mechanical moments on H does not change with changing field*. As an equation,

$$M = m_{j_1} + m_{j_2}. \tag{13.41}$$

Since there are in general several levels with the same M value, the further restriction that *no two levels with the same M cross each other*

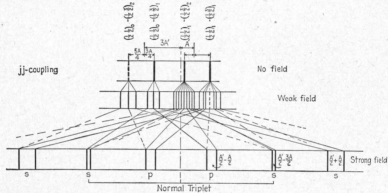

Fig. 13.11.—Paschen-Back effect for one of the jj-coupling patterns arising from the electron transition $sp \rightarrow s \cdot s$.

must be added to the above rule. As an example of the behavior of jj-coupling in a strong field, consider one of the two Paschen-Back patterns arising from the electron transition $sp \rightarrow s \cdot s$. With the set of levels shown at the left in Fig. 13.10 as initial states, and the set at the right as final states, the pattern in Fig. 13.11 is constructed. The selection rules for jj-coupling in a strong field are

$$\begin{aligned} \Delta m_{j_1} &= 0 \\ \Delta m_{j_2} &= \begin{cases} 0 \text{ for } p \text{ components} \\ \pm 1 \text{ for } s \text{ components} \end{cases} \end{aligned} \left.\begin{aligned} \\ \\ \end{aligned}\right\} \begin{aligned} &\text{or with subscripts} \\ &\text{interchanged} \end{aligned} \tag{13.42}$$

These rules are in agreement with the polarization rules that *the polarization of a line is the same in all field strengths*. In the pattern it is seen that lines tending to go from p to s or from s to p components fade out and should not be observed in a strong field. Unlike the Paschen-Back patterns for LS-coupling the lines do not resemble a normal triplet but possess an anomalous pattern. Were it not for the fine structure, the pattern shown in Fig. 13.11 would be the same as the pattern for a principal-series doublet line, $^2S_{\frac{1}{2}} - ^2P_{\frac{3}{2}}$ (see Fig. 10.9).

13.9. Complete Paschen-Back Effect.—In the three previous sections we have seen how, in a strong magnetic field, the coupling between j_1^* and j_2^*, or between L^* and S^*, is broken down and each is quantized separately with the field direction H. In calculating the energies in such cases it was tacitly assumed that the inner couplings between the individual electron spins s_i^* and orbits l_i^* were not broken down. On the classical model it was assumed, for example, that the precession of s_1^* and s_2^* around S^* and the precession of l_1^* and l_2^* around L^* are very much faster than that of S^* or L^* around H.

In a very strong magnetic field the coupling between all of the individual electron vectors may be broken down, regardless of the original coupling scheme LS or jj, so that each part will quantize separately with the field H. Under these conditions we have what is called the *complete Paschen-Back effect*[1] (see Fig. 13.12). The quantum conditions for this state of the atom are:

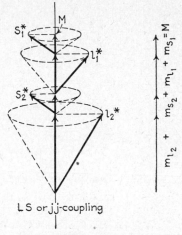

FIG. 13.12.—Classical vector model for either LS- or jj-coupling in a very strong field (complete Paschen-Back effect).

1. The projection of $s_1^* h/2\pi$ on H takes values $m_{s_1} h/2\pi$, where $m_{s_1} = \pm\frac{1}{2}$.

2. The projection of $s_2^* h/2\pi$ on H takes values $m_{s_2} h/2\pi$, where $m_{s_2} = \pm\frac{1}{2}$.

3. The projection of $l_1^* h/2\pi$ on H takes values $m_{l_1} h/2\pi$ where $m_{l_1} = 0$, $\pm 1, \pm 2, \cdots, \pm l$.

4. The projection of $l_2^* h/2\pi$ on H takes values $m_{l_2} h/2\pi$, where $m_{l_2} = 0$, $\pm 1, \pm 2, \cdots, \pm l_2$.

The complete Paschen-Back effect has never been observed for any but one-electron systems because of the enormous fields needed to produce it. For terms close to the series limit, however, it may be possible in the near future to produce the effect with the fields now available.

In a field strong enough to break down the quantization between all of the individual vectors s_1^*, s_2^*, l_1^*, and l_2^*, the chief contribution to the magnetic energy will arise from the independent couplings of these vectors with H. To this energy must be added small correction terms due to the different mutual interactions between the individual vectors. While these latter corrections will be different for LS-coupling than for jj-coupling the chief contributions will be exactly the same.

---

[1] PAULI, W., *Zeits. f. Phys.*, **16**, 155, 1923; **31**, 765, 1925; see also L. Pauling and S. Goudsmit, "Structure of Line Spectra," p. 122.

The Larmor precessions of each spin and orbit around H [see Eq. (10.4)] are given by

$$\omega_{s_1} = H \cdot 2\frac{e}{2mc}, \qquad \omega_{s_2} = H \cdot 2\frac{e}{2mc}, \qquad \omega_{l_1} = H \cdot \frac{e}{2mc}, \qquad \omega_{l_2} = H \cdot \frac{e}{2mc}.$$
(13.43)

Multiplying each of these angular velocities by the corresponding projections of the angular momentum on H gives the energies (see footnote 3 on page 157)

$$\Delta W_{s_1 H} = 2 \cdot H \cdot \frac{e}{2mc} m_{s_1}\frac{h}{2\pi}, \qquad \Delta W_{l_1 H} = H \cdot \frac{e}{2mc} m_{l_1}\frac{h}{2\pi},$$

$$\Delta W_{s_2 H} = 2 \cdot H \cdot \frac{e}{2mc} m_{s_2}\frac{h}{2\pi}, \qquad \Delta W_{l_2 H} = H \cdot \frac{e}{2mc} m_{l_2}\frac{h}{2\pi}. \tag{13.44}$$

The sum of these energies is

$$\Delta W_H = (2m_{s_1} + 2m_{s_2} + m_{l_1} + m_{l_2}) \cdot H \cdot \frac{eh}{4\pi mc}. \tag{13.45}$$

Dividing by hc, the energy in wave numbers becomes

$$-\Delta T_H = (2m_{s_1} + 2m_{s_2} + m_{l_1} + m_{l_2})\frac{He}{4\pi mc^2} \text{ cm}^{-1}. \tag{13.46}$$

To this energy must be added the small interaction energies [see Eqs. (12.5)],

$$\Gamma_1 = a_1 s_1^* s_2^* \overline{\cos (s_1^* s_2^*)}, \qquad \Gamma_3 = a_3 s_1^* l_1^* \overline{\cos (s_1^* l_1^*)},$$
$$\Gamma_2 = a_2 l_1^* l_2^* \overline{\cos (l_1^* l_2^*)}, \qquad \Gamma_4 = a_4 s_2^* l_2^* \overline{\cos (s_2^* l_2^*)}. \tag{13.47}$$

TABLE 13.5.—VERY STRONG FIELD ENERGY LEVELS FOR THE ELECTRON CONFIGURA-
TION *sp*
(Complete Paschen-Back effect)

$M = m_{s_1} + m_{s_2}$ $+ m_{l_1} + m_{l_2}$	m_{s_1}	m_{s_2}	m_{l_1}	m_{l_2}	$2m_{s_1}$	$2m_{s_2}$	$2m_{s_1}+2m_{s_2}$ $+m_{l_1}+m_{l_2}$	Γ_1	Γ_2	Γ_3	Γ_4
2	$\frac{1}{2}$	$\frac{1}{2}$	0	1	1	1	3	$a_1/4$	0	0	$a_4/2$
1	$\frac{1}{2}$	$\frac{1}{2}$	0	0	1	1	2	$a_1/4$	0	0	0
0	$\frac{1}{2}$	$\frac{1}{2}$	0	-1	1	1	1	$a_1/4$	0	0	$-a_4/2$
1	$\frac{1}{2}$	$-\frac{1}{2}$	0	1	1	-1	1	$-a_1/4$	0	0	$-a_4/2$
0	$\frac{1}{2}$	$-\frac{1}{2}$	0	0	1	-1	0	$-a_1/4$	0	0	0
-1	$\frac{1}{2}$	$-\frac{1}{2}$	0	-1	1	-1	-1	$-a_1/4$	0	0	$a_4/2$
1	$-\frac{1}{2}$	$\frac{1}{2}$	0	1	-1	1	1	$-a_1/4$	0	0	$a_4/2$
0	$-\frac{1}{2}$	$\frac{1}{2}$	0	0	-1	1	0	$-a_1/4$	0	0	0
-1	$-\frac{1}{2}$	$\frac{1}{2}$	0	-1	-1	1	-1	$-a_1/4$	0	0	$-a_4/2$
0	$-\frac{1}{2}$	$-\frac{1}{2}$	0	1	-1	-1	-1	$a_1/4$	0	0	$-a_4/2$
-1	$-\frac{1}{2}$	$-\frac{1}{2}$	0	0	-1	-1	-2	$a_1/4$	0	0	0
-2	$-\frac{1}{2}$	$-\frac{1}{2}$	0	-1	-1	-1	-3	$a_1/4$	0	0	$a_4/2$

These average cosines are evaluated just as in Sec. 10.7 [see Eq. (10.33)] to give

$$\Gamma_1 = a_1 m_{s_1} m_{s_2}, \quad \Gamma_2 = a_2 m_{l_1} m_{l_2}, \quad \Gamma_3 = a_3 m_{s_1} m_{l_1}, \quad \Gamma_4 = a_4 m_{s_2} m_{l_2}.$$
$$(13.48)$$

If now T_0 represents the hypothetical center of gravity of all the terms arising from a given electron configuration, the term value of

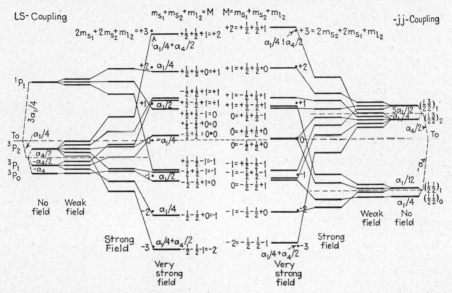

Fig. 13.13.—Very strong field energy levels for an sp electron configuration (complete Paschen Back effect).

each very strong field level will be given by the addition of Eqs. (13.46) and (13.48):

$$T_M = T_0 - (2m_{s_1} + 2m_{s_2} + m_{l_1} + m_{l_2}) \cdot \mathbf{L} - \Gamma_1 - \Gamma_2 - \Gamma_3 - \Gamma_4, \quad (13.49)$$

where $\mathbf{L} = He/4\pi mc^2 \text{ cm}^{-1}$.

As an example of the calculation of levels in a very strong magnetic field, consider the electron configuration sp. The various terms of Eq. (13.49) are tabulated in Table 13.5.

Diagrams of the energy levels for the sp configuration in LS- and jj-coupling are shown in Fig. 13.13, starting with the field-free levels on either side and ending with the very strong levels in the middle. Except for the fine structure due to the Γ factors the very strong field levels are the same for both coupling schemes. However, it is just these differences that, as the field decreases, cause one system to go over to LS-coupling and the other to jj-coupling. It is seen that throughout each diagram each level retains its total M value and further that

no two levels with the same M values cross. It should also be pointed
out that the coefficient a_1, due to the *spin-spin* interaction, is *negative* and

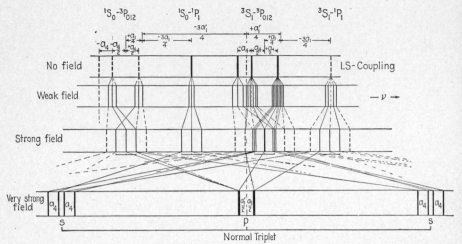

Fig. 13.14.—Complete Paschen-Back effect for the transition $sp \rightarrow s \cdot s$ (*LS*-coupling).

large in *LS*-coupling and negative but small in *jj*-coupling. The reverse
is true for the a_4 coefficient, being positive and small in *LS*-coupling
and positive and large in *jj*-coupling.

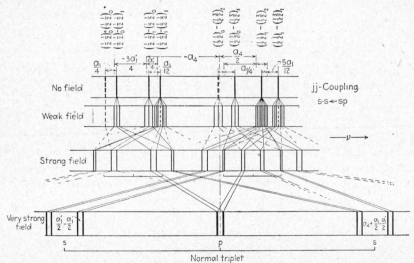

Fig. 13.15.—Complete Paschen-Back effect for the transition $sp \rightarrow s \cdot s$ (*jj*-coupling).

As an example of the spectrum lines, or pattern, to be observed
when the complete Paschen-Back effect sets in for both the initial and
final states of an atom, consider the electron transition $sp \rightarrow s \cdot s$. The

resultant patterns for all allowed transitions in *weak, strong,* and *very strong fields* are shown in Figs. 13.14 and 13.15. The initial levels giving rise to these patterns are the ones shown in Fig. 13.13. The selection rules for very strong fields may be stated as follows:

$$\Delta m_{s_1} = \Delta m_{s_2} = 0$$
$$\Delta m_{l_1} = 0$$
$$\Delta m_{l_2} = \left\{ \begin{array}{l} 0 \text{ for } p \text{ components} \\ \pm 1 \text{ for } s \text{ components} \end{array} \right\} \begin{array}{l} \text{or with subscripts} \\ \text{interchanged} \end{array} \qquad (13.50)$$

Were it not for the fine structure arising from the Γ factors, each very strong field pattern would be a normal triplet. This result is arrived at with all electron configurations. It should be noted that the two strong field patterns for jj-coupling, in Fig. 13.15, closely resemble the anomalous patterns of a principal-series doublet in a weak field.

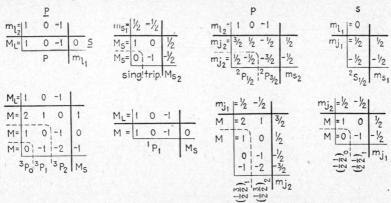

Fig. 13.16.—Magnetic quantum numbers for an sp electron configuration. (LS-coupling left and jj-coupling right.)

13.10. Breit's Scheme for the Derivation of Spectral Terms from Magnetic Quantum Numbers.

—In the early development of complex spectra a scheme for the calculation of spectral terms was put forward by Breit.[1] This scheme is of considerable importance in that it starts with the very strong field quantum numbers of each valence electron, develops successively the strong- and weak-field quantum numbers, and ends up by giving the allowed field-free levels. Consider as an example the electron configuration sp for which the field-free levels are $^3P_{0,1,2}$ and $^1P_1$.

In a very strong field each electron is designated by the four quantum numbers n, l, m_l, and m_s. Since the total quantum number takes no part in the types of terms we need only consider the quantum values $l_1 = 0$, $m_{l_1} = 0$, $m_{s_1} = \pm\frac{1}{2}$, $l_2 = 1$, $m_{l_2} = 0$, ± 1, and $m_{s_2} = \pm\frac{1}{2}$. If the coupling is to be LS, the values of m_{l_2} and m_{l_1} are written down in

[1] Breit, G., *Phys. Rev.*, **28**, 334, 1926; see also Russell, H. N., *Phys. Rev.*, **29**, 782, 1927.

a row and column as in the array in Fig. 13.16. To the left of $m_{l_1} = 0$ and below $m_{l_2} = 1$ the sum $M_L = 1$ is written. This process continued gives the strong-field quantum numbers for a P term. Combining m_{s_1} and m_{s_2} in the same way, the array shown at the top of the figure is constructed. The values $M_S = 0$ and $M_S = 0$ and ± 1 divided by the L-shaped line are just the M_S quantum numbers for singlets and triplets, respectively. Combining these two sets of M_S with the set of M_L, the two arrays in the lower left of the figure are obtained. The quantum sums divided by the dotted lines are just the weak-field quantum numbers for the $^3P_0$, $^3P_1$, $^3P_2$, $^1P_1$ terms. In the case of jj-coupling, shown at the right in the figure, the values of m_s and m_l are first combined for each electron separately to give the strong-field quantum numbers m_j. These in turn are combined to form the array shown at the bottom of the figure. These give the same runs of weak-field quantum numbers and correspond to the same four levels obtained for LS-coupling.

13.11. The Pauli Exclusion Principle.—In 1925 Pauli put forward a new principle which came to play an important rôle in the development of complex spectra (see Sec. 12.4). In its simplest form the principle may be stated as follows: *No two electrons in the same atom can have all of their quantum numbers the same.* This principle is well known as the *Pauli exclusion principle.* In order to assign quantum numbers to each electron we go to very strong magnetic fields where the coupling between the electrons is completely broken down. In such a field the four quantum numbers for any electron are n, l, m_l, and m_s.

Let us now calculate the allowed spectral terms arising from two equivalent electrons. The term *equivalent* refers to any two electrons having the same n and l values. As a first example, consider two equivalent p electrons. First all possible combinations of m_s and m_l for a single p electron are written down in two rows as follows:

$$m_s = \tfrac{1}{2} \quad \tfrac{1}{2} \quad \tfrac{1}{2} \quad -\tfrac{1}{2} \quad -\tfrac{1}{2} \quad -\tfrac{1}{2}$$
$$m_l = 1 \quad 0 \quad -1 \quad 1 \quad 0 \quad -1$$
$$(a) \quad (b) \quad (c) \quad (d) \quad (e) \quad (f)$$

It is seen that there are six possible states, (a), (b), (c), (d), (e), and (f), in which a single p electron may exist in an atom. With two equivalent p electrons Pauli's exclusion principle says that one of these quantum values m_s or m_l must be different. We therefore obtain all possible states for two electrons by writing down all combinations of the above states taken two at a time, with no two alike. They are

ab
$ac \quad bc$
$ad \quad bd \quad cd$
$ae \quad be \; ce \quad de$
$af \quad bf \quad cf \quad df \quad ef$

For each of these 15 combinations of very strong field quantum numbers we add the two values of m_s to obtain the strong-field values of M_S, and the two values of m_l to form M_L. This leads to the following tabulation:

$$M_S = 1 \quad 1 \quad 0 \quad 0 \quad 0 \quad 1 \quad 0 \quad 0 \quad 0 \quad 0 \quad 0 \quad 0 \; -1 \; -1 \; -1$$
$$M_L = 1 \quad 0 \quad 2 \quad 1 \quad 0 \; -1 \quad 1 \quad 0 \; -1 \quad 0 \; -1 \; -2 \quad 1 \quad 0 \; -1$$

The largest value of M_L is two indicating part of a D term. Corresponding values of M_S show that there are strong-field quantum numbers enough to form a ^1D term:

$$\left.\begin{matrix} M_S = 0 & 0 & 0 & 0 & 0 \\ M_L = 2 & 1 & 0 & -1 & -2 \end{matrix}\right\}{}^1D$$

Taking these out we find just enough numbers left to form a ^3P and a ^1S:

$$\left.\begin{matrix} M_S = 1 & 1 & 1 & 0 & 0 & 0 & -1 & -1 & -1 \\ M_L = 1 & 0 & -1 & 1 & 0 & -1 & 1 & 0 & -1 \end{matrix}\right\}{}^3P \qquad \left.\begin{matrix} M_S = 0 \\ M_L = 0 \end{matrix}\right\}{}^1S,$$

Two equivalent p electrons therefore give rise to ^1S, ^3P, and ^1D terms. Referring to Table 12.2 it is seen that two nonequivalent p

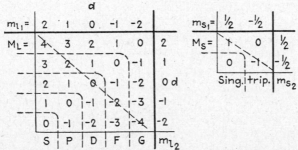

Fig. 13.17.—Magnetic quantum numbers for two similar d electrons (LS-coupling).

electrons give rise to ^1S, ^1P, ^1D, ^3S, ^3P, and ^3D terms. The Pauli exclusion principle thus excludes ^1P, ^3S, and ^3D, when the two electrons have equal n values.

The same terms are readily calculated from Breit's scheme given in the preceding section. Consider, for example, two d electrons in LS-coupling. We first write down all possible combinations of m_{s_1} and m_{s_2} in one array and those of m_{l_1} and m_{l_2} in another (see Fig. 13.17). If the total quantum numbers are different, all possible combinations of the magnetic quantum numbers are allowed. The runs $M_L = 4$ to -4, 3 to -3, 2 to -2, 1 to -1, and 0 correspond to G, F, D, P, and S terms, respectively; and the two sets of $M_S = 1, 0, -1$, and 0 correspond to triplets and singlets. These are just the terms given in Table 12.2 for $d \cdot d$.

If the two d electrons are equivalent, *i.e.*, equal values of n, certain of these terms are forbidden. If we permit the m_s values to be alike (*i.e.*, $M_S = 1$, or -1), the values of $M_L = 4, 2, 0, -2$, and -4, crossed out by the diagonal line, are forbidden. Since the values in the lower left of the array are identical with, and are a mirror image of, those in the upper right half, one of these groups must also be eliminated from the calculations.[1] Leaving out the lower left half of the array the remaining values are seen to form two runs $M_L = 3$ to -3, and 1 to -1:

$$
\begin{array}{llrrrrrrr}
M_S = & 1, & M_L = 3 & 2 & 1 & 0 & -1 & -2 & -3 \\
M_S = & -1, & M_L = 3 & 2 & 1 & 0 & -1 & -2 & -3 \\
M_S = & 1, & M_L = & & 1 & 0 & -1 \\
M_S = & -1, & M_L = & & 1 & 0 & -1
\end{array}
$$

If, on the other hand, we permit the M_L values to be alike, the values of $M_S = 1$, or -1, are forbidden. Since the two $M_S = 0$ values are identical, one of these must also be excluded. The remaining combinations are tabulated as follows:

$$
\begin{array}{llrrrrrrrrr}
M_S = 0, & M_L = 4 & 3 & 2 & 1 & 0 & -1 & -2 & -3 & -4 \\
M_S = 0, & M_L = & 3 & 2 & 1 & 0 & -1 & -2 & -3 \\
M_S = 0, & M_L = & & 2 & 1 & 0 & -1 & -2 \\
M_S = 0, & M_L = & & & 1 & 0 & -1 \\
M_S = 0, & M_L = & & & & 0
\end{array}
$$

The second and fourth rows go with the preceding tabulation to complete the quantum numbers for ^3F and ^3P terms. The remaining rows correspond to ^1G, ^1D, and ^1S terms.

Consider, as a third example, the calculation of terms arising from two equivalent p electrons in jj-coupling. The first step is to write down all possible combinations of m_s and m_l for each electron separately. This forms the two arrays at the top of Fig. 13.18. Each of the two runs of m_{j_1} combined with each of the two runs of m_{j_2} will give all possible combinations. Of the four resultant arrays there will be two like the lower right one in the figure. Since the electrons are equivalent, one of these must be entirely excluded. In the lower left-hand array, the diagonal and either the upper right or lower left half of the array must be excluded. The same is true for the lower center array. The remaining combinations are just sufficient to form the five terms $(\frac{3}{2}\,\frac{3}{2})_0$, $(\frac{3}{2}\,\frac{3}{2})_2$, $(\frac{1}{2}\,\frac{1}{2})_0$, $(\frac{1}{2}\,\frac{3}{2})_1$, and $(\frac{1}{2}\,\frac{3}{2})_2$. These correspond to the five terms $^1S_0$, $^1D_2$, $^3P_0$, $^3P_1$, and $^3P_2$ in LS-coupling, derived above.

---

[1] Each value of M_L in the lower left half of the array in Fig. 13.17 is identical with a corresponding value in the upper right half. It is observed that each pair of values arises from the same m_l values. Although the m_l subscripts are just interchanged in each of the two combinations of a pair, the equivalence of the two electrons makes the two states identical in all respects.

13.12. Pauli's g Permanence Rule.—In 1923 Pauli[1] proposed a new rule for the g factors of any given multiple term in weak and strong fields. This rule states that *the sum of the g factors for a given M is the same in all field strengths.* In a weak field the g factor of any state is given by the ratio between the magnetic moment of the atom in Bohr

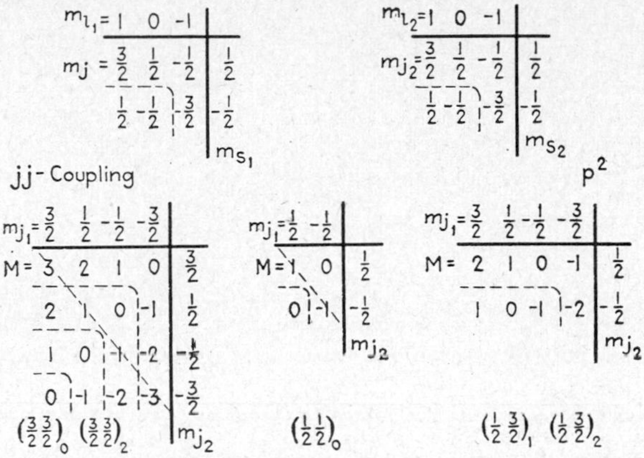

FIG. 13.18.—Magnetic quantum numbers for two similar p electrons (jj-coupling).

magnetons, $eh/4\pi mc$, and the mechanical moment in units $h/2\pi$ [see Eqs. (10.13) and (13.6)]:

$$g_{\text{weak}} = \frac{\mathbf{\mu}_J}{\mathbf{p}_J}. \tag{13.51}$$

Here

$$\mathbf{\mu}_J = \frac{\mu_J}{eh/4\pi mc} \quad \text{and} \quad \mathbf{p}_J = \frac{p_J}{h/2\pi}, \tag{13.52}$$

where, as usual, μ_J is in ergs per gauss and p_J is in erg seconds. In these units,

$$g_{\text{weak}} = \frac{\mu_J}{p_J} \cdot \frac{h/2\pi}{eh/4\pi mc} = \frac{\mu_J}{p_J} \cdot \frac{2mc}{e} = \frac{g_J M_J}{M_J}. \tag{13.53}$$

In weak or strong field the g factor is given by the ratio of the total projection of the magnetic moments on the field direction to the total projection of the mechanical moments.[2]

For LS-coupling,

$$g_{\text{strong}} = \frac{M_L + 2M_S}{M_L + M_S}. \tag{13.54}$$

[1] PAULI, W., *Zeits. f. Phys.*, **16**, 155, 1923.

[2] The weak field g-factor of Eq. (13.53) is also expressed in terms of projections. With μ_J and p_J in line with each other, see Fig. 10.6, their ratio and the ratio of their projections on any line will be the same.

For jj-coupling,

$$g_{\text{strong}} = \frac{g_1 m_{j_1} + g_2 m_{j_2}}{m_{j_1} + m_{j_2}}. \tag{13.55}$$

For a given multiple term it often happens that there are several magnetic levels with the same M value. Pauli's g permanence rule states that for given L, S, and M, or for given j_1, j_2, and M the sum of the weak-field g factors is equal to the sum of the strong-field g factors:

$$\Sigma g_{\text{weak}} = \Sigma g_{\text{strong}}. \tag{13.56}$$

Values of weak- and strong-field g factors are given in Table 13.6 for a ^3P term.

TABLE 13.6.—Pauli's g Permanence Rule for LS-coupling

Term	$M = 2$	$M = 1$	$M = 0$	$M = -1$	$M = -2$	
$^3P_2$	$\frac{3}{2}$	$\frac{3}{2}$	$\frac{3}{2}$	$\frac{3}{2}$	$\frac{3}{2}$	
$^3P_1$		$\frac{3}{2}$	$\frac{3}{2}$	$\frac{3}{2}$		Weak field
$^3P_0$			$\frac{0}{0}$			
$^3P_2$	$\frac{3}{2}$	2		1	$\frac{3}{2}$	
$^3P_1$		1		2		Strong field
$^3P_0$						
Σg	$\frac{3}{2}$	3	$\frac{0}{0}$	3	$\frac{3}{2}$	

Similarly for the two upper states arising from the sp configuration in jj-coupling we obtain the values given in Table 13.7.

TABLE 13.7.—Pauli's g Permanence Rule for jj-coupling

Term	$M = 2$	$M = 1$	$M = 0$	$M = -1$	$M = -2$	
$(\frac{1}{2}\frac{3}{2})_1$		$\frac{7}{6}$	$\frac{7}{6}$	$\frac{7}{6}$		
$(\frac{1}{2}\frac{3}{2})_2$	$\frac{3}{2}$	$\frac{3}{2}$	$\frac{3}{2}$	$\frac{3}{2}$	$\frac{3}{2}$	Weak field
$(\frac{1}{2}\frac{3}{2})_1$		$\frac{5}{3}$		1		
$(\frac{1}{2}\frac{3}{2})_2$	$\frac{3}{2}$	1		$\frac{5}{3}$	$\frac{3}{2}$	Strong field
Σg	$\frac{3}{2}$	$\frac{8}{3}$	$(\frac{8}{3})$	$\frac{8}{3}$	$\frac{3}{2}$	

One of the most important features of the g permanence rule is that the weak-field g factors can be determined without the use of the Landé g formula and the quantum-mechanical or classical model. For $^3P_2$, $M = 2$, in the above table $g_{\text{strong}} = \frac{3}{2}$. The weak-field g factor will therefore be $\frac{3}{2}$ for all weak-field $^3P_2$ levels. This leaves for $^3P_1$, $M = 1$ the value $g = 3 - \frac{3}{2} = \frac{3}{2}$. For $^3P_0$, $M = 0$, g is indeterminate in all fields.

Darwin has shown that the g permanence rule holds for all intermediate field strengths.[1]

13.13. Pauli's g Sum Rule for All Field Strengths.—In a very strong magnetic field the individual electron couplings are completely broken down and each spin and orbit becomes quantized independently with the field. Pauli showed that even under these extreme conditions *the sum of the g factors for a given M, of a given electron configuration, is constant.*[2] Starting with LS- or jj-coupling the g factor for any term in a very strong magnetic field is given by the sum of the projections on H of the magnetic moments in Bohr magnetons divided by the sum of the projections of the mechanical moments in units $h/2\pi$.

$$g_{\text{very strong}} = \left(\frac{2m_{s_1} + 2m_{s_2} + m_{l_1} + m_{l_2}}{m_{s_1} + m_{s_2} + m_{l_1} + m_{l_2}}\right). \tag{13.57}$$

Consider, for example, the terms arising from the configuration sp in LS-coupling. The g factors for weak, strong, and very strong fields are given in Table 13.8.

TABLE 13.8.—PAULI'S g SUM RULE FOR THE ELECTRON CONFIGURATION sp IN LS-COUPLING

Term	$M = 2$	$M = 1$	$M = 0$	$M = -1$	$M = -2$	
$^1P_1$		1	1	1		
$^3P_2$	$\frac{3}{2}$	$\frac{3}{2}$	$\frac{3}{2}$	$\frac{3}{2}$	$\frac{3}{2}$	Weak field
$^3P_1$		$\frac{3}{2}$	$\frac{3}{2}$	$\frac{3}{2}$		
$^3P_0$			$\frac{0}{0}$			
$^1P_1$		1		1		
$^3P_2$	$\frac{3}{2}$	2		1	$\frac{3}{2}$	Strong field
$^3P_1$		1		2		
$^3P_0$						
$^1P_1$		2		1		
$^3P_2$	$\frac{3}{2}$	1		1	$\frac{3}{2}$	Very strong field
$^3P_1$		1		2		
$^3P_0$						
$\Sigma g =$	$\frac{3}{2}$	4	$\frac{0}{0}$	4	$\frac{3}{2}$	

Consider again the terms arising from the configuration sp in jj-coupling. The g factors for weak, strong, and very strong fields are given in Table 13.9.

In general the weak-field g factors cannot be calculated from the very strong field g factors. The reason for this is that the coupling scheme is not known. When the coupling scheme is given, the strong-

---

[1] DARWIN, K., *Proc. Roy. Soc.*, **A, 118**, 264, 1928.

[2] For a discussion of the g sum rule in weak magnetic fields, see Sec. 13.5.

field g factors can be determined from the g permanence rule and hence the weak-field g factors can be evaluated (see the previous section).

13.14. Landé's Γ Permanence Rule.—Analogous to the g permanence rule we have what is known as the Γ *permanence rule* discovered by Landé. The rule may be stated as follows: *For a given multiple term, i.e., given S and L, or given j_1 and j_2, the sum of all the Γ factors for terms with the same magnetic quantum number M is a constant independent of the field strength.*

TABLE 13.9.—PAULI'S g SUM RULE FOR THE ELECTRON CONFIGURATION sp IN jj-COUPLING

Term	$M = 2$	$M = 1$	$M = 0$	$M = -1$	$M = -2$	
$(\frac{1}{2}\frac{3}{2})_1$		$\frac{7}{6}$	$\frac{7}{6}$	$\frac{7}{6}$		
$(\frac{1}{2}\frac{3}{2})_2$	$\frac{3}{2}$	$\frac{3}{2}$	$\frac{3}{2}$	$\frac{3}{2}$	$\frac{3}{2}$	Weak field
$(\frac{1}{2}\frac{1}{2})_1$		$\frac{4}{3}$	$\frac{4}{3}$	$\frac{4}{3}$		
$(\frac{1}{2}\frac{1}{2})_0$			$\frac{0}{0}$			
$(\frac{1}{2}\frac{3}{2})_1$		$\frac{5}{3}$		1		
$(\frac{1}{2}\frac{3}{2})_2$	$\frac{3}{2}$	1		$\frac{5}{3}$	$\frac{3}{2}$	Strong field
$(\frac{1}{2}\frac{1}{2})_1$		$\frac{4}{3}$		$\frac{4}{3}$		
$(\frac{1}{2}\frac{1}{2})_0$						
$(\frac{1}{2}\frac{3}{2})_1$		2		1		
$(\frac{1}{2}\frac{3}{2})_2$	$\frac{3}{2}$	1		1	$\frac{3}{2}$	Very strong field
$(\frac{1}{2}\frac{1}{2})_1$		1		2		
$(\frac{1}{2}\frac{1}{2})_0$						
$\Sigma g =$	$\frac{3}{2}$	4	$\frac{0}{0}$	4	$\frac{3}{2}$	

For LS-coupling in field-free space, or in a weak magnetic field, the Γ factor of a term is given by Eq. (12.13):

$$\Gamma_{\text{weak}} = \Gamma_3 + \Gamma_4 = AL^*S^* \cos (L^*S^*) = \tfrac{1}{2}A(J^{*2} - L^{*2} - S^{*2}), \quad (13.58)$$

where A is a coupling constant. In other words, a Γ factor, as we have already seen in Sec. 12.6 and 12.7, is just the interaction energy of any two quantum vectors. This particular Eq. (13.58) gives the Landé interval rule for the fine structure (see Sec. 12.8). Now, in a strong field, the Paschen-Back effect sets in, and L^* and S^* become independently quantized with the field H. In this case the average value of the cosine in the above equation had to be evaluated to obtain the interaction energy and the strong-field Γ factors. This average interaction energy [see Sec. 13.6, Eq. (13.28), and Sec. 10.7, Eq. (10.33)] is given by

$$\Gamma_{\text{strong}} = \Gamma_3 + \Gamma_4 = A \cdot L^*S^* \overline{\cos (L^*S^*)} = A \cdot M_L M_S. \quad (13.59)$$

Consider now the Γ permanence rule applied to a ^3P term. Since $S = 1$, $L = 1$, and $J = 0$, 1, and 2, the following Γ factors are determined.

In going from weak fields to strong fields the Γ factors always change, if at all, so that $\Sigma\Gamma$ = constant for each M. It is to be noted that the weak-field Γ's can be determined from the strong-field Γ's. The Landé interval rule is thus obtained without the use of the quantum-mechanical or classical model of the atom [Eq. (13.58)].

TABLE 13.10.—Γ PERMANENCE RULE FOR A ^3P TERM (LS-COUPLING)

Term	$M = 2$	$M = 1$	$M = 0$	$M = -1$	$M = -2$	
$^3P_2$	A	A	A	A	A	Weak field
$^3P_1$		$-A$	$-A$	$-A$		Γ factors
$^3P_0$			$-2A$			
$^3P_2$	A	0	$-A$	0	A	Strong field
$^3P_1$		0	0	0		Γ factors
$^3P_0$			$-A$			
$\Sigma\Gamma =$	A	0	$-2A$	0	A	

For jj-coupling in field-free space or in a weak magnetic field the Γ factor of a term is given by Eq. (12.25):

$$\Gamma_{\text{weak}} = \Gamma_1 + \Gamma_2 = Aj_1^*j_2^* \cos\,(j_1^*j_2^*) = \tfrac{1}{2}A\,(J^{*2} - j_1^{*2} - j_2^{*2}). \quad (13.60)$$

In a strong field, the Paschen-Back effect sets in and j_1^* and j_2^* become independently quantized with the field H. Here the average value of the above given cosine term must be evaluated to obtain the interaction energies and the strong-field Γ factors. This average interaction energy, by analogy with LS-coupling, is given by

$$\Gamma_{\text{strong}} = A \cdot j_1^*j_2^* \cos\,(j_1^*j_2^*) = A \cdot M_{j_1}M_{j_2}. \quad (13.61)$$

Consider, as an example, the two upper terms of the electron configuration sp in jj-coupling. Since $j_1 = \tfrac{1}{2}$, $j_2 = \tfrac{3}{2}$, and $J = 1$, and 2, the following weak- and strong-field Γ factors are obtained:

TABLE 13.11.—Γ PERMANENCE RULE FOR THE TWO TERMS $(\tfrac{1}{2}\,\tfrac{3}{2})_1$ AND $(\tfrac{1}{2}\,\tfrac{3}{2})_2$, ARISING FROM THE CONFIGURATION sp (jj-COUPLING)

Term	$M = 2$	$M = 1$	$M = 0$	$M = -1$	$M = -2$	
$(\tfrac{1}{2}\,\tfrac{3}{2})_1$		$-5A/4$	$-5A/4$	$-5A/4$		Weak field
$(\tfrac{1}{2}\,\tfrac{3}{2})_2$	$3A/4$	$3A/4$	$3A/4$	$3A/4$	$3A/4$	Γ factors
$(\tfrac{1}{2}\,\tfrac{3}{2})_1$		$A/4$	$-A/4$	$-3A/4$		Strong field
$(\tfrac{1}{2}\,\tfrac{3}{2})_2$	$3A/4$	$-3A/4$	$-A/4$	$A/4$	$3A/4$	Γ factors
$\Sigma\Gamma =$	$3A/4$	$-A/2$	$-A/2$	$-A/2$	$3A/4$	

13.15. Goudsmit's Γ Sum Rule.—Analogous with the g sum rule for magnetic levels in weak and strong fields is the Γ sum rule of Goudsmit.[1] This rule may be stated as follows: *For a given electron configuration the sum of the Γ values corresponding to a given value of M is independent of the field strength H.* In LS- or jj-coupling there are four interactions to be taken into account: Γ_1, Γ_2, Γ_3, and Γ_4 (see Sec. 12.7). In a very strong magnetic field, where each spin s_i^* and each orbit l_i^* are independently quantized with the field, these interaction energies are given by Eq. (13.48).

Table 13.12.—Γ Sum Rule for sp Electron Configuration (LS-coupling)

Term	$M = 2$	$M = 1$	$M = 0$	$M = -1$	$M = -2$	
$^1P_1$		0	0	0		
$^3P_2$	$a/2$	$a/2$	$a/2$	$a/2$	$a/2$	Weak field
$^3P_1$		$-a/2$	$-a/2$	$-a/2$		Γ factors
$^3P_0$			$-a$			
$^1P_1$		0	0	0		
$^3P_2$	$a/2$	0	$-a/2$	0	$a/2$	Strong field
$^3P_1$		0	0	0		Γ factors
$^3P_0$			$-a/2$			
$^1P_1$		0	$-a/2$	$a/2$		
$^3P_2$	$a/2$	$a/2$	0	$-a/2$	$a/2$	Very strong field
$^3P_1$		$-a/2$	0	0		Γ factors
$^3P_0$			$-a/2$			
$\Sigma\Gamma_4$	$a/2$	0	$-a$	0	$a/2$	

In LS-coupling Γ_1 gives the singlet-triplet intervals and is due principally to Heisenberg's resonance phenomena, Γ_2 gives the separations between multiple levels, and Γ_3 and Γ_4 give the Landé interval rule for the fine-structure separations (see Fig. 12.6). Goudsmit has applied the Γ sum rule to the Γ_3 and Γ_4 interactions and has shown that they are in general agreement with observation. Consider for example the sp configuration in weak, strong, and very strong fields. The Γ factors of the allowed terms in LS-coupling are computed from Eqs. (12.9), (13.28), and (13.48), respectively, and are given in Table 13.12.

In this particular example, where $l_1 = 0$, $\Gamma_3 = 0$. In configurations where both l's are not zero, the Γ sum rule will apply to both Γ's separately or collectively.

A similar table formed for the same configuration in jj-coupling will lead to the same Γ sums shown here for LS-coupling. It should

[1] Goudsmit, S., *Phys. Rev.*, **31**, 946, 1928; see also Pauling, L., and S. Goudsmit, "Structure of Line Spectra."

be pointed out that the Γ sum rule may also be applied and shown to hold for Γ_1 and Γ_2.

13.16. The Γ Permanence and Γ Sum Rules Applied to Two Equivalent Electrons.—Consider the permanence and sum rules as they apply to the case of two equivalent d electrons, *i.e.*, to two d electrons having the same total quantum number n. In this case the Pauli exclusion principle is in operation and the allowed terms (see Sec. 13.11) are ^1S, ^3P, ^1D, ^3F, and ^1G. In a very strong field there are 10 possible states for each d electron:

$$m_s = \tfrac{1}{2} \quad \tfrac{1}{2} \quad \tfrac{1}{2} \quad \tfrac{1}{2} \quad \tfrac{1}{2} \qquad -\tfrac{1}{2} \; -\tfrac{1}{2} \; -\tfrac{1}{2} \; -\tfrac{1}{2} \; -\tfrac{1}{2}$$
$$m_l = 2 \quad 1 \quad 0 \; -1 \; -2 \qquad 2 \quad 1 \quad 0 \; -1 \; -2 \tag{13.62}$$

Following the first scheme developed in Sec. 13.11 for the calculation of terms arising from two equivalent electrons we combine these columns two at a time, taking no two alike. The resultant combinations should be tabulated by the reader as follows: (1) Make four columns of all possible combinations of, and giving each value of, m_{s_1}, m_{s_2}, m_{l_1}, and m_{l_2}. (2) Using the formulas for Γ_3 and Γ_4, Eq. (12.9), multiply each m_s by its own m_l times a to form the fifth and sixth columns under Γ_3 and Γ_4. (3) Since the a coefficients are identical in the two electrons, add each Γ_3 and Γ_4 to form the seventh column $\Gamma_{\text{very strong}}$. (4) Add the first four columns to form the last and eighth column of total magnetic quantum numbers $M = m_{s_1} + m_{s_2} + m_{l_1} + m_{l_2}$. We now collect all values of $\Gamma_{\text{very strong}}$ and tabulate them under corresponding values of M as shown at the top of Table 13.13.

The strong-field Γ sums may now be used to calculate the weak-field Γ factors, provided the coupling of the two electrons is specified. Suppose first that the coupling is LS. In LS-coupling the Γ factors for singlet terms are always zero. We therefore write zero in all columns for the ^1S, ^1D, and ^1G terms, as shown. Since $^3F_4$ is the only remaining term with $M = 4$, and the Γ sum for $M = 4$ is $3a/2$, we write $\Gamma = 3a/2$ for all $^3F_4$, M's. This leaves $-a/2$ for $^3F_3$, $M = 3$, which is next written in all $^3F_3$, M's. With $-3a/2$ for $^3F_4$, the Γ permanence rule, which also gives the Landé interval rule, gives $\Gamma = -a/2$ and $-2a$ for $^3F_3$ and $^3F_2$, respectively. This in turn leaves only $a/2$ for $^3P_2$, then $-a/2$ for $^3P_1$ and $-a$ for $^3P_0$.

If the coupling of the two equivalent d electrons is jj-coupling, the individual j's and the field-free terms are first determined by the scheme given in Sec. 13.11. The resultant values are given in the lower left-hand column of Table 13.13. For each d electron, separately, $j_i = \tfrac{5}{2}$ and $\tfrac{3}{2}$, for which the Γ factors are a and $-3a/2$, respectively. The Γ factors for both electrons, taken together, will be just the sum of the two individual Γ's. These inserted in the lower third of Table 13.13 agree with Goudsmit's Γ sum rule.

Table 13.13.—Γ Sum Rule for Two Equivalent d Electrons in Weak and in Very Strong Magnetic Fields

Term	$M=4$	$M=3$	$M=2$	$M=1$	$M=0$	$M=-1$	$M=-2$	$M=-3$	$M=-4$	
	$3a/2$	a	$-3a/2$	$3a/2$	$2a$	$3a/2$	$-3a/2$	a	$3a/2$	
	0	$a/2$	a	$-3a/2$	a	$-3a/2$	a	$a/2$	0	
		$-a/2$	0	$-a$	0	$-a$	0	$-a/2$		Very strong field Γ factors
			$-a$	$a/2$	$-a$	$a/2$	$-a$			
			$a/2$	$-a/2$	$-2a$	$-a/2$	$a/2$			
			$a/2$	0	$-a/2$	0	$a/2$			
			0	0	$-a/2$	0				
					$-a/2$					
					$-a/2$					
ΣΓ	$3a/2$	a	$-a/2$	$-a$	$-2a$	$-a$	$-a/2$	a	$3a/2$	
$^1G_4$	0	0	0	0	0	0	0	0	0	
$^3F_4$	$3a/2$	$3a/2$	$3a/2$	$3a/2$	$3a/2$	$3a/2$	$3a/2$	$3a/2$	$3a/2$	
$^3F_3$		$-a/2$	$-a/2$	$-a/2$	$-a/2$	$-a/2$	$-a/2$	$-a/2$		
$^3F_2$			$-2a$	$-2a$	$-2a$	$-2a$	$-2a$			Weak field Γ factors LS-coupling
$^1D_2$			0	0	0	0	0			
$^3P_2$			$a/2$	$a/2$	$a/2$	$a/2$	$a/2$			
$^3P_1$				$-a/2$	$-a/2$	$-a/2$				
$^3P_0$					$-a$					
$^1S_0$					0					
$(\frac{3}{2}\,\frac{5}{2})_4$	$-a/2$	$-a/2$	$-a/2$	$-a/2$	$-a/2$	$-a/2$	$-a/2$	$-a/2$	$-a/2$	
$(\frac{3}{2}\,\frac{5}{2})_3$		$-a/2$	$-a/2$	$-a/2$	$-a/2$	$-a/2$	$-a/2$	$-a/2$		
$(\frac{3}{2}\,\frac{5}{2})_2$			$-a/2$	$-a/2$	$-a/2$	$-a/2$	$-a/2$			
$(\frac{3}{2}\,\frac{5}{2})_1$				$-a/2$	$-a/2$	$-a/2$				
$(\frac{5}{2}\,\frac{5}{2})_4$	$2a$	$2a$	$2a$	$2a$	$2a$	$2a$	$2a$	$2a$	$2a$	Weak field Γ factors jj-coupling
$(\frac{5}{2}\,\frac{5}{2})_2$			$2a$	$2a$	$2a$	$2a$	$2a$			
$(\frac{5}{2}\,\frac{5}{2})_0$					$2a$					
$(\frac{3}{2}\,\frac{3}{2})_2$			$-3a$	$-3a$	$-3a$	$-3a$	$-3a$			
$(\frac{3}{2}\,\frac{3}{2})_0$					$-3a$					

Table 13.14.—Triplet Separations for the Electron Configuration $3d^2$, Showing Agreement with the Landé Interval Rule and the Goudsmit Γ Sum Rule

Element	$^3F_4 - {}^3F_3 - {}^3F_2$		Interval ratio	$^3P_2 - {}^3P_1 - {}^3P_0$		Interval ratio	a cm^{-1}
Sc II	*104*	*81*	**4 : 3.1**	53	27	**2 : 1.0**	*52, 54, 53, 54*
Ti III	*238*	*184*	**4 : 3.1**	118	67	**2 : 1.1**	*119, 123, 118, 134*
V IV	*412*	*318*	**4 : 3.1**	215	117	**2 : 1.1**	*206, 212, 215, 234*
Cr V	*637*	*500*	**4 : 3.1**	368	208	**2 : 1.1**	*319, 333, 368, 416*

Suitable comparisons of the calculated Γ factors with observed spectral terms are to be found in Sc II, Ti III, V, IV, and Cr V. The observed intervals and calculated a's are given in Table 13.14.

That the coupling is Russell-Saunders is shown by the interval ratios given in the third and fifth columns of Table 13.14. That the Γ sum rule holds is shown by the a coefficients in the last column. Perfect agreement would find each of the a coefficients the same for each of the four intervals. The same a coefficients calculated from the configuration $3d4s$ in the same elements are 49, 144, 240, and 365 cm^{-1}, respectively, in good agreement with those tabulated.

Problems

1. Calculate the relative separations and intensities for the Zeeman pattern arising from the transition $^3F_4 - ^3G_4$.

2. Calculate the Zeeman patterns for the transition $^3P_1 - ^3D_2$ ($sp-sd$) in LS- and in jj-coupling.

3. Show that Pauli's g sum rule holds for the terms arising from a $p \cdot p$ configuration in LS- and in jj-coupling.

4. Find the relative intensities of the lines comprising the Paschen-Back pattern at the bottom of Fig. 13.9. See Fig. 13.8 for the levels, and use the sum rules.

5. Compute the terms arising from two similar f electrons.

6. Show that the Γ sum rule holds in weak, strong, and very strong fields for a pd electron configuration (a) in LS-coupling and (b) in jj-coupling.

CHAPTER XIV

COMPLEX SPECTRA

Prior to 1922 only singlet, doublet, and triplet series of spectrum lines were recognized by experimental and theoretical physicists. It was well known that these series had been found only in the groups of elements at both sides or edges of the periodic table, and that the spectra of the elements in the center of the table were very complex. The titanium spectrum, or the iron spectrum, for example, was known to contain hundreds of lines distributed apparently at random throughout the visible, the near ultra-violet, and the near infra-red spectrum.

As early as 1901, however, a fairly complete analysis of the complex spectrum of rhodium had been made by Snyder.[1] In this spectrum some 470 lines were grouped together in an array of equal frequency differences tying together what is now known as the main energy level structure of rhodium. In addition Snyder had been able to link together several hundred lines in ruthenium, iridium, nickel, platinum, and osmium. The significance of Snyder's work was not realized until some 25 years later.

In 1922 the complex spectrum of manganese was analyzed by Catalan,[2] and a part of the chromium spectrum by Gieseler.[3] The manganese spectrum was shown to contain a number of triplet series, some members of which formed groups of lines more complex than had ever been assigned to triplets. In the hands of Sommerfeld these complex groups of lines were shown to arise from multiple energy levels and were not to be associated with triplets. This marked the beginning of complex-spectrum analysis.

The chief characteristics of complex spectra may be briefly described in terms of the energy levels. In the place of series of singlet, doublet, and triplet levels, there are, in general, multiple levels composed of four, five, six, seven, or eight regularly spaced levels. Such multiple levels are frequently called *quartet, quintet, sextet, septet,* and *octet levels.* It is found experimentally that the multiplicities of the levels belonging to a given spectrum will either be all *even* or all *odd.* In the cobalt arc spectrum, for example, the levels are doublets, quartets, and sextets, whereas in the arc spectrum of iron they are triplets, quintets, and septets.

---

[1] SNYDER, C. P., *Astrophys. Jour.*, **14**, 179, 1901.
[2] CATALAN, M. A., *Phil. Trans. Roy. Soc.*, **A, 223**, 127, 1922.
[3] GIESELER, H., *Ann. d. Phys.*, **69**, 147, 1922.

Before going further it should be pointed out that just as S terms are always single, P terms never reveal more than three fine-structure levels, D terms never more than five, F terms never more than seven, etc. This anomaly, which is often confusing to the beginner, really simplifies complex-spectrum analysis. This will become apparent in the following treatment of complex spectra and the vector model. We shall find, for example, that a ^4P, a ^5P, a ^6P, etc., term will each have only three fine-structure levels. That they really belong to quartet, quintet, sextet, etc., systems is shown when the atom is placed in a weak magnetic field and the Zeeman effect is observed. It is little wonder therefore that the principal series discovered by Catalan in manganese were first called triplets in place of sextets and octets as they are now shown to be.

14.1. The Displacement Law.—In 1919 Kossel and Sommerfeld[1] promulgated the displacement law for the spectra of the neutral and singly ionized atoms. This law states that *the spectrum and energy levels of any neutral atom of atomic number Z closely resemble the spectrum and energy levels of the ionized atom Z + 1 succeeding it in the periodic table.* In the preceding chapters, for example, we have seen how the doublet series of the alkali metals Li, Na, K, Rb, and Cs resemble the doublet series of the ionized alkaline earths Be, Mg, Ca, Sr, and Ba (see Figs. 5.2 and 6.5). This law will, in the following sections, be seen to hold in complex spectra.

14.2. Alternation Law of Multiplicities.—Along with the displacement law just discussed another important law has developed known as the *alternation law of multiplicities.* In short this law may be stated as follows: *Spectral terms arising from successive elements in the periodic table alternate between even and odd multiplicities* We shall give, for example, the alternation of multiplicities as they are found in the elements of the first long period (Table 14.1).

TABLE 14.1.—ALTERNATION LAW OF MULTIPLICITIES FOR THE ELEMENTS IN THE FIRST LONG PERIOD

K I	Ca I	Sc I	Ti I	V I	Cr I	Mn I	Fe I	Co I	Ni I	Cu I	Zn I	Ga I	Ge I
				Sing.		(Sing.)		(Sing.)		Sing.		Sing.	Sing.
Doub.		Doub.		Doub.		(Doub.)		Doub.		Doub.		Doub.	
	Trip.		Trip.		Trip.		Trip.		Trip.		Trip.		Trip.
		Quar.		Quar.		Quar.		Quar.		Quar.			
			Quin.		Quin.		Quin.		Quin.				
				Sex.		Sex.		Sex.					
					Sept.		Sept.						
						Oct.							

All but singlets in Cr and Fe, and doublets in Mn, have been observed. Photographs of multiplets illustrating term multiplicities for these elements are given in Fig. 14.1. The multiplicity and term designation

---

[1] KOSSEL, W., and A. SOMMERFELD, *Verh. d. Deutsch. Phys. Ges.*, **21**, 240, 1919.

of each multiplet are given above each photograph. Wave-lengths of the strongest lines in each multiplet, bracketed by the heavy lines,

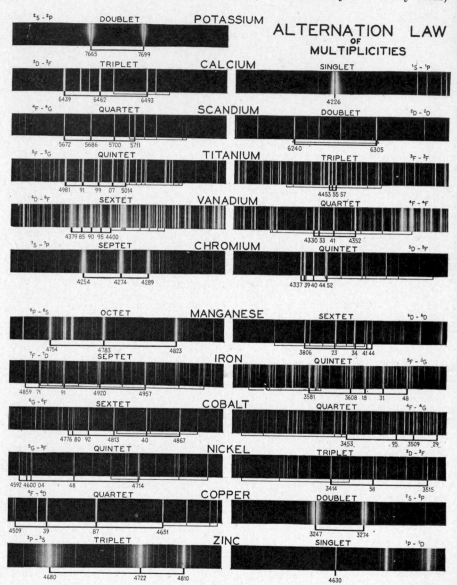

Fig. 14.1.—Illustrating the alternation law of multiplicities for the elements in the first long period. Photographs taken by the author with a 15-ft. Rowland grating and mounting.

are given below each picture. The centers of the potassium-doublet, the calcium-singlet, and the copper-doublet lines show *self-reversal* due to absorption. It may be noted that a triplet multiplet may be made up of as many as seven lines whereas an octet multiplet may contain as few as three. The faint lines symmetrically located on each side of each of the zinc triplet lines are *grating ghosts*. Since both the alternation and displacement laws are valid, a combination of the two shows that a table similar to the one above may be formed from the spectra of the same atoms singly ionized.

TABLE 14.2.—ALTERNATION LAW OF MULTIPLICITIES FOR THE SINGLY IONIZED
ELEMENTS IN THE FIRST LONG PERIOD

Ca II	Sc II	Ti II	V II	Cr II	Mn II	Fe II	Co II	Ni II	Cu II	Zn II	Ga II	Ge II	As II
	Sing.		(Sing.)		(Sing.)		(Sing.)		Sing.		Sing.		Sing.
Doub.		Doub.		Doub.		(Doub.)		Doub.		Doub.		Doub.	
	Trip.		Trip.		(Trip.)		Trip.		Trip.		Trip.		Trip.
		Quar.		Quar.		Quar.		Quar.		Quar.			
			Quin.		Quin.		Quin.		(Quin.)				
				Sex.		Sex.		(Sex.)					
					Sept.		(Sept.)						
						(Oct.)							

It is to be noted that the tables are approximately the same as far as observed multiplicities are concerned, and that the elements have been shifted one place to the left.

A table for doubly ionized atoms may be formed in exactly the same way by shifting the elements one more column to the left. Observations show that this displacement of multiplicities is valid as far as the eighth and ninth stages of ionization, and there is no reason to doubt that it will be valid until the atoms are completely stripped of all extranuclear electrons.

14.3. The Vector Model for Three or More Valence Electrons.—It is an easy step from the vector model for two electrons to the model for three or more electrons. This step is made with the aid of the branching rule (see Sec. 12.13). We shall start with an atom stripped of all but one valence electron and return electrons to it, one by one, until the atom is neutralized. Let the individual quantum numbers of the electrons be s_1, s_2, s_3, . . . , l_1, l_2, l_3, . . . , j_1, j_2, j_3, . . . If we assume LS-coupling among the electrons we begin by successively adding the spins to form a resultant S. With each $s_i = \frac{1}{2}$,

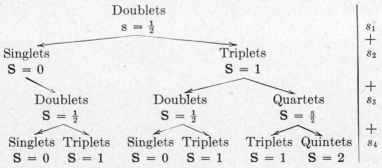

In general the addition of an electron to any multiple term raises and lowers the multiplicity by one. This in terms of the vector model is shown in Fig. 14.2a, for the case where $s = \frac{1}{2}$ is added to a quartet

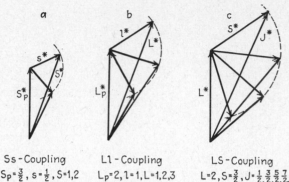

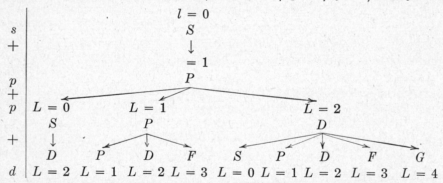

Fig. 14.2.—Vector diagrams of the addition of one electron to the parent term of an ionized atom.

term with $S = \frac{3}{2}$ to give triplets, $(S = 1)$, and quintets, $(S = 2)$. S_P represents a parent S to which a single electron spin s is added.[1]

Adding l's in the same fashion, take $l_1 = 0$, $l_2 = 1$, $l_3 = 1$, and $l_4 = 2$:

$$
\begin{array}{c|c}
s & l = 0 \\
+ & S \\
 & \downarrow \\
 & = 1 \\
p & P \\
+ & \\
p & L = 0 \qquad L = 1 \qquad L = 2 \\
 & S \qquad\qquad P \qquad\qquad D \\
+ & \downarrow \\
d & D \quad P \quad D \quad F \quad S \quad P \quad D \quad F \quad G \\
 & L=2 \ L=1 \ L=2 \ L=3 \ L=0 \ L=1 \ L=2 \ L=3 \ L=4
\end{array}
$$

The two p electrons are assumed to have different total quantum numbers. Similar electrons will be treated in the next chapter. The addition of l's according to the vector model is shown in Fig. 14.2b, for the case where a p electron, $(l = 1)$, is added to a D term, $(L = 2)$, to form the resultant terms P, D, and F with $L = 1$, 2, and 3, respectively.

If we now add spins and orbits simultaneously the branching rule gives the terms shown at the top of page 253.

Combining any resultant spin S with a resultant L will, just as in the case of two electrons (see Sec. 12.3), give the resultant J values. Briefly the J values of a given multiple term are just given by the sum and

---

[1] The small letter s, used for the electron spin, and the capital letter S, used for spin resultant, should not be confused with s for an electron with $l = 0$, and S for a term with $L = 0$, respectively.

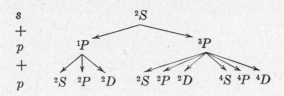

difference of L and S and all intervening values differing by unity. Combining $S = \frac{3}{2}$ with $L = 0$, 1, 2, and 3, J values corresponding to $^4S_{\frac{3}{2}}$, $^4P_{\frac{1}{2},\frac{3}{2},\frac{5}{2}}$, $^4D_{\frac{1}{2},\frac{3}{2},\frac{5}{2},\frac{7}{2}}$, and $^4F_{\frac{3}{2},\frac{5}{2},\frac{7}{2},\frac{9}{2}}$ terms are obtained. Similarly combinations of $S = 3$ with $L = 0$, 1, 2, and 3, lead to $^7S_3$, $^7P_{2,3,4}$, $^7D_{1,2,3,4,5}$, and $^7F_{0,1,2,3,4,5,6}$. S terms are never more than single, P terms triple, D terms quintuple, etc. A term is called a *triplet*, *quartet*, *quintet*, etc., because its spin resultant $S = \frac{2}{2}$, $\frac{3}{2}$, $\frac{4}{2}$, $\cdots$, regardless of the number of fine-structure levels it may contain. It is only when $L \geqslant S$ that the term will contain the maximum number of fine-structure levels $2S + 1$, from which the whole system of terms with the same S derive their name *quartet*, *quintet*, *sextet*, etc. This maximum multiplicity for each given S is called the *permanent multiplicity*.

In deriving the spectral terms arising from Jj-coupling we need consider only the addition of one electron to a parent system already made up of one or more valence electrons. The parent system of terms represents the energy levels of an ionized atom, to which we add one electron with Jj-coupling to form energy levels for the neutral atom or an atom in one lower stage of ionization. Consider as parent terms, for example, those arising from the configuration sp. They are $J = 1$, 0, 1, and 2. Adding now a p electron we obtain the following:

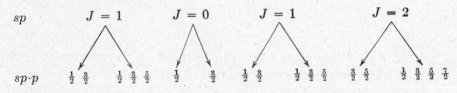

These correspond exactly with the 18 terms obtained for the same resultant electron configuration in LS-coupling: $^2S_{\frac{1}{2}}$, $^2P_{\frac{1}{2},\frac{3}{2}}$, $^2D_{\frac{3}{2},\frac{5}{2}}$, $^2S_{\frac{1}{2}}$, $^2P_{\frac{1}{2},\frac{3}{2}}$, $^2D_{\frac{3}{2},\frac{5}{2}}$, $^4S_{\frac{3}{2}}$, $^4P_{\frac{1}{2},\frac{3}{2},\frac{5}{2}}$, $^4D_{\frac{1}{2},\frac{3}{2},\frac{5}{2},\frac{7}{2}}$.

The precessing vector models for LS- and Jj-coupling for complex atomic systems are represented in Fig. 14.3. Just as for two-electron systems, L_P^* and l^*, and S_P^* and s^*, precess rapidly around their respective resultants L^* and S^* which in turn precess more slowly around their resultant J^*. In Jj-coupling the spin and orbit of the added electron are coupled together and precess rapidly around their resultant j^* which in turn precesses more slowly with J_P of the parent term around J^*. It should be pointed out that in Jj-coupling the parent term

J_P may be formed by two or more electrons in LS-, jj-, or any other coupling scheme.

14.4. Terms Arising from Three or More Equivalent Electrons.—The terms arising from three or more equivalent electrons cannot be calculated

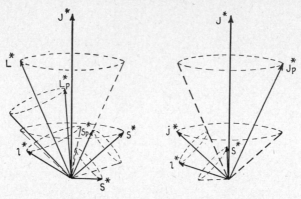

LS - Coupling   Jj - Coupling

Fig. 14.3.—Precessing vector models for complex atomic systems.

by the method outlined above. Here the Pauli exclusion principle must be taken into account and the *strong-field* or *very strong field* quantum numbers resorted to (see Sec. 13.11). Although this necessitates the postponement of the calculation of terms until the Zeeman and Paschen-Back effects have been treated in the next chapter, the results may be given here.

Table 14.3.—Spectral Terms Arising from Equivalent p and d Electrons

$$p^1, \quad {}^2P$$
$$p^2, \quad {}^1S \quad {}^1D \quad {}^3P$$
$$p^3, \quad {}^2P \quad {}^2D \quad {}^4S$$
$$p^4, \quad {}^1S \quad {}^1D \quad {}^3P$$
$$p^5, \quad {}^2P$$
$$p^6, \quad {}^1S$$

$d^1, \quad {}^2D$
$d^2, \quad {}^1S{}^1D{}^1G \quad {}^3P{}^3F$
$d^3, \quad \quad {}^2D \quad {}^2P{}^2D{}^2F{}^2G{}^2H \quad \quad {}^4P{}^4F$
$d^4, \quad {}^1S{}^1D{}^1G \quad {}^3P{}^3F \quad \quad {}^1S{}^1D{}^1F{}^1G{}^1I \quad {}^3P{}^3D{}^3F{}^3G{}^3H \ {}^5D$
$d^5, \quad \quad {}^2D \quad {}^2P{}^2D{}^2F{}^2G{}^2H{}^2S{}^2D{}^2F{}^2G{}^2I{}^4P{}^4F \quad \quad {}^4D{}^4G \ {}^6S$
$d^6, \quad {}^1S{}^1D{}^1G \quad {}^3P{}^3F \quad \quad {}^1S{}^1D{}^1F{}^1G{}^1I \quad {}^3P{}^3D{}^3F{}^3G{}^3H \ {}^5D$
$d^7, \quad \quad {}^2D \quad {}^2P{}^2D{}^2F{}^2G{}^2H \quad \quad {}^4P{}^4F$
$d^8, \quad {}^1S{}^1D{}^1G \quad {}^3P{}^3F$
$d^9, \quad \quad {}^2D$
$d^{10}, {}^1S$

It is important that we note here the ${}^1S_0$ term arising from six equivalent p electrons or from ten equivalent d electrons. Omitting these configurations in the tables, the upper half of each table is identical with the lower half.

14.5. The Landé Interval Rule.—The Landé interval rule, as already shown in Sec. 12.8, applies to the special case of Russell-Saunders coupling and gives the interval rule for the fine structure of each multiple level.

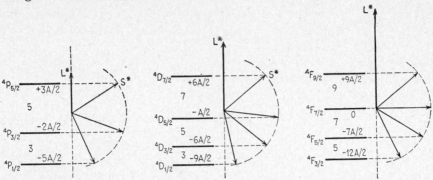

Fig. 14.4a.—Graphical representation of the Landé interval rule for ^4P, ^4D, and ^4F terms.

If, for example, the spins of three or more electrons are coupled together to form a resultant S and the l's coupled together to form a resultant L, the derivation of the interval rule becomes identical with the derivation for two electrons. The interval rule is written, therefore,

$$\Gamma = AL^*S^* \cos (L^*S^*) = \tfrac{1}{2}A(J^{*2} - L^{*2} - S^{*2}), \quad (14.1)$$

where A is a constant for a given multiple term and is given by

$$A = a_3\alpha_3 + a_4\alpha_4. \quad (14.2)$$

A comparison of Fig. 14.3 with Fig. 12.5 shows that a_3 and a_4 are the coupling coefficients for the parent term and the added electron, respectively, and α_3 and α_4 are given by Eqs. (12.10) and (12.11), where s_1^* is replaced by S_P^*, and l^* by L_P^*. In other words, A is a measure of the sum of the energies of interaction between each electron spin and its own orbit. When the constant A is expressed in wave numbers, Eq.

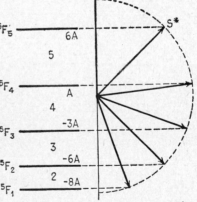

Fig. 14.4b.—Graphical representation of the Landé interval rule for a ^5F term.

(14.1) gives the wave-number shift of each fine-structure level J from the hypothetical center of gravity of the multiple level. Consider, for example, a ^4F term, where $S = \tfrac{3}{2}$, $L = 3$, and $J = \tfrac{3}{2}, \tfrac{5}{2}, \tfrac{7}{2},$ and $\tfrac{9}{2}$. Equation (14.1) gives $\Gamma = -6A, -\tfrac{7}{2}A, 0, +\tfrac{9}{2}A$. A graphical representation of these four levels is shown at the right in Fig. 14.4a. Since A, L^*, and S^* are fixed in magnitude, the projection of S^* on L^* is proportional to cos (L^*S^*) and hence proportional to the interaction energy Γ. The differences have the ratio $5:7:9$. By Eq. (14.1) the difference between one level J and the next level $J + 1$ is given by

$$\Delta\Gamma = A(J + 1), \tag{14.3}$$

i.e., by the larger of the two J's. From Fig. 14.4a it may be seen that the interval ratios for ^4P and ^4D terms are $3:5$ and $3:5:7$, respectively. For a ^5F term, shown in Fig. 14.4b with $J = 1, 2, 3, 4$, and 5, the interval ratios are $2:3:4:5$.

Of the many examples revealing good LS-coupling and the Landé interval rule in complex spectra, only a few will be given as illustrations (see Table 14.4).

TABLE 14.4.—OBSERVED FINE-STRUCTURE INTERVALS ILLUSTRATING THE LANDÉ INTERVAL RULE FOR LS-COUPLING

Element	Terms	Observed intervals in centimeters	Observed ratios	Theoretical ratios
Sc I	$^4F_{\frac{3}{2},\frac{5}{2},\frac{7}{2},\frac{9}{2}}$	37.49, 52.60, 67.07	5.03, 7.05, 9.00	$5:7:9$
Ti I	$^5F_{1,2,3,4,5}$	58.00, 86.23, 113.89, 140.13	2.07, 3.08, 4.06 5.00	$2:3:4:5$
V I	$^6F_{\frac{1}{2},\frac{3}{2},\frac{5}{2},\frac{7}{2},\frac{9}{2},\frac{11}{2}}$	40.88, 68.57, 94.10, 118.59, 141.98	3.17, 5.31, 7.29, 9.19, 11.00	$3:5:7:9:11$
Fe I	$^7F_{0,1,2,3,4,5,6}$	−25.55, −52.34, −81.56, −114.26, −150.81, −195.44	1.00, 2.05, 3.19, 4.47, 5.90, 7.65	$1:2:3:4:5:6$
Mn I	$^8P_{\frac{5}{2},\frac{7}{2},\frac{9}{2}}$	129.18, 173.71	7.00, 9.41	$7:9$

14.6. Inverted Terms.—In some elements it is observed that nearly all of the terms have *inverted fine structure*, whereas in others they are nearly all *normal*. A normal term is defined as one in which the fine-structure level with the smallest J value lies deepest on the energy level diagram, and an inverted term is one in which the largest J value lies deepest. The ^7F term given for iron in Table 14.4 is a good example of an inverted term. The others given there are normal.

A correlation of spectral terms as either normal or inverted shows that (1) normal terms arise from electron configurations involving less than half an incompleted subshell of electrons, and (2) inverted terms arise from configurations involving more than half an incompleted subshell of electrons. Since normal terms have already been treated in the previous section and shown to follow the interval rule, only inverted terms need be treated here.

First a vector-model treatment of one of the causes of inverted terms will be given. Consider for this example the two multiplet terms $^7P_{2,3,4}$ and $^5P_{3,2,1}$ as they arise from the addition of a p electron to the ion term $d^5, {}^6S_{\frac{5}{2}}$. This addition is shown graphically by vector diagrams in Fig. 14.5. The spin s^* of the p electron is added to the spin resultant S_P^* of the parent term ^6S to form the S^* of a septet or a quintet. With no orbit resultant L_P^* of the parent term, the orbit l^* of the p electron becomes the resultant L^*, i.e., $L^* = l^*$. In combining S^* with L^*, to form resultants J^*, S^* is held fixed and L^* shown in the allowed positions where J^* (not shown) gives $J = 2, 3, 4$, and $J = 3, 2, 1$. Now the spread of both of these multiplets depends upon two couplings: first, the spin-orbit coupling of the p electron which is given by

$$\Gamma' = a' s^* L^* \ \overline{\cos\ (s^* L^*)} \tag{14.4}$$

and, second, the coupling between S_P^* and the orbit L^*, which is given by

$$\Gamma'' = a'' S_P^* L^* \ \overline{\cos\ (S_P^* L^*)}. \tag{14.4a}$$

Applying the cosine law for triangles,

$$\Gamma' = a' \frac{S^{*2} + s^{*2} - S_P^{*2}}{4S^{*2}} (J^{*2} - L^{*2} - S^{*2}), \tag{14.5}$$

$$\Gamma'' = a'' \frac{S^{*2} + S_P^{*2} - s^{*2}}{4S^{*2}} (J^{*2} - L^{*2} - S^{*2}). \tag{14.5a}$$

Adding these,

$$\Gamma = \Gamma' + \Gamma'' = \left[a' \frac{S^{*2} + s^{*2} - S_P^{*2}}{4S^{*2}} + a'' \frac{S^{*2} + S_P^{*2} - s^{*2}}{4S^{*2}} \right]$$
$$(J^{*2} - L^{*2} - S^{*2}). \tag{14.6}$$

Since for a given multiplet the values in the bracket are constant, the fine structure will follow the Landé interval rule. Substituting the values of S, s, S_P, L, and J in this formula, the following values are obtained:

$$^7P_4, \ \Gamma = +\tfrac{3}{6}a' + 1\tfrac{5}{6}a''; \qquad ^5P_3, \ \Gamma = -\tfrac{2}{6}a' + 1\tfrac{4}{6}a'';$$
$$^7P_3, \ \Gamma = -\tfrac{1}{6}a' - \tfrac{5}{6}a''; \qquad ^5P_2, \ \Gamma = +\tfrac{1}{6}a' - \tfrac{7}{6}a'';$$
$$^7P_2, \ \Gamma = -\tfrac{4}{6}a' - 2\tfrac{0}{6}a''; \qquad ^5P_1, \ \Gamma = +\tfrac{3}{6}a' - 2\tfrac{1}{6}a''.$$

Since a' and a'' are magnetic in character, and therefore positive, the ^7P term can only be normal. If, however, a' is greater than $7a''$, the ^5P term will be inverted. This may be seen from the diagrams of Fig. 14.5, for in the ^5P diagram the component of s^* along S^* adds to S^* and in ^5P it subtracts. If, therefore, the $s^* L^*$ interaction is sufficiently strong, the energy will be greatest when the component of s^* is most nearly parallel to L^*. This state corresponds to $^7P_4$ on the one hand and $^5P_1$ on the other. A good example of this is observed in the chromium spectrum where the two terms arising from $3d^5 4p$ follow the Landé interval rule and have the separations 112.5 and 81.4 cm^{-1} for $^7P_{2,3,4}$ and -5.7 and -8.8 cm^{-1} for $^5P_{3,2,1}$ for which the coupling coefficients $a' = 104.2$ cm^{-1} and $a'' = 12.4$ cm^{-1}.

The most common cause for the inversion of spectral terms is to be attributed to more than half-filled, but incomplete, subshells of electrons. Although the derivation of spectral terms arising from more than two equivalent electrons will not be given until the next

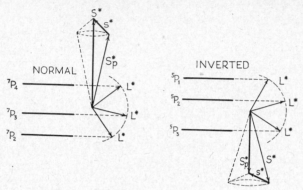

Fig. 14.5.—Vector diagrams illustrating the addition of a p electron to a parent term $d^5,{}^6S_{\frac{5}{2}}$ to form a normal ^7P and an inverted ^5P term.

chapter, the question of inversion can be treated here. To treat the interaction energies of more than a half shell of equivalent electrons we resort to Goudsmit's Γ sum rule (see Sec. 13.15). Consider, for example, the electron configuration d^8, which gives rise (see Table 14.3) to the same types of terms as d^2, viz., ^1S, ^3P, ^1D, ^3F, and ^1G. To show that the ^3P and ^3F terms from the former are inverted, the procedure described in Sec. 13.5 may be employed. The 10 possible states for one d electron are first written down as in Eq. (13.62). We next combine these states taking eight at a time with no two alike. The resultant 45 combinations should be tabulated as there described. Each spin m_{s_i} is multiplied by its own m_{l_i} to obtain individual Γ_i's. These are summed over the eight electrons to obtain Γ for each of the 45 combinations and then tabulated under the corresponding values of M as shown in Table 13.13.

$$\Gamma = \Sigma \Gamma_i \qquad \text{and} \qquad M = \Sigma m_{s_i} + \Sigma m_{l_i}.$$

When this table is completed the Γ sums will be:

$M =$	4	3	2	1	0	-1	-2	-3	-4
$\Sigma\Gamma =$	$-\dfrac{3a}{2}$	$-a$	$+\dfrac{a}{2}$	$+a$	$+2a$	$+a$	$+\dfrac{a}{2}$	$-a$	$-\dfrac{3a}{2}$

Following the scheme already described in Sec. 13.15 these give for the two triplet terms arising from d^8,

$$^3F_4, \ \Gamma = -\frac{3a}{2}; \qquad ^3P_2, \ \Gamma = -\frac{a}{2};$$

$$^3F_3, \ \Gamma = +\frac{a}{2}; \qquad ^3P_1, \ \Gamma = +\frac{a}{2};$$

$$^3F_2, \ \Gamma = +2a; \qquad ^3P_0, \ \Gamma = +a.$$

Where observed these terms are found to be inverted.

Finally we shall mention that large group of inverted terms that arise from the branching rule. If to an inverted parent term of an ion we add another arbitrary electron, the new terms will in general be inverted. The reason for this is readily seen when we remember that in LS-coupling the l^* of the added electron couples with the parent L_P^*, and the spin s^* couples with the parent S_P^*. If the spin-orbit interaction of the added electron is small compared with the $S_P^* L_P^*$ interaction, all of the resultant terms will be inverted. If the former is large, some of the terms may be normal and the others inverted. Because of the many possibilities that come under this heading further discussion will be left until specific examples come up in the following sections.

14.7. Hund's Rule.—Hund's rule, given for two electrons in Sec. 12.7, may be restated here to apply to complex spectra in general. *Out of all the terms with the same L value arising from a given electron configuration: (1) the term with the highest multiplicity, i.e., highest S value, will in general lie deepest; and (2) of these the term with the highest L value will lie deepest.*[1] Experimentally this rule is observed to hold for many electron configurations, and especially for configurations involving the *normal state*, or the so-called *ground state*, of many atoms. Very good examples of Hund's rule will be encountered in the following sections of this chapter in the discussion of the energy levels arising from the elements nitrogen, carbon, oxygen, scandium, titanium, manganese, etc. It should be pointed out that the deepest lying term *i.e.*, the normal state, in all atoms in all observed stages of ionization is the one given by Hund's rule.

14.8. The Nitrogen Atom.—As examples of three-valence-electron systems, let us first consider the elements in Group VB of the periodic table (see Table 5.1). According to the Bohr-Stoner scheme of the building up of the elements the normal states of these elements are given by the configurations ·

N, $1s^2 \ 2s^2 \ \mathbf{2p^3}$
P, $1s^2 \ 2s^2 \ 2p^6 \ 3s^2 \ \mathbf{3p^3}$
As, $1s^2 \ 2s^2 \ 2p^6 \ 3s^2 \ 3p^6 \ 3d^{10} \ 4s^2 \ \mathbf{4p^3}$
Sb, $1s^2 \ 2s^2 \ 2p^6 \ 3s^2 \ 3p^6 \ 3d^{10} \ 4s^2 \ 4p^6 \ 4d^{10} \ 5s^2 \ \mathbf{5p^3}$
Bi, $1s^2 \ 2s^2 \ 2p^6 \ 3s^2 \ 3p^6 \ 3d^{10} \ 4s^2 \ 4p^6 \ 4d^{10} \ 4f^{14} \ 5s^2 \ 5p^6 \ 5d^{10} \ 6s^2 \ \mathbf{6p^3}$

[1] See HUND, F., "Linienspektren," p. 124, 1927.

The last three equivalent p electrons (**in heavy type**) represent the three valence electrons of each atom and are responsible for the optical spectra.   As a typical example of these spectra we shall consider nitrogen in some detail.

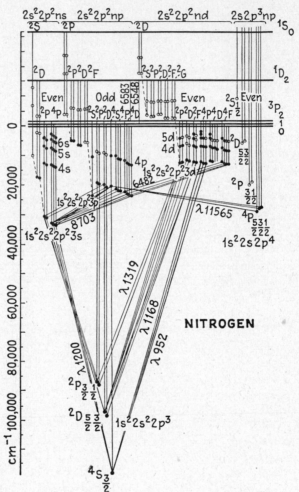

Fig. 14.6.—Energy level diagram of nitrogen.

The electrons $2p^3$ form an incomplete subshell of electrons and (see Table 14.3) give rise to the terms ^4S, ^2P, and ^2D.   Applying Hund's rule, the lowest of these should be ^4S, followed by ^2D and ^2P.   As seen by the energy level diagram in Fig. 14.6, these are exactly the terms observed and in the correct order.   When the nitrogen atom is excited, one of the $2p$ electrons is raised to one of the unoccupied orbits $3s$, $3p$, $3d$, $4s$, $4p$, $4d$, . . . Excited to a $3s$ orbit the electron configuration becomes $1s^22s^22p^23s$, which, as shown by the branching rule, gives rise to the following terms:

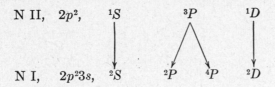

N II, $2p^2$, ^1S ^3P ^1D

N I, $2p^23s$, ^2S ^2P ^4P ^2D

All but the incompleted subshells of electrons are usually omitted.

The parent terms given above are the lowest levels of the singly ionized atom, a two-valence-electron system, and are shown at the top of the energy level diagram as series limits. From the displacement law, N II is similar to C I, with the low states ^1S, ^1D, and ^3P arising from $2p^2$ in agreement with theory. Of the terms ^2S, ^2P, ^4P, and ^2D, all but the ^2S built upon ^1S of the ion N II have been observed by combinations with the lower terms. These combinations involve the transition of the $3s$ electron to a $2p$ state ($\Delta l = 1$).

Excited to a $4s$, $5s$, $6s$, . . . state the same term types given above arise to form series of terms approaching as limits the ion terms from which they are shown to branch.

Excited to a $3p$ state the electron configuration becomes $1s^22s^22p^23p$, which abbreviated is $2p^23p$, and by the branching rule gives rise to the following terms:

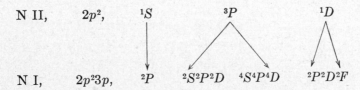

N II, $2p^2$, ^1S ^3P ^1D

N I, $2p^23p$, ^2P $^2S^2P^2D$ $^4S^4P^4D$ $^2P^2D^2F$

The parent terms are again the low levels of the ion N II. Of the resultant terms all but the ^2S and ^2F have been observed in combination with those of $2p^23s$.

Similarly the excitation of an electron to a $3d$ state gives rise to the terms:

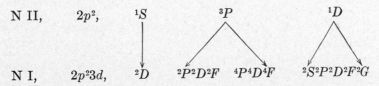

N II, $2p^2$, ^1S ^3P ^1D

N I, $2p^23d$, ^2D $^2P^2D^2F$ $^4P^4D^4F$ $^2S^2P^2D^2F^2G$

Of these terms only those built upon ^3P of the ion are observed. In this connection it is to be noted that no term above the ^3P series limit has been observed in nitrogen. The longest observed series of terms are the ^4P terms of $2p^2nd$, where $n = 3, 4, 5, 6,$ and 7.

The observed spectrum lines of the neutral atom of nitrogen lie in two widely separated regions of the spectrum: one group of lines is in the extreme ultra-violet and the other is in the visible and near infrared. This is due to the enormous amount of energy required to raise a $2p$ electron to a $3s$ state, as compared with the difference between the $3s$ and other excited states (see Fig. 14.6). A schematic diagram of

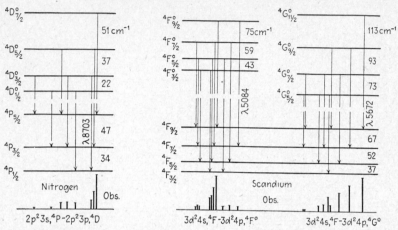

Fig. 14.7.—Quartet multiplets observed in nitrogen and scandium.

typical quarter multiplets is given in Fig. 14.7. The fine structure of the multiple levels is spread out to show the Landé interval rule. The observed lines are plotted below to a wave-number scale.

The low $2p^3,{}^2P$ and $2p^3,{}^2D$ levels in nitrogen are metastable in that, once an atom is in one of these states, a transition into a lower state is forbidden. Similarly the $2p^2,{}^1S$ and $2p^2,{}^1D$ states of the ion are metastable. Bowen has pointed out, however, that transitions within a configuration sometimes occur in gaseous nebulae where densities are very low.[1] Transitions from $^1D_2$ to $^3P_2$ and $^3P_1$, shown in the figure, account for two of the many nebular lines λ6548 and λ6583.

14.9. The Scandium Atom.—The scandium atom and its spectrum will be taken up next, as an element characteristic of Group IIIA of the periodic table (Table 5.1). The normal state of the neutral scandium atom is given by the complete electron configuration,

$$\text{Sc, } 1s^22s^22p^63s^23p^64s^23d.$$

With all but one electron forming completed subshells, the normal state, as observed, is given by the one $3d$ electron as ^2D. Observation shows that when the scandium atom is excited, it is easier to raise one

[1] Bowen, I. S., Astrophys. Jour., **67**, 1, 1928.

of the $4s$ electrons to an outer orbit than it is to raise the last bound
$3d$ electron.   It is for this reason that the neutral scandium atom is to
be classified as a three-electron system.   In order to build up an energy

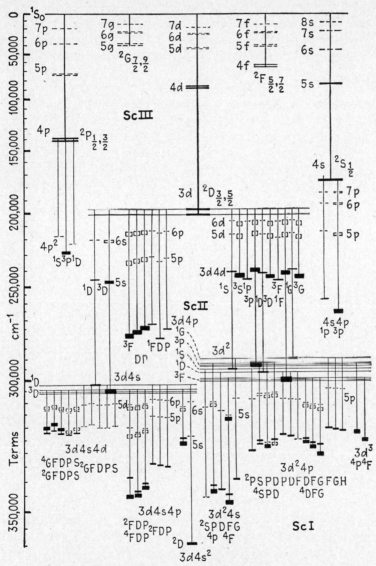

Fig. 14.8.—Energy level diagram of scandium.

level diagram it is convenient to start with the atom stripped of the
three outer electrons $4s^2 3d$ and then allow them to return one at a
time.

The energy state of the scandium atom triply ionized is represented by a horizontal line at the top of Fig. 14.8. Containing only closed sub-shells of electrons, this state is designated $^1S_0$. If now one electron is allowed to return to the atom it may go into any one of the unoccupied s, p, d, f, . . . orbits, *i.e.*, any one of the ^2S, ^2P, ^2D, ^2F, . . . states shown in the top part of the diagram. Of all the doublet levels observed, $3d,{}^2D$ lies deepest. This is in agreement with the prediction made by Bohr and shows that a $3d$ electron is more tightly bound to the scandium atom than a $4s$ electron (see Sec. 17.1).

With one electron in the lowest state $3d,{}^2D$, we now allow a second electron to return to the atom in different allowed orbits and thus build up the Sc II levels. If the second electron is returned to an s orbit, the resultant configuration becomes $3dns$ giving rise to ^1D and ^3D terms. Taking $n = 4$, 5, 6, $\cdots$, these form series of D terms approaching $3d,{}^2D$ as a limit.

Returning the second electron to a p orbit, and utilizing the branching rule, the following terms are derived:

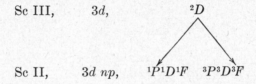

Sc III, $3d$, ^2D

Sc II, $3d\ np$, $^1P^1D^1F$ $^3P^3D^3F$

Setting $n = 4$, 5, 6, $\cdots$, these should all form series approaching $3d,{}^2D$ of Sc III as a limit. Only the first members of this set of series have been observed to combine with ^1D and ^3D of $3d4s$. Photographs of two of the resultant triplet multiplets $^3D - {}^3D°$ and $^3D - {}^3F°$ are given in Fig. 17.7.

Returning the second electron to a d state gives rise to the following terms:

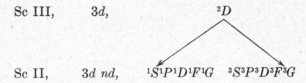

Sc III, $3d$, ^2D

Sc II, $3d\ nd$, $^1S^1P^1D^1F^1G$ $^3S^3P^3D^3F^3G$

These form five series of singlets and five series of triplets approaching $3d,{}^2D$ as a limit. The second members of these series are the levels shown in Fig. 12.4 in combination with the triads of $3d4p$. The first member of the configuration series, *viz.*, $3d3d$, finds both electrons in the same orbits so that the Pauli exclusion principle comes in to exclude three triplets and two singlets. All predicted terms and no others are observed for $3d^2$. The higher series members shown in Fig. 14.8 in brackets are predicted but not observed.

In turning to the neutral scandium atom we find that the main energy level diagram is built upon two parent configurations $3d4s$ and $3d^2$ of the ion. Starting at the lower left in the figure we have the terms arising from the addition of a $4d$ electron to $3d4s$. These are obtained as follows:

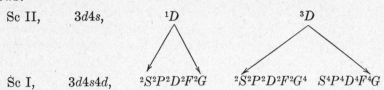

Sc II, $3d4s$, ^1D ^3D

Sc I, $3d4s4d$, $^2S^2P^2D^2F^2G$ $^2S^2P^2D^2F^2G^4$ $S^4P^4D^4F^4G$

Of these terms five doublets and three quartets have been found.

The second group of terms shown are those attributed to $3d4s4p$. All predicted terms are observed for this first member of the series but none of those for $5p$, $6p$, etc.

In the third set of series $3d4sns$ the first member $3d4s4s$ comprises the normal state of the neutral atom.

The fourth group of series $3d^2ns$ is built upon $3d^2$ of Sc II. These terms arise as follows:

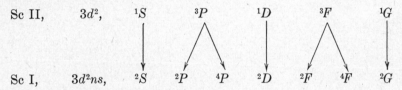

Sc II, $3d^2$, ^1S ^3P ^1D ^3F ^1G

Sc I, $3d^2ns$, ^2S ^2P ^4P ^2D ^2F ^4F ^2G

With the exception of ^2S the first member of each of these series has been identified.

Similarly the fifth group of series $3d^2np$ are built upon $3d^2$ as follows:

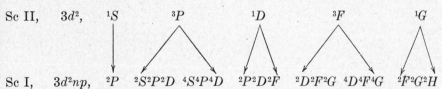

Sc II, $3d^2$, ^1S ^3P ^1D ^3F ^1G

Sc I, $3d^2np$, ^2P $^2S^2P^2D$ $^4S^4P^4D$ $^2P^2D^2F$ $^2D^2F^2G$ $^4D^4F^4G$ $^2F^2G^2H$

Nearly all of these have been observed for the lowest configuration $3d^24p$. The remaining terms, ^3P and ^3F, arise from the configuration $3d^3$.

Schematic diagrams of the fine structure of two quartet multiplets are shown in Fig. 14.7. Photographs of the same two multiplets are reproduced at the top in Fig. 17.11. Altogether about 160 lines have been identified as belonging to the Sc II spectrum, and about 360 lines have been identified as belonging to Sc I.[1]

[1] RUSSELL, H. N., and W. F. MEGGERS, U. S. Bur. Standards, Sci. Papers, 22, 329, 1927.

The displacement law of multiplicities predicts that the Sc I, Ti II, V III, . . . spectra should resemble each other in general structure and multiplicity. The corresponding multiplets in Fig. 17.11 illustrate the observed similarity.

14.10. The Oxygen Atom.—As examples of four-valence-electron systems we shall first consider the simpler elements oxygen, sulphur, selenium, tellurium, and polonium. According to the Bohr-Stoner scheme of the building up of the elements, the last four electrons bound

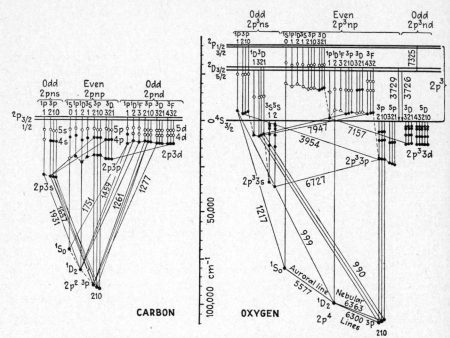

Fig. 14.9.—Energy level diagrams of carbon and oxygen.

to each of these atoms are equivalent p electrons (see Table 5.3). As a typical example of these elements we shall consider oxygen in some detail. The low levels in the oxygen atom (see Fig. 14.9) are given by the configuration $1s^2 2s^2 2p^4$ (abbreviated $2p^4$). Four equivalent p electrons give rise to exactly the same terms as two equivalent p electrons, ^1S, ^3P, and ^1D. The only difference between the two is that in p^4 the ^3P term is inverted and in p^2 it is normal. The energy level diagram of carbon has been given in the same figure for comparison purposes. Although the low set of terms is alike for both atoms the higher term structures are quite different. For carbon the excitation of a $2p$ electron to a $3s$ orbit gives rise to a ^1P and a ^3P term, whereas in oxygen the terms are as follows:

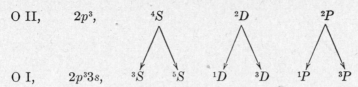

O II, $2p^3$, ^4S ^2D ^2P

O I, $2p^33s$, ^3S ^5S ^1D ^3D ^1P ^3P

Both ^3S and ^5S form series approaching ^4S as a limit; ^1D and ^3D form series approaching ^2D as a limit; and ^1P and ^3P form series approaching ^2P as a limit. The terms arising from the next configuration in oxygen are those of $2p^33p$ built upon $2p^3$ of the ion. They are:

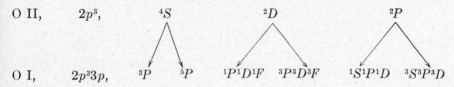

O II, $2p^3$, ^4S ^2D ^2P

O I, $2p^33p$, ^3P ^5P $^1P^1D^1F$ $^3P^3D^3F$ $^1S^1P^1D$ $^3S^3P^3D$

The one quintet, four of the seven triplets, and one of the six singlets have been identified.

Wave-lengths of some of the strongest lines in oxygen are indicated in the diagram. Special mention should be made of the *auroral green line* λ5577, and the red *nebular* lines λ6300 and λ6363. These lines arise from what are commonly called *forbidden jumps*. The auroral line has been reproduced in the laboratory by Kaplan, and others, and its Zeeman effect has been studied by MacLennan and by Paschen. The two nebular lines have been produced in the laboratory by Hopfield. Other nebular lines arise from similar transitions between the low states of O II. These are shown at the top and right in Fig. 14.9.

14.11. The Titanium Atom.—One of the most complete analyses of a really complex spectrum has been made for the titanium atom.[1] This analysis, which has been carried out chiefly by Russell, includes 43 singlet levels, 65 triplet levels, and 34 quintet levels and involves about 1400 spectrum lines. In singly ionized titanium some 33 doublet and 17 quartet levels, involving about 500 so-called *spark lines*, have been identified. These constitute practically all of the lines commonly observed in the titanium arc or spark.

In the doubly ionized spectrum, Ti III, 7 singlet and 12 triplet levels involving some 90 spectrum lines have been observed.[2]

In the triply ionized spectrum, Ti IV, 12 doublet levels involving 31 lines have been identified.[3]

[1] Kiess, C. C., and H. K. Kiess, *Jour. Wash. Acad. Sci.*, **13**, 270, 1923; *Jour. Opt. Soc. Amer.*, **8**, 607, 1924; Gieseler, H., and W. Grotrian, *Zeits. f. Phys.*, **25**, 342, 1924; Russell, H. N., *Astrophys. Jour.*, **66**, 347, 1927.

[2] Russell, H. N., and R. J. Lang, *Astrophys. Jour.*, **66**, 13, 1927.

[3] Gibbs, R. C., and H. E. White, *Proc. Nat. Acad. Sci.*, **12**, 448, 598, 1926; see also Russell, H. N., and R. J. Lang, *Astrophys. Jour.*, **66**, 13, 1927.

A great deal of information concerning the outer structure of the titanium atom can be obtained by bringing together the energy levels of Ti I, II, III, and IV, into a single diagram similar to the one given for scandium in Fig. 14.8. Because of the complexity of the titanium diagram only the part due to the neutral atom will be given (see Fig. 14.10). The multiple levels belonging to the different electron configura-

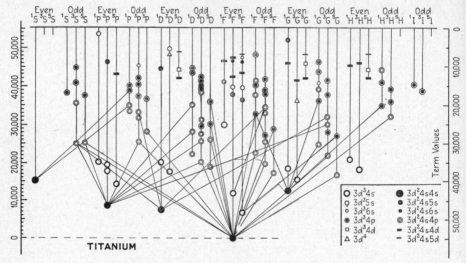

TITANIUM

FIG. 14.10.—Energy level diagram of titanium.

tions are given by the legend at the lower right in the figure. The normal state of the atom is given by the abbreviated electron configuration $4s^2 3d^2$. All of the predicted terms ^1S, ^3P, ^1D, ^3F, and ^1G are observed. In agreement with Hund's rule the ^3F lies deepest. Not far above the normal state lies a ^5F term arising from the configuration $3d^3 4s$. This multiple level as well as all levels lying below the first *odd* ^5G are metastable levels. Nearly all of the predicted terms arising from $3d^3 4s$ are found. As shown by the branching rule, these terms are:

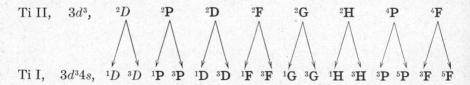

The observed terms of Ti I and Ti II are given in heavy type.

The next higher terms in the figure arise from the *odd* configurations $3d^3 4p$ and $3d^2 4s 3p$ and are frequently referred to as *middle terms*. These combining with the low *even* terms give rise to the major part of the observed titanium spectrum. According to the selection rules, odd terms

combine with even terms or even terms with odd. Expressed in terms
of the electron configurations:

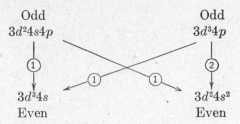

The transitions $3d^34p$ to $3d^24s^2$ give rise to some of the strongest lines
in the titanium spectrum and constitute double electron jumps $4p$ to
$4s$ ($\Delta l = 1$) and $3d$ to $4s$ ($\Delta l = 2$). The titanium triplet shown in Fig.
14.1 is a photograph of the double electron jump $3d^24s^2, {}^3F - 3d^34p, {}^3F^\circ$.
A very plausible explanation of the great strength of such lines has
been given by Condon.[1] By a quantum-mechanical treatment Condon
has shown that the terms of two configurations having the same sign

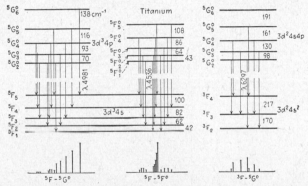

FIG. 14.11.—Schematic diagram showing the fine structure of quintet-quintet combinations and triplet-quintet intercombinations in titanium.

(odd or even), and lying close together or overlapping each other, belong
in part to both configurations. Because of a sort of resonance or periodic
interchange of states, the atom may be thought of as jumping back
and forth between two states having the same quantum numbers,
without radiation. In this sense Condon has shown that double-electron
transitions may be reduced to single-electron transitions (see Sec. 19.3).

Intercombinations between singlet and triplet levels and between
triplet and quintet levels are also commonly observed. A schematic
diagram of an intercombination multiplet is shown in Fig. 14.11, along
with two quintet-quintet combination multiplets. A photograph of the
${}^5F-{}^5G^\circ$ multiplet is reproduced at the top of Fig. 17.12 and at the left

[1] CONDON, E. U., *Phys. Rev.*, **36**, 1121, 1930.

in Fig. 14.1. The wave-lengths, frequencies, and relative intensities of these lines are given in Table 14.5. The photographs of the corresponding multiplet in singly ionized vanadium and doubly ionized chromium (see Fig. 17.12) illustrate the displacement law of multiplicities.

TABLE 14.5.—QUINTET MULTIPLET OBSERVED IN TITANIUM (FIG. 17.12)

	$^5G_6^\circ(137.7)$	$^5G_5^\circ(115.6)$	$^5G_4^\circ(93.0)$	$^5G_3^\circ(70.1)$	$^5G_2^\circ$
$^5F_5$	100	8.8	0.3		
	4981.75	5016.17	5045.43		
	20067.7	*19930.0*	*19814.4*		
(*100.2*)					
$^5F_4$		75.2	12.2	0.6	
		4991.08	5020.04	5043.59	
		20030.2	*19914.6*	*19821.6*	
(*81.8*)					
$^5F_3$			56.2	11.9	0.5
			4999.50	5022.87	5040.63
			19996.4	*19903.41*	*19833.3*
(*62.2*)					
$^5F_2$				41.0	8.2
				5007.22	5024.85
				19965.6	*19895.6*
(*41.9*)					
$^5F_1$					29.2
					5014.28
					19937.5

14.12. The Manganese Atom.—A general treatment of complex spectra can hardly be complete without some mention of the well-known arc spectrum of manganese. There are two reasons for this; (1) The energy level diagram is made up of terms of high multiplicity, quartets, sextets, and octets. (2) Some of the multiple levels are inverted and others are normal. This latter is due chiefly, but not altogether, to the fact that *the system of normal multiplets arises from five equivalent d electrons* (*i.e.*, half a subshell) *and two other arbitrary valence electrons, and the system of inverted multiplets arises from six equivalent d electrons* (*i.e.*, more than half a subshell) *and one arbitrary electron* (see Fig. 14.12).

The normal state of manganese is given by $3d^54s^2,^6S_{\frac{5}{2}}$. Although theory predicts other terms for the same configuration, only the ^6S has been observed. If one of the $4s$ electrons is raised to a $4p$ state, the most probable of the predicted states are the ^8P, ^6P, ^6P, and ^4P states observed. A schematic diagram of the origin of these levels is shown at the left in Fig. 14.13. Starting at the extreme left with the term $3d^5,^6S$, of doubly ionized manganese, a $4s$ electron is added to form $^5S_2$ and $^7S_3$ terms in singly ionized manganese. The observed separation of these two S terms, 9473 cm^{-1}, is due to the interaction between $S = \frac{5}{2}$ of the parent term and $s = \frac{1}{2}$ of the added electron. These levels

are the series limits at the left in Fig. 14.12. The addition now of a
$4p$ electron raises and lowers the multiplicity again and adds an l value

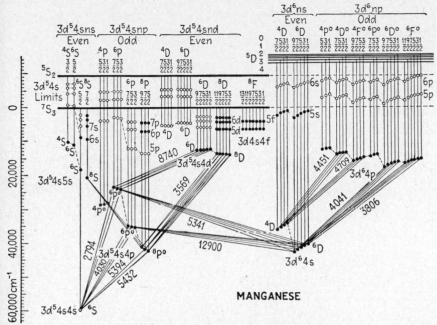

Fig. 14.12.—Energy level diagram of manganese.

of one to each term to form P terms. It should be noted that the
fine structure is drawn to one scale and the multiple-term separations

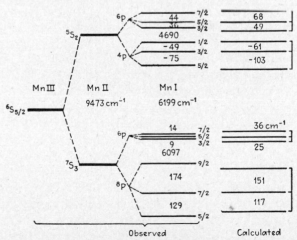

Fig. 14.13.—Schematic representation of the branching rule for the p terms in manganese.
Configuration $3d^5s\,4p$.

to another. The interaction between the spin of the $4p$ electron and
S, the spin resultant of $3d^5 4s$, separates the upper P terms by about

4700 cm⁻¹ and the lower terms by about 6100 cm⁻¹. The observed order ⁸P, ⁶P, ⁴P, ⁶P indicates that the interaction between the spins of 4s and 4p is considerably greater than that between the spin of 4p and the spin of 3d⁵. We shall return to the calculation of the fine structure shown at the right in Fig. 14.13.

If one of the 4s electrons from the normal state of manganese is excited to a 3d orbit, the most probable among the many terms predicted for the new configuration 3d⁶4s are the ⁶D and ⁴D terms observed. Being built upon the inverted 3d⁶,⁵D term of Mn II, both of these D terms are inverted.

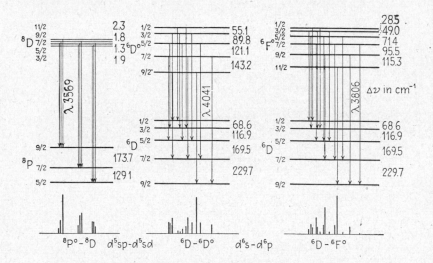

OCTET AND SEXTET MULTIPLETS IN MANGANESE

FIG. 14.14.—Schematic diagram of three multiplets observed in manganese.

Similarly the excitation of a 4s electron from the metastable configuration 3d⁶4s of manganese to a 4p orbit gives a triad of inverted quartets and a triad of inverted sextet terms, again built upon 3d⁶,⁵D of the ion.

Schematic diagrams of three manganese multiplets are shown in Fig. 14.14. The octet multiplet at the left belongs to the normal set of energy levels and is due to the configuration combination 3d⁵4s4p–3d⁵4s4d. The two inverted sextet multiplets arise from the configuration combination 3d⁶4s–3d⁶4p. Photographs of these latter two multiplets are given in Fig. 14.15. By drawing the initial and final states to scale and at an angle to each other the spectrum lines are seen to come at the intersection of the respective initial and final levels. This is only possible where the spectrum lines are on a linear frequency scale. The spectrograms were taken with a 15-ft. Rowland grating and mounting where the wave-length scale is practically linear. Over a short range of wave-lengths the frequency scale is practically linear also. The *self-reversed* triplet in the upper photograph is due to transitions from the lower ^6P term of $3d^54s4p$ to the normal state of the atom $3d^54s^2,^6S_{\frac{5}{2}}$.

We shall return now to the calculation of the fine structure of the P terms shown in Fig. 14.13. The splitting in each of these four terms is attributed to the interaction between the spin resultant S^* and the

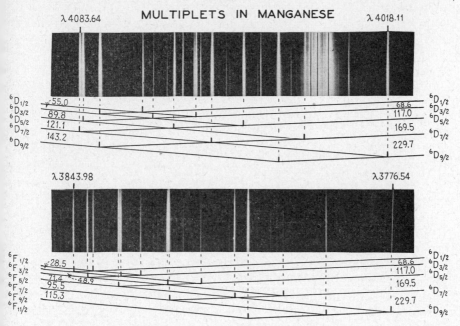

Fig. 14.15.—Photographs of two sextet multiplets observed in the arc spectrum of manganese.

orbit l^* of the p electron. If this interaction were due only to the coupling of the spin of the $4p$ electron and its own orbit it is readily seen, either from Eq. (14.5) or from the vector-model diagrams, that the octet and upper sextet terms should both be *normal*, whereas the quartet and lower sextet terms should be *inverted*. A study, however, of the observed intervals as well as the four vector diagrams for each of the four P terms shows that the spin of the $5s$ electron also couples quite strongly with l. Further consideration shows that the spin resultant of $3d^5$ also couples (but weakly) with l. The three interactions can be written in the usual way by

$$\Gamma_p = a_p s_p^* l_p^* \, \overline{\cos\,(s_p^* l_p^*)},$$
$$\Gamma_s = a_s s_s^* l_p^* \, \overline{\cos\,(s_s^* l_p^*)},$$
$$\Gamma_d = a_d S_d^* l_p^* \, \overline{\cos\,(S_d^* l_p^*)},$$

where s_p, s_s, and S_d are the spins of the $4p$, $4s$, and $3d^5$ electrons, respectively, and l_p is the orbit of the $4p$ electron. Although the exact coupling is not known we shall assume, as a first approximation, that Eq. (14.5) applies. In this equation, s^* becomes the interacting spin in question and S_P the sum of the remaining spins. When the allowed values of S, s, S_P, L, and J are substituted, Γ sums, $i.e.$, $\Gamma = \Gamma_p + \Gamma_s + \Gamma_d$, are obtained for each level. From these the total width of each term is set equal to the observed separations as follows:

$$^8P, \quad \tfrac{8}{7}a_p + \tfrac{8}{7}a_s + \tfrac{4 \cdot 0}{7}a_d = \quad 303 \text{ cm}^{-1};$$

$$^6P, \quad -\tfrac{6}{7}a_p + \tfrac{6}{5}a_s + \quad 6a_d = \quad 23 \text{ cm}^{-1};$$

$$^4P, \quad -\tfrac{8}{7}a_p - \tfrac{8}{7}a_s + \tfrac{2 \cdot 8}{5}a_d = \quad -124 \text{ cm}^{-1};$$

$$^6P, \quad \tfrac{6}{5}a_p - \tfrac{6}{7}a_s + \quad 6a_d = \quad 80 \text{ cm}^{-1}.$$

Solving these equations for values of the a_i's we obtain the average values,

$$a_p = 108.9 \text{ cm}^{-1}, \qquad a_s = 81.4 \text{ cm}^{-1}, \qquad a_d = 9.5 \text{ cm}^{-1}.$$

Substituting these back in the equations, the calculated separations shown in Fig. 14.13 are obtained. Although not perfect the agreement is quite good. If either the small coefficient a_d or the larger one a_s is neglected, the agreement between the observed and calculated values becomes very poor.

In complex spectra, such as manganese, one cannot help but notice that only a few of the terms predicted for each configuration have been observed. Furthermore the observed terms are seen to be just those having, first, the high S values and, second, the high L values. This always includes the lowest term in each configuration. An explanation in terms of the vector model is that in exciting an atom to one of these states there is a minimum of angular readjustment among the various quantum vectors common to both initial and final states.

14.13. The Rare-gas Atoms, Neon, Argon, Krypton, and Xenon.—Of the complex atomic systems treated thus far in this chapter the most prominent electron configurations to be formed are those whose terms follow the Landé interval rule and reveal LS-coupling. The rare gases, on the other hand, form a group of atomic systems that reveal fairly good Jj-coupling.

As mentioned in Chap. I, Paschen (in 1919) published an analysis of the neon spectrum in which he had identified 132 series of singlets. Since then fairly complete analyses have been made of A, Kr, and Xe. The series of these spectra, following Paschen, are found to be combinations between 4 series of s terms, 10 series of p terms, 12 series of d terms, and 12 series of f terms. These terms were all so named because they were observed to combine with each other like s, p, d, and f terms in the alkalies. We now know that s, p, d, and f refer to one of the six electrons taking part in producing the series terms.

An energy level diagram of xenon is shown in Fig. 14.16 as a typical example of the rare gases. The normal $^1S_0$ state is given by completed subshells of electrons only, the last of which (see Table 5.3) is $5p^6$. The

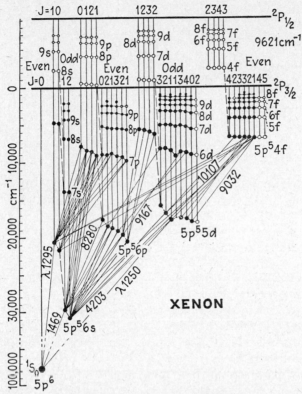

FIG. 14.16.—Energy level diagram of xenon.

excitation of one of these electrons to the first s orbit forms the configuration $5p^56s$, which gives rise to the same terms as $5p6s$ in tin (see Table 14.3).

Xe II,	$5p^5$,	$^2P_{\frac{1}{2}\frac{3}{2}}$		$^2P_{\frac{1}{2}}$		$^2P_{\frac{3}{2}}$	
Xe I,	$5p^56s$,	$^3P_{0,1,2}$ $^1P_1$		$(\frac{1}{2}\frac{1}{2})_0$ $(\frac{1}{2}\frac{1}{2})_1$		$(\frac{3}{2}\frac{1}{2})_2$ $(\frac{3}{2}\frac{1}{2})_1$	
		LS-coupling			Jj-coupling		

In xenon the coupling is Jj- with the spin-orbit interaction of the five p electrons very large as compared with the spin-spin interaction between $6s$ and $5p^5$. The spin-orbit interaction is shown by the magnitude of the ^2P interval at the top of the energy level diagram in Fig. 14.16, 9621 cm^{-1}. These are the limits of all the Xe I series.

The excitation of one of the $5p^6$ electrons to a $6p$ orbit gives rise to the following terms:

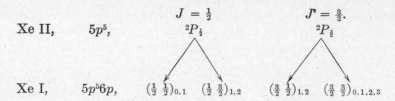

$$J = \tfrac{1}{2} \qquad J' = \tfrac{3}{2}.$$

Xe II, $5p^5$, $^2P_{\frac{1}{2}}$ $^2P_{\frac{3}{2}}$

Xe I, $5p^56p$, $(\tfrac{1}{2}\,\tfrac{1}{2})_{0,1}$ $(\tfrac{1}{2}\,\tfrac{3}{2})_{1,2}$ $(\tfrac{3}{2}\,\tfrac{1}{2})_{1,2}$ $(\tfrac{3}{2}\,\tfrac{3}{2})_{0,1,2,3}$

The 10 terms in Jj-coupling correspond to $^1S_0$, $^1P_1$, $^1D_2$, $^3S_1$, $^3P_{0,1,2}$, $^3D_{1,2,3}$ in LS-coupling. The $^2P_{\frac{1}{2},\frac{3}{2}}$ interval being large, these 10 levels are split into two groups of 4 and 6 as shown, and are the first members of 10 series approaching the double limit given above. Because the excited electron is in a p orbit the terms behave as p terms.

Similarly the excitation of one of the $5p$ electrons from the normal state of the atom to a $5d$ gives rise to the following terms:

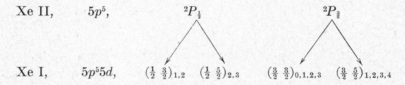

Xe II, $5p^5$, $^2P_{\frac{1}{2}}$ $^2P_{\frac{3}{2}}$

Xe I, $5p^55d$, $(\tfrac{1}{2}\,\tfrac{3}{2})_{1,2}$ $(\tfrac{1}{2}\,\tfrac{5}{2})_{2,3}$ $(\tfrac{3}{2}\,\tfrac{3}{2})_{0,1,2,3}$ $(\tfrac{3}{2}\,\tfrac{5}{2})_{1,2,3,4}$

These 12 terms in Jj-coupling correspond to $^1P_1$, $^1D_2$, $^1F_3$, $^3P_{0,1,2}$, $^3D_{1,2,3}$, and $^3F_{2,3,4}$ in LS-coupling. With the exception of one term these two groups of terms have been observed in xenon as the first members of series approaching the double limit.

The spectra of neon, argon, and krypton are so nearly like xenon that their energy levels and diagrams may be closely represented by lowering the upper limit $^2P_{\frac{1}{2}}$ of Xe, with all of the series approaching it, until the ^2P interval is 782, 1431, and 5371 cm^{-1}, respectively.

Selection rules for jj-coupling (see Sec. 12.14), which also apply here, show that transitions from the 10 $even$ series of p terms $5p^5np$ to the 4 lowest s terms, $(5p^56s)$, give rise to 30 principal series of spectrum lines. These are just the 30 series observed first by Paschen in the neon spectrum. Transitions from the 4 series of s terms, $(5p^5ns)$, to the lowest p terms, $(5p^56p)$, give rise to 30 sharp series of lines also observed by Paschen in neon.

Observed transitions from the odd f terms, $(5p^5nf)$, to the $even$ s terms, $(5p^56s)$, were first thought to be forbidden transitions but are now known to be allowed transitions on the double-electron-jump hypothesis. An f electron jumps to a $5p$ orbit while a $5p$ electron jumps to a $6s$ orbit. It should be mentioned that a majority of the lines observed in neon have also been observed in A, Kr, Xe, and Rn.

The normal state $^1S_0$ of each of the rare gases lies far below the first excited states and is determined by only six possible lines in the extreme ultra-violet region of the spectrum. Three of these six lines, observed in xenon, are shown in the diagram.   It should be mentioned in passing that no levels above the lower series limit $^2P_{\frac{3}{2}}$ have ever been observed. The imaginary lowering of the $^2P_{\frac{1}{2}}$ limit to form the term diagrams for

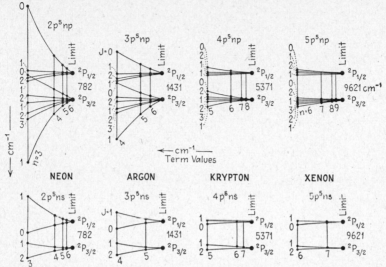

FIG. 14.17.—Fine structure of the s and p terms in neon, argon, krypton, and xenon.

Kr, A, and then Ne brings successively higher series members below $^2P_{\frac{3}{2}}$, where they are subsequently observed.   This disappearance of spectral terms that lie above a series limit is due to the phenomenon of *autoionization* (see Chap. XIX).

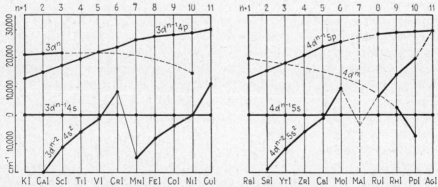

FIG. 14.18.—Deep lying electron configurations in the elements of the first and second long periods, illustrating breaks in the building up of the s and d shells of electrons.

To show the general change taking place in the term fine structure as we go from Ne to A to Kr and to Xe, this structure for s and p series has been plotted to scale in Fig. 14.17.   At the left the coupling is neither LS nor Jj but something between the two.

14.14. The Normal States of the Elements in the First and Second Long Periods.—It was pointed out in Chap. V that certain irregularities in the Bohr-Stoner scheme of the building up of the elements occur in the first and second long periods. Energy level diagrams of all but one of the known elements in these two periods have made possible the construction of Fig. 14.18.[1] Here the deepest level in each of four of the deepest lying configurations $d^{n-2}s^2$, $d^{n-1}s$, $d^{n-1}p$, and d^n has been plotted with respect to $d^{n-1}s$ of the same element as zero. It is observed that, while there is a regular progression of the configurations $d^{n-1}p$ across each period, there is an apparent breaking up of the $d^{n-2}s^2$ curve into two similar parts. This is only apparent, for when the $d^{n-2}s^2$ curve is used as the origin in plotting, the other two curves for $d^{n-1}s$ and $d^{n-1}p$ appear as the broken curves. The curves plotted either way show, however, a gradual increase in the binding of $3d$ or $4d$ electrons over $4s$ and $5s$ electrons as we progress from element to element. With the addition of one, two, and three d electrons there is a strong tendency to complete half a subshell of electrons so that with the addition of a fourth d electron to form the normal state of Cr, or Mo, one of the s electrons also goes over into a d state to yield $3d^5 4s$, or $4d^5 5s$. With the shell half filled, the next electron added to form the next element goes into a $4s$ or $5s$ orbit to again fill the s subshell. At the approach of a complete subshell of d electrons we observe that additional d electrons are again added at the expense of the s subshells. No such anomalies are found to exist in the sequences of elements where p electrons are added.

14.15. Houston's Treatment of One s Electron and One Arbitrary Electron.—A quantum-mechanical treatment of the fine structure due to the interaction of one s electron with one arbitrary electron has been made by Houston,[2] by applying the Darwin-Pauli treatment of the electron to the Schrödinger wave equation for two electrons. By setting up suitable wave functions, based upon Schrödinger's theory, solutions for the spin-spin resonance interaction between the two electrons and the spin-orbit interaction for the arbitrary electron are obtained. The treatment is one involving perturbation methods in which only the first-order perturbation to the energy is evaluated. Houston's results may be given most easily by his resultant equations;

$$\text{Singlet } {}^1\Gamma_L = \tfrac{1}{2}A[(X - 1) + \{(X + 1)^2 + 4L(L + 1)\}^{\frac{1}{2}}] \qquad (14.7a)$$

$$\text{Triplet}\begin{cases} {}^3\Gamma_{L+1} = A \cdot L & (14.7b) \\ {}^3\Gamma_L \ \ = \tfrac{1}{2}A[(X - 1) - \{(X + 1)^2 + 4L(L + 1)\}^{\frac{1}{2}}] & (14.7c) \\ {}^3\Gamma_{L-1} = -A(L + 1) & (14.7d) \end{cases}$$

[1] GIBBS, R. C., and H. E. WHITE, *Nat. Acad. Sci.*, **14**, 559, 1928.
[2] HOUSTON, W. V., *Phys. Rev.*, **33**, 297, 1929.

where A is a measure of the spin-orbit interaction of the arbitrary electron and is given by $a/2$, a defined in Eq. (12.2), and X is a parameter which measures the magnitude of the spin-spin interaction. The second of these enters into the two terms having equal J values only, and not into the two outer triplet terms at all. These four interaction energies are plotted in Fig. 14.19 for a ps electron configuration. If $X >> A$, we have LS-coupling with the singlet high above the triplet

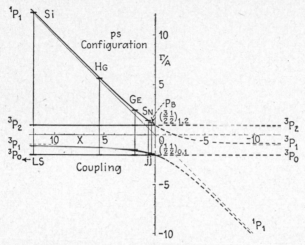

FIG. 14.19.—Theoretical curves for the fine structure of a ps electron configuration. Observed triplets and singlets are shown to be in good agreement with theory. (*After Houston.*)

and the triplet fine structure following the interval rule with the ratio 2:1. If $X << A$ we have jj-coupling with the same outside triplet separation. This is just the result obtained from the classical theory given in Secs. 12.7, 12.8, and 12.9 (see also Fig. 12.13). For negative values of X the middle triplet level becomes the singlet, and the singlet level becomes the triplet. Such cases of the singlet lying below the triplet are observed in the diffuse series of Cd and Hg.

Observed triplet and singlet intervals for Si, Hg, Ge, Sn, and Pb are seen (in Fig. 14.19) to fit the theoretical curves to a remarkable degree of accuracy. In plotting the observed terms, the value of A is first determined by dividing the observed intervals $^3P_0 - {}^3P_2$ by three. This gives a value of A in wave numbers which, with the observed intervals of $^1P_1$ and $^3P_1$ substituted in Eqs. (14.7a) and (14.7c), respectively, gives two values of X. These are averaged and the terms plotted at that X. The configurations plotted are: Se, $3p4s$; Hg, $6p6s$; Ge, $4p5s$; Sn, $5p6s$; Pb, $6p7s$.

Many other configurations are found to fit these curves at large values of X (not shown in the figure), where the singlet lies far above the triplet and the triplets have the ratio 2:1. This figure is also to be compared with the observed silicon series in Fig. 12.13.

In addition to the interaction energies Houston's formulas include the Landé g factors for the weak-field Zeeman effect. They are:

$$\text{Singlet } {}^1g_L = 1 + \frac{1}{2L(L+1)} - \frac{X+1}{2L(L+1)[(X+1)^2 + 4L(L+1)]^{\frac{1}{2}}} \tag{14.8a}$$

$$\text{Triplet} \begin{cases} {}^3g_{L+1} = \dfrac{L+2}{L+1} & (14.8b) \\[2mm] {}^3g_L = 1 + \dfrac{1}{2L(L+1)} + \dfrac{X+1}{2L(L+1)[(X+1)^2 + 4L(L+1)]^{\frac{1}{2}}} & (14.8c) \\[2mm] {}^3g_{L-1} = \dfrac{L-1}{L} & (14.8d) \end{cases}$$

For the outside triplet terms these formulas give the same g factors as before and are independent of the coupling scheme. According to the g sum rule, the sum of the g's for the two terms with the same J value is the same for all couplings and all field strengths. This is given by the sum of Eqs. (14.8a) and (14.8c):

$$\sum g_L = 2 + \frac{1}{L(L+1)}. \tag{14.9}$$

The X values obtained for Sn and Pb from Fig. 14.19 and substituted in the above given equations yield g factors in excellent agreement with experimental values obtained from the Zeeman effect. The following calculated values were obtained by Houston.

Table 14.6.—Calculated and Observed g Factors for Sn and Pb
(After Houston)

Element	Term	Obs.	Calc.	Element	Term	Obs.	Calc.
Sn	${}^1P_1$	1.125	1.123	Pb	${}^1P_1$	1.150	1.148
	${}^3P_1$	1.375	1.377		${}^3P_1$	1.350	1.352
	Σg	2.500	2.500		Σg	2.500	2.500

The application of Houston's formulas to configurations of the type p^5s and d^9s has been carried out by Laporte and Inglis,[1] and by Condon and Shortley.[2] This extension is possible for two reasons: first, the terms are of the same type with the same J values, and, second, the outside triplet separation is just the same as for one electron except that

[1] Laporte, O., and D. R. Inglis, Phys. Rev., **35**, 1337, 1930.
[2] Condon, E. U., and G. H. Shortley, Phys. Rev., **35**, 1342, 1930.

it is inverted. This latter result means only that the above given A factor is negative instead of positive. In order that the singlet be above the inverted triplet, as observed, X must also be negative.

Substituting $-X'$ for X and $-A'$ for A in Eqs. (14.7a, b, c, and d), formulas for the configurations p^5s, d^9s, and $f^{13}s$ are obtained. Curves plotted from these new equations are given in Fig. 14.20, along with the observed intervals for a number of elements. It will be noted that, even for highly ionized atoms like In IV and Sn V, the observed intervals are in excellent agreement with theory. The configurations

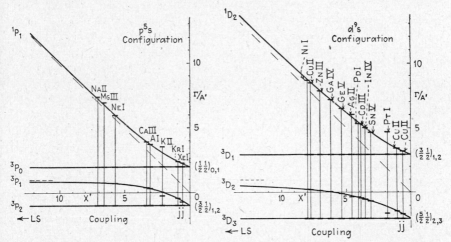

Fig. 14.20.—Fine-structure curves for the configurations p^5s and d^9s. Observed terms are shown to agree with the theoretical curves. (*After Laporte and Inglis.*)

plotted in the left-hand figure are: Ne I, Na II, and Mg III, $2p^53s$; A I, K II, and Ca III, $3p^54s$; Kr I, $4p^55s$; Xe I, $5p^56s$. Those in the right-hand figure are: Ni I, Cu II, Zn III, Ga IV, and Ge V, $3d^94s$; Pd I, Ag II, Cd III, In IV, and Sn V, $4d^95s$; Pt I, $5d^96s$; Cu II, $3d^96s$; Cu II, $3d^97s$.

14.16. Slater's Multiplet Relations.—A general first-order perturbation treatment of the interaction between two arbitrary electrons in a central force field has been attempted by Slater. Again taking into account the Heisenberg electrostatic resonance interaction, but neglecting spin-orbit interactions, he obtained equations for the relative intervals between the different triplets and singlets belonging to the same electron configuration. Although Slater's calculations are beyond the scope of this book, we may consider briefly some of his results.[1] In titanium, for example, the lowest configuration $3d^24s^2$ gives rise to two triplets and three singlets, ^3P, ^3F, ^1S, ^1D, and ^1G. Assuming certain values for the coupling parameters in his equations, Slater obtains the following interval ratios between levels:

[1] SLATER, J. C., *Phys. Rev.*, **34**, 1293, 1929.

Value	$^3F - {}^3P$	$^3F - {}^1G$	$^3F - {}^1D$	$^3F - {}^1S$
Observed.................	8500 cm^{-1}	12100 cm^{-1}	7200 cm^{-1}	15100 cm^{-1}
Calculated................	98	113	67	265

One of the important features of these calculations is the order of the terms. Both the observed and calculated order starting with the lowest term is ^3F, ^1D, ^3P, ^1G, and ^1S.

In general, Slater's results show that one cannot always rely upon Hund's rule for excited configurations.

14.17. Multiplet Relations of Goudsmit and Inglis.—An extension of Houston's and Slater's quantum-mechanical treatment of two electrons has been made by Goudsmit[1] and Inglis.[2] Taking into account the electrostatic spin-spin interaction, as well as the spin-orbit interaction, equations have been derived for two or more arbitrary electrons. Though their mathematical treatment will not be given here, their results are of great importance and will be given. In Houston's beautiful account of one s electron and one arbitrary electron, there were but two interactions to be taken into account. With two or more arbitrary electrons the number of interactions is greatly increased and the problem becomes very difficult. Solutions for each particular configuration can be obtained from the observed intervals, however, by adjusting the parameters in the equations until the best agreement is obtained. In the special cases of *equivalent electrons* a number of the interactions become identical and the equations are greatly simplified. These configurations are of importance in that they involve the normal states of a number of atoms. Theoretical curves for two, three, and four similar p electrons are shown in Figs. 14.21 and 14.22. Observed terms for different elements are given to show the excellent agreement with theory. The configurations plotted are shown on the diagrams. X is a measure of the electrostatic spin-spin interaction and A is a measure of the magnetic spin-orbit interaction. One rather interesting case is that of tellurium where the ^3P term is partially inverted; $^3P_0$ and $^3P_1$ fall almost together ($\Delta\nu = 44$ cm^{-1}) and about 4700 cm^{-1} above $^3P_2$. The two singlet terms in selenium have not yet been identified.

14.18. Relative Intensities of Multiplet Lines.—Extensive measurements of the relative intensities of spectrum lines have been made by a number of investigators. In many cases the observed intensities are found to be in excellent agreement with the well-known intensity formulas (see Sec. 12.15). In the titanium multiplet of Fig. 17.12 and

---

[1] GOUDSMIT, S., *Phys. Rev.*, **35**, 1325, 1930.
[2] INGLIS, D. R., *Phys. Rev.*, **38**, 862, 1931.

Table 14.5, for example, the following experimental values have been obtained by Harrison.[1]

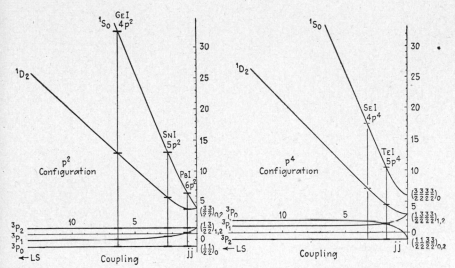

Fig. 14.21.—Fine-structure curves for the configurations p^2 and p^4. (*After Goudsmit.*) Observed terms are shown to agree with the theoretical curves.

The calculated intensities (see table of intensities in the Appendix) are given in *italics* and the observed intensities beneath them in **heavy type.**

Table 14.7.—Observed and Calculated Intensities for the Titanium Multiplet of Fig. 17.12

	$^5G_6^\circ$	$^5G_5^\circ$	$^5G_4^\circ$	$^5G_3^\circ$	$^5G_2^\circ$
$^5F_5$	*100*	*8.5*	*0.3*		
	100	**8.8**	....		
$^5F_4$		*76.2*	*12.2*	*0.6*	
		75.2	**12.2**	....	
$^5F_3$			*56.7*	*12.0*	*0.5*
			56.2	**11.9**	....
$^5F_2$				*41.2*	*8.2*
				41.0	**8.2**
$^5F_1$					*29.7*
					29.2

In some cases where the observed intensities of a multiplet do not agree with the formulas, the sum rules for the lines with a common initial or final state nevertheless hold. Harrison has shown, for certain multiplets in titanium, that while the sum rules do not always apply to a given multiplet, they may apply to a triad of multiplets. In still

[1] Harrison, G. R., *Jour. Opt. Soc. Amer.*, **17**, 389, 1928.

other cases it is necessary to take into account all of the multiplets associated with given initial and final electron configurations.

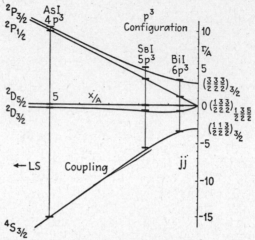

FIG. 14.22.—Fine-structure curves for the configuration p^3. (*After Inglis.*) Observed terms are shown to agree with the theoretical curves.

It has also been shown that the relative intensities between related multiplets, taken as a whole, obey the sum rules (see Sec. 12.16). For a titanium triad of quintet multiplets, for example, the following values have been obtained by Harrison and Engwicht:[1]

		d^3p		
	$^5G^\circ$	$^5F^\circ$	$^5D^\circ$	
$d^3s,\ ^5F$	90	70	50	calculated
	81	70	49	measured (without ν^4 and T corrections)
	89	70	48	measured (with ν^4 and T corrections)

The measures taken from many multiplets show that better agreement between theory and experiment is obtained when ν^4 and temperature corrections are made.

Problems

1. The following list of observed lines form a multiplet. Plot the lines to a frequency scale and, looking for equal frequency differences by marking them on a

Intensity	λ	ν	Intensity	λ	ν	Intensity	λ	ν
1	4716.41	21202.56	30	4749.84	21053.32	70	4767.97	20973.27
2	4720.22	21185.47	40	4752.30	21042.42	100	4777.69	20930.58
3	4724.74	21165.16	35	4755.28	21029.26	140	4787.84	20886.21
2	4729.98	21141.74	25	4758.70	21014.16	190	4798.27	20840.86
20	4747.96	21061.69	45	4758.81	21013.63	250	4808.87	20794.90

[1] HARRISON, G. R., and H. ENGWICHT, *Jour. Opt. Soc. Amer.*, **18**, 287, 1929.

strip of paper, find the term-intervals.   Tabulate the lines in multiplet form, as in Table 14.3.   Applying the Landé interval rule to the observed terms, determine the J, S, and L values.

2. Using the values of X as read from Fig. 14.19 for Si, Ge, and Hg, compute the g factors for each of the four terms, respectively [see Eqs. (14.8)].   Show that the g sum rule holds.

3. Derive all the terms arising from the electron configurations d^3s, d^3p, p^2d, p^4s, and d^7p.

4. Carry out the calculation of the Γ_i factors for d^8 as outlined in the middle of Sec. 14.6, and tabulate them.   From this table make another tabulation like that given in the top third of Table 13.13.   From these Γ sums determine the Γ values of the terms as shown in the middle third of Table 13.13.

CHAPTER XV

THE ZEEMAN EFFECT AND MAGNETIC QUANTUM NUMBERS IN COMPLEX SPECTRA

It is well known to spectroscopists that the Zeeman effect plays an important part in the making of any analysis of a complex spectrum. This is due largely to the fact that the Zeeman patterns for all types of transitions can be predicted with considerable accuracy. Let us start therefore with a calculation of Zeeman patterns for various types of transitions and then compare the results with the observed patterns. To do this we must first obtain an expression for the magnetic energy of an atom in any stationary state.

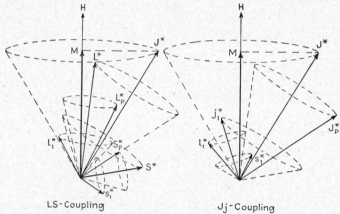

LS-Coupling   Jj-Coupling

Fig. 15.1.—Classical models for the motion of complex atoms in a weak magnetic field.

15.1. Magnetic Energy and the Landé g Factor.—In the previous chapter we have seen that the vector model for complex spectra is essentially the same as the model for two valence electrons. The extension into complex spectra was made by considering all but one of the electrons as a parent term or configuration to which the remaining electron is added (see Figs. 14.2 and 14.3).

In a weak magnetic field the atom as a whole becomes quantized and oriented to the field H, in such a way that the projection of $J^*h/2\pi$ on H is equal to $Mh/2\pi$ (see Fig. 15.1). For terms with whole-integral values of J the magnetic quantum number $M = 0, \pm 1, \pm 2, \cdots, \pm J$. For terms with half-integral values of J, $M = \pm\frac{1}{2}, \pm\frac{3}{2}, \pm\frac{5}{2}, \cdots, \pm J$. The magnetic quantum numbers for a $^5D_3$ term, for example, are $M = 3$,

2, 1, 0, -1, -2, -3, and for a $^4P_{\frac{3}{2}}$ term they are $M = \frac{5}{2}, \frac{3}{2}, \frac{1}{2}, -\frac{1}{2}, -\frac{3}{2},$ $-\frac{5}{2}$. Just as in the case of one electron the magnetic energy is determined by M, H, and the Landé g factor [see Eq. (10.17)]:

$$-\Delta T = M \cdot g \cdot \frac{He}{4\pi mc^2} \text{ cm}^{-1} = M \cdot g \cdot \mathbf{L} \text{ cm}^{-1}. \tag{15.1}$$

For a given field strength H the separations of consecutive magnetic levels for one term, relative to those of another, will be given by the g factor of each respective level. Just as in one- and two-electron systems the g factor is the ratio between the total magnetic moment of the atom in Bohr magnetons and the total mechanical moment in units of $h/2\pi$.

If the coupling is LS (*i.e.*, all spins coupled together to form S^* and all orbits coupled together to form L^*, and S^* and L^* in turn coupled together to form J^*), the g factor is obtained in exactly the same manner as it is for a single electron. S^* is thus treated like the spin of a single electron and L^* like the corresponding orbital momentum vector. From Eq. (10.11) we write

$$g = 1 + \frac{J^{*2} + S^{*2} - L^{*2}}{2J^{*2}}. \tag{15.2}$$

Should the coupling on the other hand be Jj (*i.e.*, the spin and orbit of the last bound electron coupled together to form j_1^*, and j_1^* in turn coupled together with J_P^* of the parent term of the ion to form J^*), the g factor is obtained in exactly the same manner as it is for two electrons in jj-coupling [see Eq. (13.14)]. J_P^* of the parent term is now treated like j_2, the spin-orbit resultant of a single electron to be coupled with the j_1^* of the other electron, so that

$$g = g_1 \frac{J^{*2} + j_1^{*2} - J_P^{*2}}{2J^{*2}} + g_P \frac{J^{*2} + J_P^{*2} - j_1^{*2}}{2J^{*2}}, \tag{15.3}$$

where g_1 is the g factor for the single added electron derived from Eq. (10.11), and g_P is the g factor for the parent term derived from Eq. (13.8) or (13.14). It should be pointed out that the parent term may arise from an LS- or jj-coupling scheme even though the added electron j_1^* is coupled to it finally in Jj-coupling. Tables of g factors for LS-coupling are given in the Appendix. For Jj-coupling there are so many possibilities that Eq. (15.3) must be used.

A graphical representation of the magnetic energy corresponding to the vector model, given by Eq. (15.1), is shown in Fig. 15.2 for a $^4D_{\frac{7}{2}}$ term. The vector J^* is quantized with respect to the field direction H so that its projection $M = \frac{7}{2}, \frac{5}{2}, \frac{3}{2}, \frac{1}{2}, -\frac{1}{2}, -\frac{3}{2}, -\frac{5}{2}, -\frac{7}{2}$. Multiplying J^* by the g factor $\frac{10}{7}$ and projecting on H we obtain the values of Mg. These are proportional to the magnetic energy. The result is eight equally spaced levels each separated from the next by $g \cdot \mathbf{L}$. If the Mg values are multiplied by $He/4\pi mc^2$, the figure will give the intervals in cm^{-1}.

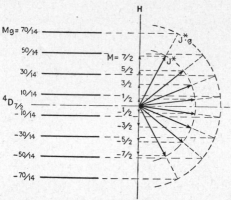

FIG. 15.2.—Schematic representation of Zeeman splitting for a $^4D_{\frac{7}{2}}$ term in a weak magnetic field.

15.2. The Calculation of Zeeman Patterns.

—As an example of the calculation of Zeeman patterns we shall first consider the theoretical patterns of $^7S_3 - {}^7P_{2,3,4}$, observed patterns for which appear in chromium (see Fig. 14.1). Since S and P terms never have more than one and three fine-structure levels, respectively, this multiplet contains but three lines. Although the lines look just like those of a principal-series triplet, the Zeeman patterns are entirely different from those shown in

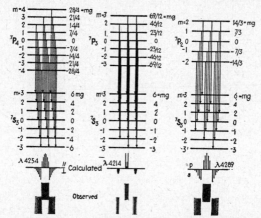

FIG. 15.3.—Zeeman effect, theoretical and observed patterns, for a $^7S_3 - {}^7P_{2,3,4}$ multiplet. (*Observed patterns are from original spectrograms by H. D. Babcock.*)

Fig. 13.4. The intervals between the three lines indicate LS-coupling with a ratio approximately 4:3. The g factors for $^7S_3$, $^7P_2$, $^7P_3$, and $^7P_4$ (see Appendix) are 2, $\frac{7}{3}$, $\frac{23}{12}$, and $\frac{7}{4}$, respectively. A graphical construction, such as that shown in Fig. 15.2, gives the intervals shown in Fig. 15.3.

With the selection rule that in any transition the magnetic quantum number M changes by $+1$, 0, or -1 only, the Zeeman patterns shown below in the same figure are obtained. Another method is to write down the Mg values for both the initial and final states of a given line with equal values of M directly above and below each other, as follows:

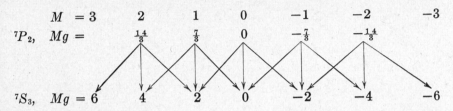

$$M = 3 \qquad 2 \qquad 1 \qquad 0 \qquad -1 \qquad -2 \qquad -3$$

$${}^7P_2, \quad Mg = \qquad \tfrac{14}{3} \qquad \tfrac{7}{3} \qquad 0 \qquad -\tfrac{7}{3} \qquad -\tfrac{14}{3}$$

$${}^7S_3, \quad Mg = 6 \qquad 4 \qquad 2 \qquad 0 \qquad -2 \qquad -4 \qquad -6$$

Vertical differences, $\Delta M = 0$, give the p components at

$$\Delta\nu = 0, \ \pm\tfrac{1}{3}\mathbf{L}, \text{ and } \pm\tfrac{2}{3}\mathbf{L} \text{ cm}^{-1}.$$

Diagonal differences, $\Delta M = \pm 1$, give the s components at

$$\Delta\nu = \pm\tfrac{4}{3}\mathbf{L}, \ \pm\tfrac{5}{3}\mathbf{L}, \ \pm\tfrac{6}{3}\mathbf{L}, \ \pm\tfrac{7}{3}\mathbf{L}, \text{ and } \pm\tfrac{8}{3}\mathbf{L} \text{ cm}^{-1}.$$

These fractions for the whole pattern are written together as

$$ {}^7S_3 - {}^7P_2, \qquad \Delta\nu = \pm\frac{(0), \ (1), \ (2), \ 4, \ 5, \ 6, \ 7, \ 8}{3}\mathbf{L} \text{ cm}^{-1}.$$

Similarly the patterns for the two other lines are calculated as

$$ {}^7S_3 - {}^7P_3, \qquad \Delta\nu = \pm\frac{(1), \ (2), \ (3), \ 21, \ 22, \ 23, \ 24, \ 25, \ 26}{12}\mathbf{L} \text{ cm}^{-1};$$

$$ {}^7S_3 - {}^7P_4, \qquad \Delta\nu = \pm\frac{(0), \ (1), \ (2), \ (3), \ 4, \ 5, \ 6, \ 7, \ 8, \ 9, \ 10}{4}\mathbf{L} \text{ cm}^{-1}.$$

The observed patterns of these three lines, reproduced at the bottom of Fig. 15.3, are from original spectrograms taken by Babcock at the Mt. Wilson Observatory. These are some of the earliest anomalous Zeeman patterns to be photographed in any laboratory.

15.3. Intensity Rules and Zeeman Patterns for Quartets, Quintets, and Sextets.—The intensity rules for the Zeeman effect in complex spectra are the same as those for one- and two-electron systems. These rules, derived from the classical orbital model of the atom and the sum rules, are given in Sec. 13.3. Since these rules involve only the J's and M's of the initial and final states they are valid for all coupling schemes. The relative intensities of the different components of a given pattern are usually represented by the heights of the lines in the schematic diagrams. It is to be noted that the component $J = 0$ to

$J = 0$ of $^7S_3 - {}^7P_3$ (Fig. 15.3) is zero as given by the intensity formulas, *i.e.*, the transition is forbidden.

A number of patterns typical of quartet and sextet multiplets in general are given in Fig. 15.4 for vanadium. Patterns typical of quintet multiplets are given in Fig. 15.5 for chromium. The calculated patterns are given above or below each observed pattern. The five lines $\lambda\lambda4352$, 4344, 4339, 4337, and 4340 are the five diagonal lines of a $^5D - {}^5F$ multiplet. It is to be noted that, as the number of components decreases in going from one pattern to the next, the separations increase. The line $\lambda4340$, $(^5D_0 - {}^5F_1)$, although partly masked by $\lambda4339$, is of particular interest in that it is one of the few spectrum lines known which remains single in all field strengths. The reason for this is that the Mg values for both the initial and final states are zero. Unresolved patterns like those of $\lambda4352$ and $\lambda4344$ are called *blends*.

The pattern $\lambda4613$ in chromium has 2.5 times the separation of a normal triplet. In general the Zeeman patterns for different combinations are so different from one another that the assignment of a completely resolved pattern to a definite multiplet is unambiguous. The importance of resolved patterns in making the analysis of an uncharted spectrum, as well as checking the analysis of a spectrum already made, cannot be overemphasized.

15.4. Paschen-Back Effect in Complex Spectra.—So far as experimental observations are concerned the Paschen-Back effect in complex spectra is practically unknown. This is due in general to the fact that even with the strongest magnetic fields attainable, the multiplet separations are many times the Zeeman separations of any one level. There is little doubt, however, that if, and when, strong enough fields are obtained the observed splitting will be very closely that predicted by theory. There is some justification for this as we shall see in the study of the Paschen-Back effect of hyperfine structure in Chap. XIX.

In a weak magnetic field a complex atom is quantized with respect to H more or less as a rigid whole. When the field becomes strong enough so that the Zeeman levels of each fine-structure level begin to overlap the patterns of the neighboring levels of the same multiplet, the strong-field Paschen-Back effect sets in and S^* and L^*, or J_P^* and j_2^*, become quantized separately with the field direction H. The quantum conditions under these circumstances are the same as those for two electrons: the projections M of S^* and L^*, or J_P^* and j_1^*, on H take integral or half integral values only, depending upon whether S and L, or J_P and j_1^*, are whole or half integral respectively. When the field becomes still stronger and the magnetic levels of one multiplet begin to overlap those from the neighboring multiplets of the same configuration, the complete Paschen-Back effect sets in and each s_i^* and l_i^* becomes quantized independently with the field H. The quantum conditions again

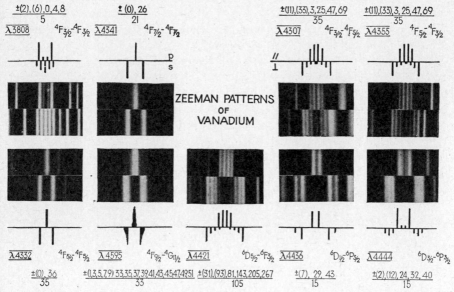

Fig. 15.4.—Zeeman patterns, observed and calculated, for typical quartet and sextet multiplet lines in vanadium. (*Observed patterns are from original spectrograms by H. D. Babcock.*)

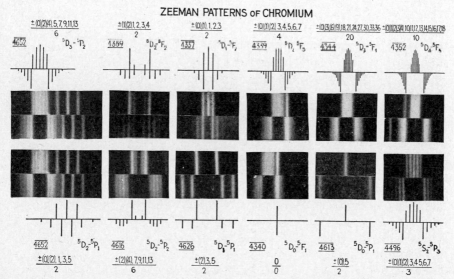

Fig. 15.5.—Zeeman patterns observed and calculated, for typical quintet multiplet lines in chromium. (*Observed patterns are from original spectrograms by H. D. Babcock.*)

are just the same as those for two-electron systems. Each spin and each orbit has a component along H. The sum of these components $\Sigma m_{s_i} + \Sigma m_{l_i}$ gives the magnetic quantum number M of the entire atomic system in that state.

When considering transitions between levels in weak, strong, and very strong fields, each multiplet in LS-coupling in a strong field will go over to a pattern resembling a normal triplet (see Fig. 13.9). In a very strong field all the lines arising from the configuration of electrons will spread out into a pattern again resembling a normal triplet (see Fig. 13.14). Patterns similar to those of Figs. 13.11 and 13.15 will result in the case of Jj-coupling. We shall now make use of the weak- and strong-field and very strong field quantum numbers to calculate the allowed spectral terms arising from given electron configurations.

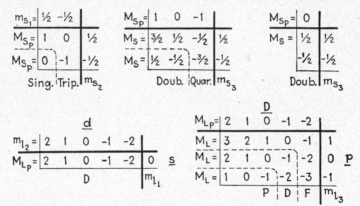

Fig. 15.6.—Combination of very strong field quantum numbers for the electron configuration dsp.

15.5. Derivation of Spectral Terms by Use of Magnetic Quantum Numbers.—In deriving spectral terms from magnetic quantum numbers, one may start with the very strong field where the coupling between all spins and orbits is broken down. Consider as a first example three arbitrary electrons, no two of which are equivalent, such as s, d, and p. For these electrons we shall have $s_1 = \frac{1}{2}, s_2 = \frac{1}{2}, s_3 = \frac{1}{2}, l_1 = 0, l_2 = 2$, and $l_3 = 1$, for which the magnetic quantum numbers are $m_{s_1} = \pm\frac{1}{2}$, $m_{s_2} = \pm\frac{1}{2}, m_{s_3} = \pm\frac{1}{2}, m_{l_1} = 0, m_{l_2} = 0, \pm1, \pm2$, and $m_{l_3} = 0, \pm1$.

Extending the scheme of Breit (see Sec. 13.10), we first combine the spins s_1 and s_2 as shown at the left in Fig. 15.6. The resultant values of M_{S_P} are cut apart by the L-shaped dotted line to form parent values for the third electron. Combining each run of M_{S_P} values with m_{s_3} we obtain three runs of M_S values. These correspond, as shown, to strong-field quantum numbers for doublet, quartet, and doublet terms. In a similar fashion the l's are combined in the lower arrays. m_{l_1} with m_{l_2} forms the run $M_{L_P} = 2, 1, 0, -1, -2$, to form the parent values for the third electron. Combining these with m_l the strong-field runs of values $M_L = 1$ to -1, 2 to -2, and 3 to -3, corresponding to P, D, and F terms, respectively, are obtained. In terms of the branching rule these resultant values would be written down from the parent terms as follows:

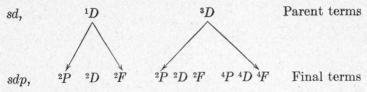

The first and fourth arrays give the first row; and the second, third, and fifth arrays give the last row. If now each final run of M_S values is combined with each run of M_L values, all of the weak-field quantum numbers of the above *final terms* are obtained. This has been done

$M_L=$	3	2	1	$\overset{F}{0}$	-1	-2	-3	
$M =$	$9/2$	$7/2$	$5/2$	$3/2$	$1/2$	$-1/2$	$-3/2$	$3/2$
$M =$	$7/2$	$5/2$	$3/2$	$1/2$	$-1/2$	$-3/2$	$-5/2$	$1/2$
$M =$	$5/2$	$3/2$	$1/2$	$-1/2$	$-3/2$	$-5/2$	$-7/2$	$-1/2$
$M =$	$3/2$	$1/2$	$-1/2$	$-3/2$	$-5/2$	$-7/2$	$-9/2$	$3/2$

$$^4F_{3/2}\quad {}^4F_{5/2}\quad {}^4F_{7/2}\quad {}^4F_{9/2}\quad M_S$$

Fig. 15.7.—Combination of the strong-field quantum numbers of a ^4F term showing the formation of resultant weak-field quantum numbers.

for the ^4F term in Fig. 15.7. The others will be left as exercises for the reader.

15.6. Equivalent Electrons and the Pauli Exclusion Principle.—In the calculation of spectral terms arising from two or more equivalent electrons we must take the Pauli exclusion principle into account and start with the very strong field quantum numbers (see Sec. 13.11). Consider as an example three equivalent p electrons. We first write down the six possible states for a single p electron in a very strong field. They are:

$$
\begin{array}{ccccccc}
m_s = & \tfrac{1}{2} & \tfrac{1}{2} & \tfrac{1}{2} & -\tfrac{1}{2} & -\tfrac{1}{2} & -\tfrac{1}{2} \\
m_l = & 1 & 0 & -1 & 1 & 0 & -1 \\
& (a) & (b) & (c) & (d) & (e) & (f)
\end{array}
\tag{15.4}
$$

Since the exclusion principle requires that no two electrons have all quantum numbers n, l, m_s or m_l alike we collect all possible combinations of the above states three at a time, with no two alike. They are:

TABLE 15.1

abc	acd	adf	bcf	cde
abd	ace	aef	bde	cdf
abe	acf	bcd	bdf	cef
abf	ade	bce	bef	def

Writing M_S for Σm_s and M_L for Σm_l, the results are tabulated as follows:

$$\begin{aligned}
&\text{For } M_S = \tfrac{3}{2}, &&M_L = 0 \\
&\text{For } M_S = \tfrac{1}{2}, &&M_L = 0, \quad 2, 1, 0, -1, -2, \quad 1, 0, -1 \\
&\text{For } M_S = -\tfrac{1}{2}, &&M_L = 0, \quad 2, 1, 0, -1, -2, \quad 1, 0, -1 \\
&\text{For } M_S = -\tfrac{3}{2}, &&M_L = 0
\end{aligned} \qquad (15.5)$$

These are just the strong-field values for ^4S, ^2D, and ^2P terms (see Table 14.3).

In a similar calculation for four equivalent p electrons we write down the same six possible states for one p electron [Eq. (15.4)] and take all possible combinations of four states at a time with no two alike. They are:

TABLE 15.2

abcd	abde	acde	adef	bcef
abce	abdf	acdf	bcde	bdef
abcf	abef	acef	bcdf	cdef

When m_s and m_l values are summed for each combination and tabulated one finds:

$$\begin{aligned}
&\text{For } M_S = 1, &&M_L = 1, 0, -1 \\
&\text{For } M_S = 0, &&M_L = 1, 0, -1, \quad 2, 1, 0, -1, -2, \quad 0 \\
&\text{For } M_S = -1, &&M_L = 1, 0, -1
\end{aligned}$$

corresponding to ^1S, ^3P, and ^1D terms. These are exactly the terms arising from two similar p electrons (see Table 14.3).

For five equivalent p electrons there are just six combinations, taking five states at a time. They are

abcde abcdf abcef abdef acdef bcdef

When summed and tabulated as before one finds:

$$\begin{aligned}
&\text{For } M_S = \tfrac{1}{2}, &&M_L = 1, 0, -1 \\
&\text{For } M_S = -\tfrac{1}{2}, &&M_L = 1, 0, -1
\end{aligned}$$

These are just the same values given in Eq. (15.4) for one electron and give rise to a ^2P term.

For six equivalent p electrons there is but one combination of the very strong field quantum numbers, taking six states at a time, with no two alike, and that is $abcdef$. The sum gives $M_S = 0$ and $M_L = 0$, a $^1S_0$ term. Here we see that six p electrons with the same total quantum number, by Pauli's exclusion principle, close a subshell and have zero as a resultant angular momentum (see Table 14.3). The table of p electrons is symmetrical about the center where the greatest multiplicities and the greatest number of magnetic levels arise.

In the calculation of terms arising from equivalent electrons in jj-coupling we need only go to the strong-field quantum numbers. The reason for this is that here each electron is specified by four quantum numbers and it is not necessary to go to very strong fields to separate them as in LS-coupling. As a single example of the calculations let us consider three equivalent p electrons. The six possible states for a p electron in a strong field are

$$
\begin{array}{ccccccc}
j = & \tfrac{3}{2} & \tfrac{3}{2} & \tfrac{3}{2} & \tfrac{3}{2} & \tfrac{1}{2} & \tfrac{1}{2} \\
m_j = & \tfrac{3}{2} & \tfrac{1}{2} & -\tfrac{1}{2} & -\tfrac{3}{2} & \tfrac{1}{2} & -\tfrac{1}{2} \\
& (a) & (b) & (c) & (d) & (e) & (f)
\end{array}
$$

Since the Pauli exclusion principle requires that no two electrons have all the quantum numbers n, l, j, and m_j alike, we collect all possible combinations of the above given states three at a time, with no two alike. These will be just the combinations given in Table 15.1. Summing up the values of m_j for each of the 20 combinations the results may be tabulated as follows:

For $j_1 = \tfrac{3}{2}$, $j_2 = \tfrac{3}{2}$, $j_3 = \tfrac{3}{2}$, $m_j = \tfrac{3}{2}, \tfrac{1}{2}, -\tfrac{1}{2}, -\tfrac{3}{2}$

For $j_1 = \tfrac{3}{2}$, $j_2 = \tfrac{3}{2}$, $j_3 = \tfrac{1}{2}$, $m_j = \tfrac{1}{2}, -\tfrac{1}{2}, \tfrac{5}{2}, \tfrac{3}{2}, \tfrac{1}{2}, -\tfrac{1}{2}, -\tfrac{3}{2}, -\tfrac{5}{2}, \tfrac{3}{2}, \tfrac{1}{2}, -\tfrac{1}{2}, -\tfrac{3}{2}$

For $j_1 = \tfrac{3}{2}$, $j_2 = \tfrac{1}{2}$, $j_3 = \tfrac{1}{2}$, $m_j = \tfrac{3}{2}, \tfrac{1}{2}, -\tfrac{1}{2}, -\tfrac{3}{2}$

These correspond to the five terms $(\tfrac{3}{2} \tfrac{3}{2} \tfrac{3}{2})_{\tfrac{3}{2}}$, $(\tfrac{3}{2} \tfrac{3}{2} \tfrac{1}{2})_{\tfrac{1}{2}}$, $(\tfrac{3}{2} \tfrac{3}{2} \tfrac{1}{2})_{\tfrac{3}{2}}$, $(\tfrac{3}{2} \tfrac{1}{2} \tfrac{1}{2})_{\tfrac{3}{2}}$, and $(\tfrac{3}{2} \tfrac{1}{2} \tfrac{1}{2})_{\tfrac{3}{2}}$, which go over in LS-coupling to $^2P_{\tfrac{3}{2}}$, $^2P_{\tfrac{1}{2}}$, $^2D_{\tfrac{3}{2}}$, $^2D_{\tfrac{3}{2}}$, and $^4S_{\tfrac{3}{2}}$ (see Fig. 14.22).

We shall now turn to the more complicated cases of equivalent d electrons. Two equivalent d electrons have already been treated in Sec. 13.11 and shown to give rise to ^1S, ^3P, ^1D, ^3F, and ^1G terms. For three or more electrons we continue the same scheme by first writing down the 10 possible states for one d electron:

$$
\begin{array}{ccccccccccc}
m_s = & \tfrac{1}{2} & \tfrac{1}{2} & \tfrac{1}{2} & \tfrac{1}{2} & \tfrac{1}{2} & -\tfrac{1}{2} & -\tfrac{1}{2} & -\tfrac{1}{2} & -\tfrac{1}{2} & -\tfrac{1}{2} \\
m_l = & 2 & 1 & 0 & -1 & -2 & 2 & 1 & 0 & -1 & -2 \\
& (a) & (b) & (c) & (d) & (e) & (f) & (g) & (h) & (i) & (j)
\end{array} \quad (15.6)
$$

For d^3 we take these three at a time with no two alike and find 120 combinations that have to be collected and segregated. The resultant sums will correspond exactly to the terms given in Table 14.3. For d^4, taking four at a time with no two alike, there are 210 possible combinations to be evaluated. Such calculations become tedious and cumbersome, to say the least, but fortunately a shorthand method has been discovered by Gibbs, Wilber, and White,[1] and by Russell.[2] We shall first apply this scheme to three equivalent d electrons.

Referring to Eq. (15.6) take only those combinations of numbers three at a time where all three m_s values are plus and those where all three are minus. These in terms of the letters are

$$
\begin{array}{llllll}
abc & ace & bde & fgh & fhj & gij \\
abd & ade & cde & fgi & fij & hij \\
abe & bcd &   & fgj & ghi \\
acd & bce &   & fhi & ghj
\end{array}
$$

Summing the corresponding values of the quantum numbers we obtain for the plus values

$$M_S = \tfrac{3}{2}, \quad M_L = 3, 2, 1, 0, -1, -2, -3, \quad 1, 0, -1$$

and for the minus values   (15.7)

$$M_S = -\tfrac{3}{2}, \quad M_L = 3, 2, 1, 0, -1, -2, -3, \quad 1, 0, -1.$$

These correspond to parts of ^4P and ^4F terms, the rest of which will be obtained from the following process. Of the 100 remaining combinations to be made and summed each one will have two of the m_s values plus and the other one minus, or vice versa. If in each of these 100 combinations the two m_s values that are alike are considered alone, they will contain just the combinations that give triplets for two equivalent d electrons: these are ^3P and ^3F. The third electron in all combinations has an opposite sign and corresponds to the values for a single d electron. Combining the triplets that arise from d^2 with the doublet that arises from d in all possible ways to form doublets, we obtain just the 100 combinations desired. This is done quickly by the branching rule as follows:

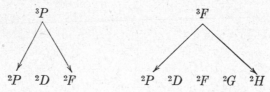

This final set of terms has M_S values of $+\tfrac{1}{2}$ and $-\tfrac{1}{2}$. Striking out one P and one F term to go with Eq. (15.7), we have left ^2P, ^2D, ^2D, ^2F, ^2G, and ^2H. The resultant terms for three equivalent d electrons are

$$d^3, \quad ^2D, \quad ^2P, \ ^2D, \ ^2F, \ ^2G, \ ^2H, \quad ^4P, \ ^4F.$$

Assume, as another example, that the correct terms have been derived for d, d^2, d^3, and d^4 and we wish to calculate the terms for d^5. Referring

[1] GIBBS, R. C., D. T. WILBER, and H. E. WHITE, Phys. Rev., **29**, 790, 1927.
[2] RUSSELL, H. N., Phys. Rev., **29**, 782, 1927.

to Eq. (15.6) we take only those combinations five at a time where all five m_s values are plus, or all five minus. These are *abcde* and *fghij* Summing these we have for the plus values

$$M_S = \tfrac{5}{2}, \qquad M_L = 0$$

and for the minus values

$$M_S = -\tfrac{5}{2}, \qquad M_L = 0. \tag{15.8}$$

These are just one-third the values needed to form a ^6S term.

There will now be a set of combinations from Eq. (15.6) in which four spins will be plus and the fifth one minus, or vice versa. That part of the combinations in which four of the spins add gives quintets. From Table 14.1 we find for d^4 one quintet only, ^5D. The fifth electron with opposite sign corresponds to ^2D. Combining these in all possible ways we get

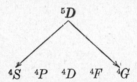

Striking out the S term to go with Eq. (15.8), we have left parts of ^4P, ^4D, ^4F, and ^4G terms. It should be pointed out here that we now have those parts of the ^6S term for which $M_S = \tfrac{5}{2}, \tfrac{3}{2}, -\tfrac{3}{2},$ and $-\tfrac{5}{2}$, and those parts of each quartet term for which $M_S = \tfrac{3}{2}$ and $-\tfrac{3}{2}$.

Again there will be a set of combinations from Eq. (15.6) in which three spins will be plus and the two others minus, or vice versa. The combinations of d^3 have already been shown to give ^4P and ^4F terms, and the combinations of d^2 to give ^3P and ^3F terms. Combining these in all possible ways to form doublets,

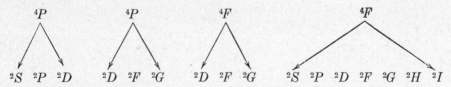

Striking out one S term to complete the ^6S term above, and one each of P, D, F, and G, to complete the ^4P, ^4D, ^4F, and ^4G terms, respectively, we have the remaining terms as doublets. The resultant terms arising from five equivalent d electrons are, therefore,

$$d^5, \quad ^2D, \quad ^2P, \, ^2D, \, ^2F, \, ^2G, \, ^2H, \quad ^2S, \, ^2D, \, ^2F, \, ^2G, \, ^2I, \quad ^4P, \, ^4F, \quad ^4D, \, ^4G, \quad ^6S.$$

Since a subshell of d electrons lacking n electrons to complete it will give rise to exactly the same terms as a configuration of n equivalent electrons, written symbolically $d^{10-n} = d^n$, the lower half of Table 14.3 is symmetrical with the upper half.

A continuation of this process for equivalent f electrons leads to the terms given in the tables in the Appendix. The number of possible combinations for each configuration of equivalent electrons is given in parentheses at the beginning of each row. These numbers are computed from the well-known combination-theory formula for p things taken q at a time.

$$\text{Number of combinations} = \frac{p!}{q!(p-q)!}. \qquad (15.9)$$

This number is equal to the number of Zeeman levels for the entire configuration. For d^2, for example, the terms are ^1S, ^3P, ^1D, ^3F, and ^1G, for which there are $1 + 9 + 5 + 21 + 9 = 45$ Zeeman levels. Without the above presented shorthand process of making several thousand combinations, the calculations for equivalent f electrons would become very laborious.

The largest number of Zeeman levels and the highest multiplicity to be derived from equivalent electrons are from half a subshell. Furthermore, the term of highest multiplicity is an S term and, wherever observed, always lies deepest. On the quantum mechanics the configuration for an S term is spherically symmetrical about the nucleus (see Chap. IV). This is part of the explanation of the increased binding of d electrons at the expense of s electrons at Cr and Mo in the first and second long periods (see Fig. 14.18). An s electron removed from a spherically symmetrical shell s^2 leaves a spherically symmetrical distribution.

Problems

1. Compute and plot the Zeeman patterns (intervals and relative intensities) for the transitions $^7G_7 - {}^7F_6$, $^7G_6 - {}^7F_6$, $^7G_5 - {}^7F_6$, and $^8P_{\frac{5}{2}} - {}^8S_{\frac{7}{2}}$.

2. Starting with the very strong field quantum numbers, derive the terms arising from the electron configurations $3d4p5p$ and $3d^24p$ (see Secs. 15.5 and 13.11).

3. Using the shorthand method outlined in Sec. 15.6, calculate the spectral terms arising from (*a*) four equivalent d electrons, (*b*) two equivalent f electrons.

CHAPTER XVI

X-RAY SPECTRA

The story of how Röntgen[1] while experimenting with a Crookes vacuum tube in 1895 discovered a new kind of radiation now known as *x-rays*, or *Röntgen-rays*, is well known. So great was the import of Röntgen's discovery that within 3 months x-rays were being used in surgical operations in Vienna. This, along with other practical uses to be made of a single scientific discovery within so short a time, is a good example of the rôle played by modern science in the rapid advancement of civilization. In this introductory treatment of atomic spectra we are not so much concerned with the methods used in obtaining x-rays or with the uses to be made of them as with the atomic processes giving rise to x radiation[2] of which a brief account is here given.

16.1. The Nature of X-rays.—Believing that a crystal is made up of regularly spaced atoms, Laue in 1912 suggested the possibility of using a crystal as a diffraction grating. This idea was verified, at Laue's suggestion, by Friedrich and Knipping.[3] By passing a narrow beam of x-rays through a crystal and then on to a photographic plate, a characteristic diffraction pattern, composed chiefly of small symmetrically placed spots, is observed (see Fig. 16.1). These spots are called *Laue spots* and the entire pattern a *Laue pattern*. This experiment proved for the first time the wave nature of x-rays, although Haga and Wind[4] had previously shown that a beam of x-rays passing through a V-shaped split was broadened more at the narrow end than would be expected from a corpuscular theory.

The two Braggs[5] next succeeded in showing that x-ray diffraction by a crystal could be treated as specular reflection from the crystal planes, the layers of regularly spaced atoms acting as reflecting surfaces. Knowing the distance d between successive layers of atoms in the crystal

---

[1] RÖNTGEN, *Sitz-ber. Phys.-med. Ges.*, Würzburg, 1895; English translation, *Electrician*, Jan. 24, 1896, and April 24, 1896.

[2] For a more complete treatment of the general subject of x-ray spectra and their production the reader is referred to M. Siegbahn, "Spektroskopie der Röntgenstrahlen," 2d ed., 1931.

[3] LAUE, M., and W. FRIEDRICH and P. KNIPPING, *Sitz-ber. Bayer. Akad. Wiss., Math.-phys. Klasse*, p. 303, 1912; *Ann. d. Phys.*, **41**, 971, 1913.

[4] HAGA, H., and C. H. WIND, *Koninklijke Akad. Wetenschappen Amsterdam, Versl.*, **11**, 350, 1902.

[5] BRAGG, W. H., and W. L. BRAGG, "X-rays and Crystal Structure."

and the equal angles of incidence and reflection θ, the x-ray wave-length λ is given by the well-known Bragg equation

$$n\lambda = 2d \sin \theta. \tag{16.1}$$

Within the last decade Walter,[1] Bäcklin,[2] Larsson,[3] Kellström,[4] and others have obtained single-slit diffraction patterns of x-rays by sending

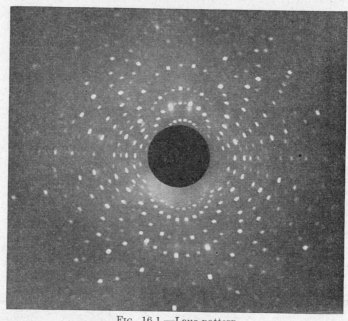

FIG. 16.1.—Laue pattern.

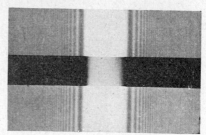

FIG. 2a.   FIG. 2b.
FIG. 16.2a.—Single-slit diffraction, 8.33 Å. (After Larsson.)
FIG. 16.2b.—Diffraction at a thin wire, 8.33 Å. (After Kellström.)

these extremely short waves through a narrow slit and then on to a photographic plate (see Fig. 16.2a). Interference fringes formed by

[1] WALTER, B., Ann. d. Phys., **74**, 661, 1924; **75**, 189, 1924.
[2] BÄCKLIN, E., Dissertation, Uppsala Univ. Årsskr., 1928.
[3] LARSSON, A., Dissertation, Uppsala Univ. Årsskr., 1929.
[4] KELLSTRÖM, G., Dissertation, Uppsala Univ. Årsskr., 1932.

the reflection of x-rays at a grazing angle from plane polished mirrors (Lloyd mirror experiment) have also been photographed by Linnik[1] and Kellström (see Fig. 16.3a).

Bergen Davis and Slack,[2] and Siegbahn,[3] have been able to refract x-rays by passing them through prisms of various materials, and Compton and Doan,[4] Siegbahn, and others have diffracted x-rays from mechanically ruled gratings. It is with ruled gratings that Osgood,[5] Thibaud,[6] and Siegbahn and Magnusson[7] and others have crossed the last gap in the electromagnetic wave chart by photographing and

Fig. 3a.   Fig. 3b.

Fig. 16.3a.—Interference, Lloyd's mirror experiment, 8.33 Å.   (After Kellström.)
Fig. 16.3b.—Diffraction at a straight edge, 8.33 Å.   (After Kellström.)

measuring the wave-lengths of spectrum lines in the region of 10 to 200 Å.

Before the wave nature of x radiation was known with certainty, Barkla and Sadler[8] had shown by the absorption of x-rays in aluminum that the penetrating radiation consisted of two groups of rays differing in penetrating power superposed on a continuous background of radiation. The more penetrating or "hard radiation" is called K radiation and the less penetrating or "soft radiation" is called L radiation.

Photographs of x-ray spectra diffracted by crystals and the measurement of their wave-lengths now show that the K radiation characteristic of a given element consists of short wave-lengths and the L radiation of longer wave-lengths. From the heavier elements in the periodic table "very soft radiations" can now be observed and their wave-lengths measured. These are called M, N, and O radiations.

[1] Linnik, W., Zeits. f. Phys., **65**, 107, 1930. For other photographs of single-slit diffraction patterns see M. Siegbahn, "Spektroskopie der Röntgenstrahlen," 2d ed. 1931.

[2] Davis Bergen, and C. M. Slack, Phys. Rev., **25**, 881, 1925.

[3] Siegbahn, M., Jour. Phys., **6**, 228, 1925.

[4] Compton, A. H., and R. L. Doan, Proc. Nat. Acad. Sci., **11**, 598, 1925.

[5] Osgood, T. H., Nature, **119**, 817, 1927; Phys. Rev., **30**, 567, 1927.

[6] Thibaud, J., Jour. de phys. et radium, **8**, 13, 1927; **8**, 447, 1927; Phys. Zeits. **29**, 241, 1928.

[7] Siegbahn, M., and T. Magnusson, Zeits. f. Phys., **62**, 435, 1930.

[8] Barkla, C. G., and C. A. Sadler, Phil. Mag., **17**, 739, 1909.

16.2. X-ray Emission Spectra and the Moseley Law.—In 1913 Moseley,[1] from a systematic study of the K radiation of Ca 20, Sc 21, Ti 22, V 23, Cr 24, Mn 25, Fe 26, Co 27, Ni 28, Cu 29, and Zn 30,

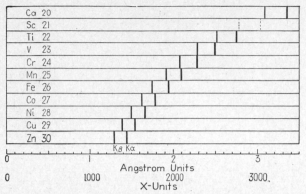

FIG. 16.4.—Wave-lengths of K-series x-ray lines.   (*After Moseley.*)

announced what is known as the *Moseley law*. In brief this law may be stated as follows: The frequency of each corresponding x-ray line is approximately proportional to the square of the atomic number of the

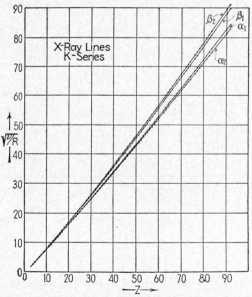

FIG. 16.4a.—Moseley law for K-series x-ray lines.

emitting element. A plot of the K lines observed and measured by Moseley is given in Fig. 16.4 to show that for each element investigated the K radiation consists of two strong spectrum lines. The gradual

[1] MOSELEY, H. G. J., *Phil. Mag.*, **26**, 1024, 1913; **27**, 703, 1914.

change in separation of, and the stepwise shift of, corresponding wavelengths in going from one element to the next are unmistakable in their meaning. For the first time one could say with certainty that the order of the chemical elements is as shown in Fig. 16.4, and also that the elements in the periodic table are constructed with extreme regularity. Prior to Moseley's discovery, cobalt and nickel, because of their atomic

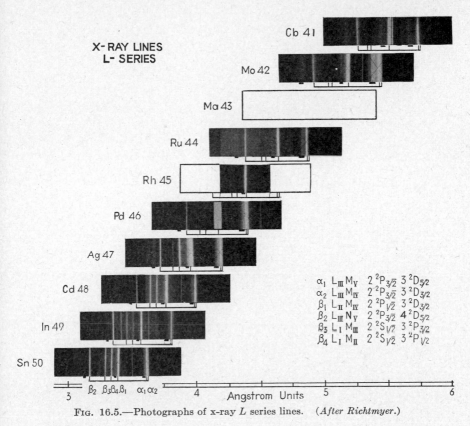

FIG. 16.5.—Photographs of x-ray L series lines. (*After Richtmyer.*)

weights 58.9 and 58.7, respectively, were listed in the order nickel, cobalt. Moseley's x-ray photographs show without doubt that so far as structure is concerned, the order is cobalt, nickel. Optical spectra are also in complete agreement with this result. In Moseley's work the x-rays were photographed in the second and third orders as diffracted from a crystal of potassium ferrocyanide (grating constant $d = 8.408$ Å).

A continuation of Moseley's early work by other investigators has shown that in the heavier elements each of the K_α and K_β lines (see Fig. 16.4) is in itself a close doublet. These four lines are usually designated K_{α_1}, K_{α_2}, K_{β_1}, and K_{β_3}. X-ray spectrograms of all available elements now show that Moseley's law continues throughout the periodic table.   From a graph similar to the one shown in Fig. 16.4a Moseley arrived at the expression

$$\nu_{\text{cm}^{-1}} = KR(Z - \sigma)^2, \tag{16.2}$$

where R is the Rydberg constant $= 109737$ cm^{-1}, and σ and K are constants.   For K_α, $\sigma = 1$ and $K = \frac{3}{4}$.   By analogy with hydrogen-like atoms and Balmer's formula [see Eq. (1.24)], Moseley wrote

$$\nu = R(Z - 1)^2\left(\frac{1}{1^2} - \frac{1}{2^2}\right). \tag{16.3}$$

In Moseley's first work $\sqrt{\nu}$ was plotted against Z.   The division of ν by the quantity R to form a dimensionless constant is due to Sommerfeld.

Like K radiation, the L radiation discovered by Barkla is also composed of a group of spectral lines.   Photographs of some of the L lines of a group of elements are shown in Fig. 16.5 and their wave-lengths are given in the following table.   These are the strong lines of the L series.

TABLE 16.1.—WAVE-LENGTHS OF L SERIES X-RAY LINES
(λ in X units)[1]

L line	Cb 41	Mo 42	Ru 44	Rh 45	Pd 46	Ag 47	Cd 48	In 49	Sn 50
α_1	5712	5395	4836	4588	4359	4145	3948	3764	3592
α_2	5718	5401	4844	4596	4367	4154	3956	3772	3601
β_1	5480	5166	4611	4364	4137	3927	3730	3548	3378
β_2	5226	4909	4362	4122	3901	3694	3506	3331	3168
β_3	5297	5005	4476	4245	4026	3824	3636	3462	3299
β_4	5331	5041	4513	4280	4062	3861	3674	3499	3336

[1] 1000 x units = 1 Ångström unit = 10^{-10} meter.

The characteristic grouping of the observed lines for each element and the regular stepwise shift in the wave-length with atomic number suggest that the Moseley law also holds for L series lines.   That it does is clearly seen in Fig. 16.6.

In the photographs of Fig. 16.5 it is observed that L_{α_2} is in each case a faint line on the long wave-length side of L_{α_1}.   In addition it is to be observed that L_{β_3} and L_{β_4} are strong lines in Sn 50, In 49, Cd 48, and Ag 47, whereas in the other elements they are faint.   This is in agreement with the general observation (see Fig. 16.6), that in going to higher atomic numbers the number of observed lines increases.   In the heaviest elements the L series is composed of as many as 20 lines.

In plotting a graph similar to that given in Fig. 16.6, Moseley obtained the same relation for L radiation that he had for K radiation (see Fig. 16.2).   For the L_{β_1} line, $\sigma = 7.4$ and $K = \frac{5}{36}$, which, by analogy with hydrogen-like orbits, is written

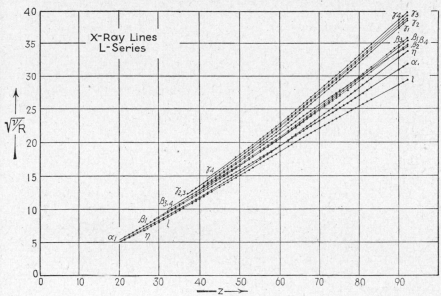

Fig. 16.6.—Moseley law for *L*-series x-ray lines.

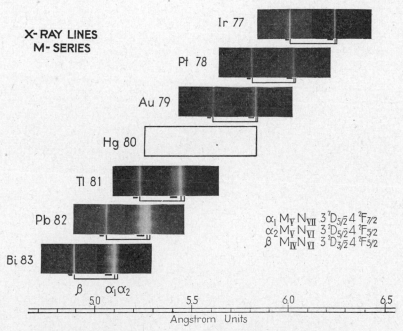

Fig. 16.7.—Photographs of *M* series x-ray lines. (*After Hirsch.*)

$$\nu = R(Z - 7.4)^2 \cdot \left(\frac{1}{2^2} - \frac{1}{3^2}\right). \tag{16.4}$$

In 1916 Siegbahn[1] discovered in the heavier elements a so-called *M radiation* and 6 years later Dolejsek[2] discovered a still softer radiation called *N radiation*. Photographs[3] of *M* series lines from a group of six elements are shown in Fig. 16.7. Like the *K* and *L* series lines, the *M* series lines follow nearly straight lines on a Moseley diagram and may be represented by Eq. 16.2. It should be pointed out in passing that the *M* and *L* radiations arising from the heavy elements are *harder* (*i.e.*, of shorter wave-length) than the *K* radiation of the light elements.

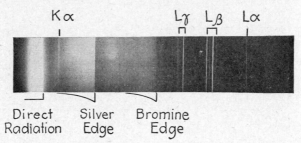

Kα   Lγ Lβ Lα

Direct   Silver   Bromine
Radiation   Edge   Edge

FIG. 16.8.—X-ray absorption edges of silver and bromine. (*After de Broglie.*)

16.3. Absorption Spectra.—In the first x-ray spectrograms taken by de Broglie in 1916 a sudden change in blackening was always noted at two discrete positions on the photographic plate. It is now known that these abrupt changes are due to the selective absorption of the silver and bromine in the photographic emulsion and that the wavelengths of the absorption edges are independent of the x-ray source used (see Fig. 16.8). Further investigation shows that, when a thin layer of some metal like Cu, Ag, Fe, or Sn, is placed just in front of the photographic plate, other absorption edges appear as characteristic of the respective element used as an absorber. With successive elements in the periodic table used as absorbing screens a regular stepwise shift of the characteristic absorption edges is observed. This may be seen in Fig. 16.9 for the elements Ag, Cd, In, Sn, Sb, Te, and I. The difference between the silver edge, which shows up on the right at the same point in each spectrum, and the other edges at the left is due to the silver absorption in the photographic plate itself (causing increased darkening) and the absorption of the radiation before reaching the plate, respectively.

[1] SIEGBAHN, M., *Verh. d. Deutsch. Phys. Ges.*, **18**, 278, 1916; *Compt. rend.*, **162**, 787, 1916.

[2] DOLEJSEK, V., *Zeits. f. Phys.*, **10**, 129, 236, 1922.

[3] These photographs are reproduced from original negatives kindly loaned by F. R. Hirsch.

A search for absorption edges over the large range of x-ray wave-lengths reveals in the heavier elements, in particular, several different edges for each element. For a given element the absorption edge occurring at the shortest wave-length is called the K absorption limit. Beyond the K limit to longer wave-lengths three relatively close absorption edges have been photographed for the elements starting at about Rb 37. These three edges are called the L limits, L_I, L_{II}, and L_{III}, in the order of their wave-lengths.[1]

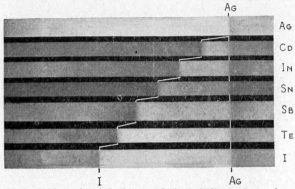

FIG. 16.9.—X-ray absorption edges of silver, cadmium, indium, tin, antimony, tellurium, and iodine. (*After Brode and Burmann.*)

At still longer wave-lengths in the heaviest elements a group of five absorption edges has been observed. These are called the M limits, M_I, M_{II}, M_{III}, M_{IV}, and M_V.

Absorption limits are of very great importance in x-ray spectra, for they furnish the clue to the origin of x-rays within the atom. A very simple and plausible theory of this was first given by Kossel.[2] A sharp absorption edge for a given element indicates that incident x-rays having a frequency greater than a certain critical frequency ν_c are largely absorbed, whereas those of lower frequency pass on through the absorption screen with little diminution in intensity. The absorbed energy $h\nu_c$, or greater, taken from the x-ray beam is used up in ejecting an electron. Such ejected electrons are called *photoelectrons*. The several K, L, and M limits observed for each element correspond therefore to the energies necessary to remove electrons from the different shells and subshells in the atom. The absorption limits thus provide a direct means by which the energy levels of an atom may be determined. This is the subject of the following section.

[1] For references concerning L absorption limits see M. Siegbahn, "Spektroskopie der Röntgenstrahlen," 2d ed., p. 271, 1931.

[2] KOSSEL, W., *Verh. d. Deutsch. Phys. Ges.*, **16**, 898, 953, 1914; **18**, 339, 1916; *Zeits. f. Phys.*, **1**, 119, 1920.

16.4. Energy Levels.—In the preceding chapters of this book we have been dealing with so-called *optical spectra, i.e.*, with radiation arising from electron transitions in the outermost part of the atom. In this chapter on x-rays, however, we are dealing with high-frequency radiations known to arise from electron transitions between the inner electron shells of the atom.

The condition for the excitation of an atom prior to its emission of x radiation consists in the complete removal of an electron from one of the completed inner subshells of electrons. This removal of an electron may be accomplished by the inelastic impact of a high-speed particle (an electron, proton, or atom), or by the absorption of a photon of energy $h\nu_c$ or greater. With an electron removed from an inner shell of the atom, an electron from one of the neighboring outer shells may jump into the unoccupied orbit, giving rise simultaneously to x radiation of energy $h\nu$ given by the energy difference between the two stationary states. Another electron from a shell still farther out may now jump into the orbit just vacated giving rise to radiation of another frequency. This process of emission will finally cease when the positively charged ion captures an electron. With this explanation we see that the absorption limits, briefly discussed in the preceding section, should theoretically give the x-ray energy levels of the atom.

In order to formulate some comprehensive picture of the atomic processes just described and the energies involved in x-ray emission and absorption, let us consider a specific example, *viz.*, the atomic system of cadmium, $Z = 48$. Cadmium is here chosen for the reason that, like He, Ne, A, Kr, Rn, Be, Mg, Ca, Sr, Ba, Zn, and Hg, it contains in the normal state only completed subshells of electrons. The complete electron configuration is given in Table 16.2.

TABLE 16.2.—ELECTRON CONFIGURATION OF NEUTRAL CADMIUM

	Shells	K	L	M	N	O
Subshells s		$1s^2$	$2s^2$	$3s^2$	$4s^2$	$5s^2$
p			$2p^6$	$3p^6$	$4p^6$	
d				$3d^{10}$	$4d^{10}$	

The x-ray notation $K, L, M, N, \ldots$ represents the main shells of electrons for which the total quantum number $n = 1, 2, 3, 4, \cdots$, respectively. In cadmium there are five completed s subshells, three completed p subshells, and two completed d subshells. These shells and subshells are represented schematically in Fig. 16.10. In terms of a quantum-mechanical model, similar to that given for rubidium in Fig. 7.1, each electron orbit in cadmium interpenetrates all other electron orbits. The circles may therefore be thought of as a sort of *time average* of the position of the electron in the atom (see Fig. 4.6).

Of all the 48 extranuclear electrons in cadmium the two $1s$ electrons are the most tightly bound to the atom, since for the greater part of the time they are inside all the remaining 46 electrons and in the field of the nucleus of charge $48e$. Second in binding energy come the $2s$ electrons, screened partially from the nucleus by the two $1s$ electrons. Third in binding energy come the six $2p$ electrons screened quite effectively from the nucleus by the four inner electrons $1s^2$ and $2s^2$. Following the L electrons the order of binding, as seen from Fig. 16.10, is $3s$, $3p$, $3d$;

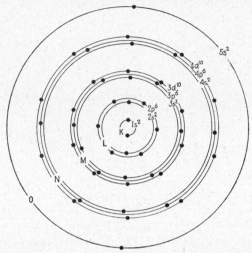

FIG. 16.10.—Cadmium shells and subshells of electrons.

$4s$, $4p$, $4d$; and $5s$, respectively. Since these binding energies are measured by the absorption edges, discussed in Sec. 16.3, an energy level diagram is obtained by plotting just the frequencies of the absorption limits.

At the bottom of Fig. 16.11 the normal state of the cadmium atom with all of its electrons is represented by a $^1S_0$ state, where $S = 0, L = 0$, and $J = 0$. The removal from the atom of one of the $5s$ electrons raises the atom to the lowest $^2S_{\frac{1}{2}}$ state, where $S = \frac{1}{2}, L = 0$, and $J = \frac{1}{2}$. This ionized state is the single limit of the regular optical series of singlets and triplets (see Fig. 11.6). The notation $5s^{-1}$ means that a $5s$ electron has been removed from the neutral atom. This leaves the atom with an incompleted subshell, a $5s$ electron.

The removal of a $1s$ electron from the neutral atom, on the other hand, raises the atom to the highest energy state K shown at the top of the figure. The removed electron is represented by $1s^{-1}$. With but one electron remaining in the $1s$ subshell this energy state is represented by $^2S_{\frac{1}{2}}$, in the notation used in *optical* spectra. The term values given at the left in the figure show that the binding energy of a $1s$ electron is about 3000 times that of a $5s$ valence electron.

In a similar fashion the removal of a $2s$ electron, designated $2s^{-1}$, from the L shell raises the atom to the state L_I. In this state the atom with one $2s$ electron in an incompleted subshell is again in a ^2S state. Now the removal of a $2p$ electron, $2p^{-1}$, from the L shell leaves an incomplete subshell $2p^5$, which, as we have seen in Sec. 15.6, gives rise to an inverted ^2P term,[1] $^2P_{\frac{3}{2}}$ and $^2P_{\frac{1}{2}}$. These correspond to the two absorption limits L_{III} and L_{II}, respectively.

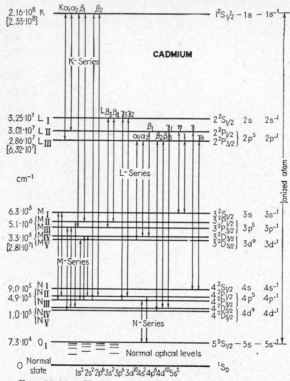

FIG. 16.11.—X-ray energy level diagram of cadmium.

Again the removal of a $3s$, $3p$, or $3d$ electron leaves incomplete subshells $3s$, $3p^5$, or $3d^9$, giving rise to a ^2S term, two ^2P terms, or two ^2D terms, respectively. In optical notation these are $^2S_{\frac{1}{2}}$, $^2P_{\frac{1}{2}}$, $^2P_{\frac{3}{2}}$, $^2D_{\frac{3}{2}}$, and $^2D_{\frac{5}{2}}$, and in x-ray notation they are M_I, M_{II}, M_{III}, M_{IV}, and M_V. A continuation of this process for the N and O shells leads to the remaining doublet levels shown in the figure. It should be pointed out that in the heavier elements of the periodic table $4f$ electrons are present and give rise to two more N levels, N_{VI} and N_{VII} ($^2F_{\frac{5}{2}}$ and $^2F_{\frac{7}{2}}$). With the exception of a very close structure, not yet mentioned, S terms in x-ray spectra

---

[1] Any subshell of electrons lacking but one electron to complete it gives rise to an inverted doublet level having an L value equal to the l value of the missing electron.

as in optical spectra are always single; other levels P, D, F, . . . are double.

Attempts by Moseley and his successors to find a simple law governing the terms, or, what is the same thing, the absorption limits ν, as a function of the atomic number Z, has led to the so-called *Moseley diagram* shown

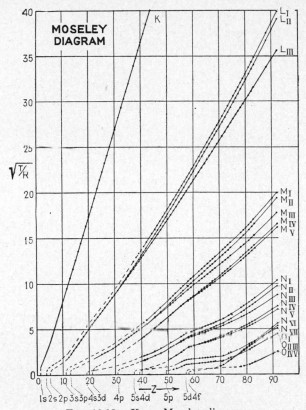

Fig. 16.12.—X-ray Moseley diagram.

in Fig. 16.12.[1] The regularities as well as the irregularities to be noted in this figure can, for the most part, be explained. This explanation will be undertaken in the following sections.

16.5. Selection and Intensity Rules.—The selection rules derived from theoretical considerations and found to hold in optical spectra also apply in x-ray spectra. These rules for the various quantum numbers n, L, and J, are[2]

[1] Bohr, N., and D. Coster, *Zeits. f. Phys.*, **12**, 342, 1923.

[2] These selection rules apply only to atoms of the cadmium type, *i.e.*, to atoms in which the energy levels arise from the absence or presence of one electron in a subshell. Although they may be applied to the chief x-ray lines of all atoms, they are only a special case of a more general set of selection rules to be given in Sec. 16.10.

$$\Delta n \qquad \text{arbitrary,}$$
$$\Delta L = +1 \text{ or } -1, \qquad (16.5)$$
$$\Delta J = +1, 0, \text{ or } -1.$$

Transitions giving rise to the K and L series lines in cadmium are shown in Fig. 16.11. Photographs of some of the strongest L and M lines are given in Figs. 16.5 and 16.7 for a few of the elements. At the right in these figures the respective transitions are designated in x-ray notation and also in optical notation. It should be noted that not all transitions allowed by the above rules have been observed. In particular the transitions L_I to L_{II}, and L_I to L_{III}, although looked for by many investigators, have not been observed with certainty. These are the transitions for which $\Delta n = 0$. In optical spectra of the alkali metals such transitions give rise to the strongest lines in the neutral spectrum. In sodium the transitions M_I to M_{II} and M_I to M_{III} give rise to the first doublet of the principal series. A plausible explanation of the absence of these lines with an appreciable intensity in x-rays is that in the intensity formulas, derived from theoretical considerations by Einstein,[1] there occurs a factor ν^4. For the transitions $\Delta n = 0$ this ν^4 factor is extremely small, as compared with other allowed transitions starting from the same initial states, and should therefore give rise to very weak lines. It must be mentioned that, as in optical spectra, a few cases are known where forbidden transitions are observed.[2]

It should be noted that when an electron jumps from a $3p$ to a $2s$ state (for example, $M_{III} \rightarrow L_I$), the atom goes from the higher energy state L_I to the lower energy state M_{III}. For this reason the transitions on all energy level diagrams are shown as double arrows. The arrows pointing up represent electron transitions of the type given in the figure with a minus sign prefixed, and the arrows pointing down represent energy changes in the emission of radiation.

The same intensity rules derived and found to hold for optical spectra are also found to hold in x-ray spectra. For observed lines not greatly different in frequency the ν^4 term in the intensity formulas may be neglected and the intensity rules applied to multiplets in Sec. 12.15 may be used. According to these formulas the theoretical intensities for the K_{α_2} and K_{α_1} lines (in optical notation $^2S_{\frac{1}{2}} - ^2P_{\frac{1}{2}}$ and $^2S_{\frac{1}{2}} - ^2P_{\frac{3}{2}}$) have the ratio 2:1. Accurate intensity measurements on some 24 elements are given in Table 16.3. The agreement between observation and theory for these lines is excellent.

[1] Einstein, A., *Verh. d. Deutsch. Phys. Ges.*, **18**, 318, 1916; *Phys. Zeits.*, **18**, 121, 1917; see also Dirac, *Proc. Roy. Soc.*, **114**, 243, 1927. There is now some question whether the ν^4 factor belongs in the intensity formulae for spectrum lines.

[2] Coster, D., *Phil. Mag.*, **43**, 1070, 1922; see also Kaufman, S., *Phys. Rev.*, **40**, 116, 1932.

TABLE 16.3.—OBSERVED RELATIVE INTENSITIES FOR THE K SERIES LINES
(*After Meyer*)[1]

Element	K_{α_1}	K_{α_2}	Element	K_{α_1}	K_{α_2}	Element	K_{α_1}	K_{α_2}
V 23	100	52.1	Ga 31	100	50.6	Zr 40	100	49.1
Cr 24	100	50.6	Ge 32	100	50.7	Cb 41	100	49.7
Mn 25	100	54.9	As 33	100	49.2	Mo 42	100	50.6
Fe 26	100	49.1	Se 34	100	50.3	Ru 44	100	51.1
Co 27	100	53.2	Br 35	100	50.9	Rh 45	100	51.2
Ni 28	100	47.6	Rb 37	100	49.3	Pd 46	100	52.3
Cu 29	100	46.0	Sr 38	100	48.6	Ag 47	100	51.7
Zn 30	100	48.9	Yt 39	100	50.0	Cd 48	100	53.8

[1] MEYER, H. T., *Wiss. Verh. a. d. Siemens Konzern*, **7**, 108, 1929; see also WILLIAMS, J. H., *Phys. Rev.*, **44**, 146, 1933.

As a second example of the intensity rules consider the strongest L series lines L_{α_1}, L_{α_2}, and L_{β_1}. These three lines arise from the transitions between the doublet levels $2p^5, {}^2P_{\frac{3}{2},\frac{1}{2}}$ and $3d^9, {}^2D_{\frac{3}{2},\frac{5}{2}}$. The predicted relative intensities are

	${}^2P_{\frac{3}{2}}$	${}^2P_{\frac{1}{2}}$	
${}^2D_{\frac{5}{2}}$	9	0	M_V
${}^2D_{\frac{3}{2}}$	1	5	M_{IV}
	L_{III}	L_{II}	

The observed intensities for eight elements are given in Table 16.4.

TABLE 16.4.—OBSERVED RELATIVE INTENSITIES FOR THE L SERIES LINES
(*After Jönsson[1] and Allison[2]*)

Element	α_1	α_2	β_1	Element	α_1	α_2	β_1
U[2] 92	9	1	4.4	Ag[1] 47	9	1	5.3
Th[2] 90	9	1.1	5.6	Pd[1] 46	9	1	5.3
Pt[1] 78	9	1	4.6	Rh[1] 45	9	1	2.8
W[1] 74	9	1	4.7	Mo[1] 42	9	1	2.8

[1] JÖNSSON, A., *Zeits. f. Phys.*, **36**, 426, 1926; **46**, 383, 1928.
[2] ALLISON, S. K., *Phys. Rev.*, **30**, 245, 1927; **32**, 1, 1928.

Peculiarly enough when ν^4 corrections are made for these lines they are far from being in agreement with theory. Bethe[1] explains this on the basis of the fact that the measured intensity is not equal to the transition probability but to the product of the life time of the initial state and the transition probability. The measurements thus indicate simply that the life time of L_I (due, *e.g.*, to a greater probability of autoionization) is

[1] BETHE, H., *Handbuch der Physik.*, Vol. 24, No. 1, p. 468, 1933.

shorter than that of $L_{II,III}$. It may be seen that the L_{α_2} lines in Fig. 16.5, where resolved, are quite faint as compared with the strongest line L_{α_1}. The L_β lines are taken from different plates and may not justly be compared.

16.6. Fine Structure of X-ray Levels.—The three L levels, the five M levels, the seven N levels, etc., may be referred to as the fine structure of x-rays. Since a fairly satisfactory account of this fine structure may be given, a treatment of the splitting of each main energy level into $2n - 1$ sublevels is made the object of this and the three succeeding sections.

It has already been pointed out that the L electrons move in an approximately Coulomb field, the two K electrons acting very much as if they had coalesced with the nucleus. This screening of the nucleus by the K electrons reduces the nuclear charge by about two, so that, neglecting for the moment the fine structure, the energy should be given by the hydrogen-like formula

$$T = \frac{RZ_{eff}^2}{n^2} = \frac{R(Z - \sigma)^2}{n^2}, \qquad (16.6)$$

where R is the Rydberg constant $= 109737$ cm^{-1}, Z_{eff} the effective nuclear charge, Z the atomic nymber, and σ the screening constant (equal to about two).

In a similar manner one can expect the M series to be given by a formula of the same type. In this instance the M electrons are screened from the nucleus by the eight L and two K electrons, thus reducing the nuclear charge by roughly ten.

In addition to this *internal screening effect* there is also a correction known as the *external screening effect*. This external screening is perhaps most easily pictured by imagining any given outer shell of Q electrons as distributed uniformly over the surface of a sphere of radius r. The potential energy of an electron within this charged shell will thus be Qe^2/r. The sum of such energy terms taken over all external subshells must be subtracted from the energy of the hydrogen-like orbit within. Referring to Fig. 16.10, it is readily seen that the energy necessary to carry an electron from the L shell through the other shells to infinity is less than the energy required to do so when the outer electrons are absent. In general this external screening is small compared with the main energy, and, since the quantum-mechanical model has all orbits interpenetrating all other orbits, it is customary to include the external with the internal screening by means of the one screening constant σ. This single constant σ will therefore represent collectively both types of screening in the following treatment.

In anticipation of the fact that the x-ray energy levels will be almost hydrogen-like, it is now an easy step from Sommerfeld's fine-structure formula for hydrogen [see Eq. (9.6)] to his x-ray formula. Replacing Z by $Z - \sigma$, or $Z - s$,

$$T = \frac{R(Z - \sigma)^2}{n^2} + \frac{R\alpha^2(Z - s)^4}{n^4}\left(\frac{n}{k} - \frac{3}{4}\right)$$
$$+ \frac{R\alpha^4(Z - s)^6}{n^6}\left(\frac{1n^3}{4k^3} + \frac{3n^2}{4k^2} - \frac{3n}{2k} + \frac{5}{8}\right)$$
$$+ \frac{R\alpha^6(Z - s)^8}{n^8}\left(\frac{1n^5}{8k^5} + \frac{3n^4}{8k^4} + \frac{1n^3}{8k^3} - \frac{15n^2}{8k^2} + \frac{15n}{8k} - \frac{35}{64}\right) +, +, +,$$

$$(16.7)$$

where $\alpha^2 = 4\pi^2e^4/h^2c^2 = 5.30 \times 10^{-5}$ is the square of Sommerfeld's fine-structure constant, R is the Rydberg constant, σ and s are screening constants, n is the total quantum number, and k is Sommerfeld's original azimuthal quantum number; $k = 1, 2, 3, \cdots$ for $s, p, d, \cdots$ electrons, respectively.

The application of this equation to observed x-ray energy levels, to be given in the three following sections, shows that the screening constants σ and s are different from each other even though, a priori, they might be expected to be the same. This equation, without the screening constant, was first derived by Sommerfeld[1] from the orbital model of hydrogen. Starting with Dirac's quantum-mechanical theory of the electron (Sec. 9.9), Gordon has arrived at exactly the same formula. With the screening constants included, the first term in the equation gives the main energy of each electron shell n, and the second, third, fourth, etc., terms give the fine-structure corrections. In Sommerfeld's early theory these latter corrections were due to the relativity change in mass of the electron, whereas, according to quantum-mechanical derivation from Dirac's theory, they are due jointly to what has been called the *electron spin-orbit interaction* and to relativity. It is for this reason that the fine-structure term differences, accounted for by the second and succeeding terms of this equation, are called *spin-relativity doublets*. In x-ray notation these are the doublet intervals $L_{II} - L_{III}$, $M_{II} - M_{III}$, $M_{IV} - M_V$, $N_{II} - N_{III}$, $\cdots$, for which Sommerfeld assigned quantum numbers $k = 1$ for L_{II}, M_{II}, N_{II}, $\cdots$, $k = 2$ for L_{III}, M_{III}, M_{IV}, N_{III}, N_{IV}, $\cdots$, $k = 3$ for M_V, N_V, N_{VI}, O_V, O_{VI}, $\cdots$; etc. It is now known that these are not the so-called azimuthal quantum numbers of the electron orbits but new quantum numbers given by the Dirac electron theory of hydrogen-like orbits. These new quantum numbers (see Sec. 9.9) are assigned the values shown on page 316.

In Gordon's derivation of the fine-structure formula, j'^2 takes the place of Sommerfeld's k^2 so that $|j'|$ becomes the analogue of the old k. One may therefore proceed to use Sommerfeld's formula, as it is given

[1] SOMMERFELD, A., "Atombau," 5th ed., p. 282.

in Eq. (16.7), for with his values of k we shall obtain the quantum-mechanical term values (see Sec. 9.9).

TABLE 16.5

Screening Doublet		Spin-relativity Doublet		Screening Doublet		Spin-relativity Doublet
$^2S_{\frac{1}{2}}$		$^2P_{\frac{1}{2}}$		$^2P_{\frac{3}{2}}$	$^2D_{\frac{3}{2}}$	$^2D_{\frac{5}{2}}$
$S = \frac{1}{2}$		$\frac{1}{2}$		$\frac{1}{2}$	$\frac{1}{2}$	$\frac{1}{2}$
$L = 0$		1		1	2	2
$J = \frac{1}{2}$		$\frac{1}{2}$		$\frac{3}{2}$	$\frac{3}{2}$	$\frac{5}{2}$
$j' = -1$		$+1$		-2	$+2$	-3

The effect of the screening constants σ and s in shifting the energy levels from those of hydrogen-like atoms to the observed x-ray levels is illustrated in Fig. 16.13. At the left the Bohr term values are given by

$$T_H = \frac{RZ^2}{n^2}. \tag{16.8}$$

Introducing the screening constant σ to account for the internal and external screening these levels are each split into n sublevels:

$$T' = \frac{R(Z - \sigma)^2}{n^2}, \tag{16.9}$$

where σ is different for the different sublevels $s, p, d, \ldots$ Adding finally the second, third, fourth, etc., terms of Eq. (16.7) simultaneously, each level, with the exception of S levels, splits into two sublevels. It should be noted that the values of n and k are those of the electron that has been removed from the atom. These same n values are often used in front of ^2S, ^2P, ^2D, etc., to distinguish them from each other. The intervals $L_I - L_{II}$, $M_I - M_{II}$, $M_{III} - M_{IV}$, $\cdots$ are generally called *Screening doublets*. In optical notation (see Table 16.5 above) these are the levels having the same n, S, and J values but different L values.

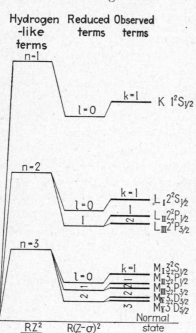

FIG. 16.13.—The splitting up of energy levels according to Sommerfeld's formula.

16.7. Spin-relativity Doublets (Regular Doublets).—The term *spin-relativity doublet* refers in general to each pair of energy levels having the same n, S, and L values but different J values. In x-ray notation these are the intervals $L_{II} - L_{III}$, $M_{II} - M_{III}$, $M_{IV} - M_V$, $N_{II} - N_{III}$,

$N_{IV} - N_{V}$, $N_{VI} - N_{VII}$, $O_{II} - O_{III}$, $O_{IV} - O_{V}$, etc., which prior to the quantum mechanics were called *regular doublets*. The intervals between each of these doublets in the various elements in the periodic table are known accurately from observed differences between a number of x-ray spectrum lines (see Figs. 16.5 and 16.7).

The substitution in Sommerfeld's formula of the known quantum numbers n and k for a given doublet leads to the so-called *regular doublet law*. Substituting in Eq. (16.7), one obtains two equations for each doublet. For the L doublet ($2^2P_{\frac{1}{2}} - 2^2P_{\frac{3}{2}}$),

$$T_{L_{II}} = \frac{R(Z - \sigma)^2}{2^2} + \frac{R\alpha^2(Z - s)^4}{2^4}\left\{\frac{5}{4} + \frac{21}{8}\frac{\alpha^2}{2^2}(Z - s)^2\right.$$
$$\left. + \frac{429}{64}\frac{\alpha^4}{2^4}(Z - s)^4 + \cdots\right\}, \quad (16.10)$$

$$T_{L_{III}} = \frac{R(Z - \sigma)^2}{2^2} + \frac{R\alpha^2(Z - s)^4}{2^4}\left\{\frac{1}{4} + \frac{1}{8}\frac{\alpha^2}{2^2}(Z - s)^2\right.$$
$$\left. + \frac{5}{64}\frac{\alpha^4}{2^4}(Z - s)^4 + \cdots\right\}. \quad (16.11)$$

Now if $\Delta\nu$ represents the difference between these two equations, then

$$\Delta\nu = \frac{R\alpha^2(Z - s)^4}{2^4}\left\{1 + \frac{5\alpha^2}{8}(Z - s)^2 + \frac{53\alpha^4}{128}(Z - s)^4 + \cdots\right\}. \quad (16.12)$$

Although only the first term of the analogous Eq. (9.6) is required in describing the hydrogen fine structure, Sommerfeld[1] has shown that the first term of this equation does not suffice to determine s and that higher terms are necessary.

From the observed x-ray lines, shown in Fig. 16.5 and tabulated in Table 16.1, the following screening constants (Table 16.6) are computed:

TABLE 16.6.—SCREENING CONSTANTS s FOR THE SPIN-RELATIVITY DOUBLET $L_{II} - L_{III}$
(*After Sommerfeld*)

Element Z		$\Delta\nu/R$	$Z - s$	s
Cb	41	6.90	37.53	3.47
Mo	42	7.70	38.50	3.50
Ru	44	9.49	40.54	3.46
Rh	45	10.48	41.53	3.47
Pd	46	11.57	42.55	3.45
Ag	47	12.69	43.52	3.48
Cd	48	13.96	44.52	3.48
In	49	15.29	45.50	3.50
Sn	50	16.72	46.51	3.49

---

[1] SOMMERFELD, A., "Atombau," 5th ed., p. 300.

It is observed that s is practically a constant independent of Z. For some 40 elements from $Z = 41$ to $Z = 92$ Sommerfeld obtained an average value

$$s = 3.50 \pm 0.05. \tag{16.13}$$

In a similar fashion Eq. (16.7) gives for the $M_{\text{II}} - M_{\text{III}}$ doublet $(3^2P_{\frac{1}{2}} - 3^2P_{\frac{3}{2}})$,

$$\Delta\nu = \frac{R\alpha^2(Z-s)^4}{3^4}\left\{\frac{3}{2} + \frac{279\alpha^2}{288}(Z-s)^2 + \frac{13059\alpha^4}{20736}(Z-s)^4 + \cdots\right\}. \tag{16.14}$$

From the observed doublet separations of the elements $Z = 37$ to $Z = 92$, Wentzel[1] has shown that s is again constant throughout (see Table 16.7) and has the average value

$$s = 8.5 \pm 0.4. \tag{16.15}$$

Table 16.7.—Screening Constants s for the Spin-relativity Doublet $M_{\text{II}}-M_{\text{III}}$
(*After Wentzel*)

Cb 41	Mo 42	Ru 44	Rh 45	Pd 46	Ag 47	Cd 48	In 49	Sn 50
8.50	8.56	8.52	8.50	8.52	8.58	8.28	8.56	8.48

Similar calculations carried out for other spin-relativity doublets have yielded the following average values for s.

Table 16.8.—Screening Constants s for Spin-relativity Doublets
(*After Sommerfeld and Wentzel*)

$2^2S_{\frac{1}{2}}$ L_{I}	$2^2P_{\frac{1}{2}} - 2^2P_{\frac{3}{2}}$ $L_{\text{II}} - L_{\text{III}}$	$3^2S_{\frac{1}{2}}$ M_{I}	$3^2P_{\frac{1}{2}} - 3^2P_{\frac{3}{2}}$ M_{II} M_{III}	$3^2D_{\frac{3}{2}} - 3^2D_{\frac{5}{2}}$ M_{IV} M_{V}	$4^2S_{\frac{1}{2}}$ N_{I}	$4^2P_{\frac{1}{2}} - 4^2P_{\frac{3}{2}}$ N_{II} N_{III}
2.0	3.50	6.8	8.5	13	14	17

The method used in determining the screening constants for the single L_{I}, M_{I}, and N_{I} levels is given in Sec. 16.8. Attempts to calculate s from theory alone have been made by Pauling.[2] By a first-order perturbation treatment of the problem Pauling has been able to calculate values which, in general, are in quite good agreement with those given above.

16.8. The Regular-doublet Law.—The regular-doublet law, well-known in x-ray spectra, refers to the apparent law governing the spin-relativity doublets $L_{\text{II}} - L_{\text{III}}$, $M_{\text{II}} - M_{\text{III}}$, $M_{\text{IV}} - M_{\text{V}}$, $N_{\text{II}} - N_{\text{III}}$, etc. Neglecting higher terms in Eq. (16.12), or Eq. (16.14), the law may be expressed by the first term of the equation as follows: *The doublet separation, $\Delta\nu$ in wave numbers, for any spin-relativity doublet is approximately proportional to the fourth power of the effective atomic number*

[1] See Wentzel, G., *Zeits. f. Phys.*, **16**, 46, 1923.
[2] Pauling, L., *Zeits. f. Phys.*, **40**, 344, 1927.

$Z - s$. As an example of the validity of this law consider the $L_{II} - L_{III}$ doublet. For this doublet (see Table 16.8) $s = 3.5$, and $\Delta\nu$, to a first approximation, is given by

$$\Delta\nu = \frac{R\alpha^2}{2^4}(Z - 3.5)^4. \qquad (16.16)$$

Now the values of $\Delta\nu$ for some 70 elements are known quite accurately from the average of several observed x-ray doublet intervals $K_{\alpha_1} - K_{\alpha_2}$, $L_{\beta_1} - L_{\alpha_2}$, $L_{\eta} - L_l$, $L_{\beta_6} - L_{\delta_6}$ and the absorption limits $L_{II} - L_{III}$. The average values of $\Delta\nu$ are plotted in Fig. 16.14 with four different sets of ordinates $\sqrt[2]{\Delta\nu/R}$, $\sqrt[3]{\Delta\nu/R}$, $\sqrt[4]{\Delta\nu/R}$, and $\sqrt[5]{\Delta\nu/R}$. The $\sqrt[4]{\Delta\nu/R}$

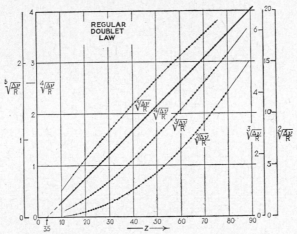

FIG. 16.14.—The regular-doublet law for L doublets in x-ray spectra.

curve, with an intercept at 3.5, shows that the fourth power law [Eq. (16.16)] gives the best agreement.

16.9. Screening Doublets and the Irregular-doublet Law.—Making a systematic study of L series lines, Hertz[1] in 1920 announced what is known as the *irregular-doublet law*. This law applies to those pairs of energy levels having the same n, S, and J values but different L values and states that *the difference between the square roots of the term values of a given doublet is a constant independent of the atomic number Z*. This law found by Hertz to hold for the L_I and L_{II} levels of the six elements Cs, Ba, La, Ce, Pr, and Nd is now known to hold for all doublets $L_I - L_{II}$, $M_I - M_{II}$, $M_{III} - M_{IV}$, $N_I - N_{II}$, $N_{III} - N_{IV}$, and $N_V - N_{VI}$ (see Fig. 16.12). That the law is only approximately true is shown by the values of $\Delta\sqrt{T/R}$ given in the last column of Table 16.9. A general widening of the interval with increasing Z is observed.

In formulating the irregular-doublet law Hertz began with the equation

[1] HERTZ, G., *Zeits. f. Phys.*, **3**, 19, 1920.

$$T = \frac{R(Z - \sigma)^2}{n^2}. \tag{16.17}$$

Transposing R and taking the square root, this equation becomes

$$\sqrt{\frac{T}{R}} = \frac{Z - \sigma}{n}. \tag{16.18}$$

If now σ_1 and σ_2 are the screening constants for the two levels of a doublet, the difference is written

$$\Delta\sqrt{\frac{T}{R}} = \frac{\sigma_1 - \sigma_2}{n} = \frac{\Delta\sigma}{n} = \text{constant}. \tag{16.19}$$

Referring to Fig. 16.16 the factor $\sigma_1 - \sigma_2$ is seen to be practically a constant for the two levels forming an irregular doublet. This is

TABLE 16.9.—THE IRREGULAR-DOUBLET LAW FOR THE X-RAY LEVELS L_I AND L_{II}

Element		$\sqrt{T/R}$ (L_I)	$\sqrt{T/R}$ (L_{II})	$\Delta\sqrt{T/R}$
Cs	55	20.538	19.873	0.665
Ba	56	21.022	20.355	0.667
La	57	21.514	20.837	0.677
Ce	58	21.984	21.310	0.674
Pr	59	22.456	21.785	0.671
Nd	60	22.939	22.260	0.679
Tb	65	25.349	24.664	0.685
Yb	70	27.830	27.120	0.710
Re	75	30.381	29.667	0.714
Hg	80	33.051	32.349	0.702
Th	90	38.844	38.055	0.789
U	92	40.053	39.256	0.797

the irregular-doublet law more recently referred to as the screening-doublet law.

Sommerfeld has shown that a refinement of the irregular-doublet law is brought about by the use of the so-called *reduced terms* [Eq. (16.9)] rather than the observed terms (see Fig. 16.13). With values of the screening constants s determined from the spin-relativity doublets of the preceding section, the higher terms of Eq. (16.7) can be calculated and the corrected, or reduced, terms

$$T' = \frac{R(Z - \sigma)^2}{n^2} \tag{16.20}$$

evaluated. Dropping all but the first two terms in Eq. (16.7), and substituting the value of T', we obtain

$$T' = T - \frac{R\alpha^2(Z - s)^4}{n^4}\left(\frac{n}{k} - \frac{3}{4}\right). \tag{16.21}$$

Here T represents the observed term values given directly by the absorption limits.

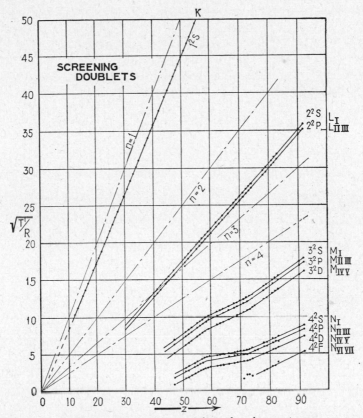

Fig. 16.15.—Moseley diagram for reduced x-ray terms.

A Moseley diagram of reduced terms is shown in Fig. 16.15. For given n the resultant curves are now quite parallel to each other. The parallelism is more accurately shown by the following Table 16.10.

TABLE 16.10.—THE IRREGULAR-DOUBLET LAW FOR REDUCED TERMS
(*After Sommerfeld*)

	Cs 55	Ba 56	La 57	Ce 58	Pr 59	Nd 60	Sa 62	Gd 64	Dy 66	Er 68
$\Delta\sqrt{T'/R}$ $2^2S - 2^2P$	0.59	0.59	0.60	0.59	0.59	0.59	0.59	0.58	0.58	0.58
$\Delta\sqrt{T'/R}$ $3^2S - 3^2P$	0.54	0.54	0.51	0.54	0.56	0.51	0.51	0.53	0.54	0.53
$\Delta\sqrt{T/R}$ $3^2P - 3^2D$	1.21	1.19	1.20	1.19	1.19	1.19	1.20	1.19	1.18	1.19

Although the values shown here are quite constant, some of the values, for elements not given in the table, deviate slightly more from the average value. It should be pointed out that there are no spin-relativity doublets from which to calculate s and σ for the ^2S levels. Wentzel,[1] however, making the assumption that the irregular-doublet law is valid for the reduced terms, has adjusted the screening constants s for these

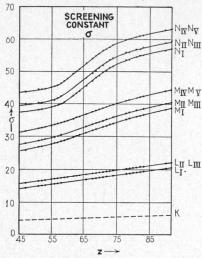

FIG.   16.16.—Screening   constants σ. *(After Sommerfeld.)*

levels until the curves for 2^2S, 3^2S, and 4^2S (see Fig. 16.15) are parallel to the center curves as shown. These values of S have been included in Table 16.8.

In Fig. 16.15 the dashed lines through the origin represent hydrogen-like atoms for which there is no screening. The difference between these ideal curves and the corresponding reduced curves $\left(\dfrac{Z}{n} - \dfrac{Z - \sigma}{n}\right)$, multiplied by n, gives directly the screening constant σ plotted in Fig. 16.16. The sudden change in the slope of the M and N curves at approximately $Z = 57$ and $Z = 71$ shows the increased screening effect of the $4f$ electrons added in the rare-earth elements. Their addition causes an increase in the external screening discussed in Sec. 16.6. As Sommerfeld[2] shows, the corresponding increase in the screening constant for a state of total quantum number n is directly proportional to n^2 and inversely proportional to the effective nuclear charge; hence the effect is relatively slight for states of low quantum number, as is, indeed, borne out by the figure. Similar screening effects are shown by the Moseley diagram of Fig. 16.12 for the sequence of elements where $3d$ and $4d$ electrons are added.[3]

The irregular-doublet law has an aspect other than that of the parallelism of L_I and L_{II} on a Moseley diagram, *viz.*, the frequency difference $\Delta \nu = T_{L_I} - T_{L_{II}}$ is very nearly a linear function of the atomic number Z. Although the x-ray transitions L_{II} to L_I have not yet been observed, this law is of considerable importance in optical spectra where

---

[1] WENTZEL, G., *Zeits. f. Phys.*, **16**, 46, 1923.

[2] SOMMERFELD, A., "Atombau," 5th ed., p. 427.

[3] These sequences of elements and the screening effect due to the addition of $3d$ and $4d$ electrons have been treated theoretically by L. Pauling, *Zeits. f. Phys.*, **40**, 344, 1927. See also L. Pauling and S. Goudsmit, "Structure of Line Spectra," p. 187.

the corresponding transitions are observed. Let us start with Hertz's
Eq. (16.17),

$$\Delta\nu = \Delta T = \frac{R}{n^2}\{(Z - \sigma_1)^2 - (Z - \sigma_2)^2\}. \tag{16.22}$$

Upon multiplying out, one obtains

$$\frac{\Delta\nu}{R} = 2\frac{(\sigma_2 - \sigma_1)}{n^2}\left\{Z - \frac{\sigma_1 + \sigma_2}{2}\right\} = c_1(Z - c_2). \tag{16.23}$$

Plots of $\Delta\nu/R$ for the intervals $L_I - L_{II}$, $M_I - M_{II}$, $M_{III} - M_{IV}$, $N_I - N_{II}$,
and $N_{III} - N_{IV}$ given in Fig. 16.17 show, at least over short ranges of
Z, how closely this law applies.
These curves are to be compared
with the $\sqrt[4]{\nu}$ law for the regular
doublet (Fig. 16.14).

**16.10. A Predicted Multiplet
Structure in X-rays.**—In Sec. 16.4
the cadmium atom was chosen as a
suitable example for the discussion
of the origin of x-ray energy levels
for the reason that all subshells of
electrons are complete in the neutral
atom and the resultant angular
momentum of all the extranuclear
electrons is zero. The removal of an
inner electron from the atom in this
simple case would leave the atom
with the same angular momentum as that of the removed electron,

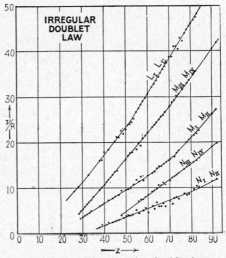

FIG. 16.17.—The irregular-doublet law.

either $l + \frac{1}{2}$ or $l - \frac{1}{2}$. If, on the other hand, an atom with an incomplete
valence-electron subshell is considered, the resultant angular momentum
J_1 of this *outer shell* must be combined with the resultant angular momentum J_2 of the *inner shell* to give the resultant angular momentum J of
the atom. This, by analogy with optical spectra, may be accomplished
in such a way as to give several different J's for the same x-ray level J_2.
The energy difference between the various possible J's will depend on the
type of coupling that may arise between the two J_i's. For heavy elements, in general, intermediate shells of electrons will screen quite
effectively the inner shell from the outer shell, and the coupling will be
closely JJ. For the lighter elements, where the two shells are not
screened from each other, the electron spins may interact strongly and
the coupling will then be closely LS. X-ray energy levels for most
elements are therefore expected to show a multiplet fine structure similar
to that observed in optical spectra.

Attempts to observe this predicted structure in x-ray lines have been made by a number of investigators. Coster and Druyvesteyn,[1] and Van der Tuuk,[2] for example, have observed complicated structures in the N levels of the rare-earth elements. Because of the lack of sufficient resolving power in x-ray apparatus detailed studies of these multiplet structures have not yet been made. This multiplet structure is not to be confused with the x-ray satellites to be discussed in the following section. The selection and intensity rules for these more complex atoms may be given here since they are the same as those used in optical spectra (see Secs. 12.14 and 12.15).

The selection rules for x-rays are:

$$
\begin{array}{ll}
LS\text{-coupling} & JJ\text{-coupling} \\
\Delta S = 0 & \Delta J_1 = 0 \\
\Delta L = +1,\, 0,\, -1 & \left.\Delta J_2 = +1,\, 0,\, -1\right\} \text{or vice versa} \\
\Delta J = +1,\, 0,\, -1 & \Delta J = +1,\, 0,\, -1
\end{array}
$$

subject to the further restriction that odd terms combine only with even terms.

Since the splitting of x-ray energy levels, due to a resultant angular momentum of the valence electrons, is in general very small, a number of the radiated lines will fall together as a single line. For this reason, and by virtue of the fact that the sum rules are valid for multiplets, the selection and intensity rules given in Sec. 16.5 will, when applied to the one-electron jumping in the inner part of the atom, describe adequately the observed lines.

16.11. X-ray Satellites.—X-ray satellites are those relatively weak lines often observed close to and on the high-frequency side of the chief x-ray diagram lines. These satellites, sometimes called *non-diagram lines*, were first discovered by Siegbahn and Stenström[3] on the high-frequency side of the K series lines of the elements Na 11 through Zn 30. Since their discovery an extensive investigation of the L series lines by Richtmyer and Richtmyer[4] and others has shown that a number of satellites appear on the high-frequency side of the chief L lines of most of the elements from Cu 29 through U 92. Similarly, Hirsch[5] and others have shown that M series satellites are to be found in the elements Yb 70 through U 92. The regions of a number of these satellites are marked in Figs. 16.5 and 16.7 and may in some of the reproductions be traced from one element to the next. Semi-Moseley plots of the satellites of

[1] COSTER, D., and M. J. DRUYVESTEYN, *Zeits. f. Phys.*, **40**, 765, 1927.

[2] VAN DER TUUK, J. II., *Zeits. f. Phys.*, **44**, 737, 1927.

[3] SIEGBAHN, M., and W. STENSTRÖM, *Phys. Zeits.*, **17**, 48, 318, 1916.

[4] RICHTMYER, F. K., and R. D. RICHTMYER, *Phys. Rev.*, **34**, 574, 1929; see also RICHTMYER, F. K., and S. KAUFMAN, *Phys. Rev.*, **44**, 605, 1933.

[5] HIRSCH, F. R., *Phys. Rev.*, **38**, 914, 1931.

some of the more prominent x-ray lines are given in Fig. 16.18. The square roots of $\Delta\nu/R$ (the difference in frequency between satellite and nearest chief x-ray line, divided by the Rydberg constant $R = 109737$ cm^{-1}) are plotted as ordinates against the atomic number Z.

The first attempt to explain x-ray satellites was made by Wentzel[1] in 1921. Wentzel's hypothesis requires essentially a double ionization of the atom by high-speed electrons followed by a single electron jump and the simultaneous emission of a radiated frequency ν_s. Because of certain apparent defects in Wentzel's theory as it was first proposed,

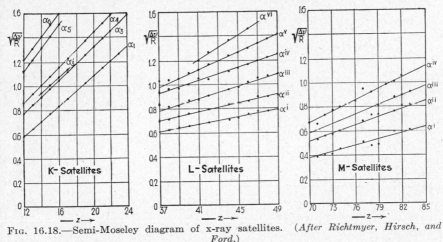

Fig. 16.18.—Semi-Moseley diagram of x-ray satellites. (*After Richtmyer, Hirsch, and Ford.*)

Richtmyer[2] advanced the theory that in a doubly ionized atom double electron jumps probably occur giving rise simultaneously to a single radiated frequency ν_s. In view of recent developments in atomic spectra it would appear that both theories are plausible and that together they explain with some satisfaction the observed satellites.

Consider first Wentzel's theory, extended by Druyvesteyn,[3] as it has been applied to the satellites of the x-ray line K_{β_1} in the elements Al 13 to Fe 26. The parent line K_{β_1} of the ordinary x-ray spectrum is due to the transition $K - M_{\text{II,III}}$ which, neglecting the fine structure $M_{\text{II}} - M_{\text{III}}$, will be written $K - M$. The well-known satellite $K_{\beta'''}$ has been assigned by Druyvesteyn to the transition $KL - LM$. This last notation indicates that in the initial state of the atom one K and one L electron is missing and that the transition of an M electron into the vacant K shell leaves the atom in a final state with one L and one M electron missing. Now the term KL is somewhat greater than the sum of the

[1] WENTZEL, G., *Ann. d. Phys.*, **66**, 437, 1921; *Zeits. f. Phys.*, **31**, 445, 1925.

[2] RICHTMYER, F. K., *Phil. Mag.*, **6**, 64, 1928; *Jour. Franklin Inst.*, **208**, 325, 1929.

[3] DRUYVESTEYN, M. J., *Zeits. f. Phys.*, **43**, 707, 1927; Dissertation, Groningen, 1928.

K and L terms of the ordinary x-ray-term scheme and the term LM is greater than the sum of the L and M terms. This follows directly from the assumption that the energy necessary to remove an L electron from an atom in which a K electron is missing is greater than that necessary to remove the same electron from a normal atom. When a K electron is missing, the inner screening is smaller by unity than in the case of the normal atom so that the binding energy of the L electron is approximately that for the corresponding electron in the element with the next higher atomic number. It therefore follows that

$$(KL)_z = K_z + L_{z+1} \tag{16.24}$$

and

$$(LM)_z = L_z + M_{z+1}. \tag{16.25}$$

The difference in frequency between the satellite $(KL - LM)_z$ and the parent line $(K - M)_z$ becomes

$$\Delta\nu = (KL_z - LM_z) - (K_z - M_z) = (L_{z+1} - L_z) - (M_{z+1} - M_z). \tag{16.26}$$

With these known differences[1] on the right Druyvesteyn obtained for $K_{\beta'''} - K_{\beta_1}$ the following values of $\Delta\nu/R$.

TABLE 16.11.—OBSERVED AND CALCULATED POSITIONS OF THE K_β SATELLITES. VALUES OF $\Delta\nu/R$
(*After Druyvesteyn*)

Element Z		Observed $\Delta\nu/R$		Calculated $L_{II,III}$	Calculated L_I
Al	13	1.79	2.23	1.82	2.34
Si	14	2.07	2.74	2.11	2.63
P	15	2.38	2.97	2.40	2.92
S	16		2.97	2.70	3.22
Cl	17		3.27	2.97	3.49
K	19		3.59	3.55	4.07
Ca	20		3.83	3.84	4.36
Sc	21		3.77	3.53	4.05
Ti	22		3.72	3.73	4.25
V	23		3.92	3.95	4.47
Cr	24		4.00	4.16	4.68
Mn	25		4.34	4.38	4.90
Fe	26		4.69	4.58	5.10

When one takes the fine structure of the L levels and neglects the relatively smaller fine structure of the M levels, Eq. (16.26) predicts a

[1] The L differences being always greater than the M differences, Eq. (16.25) indicates that the satellites will appear on the high-frequency side of the parent x-ray line (see Fig. 16.5).

fine structure for $K_{\beta'''}$. Since the $L_{II} - L_{III}$ interval is small as compared with $L_I - L_{II}$, the observed fine structure should first reveal itself as a doublet. This splitting is observed in the first three elements, Al, Si, P.

It should be pointed out that, if the fine structure of both the initial and final states is considered in the above example, many different transitions become possible. The K_β satellites should therefore be composed of a number of lines. Consider, for example, the possible ways in which satellite transitions $KL - LM$ may take place. All of the possible terms and transitions are shown in the following scheme (Table 16.12).

TABLE 16.12

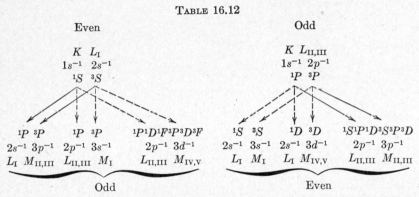

The configurations are given in terms of the missing electrons and the levels in LS-coupling. Regardless of the type of coupling to be expected between two adjacent incompleted subshells, the number of terms will be the same as that given in the table above. Of the many allowed transitions it should be noted that those given by $KL_I - L_{II,III}M_{IV,V}$ involve the double electron jump $2p3d$ to $1s2s$.[1] All double electron jumps are shown by dotted lines. In this diagram we see that both single and double electron jumps are possible. Although the double jumps are possible, they should give rise to weaker lines.[2]

Langer[3] and Wolfe[4] have suggested that the five well-known satellites of K_α (see Fig. 16.18) are to be attributed to the transitions $KL \rightarrow LL$. Following Wolfe's assignments, based upon quantitative calculations of the electron-interaction energies in a Hartree field for the potassium atom (see Fig. 7.2), a schematic energy-level diagram has been constructed in Fig. 16.19. The parent K and L levels are shown at the left with the unresolved $K_{\alpha_{1,2}}$ doublet below. The removal of a second electron from the atom splits these levels (neglecting valence electrons if

[1] The selection rules for double electron jumps are $\Delta l_1 = 1$, $\Delta l_2 = 0, 2$.
[2] A treatment of double electron jumps in x-ray spectra has been given by E. G. Ramberg, *Phys. Rev.*, **45**, 389, 1934.
[3] LANGER, R. M., *Phys. Rev.*, **37**, 457, 1931.
[4] WOLFE, H. C., *Phys. Rev.*, **43**, 221, 1933.

here are any in unclosed subshells) into singlets and triplets as shown. As pointed out by Wolfe, LS-coupling is to be expected in these levels since the spin-orbit interaction energy (shown by the $L_{II} - L_{III}$ interval) is small compared with the interaction between the two electrons (shown by the satellite separations). Five of the six allowed transitions account for the five observed satellites. The sixth allowed transition, shown as a dotted line, is a double electron transition and should give rise to a relatively weak line on the low-frequency side of $K_{\alpha'}$. The results show

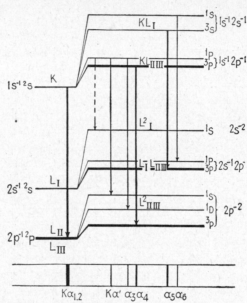

Fig. 16.19.—Splitting up of x-ray levels due to the removal of a second electron from the atom. Illustrating a possible explanation of x-ray $K\alpha$ satellites.

that Wolfe's assignments give a reasonable explanation of the K_α satellites. The K_β satellites may also be assigned in the same way to the transitions shown in Table 16.12.

Although the existing data for checking this theory are somewhat limited, double ionization followed by single, or less frequently by double, electron transitions accompanied by the simultaneous emission of a single radiated frequency appears to be a very plausible explanation of x-ray satellites in general.

There appears to be, at first sight, two processes by which double ionization of an atom may be brought about: (1) a single high-speed particle may remove both electrons, and (2) two high-speed particles may collide successively with the atom and remove one electron after the other. Du Mond and Hoyt, and others, have shown experimentally that the latter tandem process must be ruled out. From the theoretical standpoint the probability that two collisions will occur within the life time of the excited state is far too small to account for the observed satellites.

Although few quantitative data are to be found on the excitation potentials of x-ray satellites, observation supports the theory of double ionization by a single impact. Druyvesteyn has shown for example that while the parent x-ray lines $K_{\alpha_{1,2}}$ in vanadium appear at 5.45 kv., the satellites $K_{\alpha_{3,4}}$ appear only at potentials above 6.09 $\pm$ 0.1 kv. This is not in agreement with Wentzel's early suggestion that two K electrons have been removed from the atom. Assuming Wolfe's assignments are correct for $K_{\alpha_{3,4}}$ (see Fig. 16.19), the removal of one K and one $L_{II,III}$ electron from vanadium requires about the same energy as that necessary to remove a K (1s) electron from vanadium, $Z = 23$, and an $L_{II,III}$ (2p) electron from chromium, $Z = 24$. The sum of these two ionization potentials is 5.450 + 0.586 = 6.036 kv., in excellent agreement with observation. In a similar manner the L_{β_2} line (due to the transition $L_{III} - N_V$) in Ag 47 has an excitation potential of 3.34 kv., and the L_{β_2} satellites should, if attributed to the allowed transitions $L_{III}M_i - M_iN_V$, appear at about 20 per cent higher voltages, i.e., 4.00 kv. This likewise is in good agreement with experiment.

16.12. Explanation of X-ray Absorption Spectra.—In photographing x-ray absorption edges, it often happens that absorption lines are found close to and on both sides of the absorption edge. Under high dispersion and resolving power the lines on the low-frequency sides appear as absorption lines, whereas those on the high-frequency side appear as subsidiary absorption edges. In 1920 Kossel[1] made the suggestion that an inner electron, as the result of the absorption of a photon $h\nu$, need not be completely removed from the atom but instead be simply excited to one of the outer unoccupied states. The lowest possible frequency to be absorbed therefore would be given by the energy necessary to carry an inner electron to the most tightly bound but unoccupied electron orbit. These transitions are governed by the same selection rules valid in emission spectra and lie within only a few volts of the absorption edges[2] which would correspond to complete removal of the electron.

A detailed study by Kievit and Lindsey[3] of the subsidiary absorption edges, observed on the high-frequency side of the K edges of the elements Ca 20 to Zn 30, appears to confirm the theory already postulated, that they are due to the removal of more than one electron from the atom. Kronig[4] has, however, been able to explain this extended structure more satisfactorily on the basis of the existence of prohibited zones in the velocity spectrum of free electrons in crystals.

---

[1] KOSSEL, W., *Zeits. f. Phys.*, **1**, 124, 1920.

[2] SIEGBAHN, M., *Zeits. f. Phys.*, **67**, 567, 1931.

[3] KIEVIT, B., and G. LINDSEY, *Phys. Rev.*, **36**, 648, 1930.

[4] KRONIG, R. DE L., *Zeits. f. Phys.*, **70**, 317, 1931; **75**, 191, 1932.

It should be mentioned that for a given element the chief absorption edges are not always found at the same wave-length but vary somewhat by an amount that depends upon the chemical composition of the substance used in producing the edge. This shifting of the edge has been attributed by Pauling[1] to the difference in the electrostatic fields within the material used as a screen. As an example of the magnitude of the shift, the K limit of sulphur, as measured from 50 different compounds, lies between $\lambda = 4987.3$ and $\lambda = 5011.7$ X units, a maximum variation of 34.4 X units.[2]

[1] Pauling, L., *Phys. Rev.*, **34**, 954, 1929.
[2] Siegbahn, M., "Spektroskopie der Röntgenstrahlen," 2d ed., p. 284, 1931.

CHAPTER XVII

ISOELECTRONIC SEQUENCES

The term *isoelectronic sequence* as it is commonly used refers to a sequence of atoms having the same number of extranuclear electrons. In general such a sequence starts with any element in the periodic table and is followed by other elements in the order of their atomic number. Since each neutral element contains one more electron than the one just preceding it in the periodic table, each atom must be stripped, *i.e.*, ionized, of just the right number of electrons to leave it isoelectronic with the first element in the sequence. Suppose, for example, that a sequence starts with potassium, $Z = 19$. The following elements, calcium, $Z = 20$, scandium, $Z = 21$, titanium, $Z = 22$, etc., are all made isoelectronic with neutral potassium (K I) by removing one electron from calcium, yielding Ca II; two electrons from scandium, yielding Sc III; three electrons from titanium, yielding Ti IV, etc. Because each atom in such a sequence contains the same number of extranuclear electrons the energy levels and the spectrum lines arising from each atom will show remarkable similarities from element to element. Moreover, the empirical rules discovered from a study of these energy levels and spectrum lines are closely associated with the well-known x-ray doublet laws treated in the preceding chapter.

In 1923 Paschen[1] and Fowler[2] identified series of sodium-like doublets in Mg II, Al III, and Si IV.

Not long afterward, Landé pointed out the similarity between the first doublet of the principal series of these elements and the spin relativity or regular doublets $L_{II} - L_{III}$, $M_{II} - M_{III}$, $\cdots$ of x-ray spectra.[3] This correlation between x-ray and optical spectra in turn led him to the correct assignment of the quantum numbers k and j to the x-ray levels K, $L_{I,II,III}$, $M_{I,II,III,IV,V}$, etc. Similarly, de Broglie and Dauvillier[4] pointed out that the $L_{II} - L_{III}$ doublet is analogous to the P doublet of the alkalies and that these two doublets therefore must have the same azimuthal quantum numbers. At about the same time

[1] PASCHEN, F., *Ann. d. Phys.*, **71**, 142, 1923.

[2] FOWLER, A., *Proc. Roy. Soc.*, **A, 103**, 413, 1923; *Phil. Trans. Roy. Soc.*, **225**, 1, 1925.

[3] LANDÉ, A., *Zeits. f. Phys.*, **16**, 391, 1923.

[4] DE BROGLIE, L., and A. DAUVILLIER, *Jour. de phys. et radium*, **5**, 1, 1924.

Millikan and Bowen,[1] quite independently, were able to go further and show that the regular- and irregular-doublet laws of x-rays may be applied to optical doublets. Somewhat later an extension of these same laws to complex spectra was made by Gibbs and White.[2]

17.1. Isoelectronic Sequences of Atoms Containing One Valence Electron.

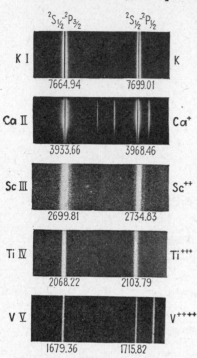

FIG. 17.1.—Photographs of the principal-series doublets $4s, {}^2S_{\frac{1}{2}} - 4p, {}^2P_{\frac{1}{2},\frac{3}{2}}$ for the isoelectronic sequence K I, Ca II, Sc III, Ti IV, and V V.

—As an example of the simplest type of isoelectronic sequence, let us consider the group of alkali-like atoms that are isoelectronic with neutral potassium, $Z = 19$, *viz.*: K I, Ca II, Sc III, Ti IV, V V, Cr VI, ... In this sequence each atom contains in addition to the closed shells of electrons one single valence electron. With a similar core of 18 electrons ($1s^2\ 2s^2\ 2p^6\ 3s^2\ 3p^6$) and one valence electron, the system of energy levels and the radiated series of spectrum lines characteristic of each element will consist of doublets.

Photographs of the first member of the principal series of the first five elements K I, Ca II, Sc III, Ti IV, and V V are reproduced in Fig. 17.1. The potassium doublet, in the far red end of the visible spectrum, and the ionized calcium doublet, in the violet, are the strongest lines in K I and Ca II. From these and other observed doublets, energy level diagrams are easily formulated for each element in the sequence. It is with these energy levels and the laws governing them that we are now concerned.

By analogy with x-ray doublets [see Eq. (16.17)], term values are given by Hertz's formula

$$T = \frac{R(Z - \sigma)^2}{n^2}. \tag{17.1}$$

From the theory of penetrating orbits on the other hand they may also be represented by (see Sec. 7.4)

$$T = \frac{R Z_o^2}{(n - \mu)^2}. \tag{17.2}$$

[1] Millikan, R. A., and I. S. Bowen, *Phys. Rev.*, **24**, 209, 1924; **25**, 295, 1925; **26**, 150, 1925; **27**, 144, 1926.

[2] Gibbs, R. C., and H. E. White, *Phys. Rev.*, **29**, 426, 1927; **29**, 655, 1927; *Proc. Nat. Acad. Sci.*, **13**, 525, 1927.

In the first formula, Z is the atomic number, n is the principal quantum number and σ is a screening constant. In the second formula Z_o is the effective nuclear charge outside the atom and μ is the quantum defect. (Z_o takes the values, unity for neutral atoms, two for singly ionized atoms, three for doubly ionized atoms, etc.) The differences between the term values of all atoms as given by the first formula and those of hydrogen-like atoms as given by

$$T = \frac{RZ^2}{n^2} \tag{17.3}$$

are accounted for by the screening constant σ, whereas in the second formula the differences are attributed to the quantum defect μ. We

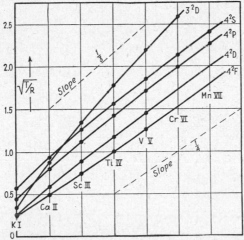

Fig. 17.2.—Moseley diagram of the isoelectronic sequence K I, Ca II, Sc III, . . . The slopes are closely $1/n$.

shall now see how both of these formulas apply separately to the doublets of an isoelectronic sequence. Transposing R in the first formula [Eq. (17.1)] and taking the square root,

$$\sqrt{\frac{T}{R}} = \frac{1}{n}(Z - \sigma). \tag{17.4}$$

In Table 17.1 and in Fig. 17.2 the observed term values for the potassium-like doublets are given, as is customary in x-rays, in terms of $\sqrt{T/R}$.

It is observed from the difference columns in Table 17.1 and from the Moseley diagram that levels with the same principal quantum number ($n = 4$) run nearly parallel. It is to be noted further that the slopes of the curves, as shown by the dotted lines, are in agreement with Eq. (17.4), i.e., they are very nearly equal to $1/n$. If the dotted lines are drawn through the zero-zero origin of coordinates, as they should be for hydrogen-like atoms, the ordinate differences between them and the plotted points will, when multiplied by n, give σ, the screening value of the 18 extranuclear electrons. These screening

TABLE 17.1.—VALUES OF $\sqrt{T/R}$ FOR THE POTASSIUM-LIKE ISOELECTRONIC SEQUENCE K I, CA II, SC III, TI IV, . . . [1]

Term	K I	Diff.	Ca II	Diff.	Sc III	Diff.	Ti IV	Diff.	V V
3^2D	0.350	0.515	0.865	0.484	1.349	0.434	1.783	0.407	2.190
4^2S	0.565	0.369	0.934	0.326	1.260	0.305	1.565	0.292	1.857
4^2P	0.448	0.353	0.801	0.319	1.120	0.298	1.418	0.288	1.706
4^2D	0.263	0.334	0.597	0.296	0.893	0.284	1.177	0.279	1.456
4^2F	0.250	0.252	0.502	0.255	0.757	0.257	1.014	0.258	1.272

[1] Term values T for a Moseley diagram are always computed with respect to the series limit as zero.

constants have been calculated and are given in Table 17.2. Since the doublet fine-structure separations of ^2P, ^2D, and ^2F are small as compared with $^2D - {}^2F$ or $^2P - {}^2D$ separations, they are neglected in the figures and in the tables.

TABLE 17.2.—VALUES OF THE SCREENING CONSTANT σ FOR THE ISOELECTRONIC SEQUENCE OF POTASSIUM-LIKE ATOMS

Electron configuration	Term	K I	Ca II	Sc III	Ti IV	V V
$3d$	3^2D	17.95	17.40	16.95	16.65	16.43
$4s$	4^2S	16.74	16.26	15.96	15.74	15.58
$4p$	4^2P	17.21	16.80	16.52	16.33	16.18
$4d$	4^2D	17.95	17.61	17.43	17.29	17.18
$4f$	4^2F	18.00	17.99	17.97	17.94	17.91

In general it is observed, as would be expected from any of the atomic models, that the screening by 18 core electrons is not so complete for penetrating s and p electrons as it is for the nonpenetrating $4f$ electrons. In the particular sequence chosen it should be noted that after K I the 3^2D states have considerably larger σ values (see Fig. 17.2). It is this change in the binding of $3d$ electrons that brings about an interruption at potassium in the building up of the elements of the periodic table.

A more general study of the electron-binding energies and the application of the x-ray laws to the alkali-like doublets throughout the periodic table is brought out in the Moseley diagram of Fig. 17.3. In this figure of five isoelectronic sequences it is observed (1) that levels with the same n value are closely parallel, (2) that the slopes of the curves for the first sequence are quite accurately $1/n$, (3) that the slopes of most curves deviate more and more from $1/n$ in going to heavier and heavier elements,

(4) that the ^2F curves start at approximately the same value for all sequences and toward heavier elements curve slightly upward, (5) that the ^2S, ^2P, and ^2D curves for heavier elements curve downward,

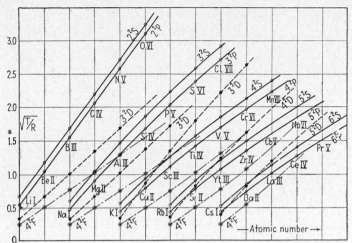

Fig. 17.3.—Moseley diagrams of the doublet levels in five periods of the periodic table. *(After Gibbs and White.)*

and (6) that the $3\,^2D$ curves change their slope abruptly between the Na and K sequences.

Although little is known concerning the energy levels of the rare-earth elements, it is suspected that the ^2F curve in the last sequence

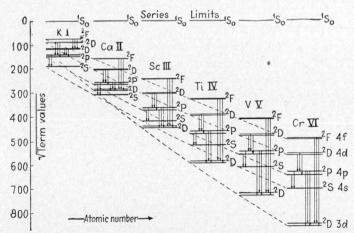

Fig. 17.4.—Energy level diagrams of the potassium-like atoms. A modified Moseley diagram. *(After White.)*

should have a much steeper slope than that indicated in the figure. This seems necessary from the standpoint of the building on of *f electrons* in the 14 rare-earth elements starting with cerium. The figure as it is now shown indicates that a 5d electron is more tightly bound to the triply ionized cerium atom, Ce IV, than is a 4f electron. A comparison of Fig. 17.3 with the x-ray Moseley diagram of Fig. 16.15 brings out a number of interesting similarities.

When values of $\sqrt{T/R}$ are plotted vertically upward as is done on a Moseley diagram, the normal state of each atom becomes the highest point on the curve. As an energy level diagram the figures are therefore inverted. By plotting $\sqrt{T/R}$ (or $\sqrt{T}$) downward, instead of upward, Fig. 17.2 may be transformed into a sequence of energy level diagrams

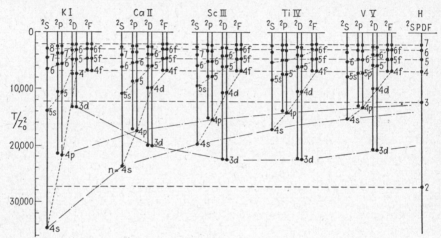

FIG. 17.5.—Energy level diagrams of the potassium-like atoms.

and a Moseley diagram combined (see Fig. 17.4). The observed transitions may now be shown in the usual manner by arrows pointing down.

Let us now turn to the second formula [Eq. (17.2)] derived for penetrating orbits and see how it applies to the energy levels of a typical isoelectronic sequence. Transposing, Eq. (17.2) may be written

$$\frac{T}{Z_o^2} = \frac{R}{(n - \mu)^2}. \tag{17.5}$$

Dividing each term value by Z_o^2 and plotting T/Z_o^2 in place of T, the energy level diagram of each element will be reduced to about the same order of magnitude. Consider, for example, the potassium-like sequence of Fig. 17.2 and Table 17.1 as it is replotted in Fig. 17.5. In this new figure the hydrogen-like states are represented by horizontal dotted lines ($\mu = 0$). The difference between these dotted lines and the plotted observed terms now give, indirectly, the quantum defect μ. Values of μ are given in Table 17.3.

Whether the differences between observed term values and those calculated for hydrogen-like atoms are to be attributed to a screening constant σ [Eq. (17.1)] or a quantum defect μ [Eq. (17.2)] depends upon the purpose for which these constants are to be used. In identifying higher members of a spectral series and in evaluating terms and series limits, the second formula is to be preferred. From the theoretical standpoint, on the other hand, the first formula is to be preferred in that

TABLE 17.3.—VALUES OF THE QUANTUM DEFECT μ FOR THE ISOELECTRONIC SEQUENCE OF POTASSIUM-LIKE ATOMS

Electron configuration	Term	K I	Ca II	Sc III	Ti IV	V V
3d	3^2D	0.143	0.688	0.776	0.757	0.717
4s	4^2S	2.230	1.858	1.619	1.444	1.308
4p	4^2P	1.769	1.504	1.322	1.179	1.069
4d	4^2D	0.198	0.640	0.637	0.602	0.566
4f	4^2F	000	0.016	0.037	0.055	0.069

quantum numbers should take integral values only. Moreover the x-ray laws have been used so successfully in the analysis of the spectra of highly ionized atoms and in the extension of isoelectronic sequences in general that the screening formulas frequently can be used to greater advantage.

17.2. Optical Doublets and the Irregular-doublet Law.—The irregular-doublet law, extended from x-ray to isoelectronic sequences in optical

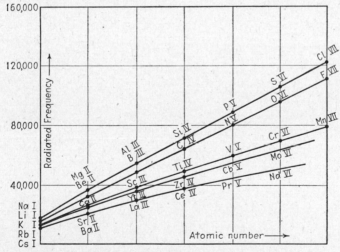

Fig. 17.6.—Illustrating the irregular-doublet law discovered in optical doublets by Millikan and Bowen. The law holds only for transitions where $\Delta n = 0$.

spectra by Millikan and Bowen, may be stated in terms of the energy levels as follows: *the difference between the square roots of the term values of the levels having the same principal quantum number n is independent of the atomic number Z*.   In other words such levels on a Moseley diagram run parallel to each other (see Fig. 16.15 and compare it with Figs. 17.2 and 17.3 for optical doublets).

As a consequence of the parallelism of any two curves on a Moseley diagram, the irregular-doublet law has another and a more useful form. In Sec. 16.9 it was shown (see Fig. 16.17) that the term differences between two levels having the same n value are linear functions of the atomic number Z.   While corresponding transitions ($\Delta n = 0$) are not observed in x-ray spectra, they are observed in optical spectra.   As an example of this form of the irregular-doublet law, a plot of the radiated frequencies due to the transitions np to ns have been plotted for five sequences of alkali-like atoms in Fig. 17.6.   Such a graph shows at a glance how remarkably exact this law holds in optical spectra.   The realization of this law furnishes a most reliable and accurate means for predicting the frequencies and wave-lengths of unidentified spectrum lines in multiply ionized atoms.

17.3. Optical Doublets and the Regular-doublet Law.—The regular-doublet law, extended by Millikan and Bowen to optical doublets, is given by the x-ray formula (see Secs. 16.6, 16.7, and 16.8)

$$\Delta \nu_{\mathrm{cm}^{-1}} = \frac{R\alpha^2(Z - s)^4}{n^3}B \tag{17.6}$$

where $\Delta \nu$ represents the fine-structure doublet separations in wave numbers, Z the atomic number, n the principal quantum number, R the Rydberg constant $= 109737$ cm^{-1}, $\alpha^2 = 5.3 \times 10^{-5}$, and

$$B = \frac{1}{k_1} - \frac{1}{k_2} = \frac{1}{k_1} - \frac{1}{k_1 + 1} = \frac{1}{k_1(k_1 + 1)}. \tag{17.7}$$

In this formula k_1 and k_2 are Sommerfeld's quantum numbers, as used in x-ray formulas.   The value of B fortunately remains the same if k_1 is replaced by the newly assigned quantum number l, where $l = 0$, 1, 2, 3, $\cdots$ for s, p, d, f, $\cdots$ electrons, respectively:

$$\Delta \nu = \frac{R\alpha^2(Z - s)^4}{n^3 l(l + 1)} \text{ cm}^{-1}. \tag{17.8}$$

This is the same formula as that derived in Chap. VIII from a different treatment [Eq. (8.25)].   From the observed separations in the lithium-like sequence of nonpenetrating $2p$ orbits, screening constants s are calculated and given in the last column of Table 17.4.

Assuming a complete screening by the two core electrons, *i.e.*, $s = 2$, $Z - s = 1, 2, 3, 4, 5,$ and 6 for Li I, Be II, B III, C IV, N V, O VI, the separations given in Col. 3 have been calculated.   Still better calculated values are obtained by first computing values of $Z - \sigma$ from the observed term values and Eq. (17.1), and substituting σ for s in Eq. (17.8).   The values computed in this way are given in Col. 4.

TABLE 17.4.—DOUBLET SEPARATIONS FOR LITHIUM-LIKE ATOMS, $2^2P_{\frac{1}{2}} - 2^2P_{\frac{3}{2}}$

Z	Atom	$\Delta\nu$ (obs.)	$\Delta\nu$ (calc.)	$\Delta\nu$ (calc.)	$Z - \sigma$, from term values	$Z - s$, from doublet separations	s
3	Li I	0.338	0.364	0.395	1.021	0.98	2.02
4	Be II	6.61	5.82	6.39	2.047	2.06	1.94
5	B III	34.4	29.4	32.1	3.064	3.12	1.88
6	C IV	107.4	93.0	100.4	4.076	4.14	1.86
7	N V	259.1	227.4	243.1	5.084	5.16	1.84
8	O VI	533.8	471.0	500.8	6.091	6.18	1.82

TABLE 17.5.—SCREENING CONSTANTS s_i CALCULATED FROM THE OBSERVED TERM VALUES AND LANDÉ'S FORMULA FOR PENETRATING ORBITS
(After Gibbs and White)[1]

Atom	$\Delta\nu$ (obs.)	Z	Z_o	s_o	Z_i	s_i	
Na I	17.18	11	1	10	7.66	3.34	
Mb II	91.55	12	2	10	9.56	2.44	
Al III	234.0	13	3	10	10.91	2.09	Third period
Si IV	461.8	14	4	10	12.08	1.92	$3^2P_{\frac{1}{2}} - 3^2P_{\frac{3}{2}}$
P V	794.8	15	5	10	13.15	1.85	
S VI	1267.1	16	6	10	14.23	1.77	
Cl VIII	1889.5	17	7	10	15.29	1.71	
K I	57.7	19	1	18	14.85	4.15	
Ca II	222.8	20	2	18	17.24	2.76	
Sc III	474.3	21	3	18	18.29	2.71	Fourth period
Ti IV	817.5	22	4	18	18.99	3.01	$4^2P_{\frac{1}{2}} - 4^2P_{\frac{3}{2}}$
V V	1264.7	23	5	18	19.54	3.46	
Cr VI	1821.5	24	6	18	19.98	4.02	
Mn VII	2464.7	25	7	18	20.15	4.85	
Rb I	237.6	37	1	36	31.23	5.77	
Sr II	801.5	38	2	36	34.81	3.19	Fifth period
Yt III	1553.7	39	3	36	36.29	2.71	$6^2P_{\frac{1}{2}} - 6^2P_{\frac{3}{2}}$
Zr IV	2484.9	40	4	36	37.10	2.90	
Cs I	554.0	55	1	54	49.55	5.45	
Ba II	1690.9	56	2	54	53.88	2.12	Sixth period
La III	3095.7	57	3	54	55.52	1.48	$7^2P_{\frac{1}{2}} - 7^2P_{\frac{3}{2}}$
Ce IV	4707.0	58	4	54	56.05	1.95	

[1] GIBBS, R. C., and H. E. WHITE, *Phys. Rev.*, **33,** 157, 1929.

A refinement of Eq. (17.6) for penetrating orbits has been given by Landé (see Sec. 8.7), in which Z^4 is split up into two parts, Z_o^2 and Z_i^2 where $Z_i = Z - s_i$, $Z_o = Z - s_o$, and Z is the atomic number.

$$\Delta\nu = \frac{R\alpha^2 Z_o^2 Z_i^2}{n_o^3 l(l+1)}. \tag{17.9}$$

Here n_o is the effective quantum number.   Values of Z_i and s_i have been calculated for the first principal doublets of four isoelectronic sequences in Table 17.5.

The large values of Z_i indicate very deep penetration of the p orbits. Regardless of what physical significance can be attached to these screen-

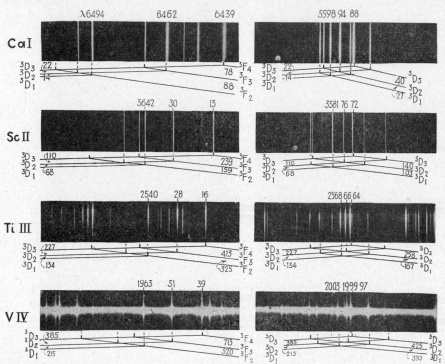

FIG. 17.7.—Photographs of triplet multiplets for the isoelectronic sequence Ca I, Sc II, Ti III, and V IV.

ing constants s_i, Eq. (17.9) serves as an excellent guide in predicting new doublet separations for spectra not yet photographed or analyzed.

17.4. Isoelectronic Sequences of Atoms Containing Two Valence Electrons.—In the previous sections of this chapter we have seen how the x-ray doublet laws apply to the optical doublets of atoms containing one valence electron.   In this and the following sections we are concerned with the extension of these laws to the complex spectra of atoms containing a number of valence electrons.   As a first step in this direction, let us consider the isoelectronic sequence of semicomplex atoms, viz., neutral calcium (Ca I), singly ionized scandium (Sc II), doubly ionized titanium (Ti III), triply ionized vanadium (V IV), etc.   In this intermediate case each atom contains, in addition to the closed subshells of 18 electrons ($1s^2\ 2s^2\ 2p^6\ 3s^2\ 3p^6$), two valence electrons. With two electrons in incomplete subshells the energy level diagram of each atom is composed of a system of singlet and triplet levels and the spectrum of each atom is made up of groups of lines called *singlets, triplets,* and *triplet multiplets.*

Photographs of two sets of these triplet multiplets are shown in Fig. 17.7 for the first four elements of the calcium-like sequence. A schematic representation of the triplet terms and intervals is given below each photograph. Upper states are shown on the left and lower states on the right.

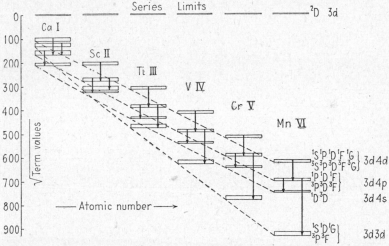

FIG. 17.8.—Modified Moseley diagram of the isoelectronic sequence Ca I, Sc II, Ti III, . . .

A modified Moseley diagram of the type constructed in Fig. 17.4 for the alkali-like atoms may also be constructed for the calcium-like sequence. To illustrate, term values of the first six elements, calcium to manganese, are plotted in Fig. 17.8. Due to the many terms arising from the four configurations shown, $3d^2$, $3d4s$, $3d4p$, and $3d4d$, only the lowest and the highest terms for each configuration are drawn. Plotted in this way all allowed terms (listed at the right in the figure) fall within the upper and lower limits of each rectangle. Grouped as they are, smooth curves can be drawn through the levels of corresponding configurations. It is observed that configurations for which the total quantum numbers of the electrons are the same run nearly parallel to one another. This is the irregular-doublet law in complex spectra.

A comparison of Fig. 17.8 and Fig. 17.4 indicates that the irregular-doublet law, as applied to radiated frequencies in Fig. 17.7, will also apply to two electron spectra. Briefly the irregular-doublet law in this, its most useful form, means that, in any transition involving no change in the principal quantum numbers of the electrons, the radiated frequencies in going from one element to the next are displaced to higher and higher frequencies by very nearly equal frequency intervals. In the calcium-like sequence, two such sets of frequencies have been observed, first the set of lines arising from the electron transition $3d4d$ to $3d4p$ and second the set of lines arising from the transition $3d4p$ to $3d4s$.[1] The allowed terms for these transitions are as follows:

Initial *even* states ^1S ^1P ^1D ^1F ^1G ^3S ^3P ^3D ^3F ^3G $3d4d$

Final *odd* states $\Big\}$
Initial *odd* states $\Big\{$ $^1P^o$ $^1D^o$ $^1F^o$ $^3P^o$ $^3D^o$ $^3F^o$ $3d4p$

Final *even* states ^1D ^3D $3d4s$

Examples of the linear progression of ν with Z are given in Table 17.6 for the line $^3F^o_4 - {}^3G_5$ as representative of the upper set of transitions and for the lines $^3D_3 - {}^3F^o_4$ and $^1D_2 - {}^1D^o_2$ as representative of the second set of transitions.

Table 17.6.—The Irregular-doublet Law Applied to Singlets and Triplets

Element	$3d4p - 3d4d$		$3d4s - 3d4p$		$3d4s - 3d4p$	
	$^3F^o_4 - {}^3G_5$	Diff.	$^3D_3 - {}^3F^o_4$	Diff.	$^1D_2 - {}^1D^o_2$	Diff.
Ca I	(13974)		15526		13986	
		(18640)		12137		9554
Sc II	32614		27663		23540	
		18700		12070		9954
Ti III	51314		39733		33494	
		18782		11838		10578
V IV	70096		51571		44072	
		18902		11733		10865
Cr V	. 88998		63304		54937	

None of the terms arising from the electron configuration $3d4d$ has as yet been determined for Ca I; however, an extrapolation by means of the second and third columns of Table 17.6 locates the $^3F^o_4 - {}^3G_5$ transition not far from 13974 wave numbers.

The almost linear displacement of frequency with atomic number, for all lines due to the transition $3d4p$ to $3d4s$, is shown graphically in Fig. 17.9. The frequency scale for each element starts 11000 wave numbers higher than the preceding element. This type of diagram shows not only the successive displacement of each singlet and triplet group of lines toward the violet by about 11000 cm^{-1} but also magnifies

[1] The many spectrum lines arising from the transition $3d4d$ to $3d4p$ are shown schematically in Fig. 12.4 for singly ionized scandium (Sc II).

many times the variations in this displacement for each individual spectrum line.

Similar studies of other two-electron isoelectronic sequences show that the irregular-doublet law may always be expected to hold. In every sequence investigated the results may be summarized as follows: (1) Curves on a Moseley diagram are smooth and almost straight. (2) Curves on a Moseley diagram having the same principal quantum numbers in the electrons run nearly parallel to each other. (3) Radiated frequencies arising from transitions involving no change in n increase almost linearly with the atomic number Z.

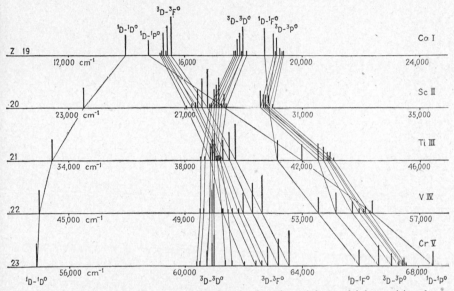

FIG. 17.9.—Illustrating the irregular-doublet law for triplet multiplets arising from the configuration transitions $3d4s - 3d4p$. The almost linear displacement of frequency with atomic number holds only for $\Delta n = 0$. (*After White.*)

A number of interesting relations may be brought out by an extension of the regular-doublet law to complex spectra. Since these relations are seldom employed in the analysis of new spectra the regular-doublet law will not be treated here.

17.5. Isoelectronic Sequences Containing Three or More Valence Electrons.[1]—An extension of the x-ray doublet laws from the optical spectra of one and two valence-electron atoms to systems containing three or more valence electrons is now but an easy step. Consider, for example, the isoelectronic sequence starting with neutral scandium, $Z = 21$. Each atom in this sequence Sc I, Ti II, V III, Cr IV, Mn V, . . . contains, in addition to the closed subshells of 18 electrons

---

[1] GIBBS, R. C., and H. E. WHITE, *Phys. Rev.*, **29**, 655, 1927; WHITE, H. E., *Phys. Rev.*, **33**, 672, 1929; **33**, 914, 1929.

$(1s^2\ 2s^2\ 2p^6\ 3s^2\ 3p^6)$, three valence electrons. As seen by the energy level diagram of neutral scandium in the lower part of Fig. 14.8, each atom in this sequence will give rise to complex systems of doublet and quartet levels.

Along with this group of elements we may also consider the isoelectronic sequence starting with neutral titanium, $Z = 22$. Each atom in this second sequence Ti I, V II, Cr III, Mn IV, Fe V, . . . contains, in addition to the same closed subshells of 18 electrons, four valence

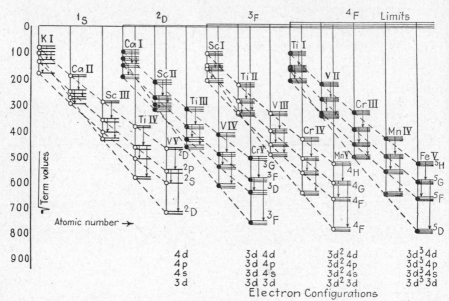

Fig. 17.10.—Modified Moseley diagram for doublets, triplets, quartets, and quintets in the first long period. (*After White.*)

electrons. As seen by the energy level diagram of neutral titanium in Fig. 14.10, each atom in this sequence will give rise to complex systems of singlet, triplet, and quintet levels.

The main features of the energy level diagram of each element in both of these sequences being known, Moseley diagrams of the type shown in Figs. 17.4 and 17.8 may be constructed. For this construction four of the lowest and most prominent electron configurations in each element have been selected:

$$3d^3,\ 3d^2 4s,\ 3d^2 4p,\ 3d^2 4d \qquad \text{for Sc I, Ti II, ...}$$
$$3d^4,\ 3d^3 4s,\ 3d^3 4p,\ 3d^3 4d \qquad \text{for Ti I, V II, ...}$$

Since each configuration gives rise to many levels, the deepest lying level is chosen as representative of that configuration on the diagrams. In accord with Hund's rule, these are the levels of largest S and L values shown schematically in Fig. 17.10. The corresponding terms of the one- and two-electron sequences of Figs. 17.4 and 17.8 are also given for comparison. It should be mentioned that if all possible levels for each configuration are known, the center of gravity of the configuration can be plotted in place of the lowest term. (Each level is assigned its quantum weight $2J + 1$.) In cases where the terms are all known, the resultant diagrams are so little different from the type here shown that the essential features of the diagram as a whole remain

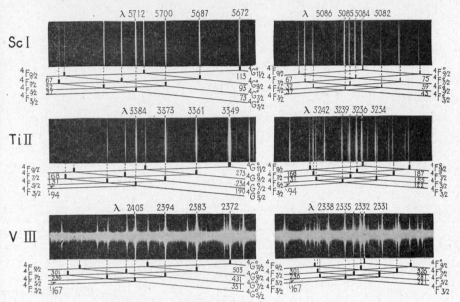

FIG. 17.11.—Photographs of quartet multiplets for the isoelectronic sequence Sc I, Ti II, and V III.

unchanged. For most purposes, one is interested in the deepest lying term of a configuration as that represents the most stable state of the atom in that electron configuration.

Photographs of two strong quartet multiplets, $^4F - {}^4F^o$ and $^4F - {}^4G^o$, arising from the electron transition $3d^2 4p$ to $3d^2 4s$ in Sc I, Ti II, and V III are shown in Fig. 17.11. Similar photographs of a quintet multiplet $^5F - {}^5G^o$, arising from the electron transition $3d^3 4p$ to $3d^3 4s$ in Ti I, V II, and Cr III are shown in Fig. 17.12. The initial and final states and their intervals are represented schematically below each photograph. Considering that these multiplets arise from different elements, they show by their similarity the remarkable likeness of different atomic systems, one with the other.

17.6. The Irregular-doublet Law in Complex Spectra.—A preliminary study of the modified Moseley diagrams in Fig. 17.10 shows that the curves for the configurations $3d^{n-1}4s$, $3d^{n-1}4p$, and $3d^{n-1}4d$ run nearly parallel to one another. This is the irregular-doublet law in complex spectra.   In contrast with this law, it is to be noted that the configurations $3d^n$ cut down across the others and become the lowest levels in the third and succeeding elements.[1]   As a consequence of the parallelism of certain curves on the Moseley diagram it was shown in Secs. 17.2 and 17.4 that the related spectral frequencies increase linearly with the

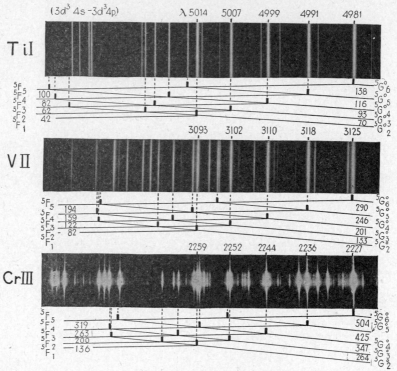

Fig. 17.12.—Photographs of quintet multiplets for the isoelectronic sequence Ti I, V II, and Cr III.

atomic number Z.   The same result is found to apply to complex spectra. Consider, for example, the electron transition $3d^2 4p$ to $3d^2 4s$ in the scandium sequence Sc I, Ti II, V III, ...   The terms arising from these configurations are

Initial *odd* states ^2P ^2S ^2P ^2D ^2P ^2D ^2F ^2D ^2F ^2G ^2F ^2G ^2H

⎰ $3d^2 4p$ ^4S ^4P ^4D ^4D ^4F ^4G

⎱ $3d^2 4s$ ^2S ^2P ^2D ^2F ^2G

Final *even* states ^4P ^4F

Of the many allowed transitions between these levels, the strongest doublets and quartets will arise from the terms in **heavy type**.   The doublet terms $^2D^o$, $^2F^o$, $^2G^o$, combining with ^2F, give rise to a strong

[1] The number n here refers to the number of valence electrons.

triad of doublets and the $^4D^o$, $^4F^o$, $^4G^o$ terms, combining with ^4F, give
rise to a strong triad of quartet multiplets. These two triads have been

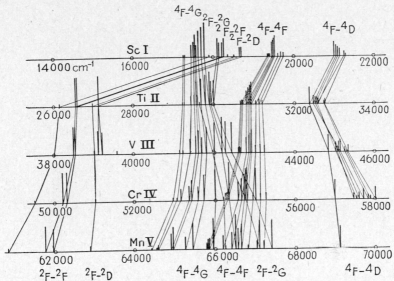

FIG. 17.13.—Illustrating the irregular-doublet law for quartet multiplets arising
from the transitions $3d^24s - 3d^24p$, in the isoelectronic sequence Sc I, Ti II, V III, . . .

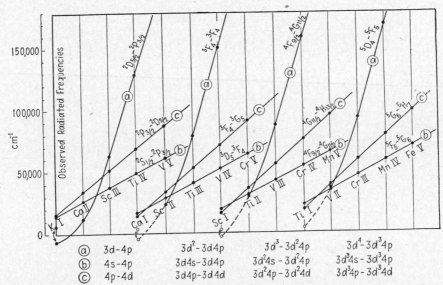

FIG. 17.14.—Showing the contrast between the irregular-doublet law (b) and (c), where
$\Delta n = 0$, and the transitions (a) where $\Delta n = 1$.

identified and plotted to frequency scales in Fig. 17.13. It is to be noted
that each scale starts 12000 wave numbers farther along than that
of the preceding element. In this way the successive displacement of

many lines toward the violet by almost equal frequency intervals is brought out most effectively. If any one particular line in this figure is plotted as a function of Z, the resultant curve, as in the case of the doublets in Fig. 17.6, is practically a straight line. Such curves are shown in Fig. 17.14 for a number of strong characteristic lines belonging to each of the four sequences starting with neutral potassium, calcium, scandium, and titanium. For transitions involving a change in the principal quantum number of one of the electrons, *i.e.*, $3d^{n-1}4p$ to $3d^n$, the curves are by no means linear but curve rapidly upward for the first three or four elements and then begin to straighten out.

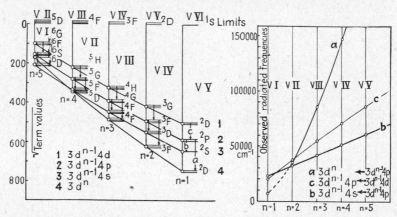

Fig. 17.15.—Modified Moseley diagram and the irregular-doublet law extended to the energy levels and radiated frequencies of the same element, vanadium, in different stages of ionization. (*After White.*)

17.7. Energy Relations for the Same Atom in Different Stages of Ionization.—A further study of the modified Moseley diagram in Fig. 17.10 shows that smooth curves can be drawn through corresponding states of the same atom in different stages of ionization. Consider, for example, singly ionized vanadium (V II), doubly ionized vanadium (V III), triply ionized vanadium (V IV), etc. The points for these atomic systems when replotted as shown at the left in Fig. 17.15 reveal a diagram similar to Fig. 17.10 for an isoelectronic sequence. With the discovery that certain curves in this figure run nearly parallel to each other, we now postulate that certain groups of spectrum lines arising from the same atom in successive stages of ionization are displaced to higher and higher frequencies by approximately equal frequency intervals. This is verified experimentally by the plot of two different electron transitions shown at the right in Fig. 17.15. Just as in the case of isoelectronic sequences these nearly straight curves involve transitions for which the total quantum numbers of the electrons do not change. The third set of transitions shown in the figure involve combinations for which the quantum number n of one of the electrons changes. In constructing Fig. 17.15 there are many terms and spectrum lines from which to choose. From any one given electron configuration, for example, there may be as many as 100 theoretically possible levels. Since all possible levels in complex spectra are seldom observed, the deepest lying term is conveniently chosen as representative of that configuration. This is quite general practice in predicting new terms and in making an analysis of a new spectrum.

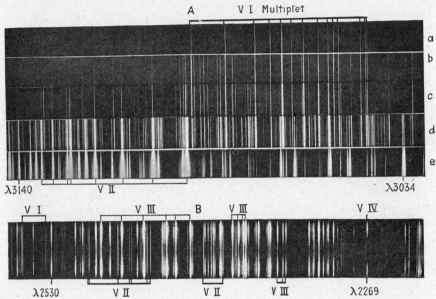

Fig. 17.16.—A. Ultra-violet spectrum of vanadium. Furnace spectra at (a) 2000° Abs., (b) 2300° Abs., (c) 2600° Abs. (d) Arc spectra. (e) Spark spectra. (After King.) B. Vanadium spectrum from a condensed spark discharge. (After White.)

A small section of the visible spectrum of vanadium is reproduced in Fig. 17.16A. This set of five spectrograms, assembled by King,[1] shows how lines and multiplets arising from transitions between low levels or between relatively high levels may be distinguished from each other as well as from lines arising from ionized atoms. At very low temperatures only the low-level lines of the neutral atom V I appear. As the temperature increases, the low-level lines of the ionized spectrum appear, first very weak, then stronger in the arc, reaching a maximum in the spark. Figure 17.16B is another section of the vanadium spectrum taken with a high-voltage spark mounted parallel to the slit of a stigmatic spectrograph. From such a spectrogram lines arising from different stages of ionization are distinguished by the region of the spark from which they appear to come. Lines from the neutral and singly ionized atoms V I and V II appear with nearly the same intensity at

[1] KING, A. S., *Astrophys. Jour.*, **60**, 282, 1924.

all points along the spark. Lines from higher stages of ionization, V III and V IV, appear strong at the electrodes and very weak, if at all, in the middle. These are but a few of the criteria that are often employed in the unraveling of an unanalyzed spectrum.

17.8. Centroid Diagrams.—The centroid diagram, introduced into atomic spectra by Mack, Laporte, and Lang,[1] is often drawn for the purpose of showing just how the energy levels of a given electron configuration change in going from one element to the next. As illustrations

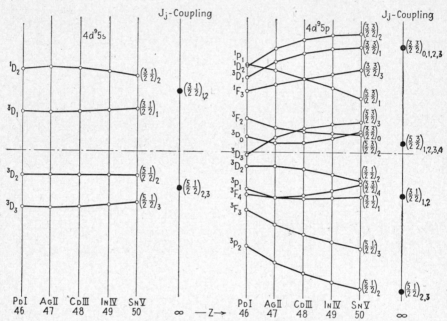

FIG. 17.17.—Centroid diagrams for two different electron configurations in the isoelectronic sequence Pd I, Ag II, Cd III, In IV, and Sn V. (*After J. E. Mack.*)

of this, two centroid diagrams for the levels arising from the electron configurations $4d^9 5s$ and $4d^9 5p$ in the sequence Pd I, Ag II, Cd III, In IV, and Sn V are given, following Mack,[2] in Fig. 17.17. Term separations are plotted vertically against atomic number Z horizontally. The straight horizontal line serves as an origin and represents the center of gravity of each system of levels, each level being assigned the usual weight $2J + 1$. Since the intervals increase rapidly from element to element the $4d^9 5s$, $^3D_1 - {}^3D_3$ interval is made the same for all elements, and all levels of the same element are plotted to that scale. Since the observed intervals show that the coupling is somewhere between LS- and jj-coupling (see Fig. 14.20), the terms are given LS-coupling designations on the left and jj-coupling designations on the right.

[1] MACK, J. E., O. LAPORTE, and R. J. LANG, *Phys. Rev.*, **31**, 748, 1928.
[2] MACK J. E., *Phys. Rev.*, **34**, 17, 1929.

From the Zeeman effect of various levels in the Pd I and Ag II spectra, as well as from the relative trends of the different levels across the diagram, one finds that the coupling is becoming more nearly of the jj type with increasing Z. For good LS-coupling the singlets should lie far above the triplets, and the triplets should follow the interval rule. For good jj-coupling the terms should form two groups for the first diagram, and four groups for the second diagram, around the points shown at the right. These points may be obtained from the spectra of the once more ionized atoms of these same elements, as well as those in the next lower state of ionization, where one can measure directly the interaction energy of $4d^9$ and $5p$, as given by the doublet intervals $^2D_{\frac{3}{2},\frac{5}{2}}$ and $^2P_{\frac{1}{2},\frac{3}{2}}$.

Similar diagrams constructed for the corresponding sequences of atoms in the first and third long periods of the periodic table show the same type of trends as are shown in Fig. 17.16. A comparison of the three periods shows that more nearly jj-coupling arises in the heavier elements Pt I, Au II, Hg III, etc., whereas more nearly LS-coupling arises in the lighter elements Ni I, Cu II, Zn III, etc. (see Fig. 14.20).

CHAPTER XVIII

HYPERFINE STRUCTURE

18.1. Introduction.—It is indeed difficult to say just when, where, and by whom hyperfine structure was first observed. For want of a more exact starting point we may begin with Michelson,[1] Fabry and Perot,[2] and Lummer and Gehrcke,[3] who constructed and employed various types of interferometers and successfully showed that many

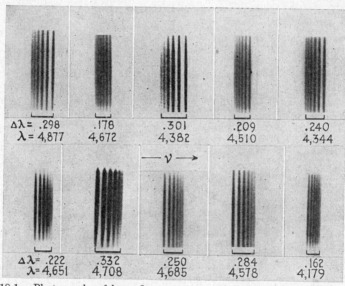

Fig. 18.1.—Photographs of hyperfine structure typical of many of the lines in praseodymium, reproduced from original negatives taken in the fourth order of the 75-ft. spectrograph on Mt. Wilson. (*After White.*)

spectrum lines are not single but made up of a number of components. In 1909 Janicki[4] published an extensive account of his observations and discovery of hyperfine structure in the spectrum lines of a large number of elements. This structure was later verified in detail by Wali-Mohammed.[5] As an example of the appearance of hyperfine-structure patterns, photographs of a number of lines arising from the rare-earth element praseodymium are reproduced in Fig. 18.1. These

[1] MICHELSON, A. A., *Phil. Mag.*, **31**, 338, 1891.

[2] FABRY, C., and A. PEROT, *Ann. de chim. et phys.* (7), **12**, 459, 1897.

[3] LUMMER, O., and E. GEHRCKE, *Ann. d. Phys.*, **10**, 457, 1903.

[4] JANICKI, L., *Ann. d. Phys.*, **29**, 833, 1909.

[5] WALI-MOHAMMED, CH., *Astrophys. Jour.*, **39**, 185, 1914.

photograms represent one of the most commonly observed forms of hyperfine structure, known as *flag patterns*, in which each line contains several components degrading in intensity and interval toward longer or shorter wave-lengths. The photographs are not to be interpreted to mean that all the lines of a given element are of the same flag-pattern type nor that each pattern contains the same number of components. On the contrary many line patterns in a given element are quite different from one another, both in spacing and in the number of components.

In terms of energy level diagrams hyperfine structure in a spectrum line is interpreted to mean that either the initial state, the final state, or both the initial and final states of the atom are not single but contain a definite structure. Early in the development of this field of investigation it was believed that each observed component of a pattern belonged to a different isotope of the same chemical element. Just as soon as hyperfine structure (hereafter to be abbreviated *hfs*) was discovered in

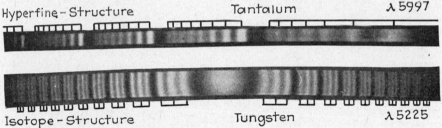

FIG. 18.2.—Photographs illustrating (a) hyperfine structure of a spectrum line as observed in tantalum, and (b) isotope structure as observed in tungsten. (*After Grace, More, MacMillan, and White.*)

elements known to have but one isotope this hypothesis was abandoned, as is always done in science, for a newer and better theory.

Apparently the first suggestion that *hfs* is to be attributed to a small magnetic moment associated with the nucleus was made by Pauli,[1] and later, but independently, by Russell.[1] Experimentalists were not long in showing that this hypothesis, in most cases, is apparently correct. Since the time that this theory was accepted generally, an isotope effect has been observed in some spectra so that now there are two types of *hfs* to be distinguished from each other. First, there is a *hfs* due to a nuclear magnetic and mechanical moment and, second, a *hfs* due to the different isotopes of the same chemical element. The first of these will be referred to as *hfs* and the second as isotope structure. In some elements *hfs* alone is observed, in others isotope structure alone is observed, and in still others both are observed.

[1] PAULI, W., *Naturwissenschaften*, **12**, 741, 1924. The suggestion that *hfs* is due probably to a spinning proton was suggested by H. N. Russell to W. F. Meggers and K. Burns, *Jour. Opt. Soc. Amer.*, **14**, 449, 1927.

Photographs of two spectrum lines are reproduced in Fig. 18.2. The tantulum line illustrates *hfs* of the flag-pattern type with eight components due to a large nuclear moment, and the tungsten line illustrates isotope structure due to the three even isotopes of tungsten. Taken with Fabry-Perot étalons these pictures differ from direct photographs of the type given in Fig. 18.1 in that each pattern is repeated several times for each line. Although there is yet much to be learned from an experimental and a theoretical standpoint, considerable progress has been made in the analysis and interpretation of *hfs*. We shall start therefore by giving the simple treatments of the subject, comparing as we go the predicted results with observation.

18.2. Hyperfine Structure and the Landé Interval Rule.—The very excellent experimental observations by Back, of the *hfs* in the spectrum lines of bismuth, and its beautiful interpretation by Goudsmit,[1] revealed

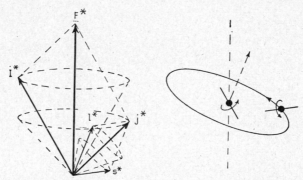

Fig. 18.3.—Orbital and vector models illustrating the coupling of a nuclear moment I^* with an electron moment j^* to form a resultant $F.^*$

for the first time that a new quantum vector should be added to the atom model, and that the Landé interval rule for fine structure also applies to *hfs*. The model proposed is essentially the one shown in Fig. 18.3, where the quantum vector j^* of one electron, or J^* representing the total mechanical moment of all the extranuclear electrons, is coupled with the quantum vector I^*, representing the total mechanical moment of the nucleus $(I^*h/2\pi)$ to form a resultant F^*. It is this resultant F^* that now represents $F^*h/2\pi$, the total mechanical moment of the atom, in place of J^* as previously stated.

Goudsmit and Back have shown that just as the interaction energy between L^* and S^* is proportional to the cosine of the angle between them [see (Eq. 8.18)], so the interaction energy between the nuclear moment I^* and the electron moment J^* is given by

$$\Gamma_F = A'I^*J^* \cos (I^*J^*), \tag{18.1}$$

[1] Goudsmit, S., and E. Back, *Zeits. f. Phys.*, **43**, 321, 1927; **47**, 174, 1928 .

where $A'I^*J^*$ is constant for each given fine-structure level J, and A' is a measure of the strength of coupling between I^* and J^*. Just as in fine structure the *starred quantities* are given by

$$J^* = \sqrt{J(J+1)}, \qquad I^* = \sqrt{I(I+1)}, \qquad F^* = \sqrt{F(F+1)}, \qquad (18.2)$$

where I takes one value only and is half or whole integral valued, and F takes values differing from each other by unity from the value $I - J$ to $I + J$ when $I \geqq J$, and from $J - I$ to $J + I$ when $J \geqq I$. The cosine term in Eq. (18.1) is evaluated by the use of Fig. 18.3 in exactly the same fashion as the cosine in LS-coupling for fine structure (see Sec. 12.6) and gives

$$\Gamma_F = \tfrac{1}{2}A'(F^{*2} - I^{*2} - J^{*2}). \qquad (18.3)$$

This is the interval rule for *hfs* energy levels.

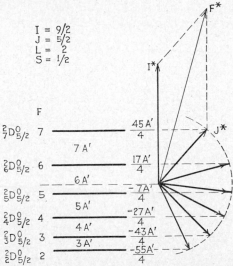

FIG. 18.4.—Vector diagram illustrating graphically the interval rule for hyperfine structure. Specific example of a $^2D_{\frac{5}{2}}$ level, where I is taken as $\frac{9}{2}$.

As an example of the application of Eq. (18.3), consider the $6p^3$, $^2D_{\frac{5}{2}}$ term in the bismuth atom where J is $\frac{5}{2}$ and the observed value of I is $\frac{9}{2}$. The allowed values of F are 2, 3, 4, 5, 6, and 7, for which the Γ_F values are $-\frac{55}{4}A'$, $-\frac{43}{4}A'$, $-\frac{27}{4}A'$, $-\frac{7}{4}A'$, $+\frac{17}{4}A'$, and $+\frac{45}{4}A'$. A graphical representation of this splitting is shown in Fig. 18.4. Drawn to scale, the projection of J^* on I^* gives $J^* \cos(J^*I^*)$, which is proportional to Γ_F. The differences between levels are seen to be $3A'$, $4A'$, $5A'$, $6A'$, and $7A'$ values proportional to the larger of the F values. This result may be derived in general by substituting first $F + 1$, then F, in Eq. (18.3) and taking the difference. Carried out, this gives

$$\Delta\Gamma = A'(F + 1). \qquad (18.4)$$

The observed intervals in the $^2D_{\frac{3}{2}}$ term of bismuth are

$$\Delta\nu = 0.563,\ 0.491,\ 0.385,\ 0.312,\ \text{and}\ 0.256\ \text{cm}^{-1}$$

with ratios closely 7:6:5:4:3.

With each fine-structure term composed of several *hfs* terms, some means of identification or designation is desired to distinguish between the latter.   Since the I value of a given atom is the same for all terms in all states of ionization, it is suggested that the new quantum number F be given by a small subscript to the left of the term type as shown in Fig. 18.4.   The complete designation of the top term in the figure would therefore be $6p^3, {}^2_7D^o_{\frac{3}{2}}$ in LS-coupling and $6p^3, {}_7(\frac{1}{2}\frac{3}{2}\frac{3}{2})^o_{\frac{3}{2}}$ in jj-coupling. Leaving off the electron configuration, a *hfs* line would be designated for example by ${}^2_6P_{\frac{3}{2}} - {}^2_7D^o_{\frac{3}{2}}$ in LS-coupling and by ${}_6(\frac{1}{2}\frac{1}{2}\frac{3}{2})_{\frac{3}{2}} - {}_7(\frac{1}{2}\frac{3}{2}\frac{3}{2})^o_{\frac{3}{2}}$ in jj-coupling.   The importance of this subscript lies in the fact that F represents the total angular momentum of the atom.

In the analysis of many spectrum lines the *hfs* of some levels is found to be *normal*, *i.e.*, smallest F value deepest, while in others it is *inverted*, *i.e.*, largest F value deepest.   In the first instance the coupling constant A' of Eq. (18.3) is *positive* and in the second instance *negative*.   The question of how both positive and negative values of A' arise from the same element and often in the same multiple term will be taken up in the following sections.

As an example of normal and inverted *hfs* a schematic diagram of the bismuth line λ4722 is shown at the left in Fig. 18.5.   The observed pattern of lines arising from transitions between the two sets of levels is shown below.   The selection rules for F in *hfs* are just the same as those for J in fine structure, *viz.*,

$$\Delta F = 0,\ \pm 1. \tag{18.5}$$

Because of the ideal coupling between I and J in nearly all *hfs*, the intensity rules and formulas derived for LS-coupling, and given in Eqs. (12.31) and (12.32), may be applied to *hfs* by replacing the electron-spin resultant S by the nuclear spin I, the orbital resultant L by the electron resultant J, and the electron resultant J by the atom resultant F.[1]

With a nuclear spin $I = \frac{9}{2}$ and a J value of $\frac{1}{2}$, the initial state in Fig. 18.5 is split into two levels $F = 4$ and 5.   Again with $I = \frac{9}{2}$ and $J = \frac{3}{2}$ the final state is split into four levels $F = 3,\ 4,\ 5,$ and 6.   [The fine structure in Bi does not show LS-coupling but very good jj-coupling (see Fig. 14.21). The transition 7s to 6p with J changing from $\frac{1}{2}$ to $\frac{3}{2}$ is an allowed transition.]   The observed line intensities are shown at the bottom of the

[1] For a derivation of *hfs* intensity rules see E. L. Hill, *Proc. Nat. Acad. Sci.*, **15**, 779, 1929.   Intensity tables are given in the Appendix.

figure by means of the microphotometer curve, for comparison with the calculated intensities given just above.

The second *hfs* pattern in Fig. 18.5 is drawn for one of the two resonance lines of manganese, an intercombination line, $\lambda5394$. With an I value of $\frac{5}{2}$, each level $J = \frac{5}{2}$ and $\frac{7}{2}$ is split into six components as shown. Applying the relative intensity formulas to the allowed transitions, the theoretical pattern shown near the bottom is obtained. For want of greater resolving power this very narrow pattern is only partially resolved as shown by the microphotometer curve at the bottom of the figure.

In making an analysis of the *hfs* of an uncharted spectrum, patterns such as we have shown here are all one has to work with. Where all

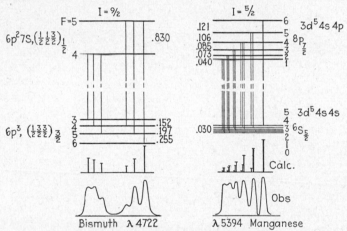

FIG. 18.5.—Schematic diagrams of the *hfs* levels and patterns of (a) $\lambda4722$ in bismuth (*after Back and Goudsmit*), and (b) $\lambda5394$ in manganese (*after White and Ritschl*).

components are completely resolved, as is easily accomplished in a simple and wide pattern like Bi, equal frequency differences enable one to construct *hfs* energy levels for the initial and final states. If there are more than two levels, the interval rule may be applied and the F values written down from the interval ratios. Knowing the J values from the fine-structure analysis, the nuclear spin I is obtained directly. These are often the steps taken in the determination of the nuclear spin I.

It should be noted that, if $I \leqq J$, the level will be broken up into $2I + 1$ *hfs* levels, whereas, if $J \leqq I$, the level will be broken up into $2J + 1$ *hfs* levels. This rule shows that, if the J values of a line are known to be large, the nuclear spin may be determined directly from the number of lines or levels and in some cases from an incompletely resolved pattern. A good example of this is to be found in praseodymium (see Fig. 18.1) where all lines that have been resolved as shown are flag patterns with six components. This can be interpreted to mean only that for Pr, $I = \frac{5}{2}$.

18.3. Nuclear Interaction with One Valence Electron.—Calculations of the interaction energy between a single arbitrary electron and a nucleus with a mechanical and magnetic moment have been made by Fermi,[1] Casimir,[2] Hargreaves,[3] Breit,[4] and Goudsmit.[5] The treatment to be given here is essentially the semiclassical treatment given by Goudsmit which leads, with suitable modifications, to the quantum-mechanical results obtained by the others. It should be pointed out at the outset that the treatment does not apply to the special case of an s electron. Suitable changes, however, will make the results applicable even here.

The interaction of a single electron with the nucleus (see Fig. 18.3) may be divided into two parts: (1) the interaction of the orbital motion l^* with the nuclear moment I^*, and (2) the interaction of the electron spin s^* with I^*. Applying classical electromagnetic theory, as has been done in Sec. 8.6 for the spin-orbit interaction, the electric field at the nucleus due to the electron at a distance r is given by

$$E = \frac{e}{r^3}\mathbf{r}.$$

Similarly the magnetic field at the nucleus due to the orbital motion of the electron is

$$H = \frac{E \times v}{c}.$$

Substituting Bohr's relation for the angular momentum

$$2\pi m\mathbf{r} \times v = l^*h,$$

the magnetic field becomes

$$H = \frac{e}{mc}l^*\frac{h}{2\pi}\left(\frac{1}{r^3}\right), \tag{18.6}$$

where m and e are the mass and charge on the electron, and r is the electron-nuclear distance. Since r is not constant in any orbit, either on the classical theory or on the quantum mechanics, $(1/r^3)$ must be averaged. Now the nucleus with a mechanical moment $I^*h/2\pi$ and a magnetic moment μ_I tends to carry out a Larmor precession around this field with an angular velocity ω_L given (see Secs. 3.7 and 8.6) by the

[1] Fermi, E., *Zeits. f. Phys.*, **60**, 320, 1930.

[2] H. B. G. Casimir, quoted in L. Pauling and S. A. Goudsmit, "The Structure of Line Spectra," p. 208.

[3] Hargreaves, J., *Proc. Roy. Soc.*, **A, 127**, 141, 1930.

[4] Breit, G., *Phys. Rev.*, **37**, 51, 1931.

[5] Goudsmit, S. A., *Phys. Rev.*, **37**, 663, 1931; see also Pauling, L., and S. A. Goudsmit, "The Structure of Line Spectra," p. 204.

product of the field strength H and the ratio between the magnetic and the mechanical moment. For this latter ratio we write

$$\frac{\mu_I}{\dfrac{I^*h}{2\pi}} = g_I \frac{e}{2mc}, \tag{18.7}$$

where $e/2mc$ is the classical ratio and g_I is an unknown factor called the *nuclear g factor.* If the nuclear moment were due to a proton in an orbit, g_I would be expected to be $\frac{1}{1838}$ that of an orbital electron. If it is due to a spinning proton, g_I should be between $4\frac{1}{2}$ and 7 times this.[1]

The precessional angular velocity becomes therefore

$$\omega_L = g_I \frac{e^2}{2m^2c^2} \frac{l^*h}{2\pi}\left(\frac{1}{r^3}\right). \tag{18.8}$$

The interaction energy is now given by the product of ω_L and the projection of the nuclear mechanical moment $I^*h/2\pi$ on l^*,

$$W_{I,l} = g_I \frac{e^2}{2m^2c^2} \frac{l^*h}{2\pi}\left(\frac{1}{r^3}\right) I^* \frac{h}{2\pi} \overline{\cos\,(I^*l^*)}. \tag{18.9}$$

Since l^* precesses around j^*, and j^* and I^* in turn precess around their resultant F^*, the above cosine must be averaged. Since the first precession is very much more rapid than the latter, we may, in the usual manner, project l^* on j^*, then j^* on I^* and get for the average cosine,

$$\overline{\cos\,(I^*l^*)} = \cos\,(I^*j^*)\,\cos\,(l^*j^*). \tag{18.10}$$

Substituting in Eq. (18.9) this gives

$$W_{I,l} = g_I \frac{e^2}{2m^2c^2} l^* \frac{h}{2\pi}\left(\frac{1}{r^3}\right) I^* \frac{h}{2\pi} \cos\,(I^*j^*)\,\cos\,(l^*j^*). \tag{18.11}$$

Since both of these angles are fixed, the cosines are readily evaluated in terms of the quantum vectors s^*, l^*, j^*, I^*, and F^*. This will be done after we obtain the interaction energy for the electron spin s^* and the nuclear spin I^*.

According to classical electromagnetic theory the mutual energy of two magnetic dipoles with moments μ_I and μ_s, and at a distance r apart, is equal to

$$W_{I,s} = \frac{\mu_I\mu_s}{r^3}\{\cos\,(\mathbf{\mu}_I\mathbf{\mu}_s) - 3\cos\,(\mathbf{\mu}_I r)\cos\,(\mathbf{\mu}_s r)\}. \tag{18.12}$$

---

[1] Recent Stern-Gerlach and Breit-Rabi experiments with hydrogen have shown that the nuclear magnetic moment of hydrogen lies between $2\frac{1}{4}$ and $3\frac{1}{2}$ *nuclear* magnetons; one nuclear magneton being defined as $eh/4\pi Mc$, where M is the mass of the proton. Because the magnetic moment of a proton appears to be considerably larger than *one nuclear magneton* the term *proton magneton* frequently used for this same unit of magnetic moment is misleading.

The nuclear magnetic moment μ_I is given by Eq. (18.7), and the magnetic moment of the spinning electron by

$$\mu_s = -2\frac{e}{2mc}s^*\frac{h}{2\pi}. \tag{18.13}$$

The mean value of the term in braces, involving the electron-nuclear distance r, is readily shown by the use of direction cosines to be[1]

$$-\tfrac{1}{2}\cos{(I^*j^*)}\{\cos{(j^*s^*)} - 3\cos{(j^*l^*)}\cos{(s^*l^*)}\}. \tag{18.14}$$

Inserting these results in Eq. (18.12),

$$W_{I,s} = +g_I\frac{e}{2mc}I^*\frac{h}{2\pi}2\frac{e}{2mc}s^*\frac{h}{2\pi}\overline{\left(\frac{1}{r^3}\right)}\frac{1}{2}\cos{(I^*J^*)}\{\cos{(j^*s^*)}$$
$$-3\cos{(j^*l^*)}\cos{(s^*l^*)}\}. \tag{18.15}$$

Adding the two interaction energies [Eqs. (18.11) and (18.15)], the total interaction for spin and orbit becomes

$$\Gamma_F = W_{I,l} + W_{I,s} = a'I^*j^*\cos{(I^*j^*)} = \tfrac{1}{2}a'(F^{*2} - I^{*2} - J^{*2}), \tag{18.16}$$

where the coefficient a' is given by

$$a' = g_I\frac{e^2h^2}{8\pi^2m^2c^2}\overline{\left(\frac{1}{r^3}\right)}\left\{\frac{l^*}{j^*}\cos{(l^*j^*)} + \frac{s^*}{2j^*}\cos{(s^*j^*)}\right.$$
$$\left. -\frac{3s^*}{2j^*}\cos{(j^*l^*)}\cos{(s^*l^*)}\right\}. \tag{18.17}$$

Upon substituting the quantum-mechanical value of $\overline{(1/r^3)}$ (see Secs. 4.9 and 8.6),

$$a' = g_I\frac{Rhc\alpha^2Z^3}{n^3l(l + \tfrac{1}{2})(l + 1)}\left\{\ \ \right\}. \tag{18.18}$$

For a given spectral term, *i.e.*, given s, l, and j, a' is a constant.

Fermi, Hargreaves, and Breit have shown from a quantum-mechanical treatment, and Goudsmit has shown from the classical theory of *energy sums*, that the terms in the braces of Eq. (18.17) are to be replaced by l^{*2}/j^{*2}. This changes the a' coefficient of Eq. (18.18) to

$$a' = g_I\frac{Rhc\alpha^2Z^3}{n^3(l + \tfrac{1}{2})j(j + 1)}. \tag{18.19}$$

Dividing by hc to obtain a' in cm^{-1}:

$$a' = g_I\frac{R\alpha^2Z^3}{n^3(l + \tfrac{1}{2})j(j + 1)}. \tag{18.20}$$

According to Eq. (18.7), the nuclear g factor is given by the ratio between the nuclear magnetic moment in Bohr magnetons, $eh/4\pi mc$, and the mechanical moment in units of $h/2\pi$. If g_I is to be expressed in

[1] See Pauling, L., and S. A. Goudsmit, "The Structure of Line Spectra," p. 206.

nuclear magnetons $(eh/4\pi Mc)$, where M is the mass of a proton, g_I in Eq. (18.20) must be divided by 1838, the ratio of the mass of the proton to the mass of the electron. The result is

$$a' = \frac{g_I}{1838} \cdot \frac{R\alpha^2 Z^3}{n^3(l + \frac{1}{2})j(j + 1)} \text{ cm}^{-1}. \tag{18.21}$$

This a' is the A' of Eqs. (18.1) and (18.3) for hydrogen-like atoms. If g_I is positive, a' is positive and the *hfs* terms will be *normal*. If g_I is negative, a' is negative and the *hfs* terms will be *inverted*. If the nuclear magnetic moment is due to a spinning proton, the g_I factor would be expected to be between $4\frac{1}{2}$ and 7.[1]

As already pointed out, the above equations have been derived for hydrogen-like atoms. Since *hfs* has not been observed in these simplest of atomic systems we must look to the more complex spectra and the heavier elements for a comparison of theory with experiment.

18.4. Nuclear Interaction with a Penetrating Electron.—In a classical treatment of fine structure Landé showed, by the use of an idealized model, that Z^4 in the resultant equation should be replaced by Z_i^2 times Z_o^2. The alkali doublet separations, for example, are given by Eq. (8.32),

$$\Delta\nu = \frac{R\alpha^2 Z_i^2 Z_o^2}{n_o^3 l(l + 1)} \text{ cm}^{-1}, \tag{18.22}$$

where Z_i is the effective nuclear charge inside the core of closed electron shells, and Z_o the effective nuclear charge outside. By analogy with this equation and its derivation, Z^3 in Eq. (18.21) is broken up into two parts so that the interaction energy of a single valence electron, screened from the nucleus by a shell of electrons, is given by [see Eq. (18.3)]

$$\Gamma_F = \frac{1}{2}a'(F^{*2} - I^{*2} - J^{*2}), \tag{18.23}$$

where

$$a' = \frac{g_I}{1838} \cdot \frac{R\alpha^2 Z_i Z_o^2}{n_o^3(l + \frac{1}{2})j(j + 1)}. \tag{18.24}$$

[1] In any experiment performed for the purpose of determining the magnetic and mechanical moments of the nucleus, μ_I and $I^*h/2\pi$ are so oriented with the field, as in the Zeeman effect, that what one measures is the component of μ_I along the field H. From the experimental value of this component the moments μ_I and $I^*h/2\pi$ are calculated from theory. In Frisch, Stern, and Estermann's experiments on the hydrogen molecule a magnetic moment of approximately $2\frac{1}{2} \pm 10$ per cent nuclear magnetons has been measured for the proton. By a different method Rabi, Kellogg, and Zacharias find a value of $3\frac{1}{4} \pm 10$ per cent nuclear magnetons. The agreement between these two values must be regarded as more important than their difference. Dividing by $I = \frac{1}{2}$ gives a value of g_I from $4\frac{1}{2}$ to 7 for the proton. This comes from Eq. (18.7), for, if the ratio $\dfrac{\mu_I}{I^*h/2\pi}$ gives the g_I factor, then the ratio of their components along any line will also give the same ratio.

See Frisch, R., and O. Stern, *Zeits. f. Phys.*, **85**, 4, 1933; Estermann, I., and O. Stern, *Zeits. f. Phys.*, **85**, 16, 1933. Rabi, I. I., J. M. B. Kellogg, and J. R. Zacharias, *Phys. Rev.*, **46**, 157, 1934.

The latter equation is somewhat simplified by substituting the observed fine-structure doublet separation [Eq. (18.22)]. This gives

$$a' = \frac{g_I}{1838} \cdot \frac{\Delta\nu l(l+1)}{Z_i(l+\frac{1}{2})j(j+1)}. \tag{18.25}$$

A graphical comparison of this equation with the observed hfs of the $7p,{}^2P_{\frac{1}{2},\frac{3}{2}}$ levels in doubly ionized thallium is made in Fig. 18.6. The calculated hfs separations are shown in Fig. 18.6B, the observed separations in Fig. 18.6D. The relative intervals are not in good agreement. It should be noted that, since g_I for the Tl nucleus is unknown from theory, the lower level in each part of the figure has been taken arbitrarily to have the same separation as the observed.

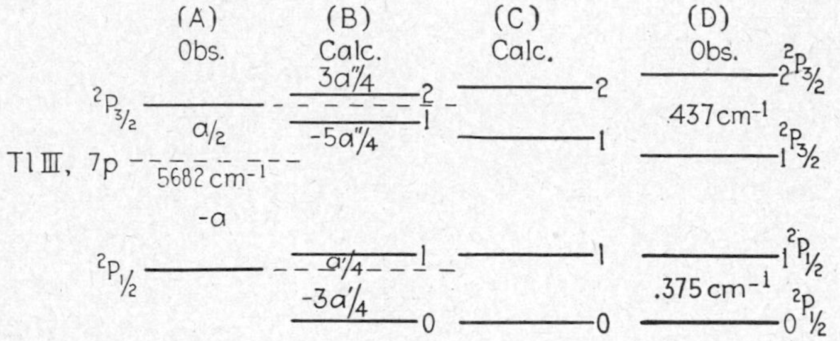

Fig. 18.6.—Graphical comparison of calculated and observed hfs in thallium. (A) Observed doublet separation. (B) Relative separations according to Eqs. (18.23) and (18.25). (C) Relativity corrections added. (D) Observed hfs separations.

Breit[1] and Racah[2] have shown that relativity corrections are different for the two levels of a doublet and must be taken into account. The relativity corrections to be added to Eq. (18.25) are obtained by multiplying a' by κ/λ, where

$$\kappa = \frac{4j(j+\frac{1}{2})(j+1)}{(4\rho^2-1)\rho}, \qquad \rho^2 = (j+\frac{1}{2})^2 - (\alpha Z_i)^2, \tag{18.26}$$

$$\lambda = \left[\frac{2l(l+1)}{(\alpha Z_i)^2}\right][\{(l+1)^2 - (\alpha Z_i)^2\}^{\frac{1}{2}} - 1 - \{l^2 - (\alpha Z_i)^2\}^{\frac{1}{2}}]. \tag{18.27}$$

Equation (18.25) becomes therefore

$$a' = \frac{g_I}{1838} \cdot \frac{\Delta\nu l(l+1)\kappa}{Z_i(l+\frac{1}{2})j(j+1)\lambda}. \tag{18.28}$$

Substituting the known values in these equations and assuming the same separation for the ${}^2P_{\frac{1}{2}}$ hfs, the ${}^2P_{\frac{3}{2}}$ separation in Fig. 18.6C is obtained. Although there is better agreement with observation, the discrepancy is still rather large.

[1] G. Breit, see Goudsmit, S. A., Phys. Rev., 43, 636, 1933.
[2] Racah, G., Zeits. f. Phys., 71, 431, 1931.

As stated above, the equations thus far developed should not apply to s orbits. McLennan, McLay, and Crawford[1] have shown, however, that the equations do seem to be approximately correct even for this special case. Goudsmit has suggested that we write for s electrons,

$$a' = \frac{g_I}{1838} \cdot \frac{8R\alpha^2 Z_i Z_o^2}{3n_o^3} \kappa \qquad (18.28a)$$

As examples of the application of Eqs. (18.28) and (18.28a), we substitute observed *hfs* separations from a known spectrum and calculate nuclear g_I factors. Such calculations are given in Table 18.1 for the doubly ionized atom of thallium. The observed *hfs* separations are given in Col. 2. With a nuclear moment $I = \frac{1}{2}$, the a' factors, given in Col. 3, are obtained from Eq. (18.23). Many calculations of Z_i from fine-structure term values show that, throughout the periodic table,

TABLE 18.1.—NUCLEAR g_I FACTORS CALCULATED FROM THE OBSERVED *Hfs* IN TL III

Term		$\Delta\nu$	a'	κ	λ	Z_i	Z_0	g_I
$6s$,	$^2S_{\frac{1}{2}}$	6.4 cm^{-1}	6.4 cm^{-1}	2.31		81	3	3.7
$7s$,	$^2S_{\frac{1}{2}}$	1.37	1.37	2.31		81	3	2.94
$7p$,	$^2P_{\frac{1}{2}}$	0.375	0.375	2.08	1.17	77	3	2.96

$Z_i \cong Z$ for s electrons and $Z_i \cong Z - 4$ for p electrons. The lack of agreement between the values obtained in the table as well as in other elements in the periodic table indicates that the above presented theoretical treatment of *hfs* is not complete and must still be modified further. For this reason too much weight should not be given to such calculations. It should be noted, however, that the magnitude of the calculated g_I factors should be about right and is about what one would expect if the nuclear moments are to be attributed to positively charged particles in the nucleus.

18.5. Classical Explanation of Normal and Inverted *Hfs*.—Classically it is not difficult to show that for each level of a fine-structure doublet arising from a single valence electron the orbital interaction of the electron with the nucleus tends to produce a normal *hfs* splitting of both levels. The electron-spin interaction with the nucleus, however, tends to invert the *hfs* of the term $j = l + \frac{1}{2}$ and to widen that of $j = l - \frac{1}{2}$. This may be seen from the classical orbital model in Fig. 18.3. The orbital motion of the electron produces a magnetic field at the nucleus which is opposite in direction to its mechanical moment $l^*h/2\pi$. The most stable state for the nucleus in this field, and therefore the state of least

---

[1] McLENNAN, J. C., A. B. McLAY, and M. F. CRAWFORD, *Proc. Roy. Soc.*, A, **133**, 652, 1931.

energy, will be the one for which the nuclear magnetic moment is most nearly parallel to the field of the electron. If this magnetic moment is due to something like an orbital or spinning proton, this will be the state for which the mechanical moments I^* and J^* are oppositely directed. These are the hfs states $^2_1P_{\frac{3}{2}}$ and $^2_0P_{\frac{1}{2}}$ in Fig. 18.6.

If we now think of the spinning electron and the nucleus as small magnets acting on each other at some distance from each other, the most stable position of the two will be that for which their magnetic moments are in opposite directions and the mechanical moments are in the same direction. These correspond to the $^2_2P_{\frac{3}{2}}$ and $^2_1P_{\frac{1}{2}}$ states in Fig. 18.6. Since the orbital interaction with the nucleus is greater than the spin interaction, the hfs of both levels is normal. Although the greater splitting is observed in the $7p,^2P_{\frac{3}{2}}$ level in Tl III (see Table 18.1) the a' coefficient, which measures the total interaction with the nucleus, is greatest for the $7p,^2P_{\frac{1}{2}}$ level.

Fermi has shown from a quantum-mechanical treatment of s electrons that the interaction with the nucleus is opposite in sign to that of the spin of an arbitrary electron, *i.e.*, it has the same sign as an orbital interaction. Classically, therefore, an s electron may be thought of as a cloud of negative charge, distributed as shown in Figs. 4.6 and 4.7 and rotating about the nucleus. A positive charge rotating at the center of this spinning negative cloud is most stable when the magnetic moments are parallel and the mechanical moments are opposite. This shows that s electrons also give rise to normal hfs, as observed. Because of the deep penetration of an s electron on the classical theory, or the large probability density near the nucleus on the quantum-mechanical model, the interaction between s^* and I^* and hence the hfs for $^2S_{\frac{1}{2}}$ states should be very large.

18.6. Hyperfine Structure in Atoms with Two or More Valence Electrons.—In 1927 Meggers and Burns[1] published an account of the hfs in the lanthanum spectrum, at which time they pointed out that the largest structures were always observed for configurations involving a single unbalanced s electron. They also pointed out at the same time that, while certain levels revealed wide structures, others of the same multiplet were either single or else very narrow and unresolved. In the $6s5d,^3D_{1,2,3}$ terms of La II, for example, the two outer levels $^3D_1$ and $^3D_3$ show a wide splitting, whereas the middle level $^3D_2$ shows practically none. An explanation of this anomaly in terms of the vector model has been given by White,[2] and equations for the splitting have been given by Goudsmit and Bacher.[3]

[1] Meggers, W. F., and K. Burns, *Jour. Opt. Soc. Amer.*, **14**, 449, 1927.

[2] White, H. E., *Phys. Rev.*, **34**, 1288, 1929; **34**, 1397, 1404, 1929; **35**, 441, 1930; *Proc. Nat. Acad. Sci.*, **16**, 68, 1930.

[3] Goudsmit, S. A., and R. F. Bacher, *Phys. Rev.*, **34**, 1499, 1501, 1929.

In Fig. 18.7 we picture, on both the classical model and on the quantum-mechanical model, an atom with two valence electrons, one in a *penetrating s* orbit and the other in a *nonpenetrating d* orbit. A vector diagram for the same atom in *LS*-coupling is drawn schematically at the left. From this picture it is easy to see how the penetrating electron has an opportunity of coupling strongly with the outer electron when it is outside the core and also with the nucleus when it is inside the core. Thus the *s* electron may greatly strengthen the coupling between the electron resultant J^* and the inner nuclear resultant I^*. Due to the screening of the nucleus by the core electrons, the interaction between the nucleus and the *d* electron is small compared with that between s_1^* and I^*. For strong coupling with the nucleus the electron must not only be *deeply penetrating* but also *tightly bound*. All *s* orbits, for

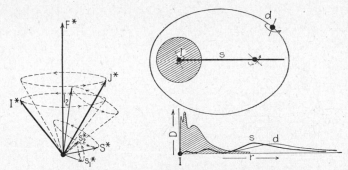

FIG. 18.7.—Vector and orbital model for the interaction of a penetrating *s* electron and a nonpenetrating *d* electron with a nuclear moment.

example, will be deeply penetrating, but only those that spend a considerable amount of their time near the nucleus will couple strongly with I^* and give wide *hfs*.

Due to the large spin-spin interaction of the electrons in *LS*-coupling, s_1^* and s_2^* precess rapidly around their mechanical resultant S^*. Due to the somewhat weaker coupling between the spin s_2^* and the orbit l_2^* of the *d* electron, S^* and l_2^* precess more slowly around their mechanical resultant J^*. Finally J^* and I^* are coupled weakly together and precess slowly around their mechanical resultant F^*. The relative frequencies of these precessions are given by, and follow directly from, the observed energy differences, *i.e.*, by the *singlet-triplet* intervals, the *triplet fine-structure* intervals, and the *hfs* intervals, respectively.

The well-known general relation that the energy of interaction between any two magnetic moments is proportional to the cosine of the angle between them (see Sec. 8.6) enables one to write

$$\Gamma_F = a' I^* s_1^* \overline{\cos (I^* s_1^*)} \tag{18.29}$$

for the energy of interaction between an *s* electron and the nuclear moment. Owing to the above mentioned classical precessions, cos (I^*s^*) must be averaged. Projecting the rapidly precessing s_1^* on S^*, then the less rapidly precessing S^* on J^*, and finally the slowly precessing J^* on I^*, we obtain

$$\overline{\cos\ (I^*s_1^*)} = \cos\ (I^*J^*)\ \cos\ (J^*S^*)\ \cos\ (S^*s_1^*), \tag{18.30}$$

giving for Eq. (18.29),

$$\Gamma_F = a'I^*s_1^*\ \cos\ (I^*J^*)\ \cos\ (J^*S^*)\ \cos\ (S^*s_1^*). \tag{18.31}$$

This may be written in the generally observed form of Eq. (18.1):

$$\Gamma_F = A'I^*J^*\ \cos\ (I^*J^*), \tag{18.32}$$

where

$$A' = a'\frac{s_1^*}{J^*}\ \cos\ (J^*S^*)\ \cos\ (S^*s_1^*). \tag{18.33}$$

Since each of the angles is constant, all three cosine terms are readily evaluated in terms of the mechanical moment vectors to give for LS-coupling

$$\Gamma_F = \tfrac{1}{2}A'(F^{*2} - I^{*2} - J^{*2}), \tag{18.34}$$

where

$$A' = a'\frac{J^{*2} + S^{*2} - l_2^{*2}}{2J^{*2}} \cdot \frac{S^{*2} + s_1^{*2} - s_2^{*2}}{2S^{*2}}. \tag{18.35}$$

One interesting result regarding this equation is that A', as shown by Goudsmit and Bacher, may be simplified by expressing it in terms of the electron g factor. Substituting $\tfrac{1}{2}$ for s_1 and for s_2 and the value of g as given by Eq. (13.8), the A' factor for LS-coupling reduces to

$$A' = \tfrac{1}{2}a'(g - 1) \tag{18.36}$$

If the coupling between the s electron and the outer electron is jj, the average cosine is obtained in a similar fashion by projecting I^* on J^*, then J^* on s_1^*, to give

$$\overline{\cos\ (I^*s_1^*)} = \cos\ (I^*J^*)\ \cos\ (J^*s_1^*). \tag{18.37}$$

This again leads to Eqs. (18.32) and (18.34), where, for jj-coupling,

$$A' = a'\frac{s_1^*}{J^*}\ \cos\ (J^*s_1^*) = a'\frac{J^{*2} + s_1^{*2} - j_2^{*2}}{2J^{*2}}. \tag{18.38}$$

As an example of the application of these equations let us first consider an sd electron configuration in LS-coupling and calculate the relative separations of the hfs in each of the ^3D terms. Graphically this has been done in Fig. 18.8 for the case where $I = \tfrac{1}{2}$. The first step is to calculate the A' coefficient for each of the three terms. The quantum values to be substituted in Eq. (18.35) are: $s_1 = s_2 = \tfrac{1}{2}$, $S = 1$, $l = 2$, $J = 1$, 2, and 3. These give the values $A' = -\tfrac{1}{4}a'$, $\tfrac{1}{12}a'$, and $\tfrac{1}{6}a'$ for $^3D_1$, $^3D_2$, and $^3D_3$, respectively. The same values of A' can be calculated more quickly from the g factors $\frac{1}{2}$, $\frac{7}{6}$, and $\frac{4}{3}$, and Eq. (18.36) (see Table IV in the Appendix). Substituting in Eq. (18.34), along with $I = \frac{1}{2}$ and the J values 1, 2, and 3, the relative separations shown in the center of Fig. 18.8 are obtained. The observed levels plotted at the right are

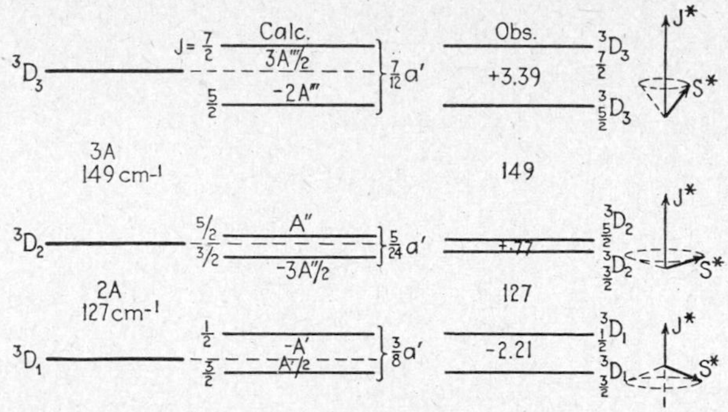

Fig. 18.8.—Calculated and observed *hfs* intervals for an *sd* configuration ^3D term in thallium.

those of the configuration $6s7d$ in singly ionized thallium (Tl II). The observation of normal splitting in $^3D_3$ and of inverted splitting in $^3D_1$ substantiates here, as it does in many other cases, the supposition that the penetrating s electron is responsible for the strong coupling of J^* with the nucleus.

TABLE 18.2.—COUPLING COEFFICIENT a' FOR A $6s$ ELECTRON IN TL II; CALCULATED FROM THE OBSERVED SEPARATIONS

Configuration	Term	$\Delta\nu_{(obs.)}$	A'	a'	Configuration	Term	$\Delta\nu_{(obs.)}$	A'	a'
6s6d	$^3D_3$	+3.33	+0.95	+5.70	6s5f	$^3F_4$	+3.31	+0.735	+5.88
	$^3D_2$	+0.55	+0.22	+2.64		$^3F_3$	−0.68	−0.194	+4.66
	$^3D_1$	−2.12	−1.41	+5.64		$^3F_2$	−2.49	−0.996	+5.97
6s7d	$^3D_3$	+3.39	+0.97	+5.82	6s6f	$^3F_4$	+3.35	+0.745	+5.96
	$^3D_2$	+0.78	+0.31	+3.72		$^3F_3$	−2.24	−0.640	+15.4
	$^3D_1$	−2.21	−1.47	+5.88		$^3F_2$	−2.58	−1.030	+6.18
6s8d	$^3D_3$	+3.45	+0.99	+5.94					
	$^3D_2$	+1.66	+0.66	+7.92					
	$^3D_1$	−2.25	−1.50	+6.00					

Referring to Eq. (18.33) we find that for a given multiple term like ^3D the coefficient a', the spin s_1^*, and cos $(S^*s_1^*)$ are constants for all values of J. The splitting factor A' is therefore proportional to $1/J^*$ cos (J^*S^*). The vector diagrams at the right in Fig. 18.8 are drawn to show this relation. As the J^* value decreases, the cosine of the angle goes from a positive to a negative value. That the splitting in Tl II is due chiefly to the $6s$ electron may be shown by substituting the observed separations of many different levels in Eqs. (18.34) and (18.35) and calculating the coefficient a'. This has been done in Table 18.2.

It is seen that the lower level of each triplet shows inverted *hfs*. At the same time the values of a' for the lower and upper level of each triplet are closely the same. The center level in each case is in poor agreement with the others. This latter is to be expected since the fine-structure intervals of the triplet show departures from the Landé interval rule for triplets. Because the two outside levels have the same g factors in all coupling schemes, they should show agreement if our assumptions are correct. Goudsmit has pointed out that by taking all levels with the same J value into account the energy sum rules will apply to those levels of the same configuration. This has been verified experimentally by McLennan, McLay and Crawford[1] for Tl II. Taking into account only the outside triplet separations in Table 18.1, an average value $a' = 5.90$ cm^{-1} is calculated as the coupling coefficient for a $6s$ electron in thallium.

If for a two-electron system both electrons are in s orbits, both may couple strongly with the nucleus and contribute appreciably to the splitting. In such cases the vector model of Fig. 18.7 is greatly simplified and the interaction of each electron with the nucleus will be given by Eq. (18.29). The two energies when added together and the cosines averaged and evaluated in the usual fashion give again Eq. (18.34) as the resultant interaction energy, where

$$A' = \tfrac{1}{2}(a'_{s_1} + a'_{s_2}).   (18.39)$$

Here a'_{s_1} is the coupling coefficient for one of the s electrons and a'_{s_2} the coefficient for the other. The derivation of this equation will be left as an exercise for the reader. If the electrons are in s orbits with the same total quantum number, there will be but one term, *viz.*, $^1S_0$, and this cannot possibly show any splitting with $J = 0$. The only possibility of observing *hfs* due to the coupling of two s electrons with I^* will arise in $^3S_1$ terms where the total quantum numbers are different. In Tl II the series of $^3S_1$ terms arising from the configurations $6sns$, where $n = 7, 8, 9, \cdots$, has been observed to have *hfs*. Assuming the value $a' = 5.90$ cm^{-1} as the coupling coefficient of the $6s$ electron common to each configuration (see Table 18.2), the following values are calculated for $7s$ and $9s$ electrons:

Configuration	Term	$\Delta\nu$	A'	a'_{s_1}	a'_{s_2}
$6s7s$	$^3S_1$	4.97	3.31	5.90	0.72
$6s9s$	$^3S_1$	4.52	3.01	5.90	0.12

[1] McLennan, J. C., A. B. McLay, and M. F. Crawford, *Proc. Roy. Soc.*, A, **133**, 652, 1931.

A comparison of the three values 5.90 for $6s$, 0.72 for $7s$, and 0.12 for $9s$ indicates the rapid decrease in the coupling with the nucleus with increasing total quantum number. The conditions for wide hfs therefore specify that at least one electron be not only deeply penetrating, as all s orbits are, but that it also be tightly bound to the atom.

18.7. Hyperfine Structure in Complex Spectra.—Attempts to correlate observed hfs in complex spectra with theory have in some respects been more successful than in the simpler cases of one-electron systems. As shown in the last section this is due largely to the general observation that nearly all wide structures and patterns arise from configurations in which there is a single tightly bound s electron. The classical and quantum-mechanical model for a complex atom may be represented by Fig. 18.7. This figure is generalized by letting the s, l, and j of the nonpenetrating electron represent the resultant S, L, and J of several nonpenetrating electrons. In such a system the penetrating s electron couples strongly with the outer electrons when it is *outside* the core and with the nucleus when it is *inside* the core. The treatment for several electrons will therefore be essentially the same as that given in the preceding section for two valence electrons. Replacing l_2^*, s_2^*, and j_2^* in Eqs. (18.35) and (18.38) is L_P^*, S_P^*, and J_P^*, the interaction energy for complex spectra becomes

$$\Gamma_F = \tfrac{1}{2}A'(F^{*2} - I^{*2} - J^{*2}), \qquad (18.40)$$

where, for LS-coupling,

$$A' = a'\frac{J^{*2} + S^{*2} - L_P^{*2}}{2J^{*2}} \cdot \frac{S^{*2} + s_1^{*2} - S_P^{*2}}{2S^{*2}} \qquad (18.41)$$

and, for Jj-coupling,

$$A' = a'\frac{J^{*2} + s_1^{*2} - J_P^{*2}}{2J^{*2}}. \qquad (18.42)$$

Here S_P, L_P, and J_P represent the resultants of the nonpenetrating electrons, s_1 the spin of the penetrating s electron, and S and J the total resultants of all the electrons together.

Let us now apply these equations to a specific example where hfs separations have been observed. In the neutral spectrum of lanthanum the first excited state is a ^4F term arising from $5d^26s$. Three of the four levels in this term have quite wide hfs whereas the fourth is relatively narrow. The observed intervals are shown at the right in Fig. 18.9. To calculate relative splittings for each level, we first evaluate A' coefficients for each. The observed fine-structure intervals of 341.8, 484.6, and 627.0 cm^{-1} have the ratios $\tfrac{5}{2} : \tfrac{7}{2} : \tfrac{9}{2}$, revealing good LS-coupling between electrons. From the configuration and term $5d^26s, {}^4F$ we have the quantum values $S = \tfrac{3}{2}$, $s_1 = \tfrac{1}{2}$, $S_P = 1$, $L_P = 3$, and $J = \tfrac{3}{2}$, $\tfrac{5}{2}$, $\tfrac{7}{2}$, and $\tfrac{9}{2}$. Substituted in Eq. (18.41), we obtain $A' = \tfrac{1}{5}a'$, $\tfrac{1}{105}a'$, $\tfrac{5}{63}a'$, and $\tfrac{1}{9}a'$

for $^4F_{\frac{9}{2}}$, $^4F_{\frac{7}{2}}$, $^4F_{\frac{5}{2}}$, and $^4F_{\frac{3}{2}}$, respectively. Substituting these in Eq. (18.40) the over-all separations $-\frac{1}{5}^2a'$, $\frac{4}{21}a'$, $\frac{2}{9}^0a'$, and $\frac{3}{9}^5a'$, shown at the left in Fig. (18.9), are obtained. The calculated intervals in the first column are obtained by computing a constant a' from $^4F_{\frac{9}{2}}$ and using this for all four levels. Better agreement between calculated and observed intervals is obtained by taking the orbital motions of the $5d$ electrons into account.[1] Assuming that the interaction will be given to a first approximation by $a''L^*I^* \cos (L^*I^*)$, the energy will be given by Eq. (18.40), where $A' = a''(J^{*2} + L^{*2} - S^{*2})/2J^{*2}$. Substituting the ^4F quantum numbers, the energy contributions $\frac{9}{5}^6a''$, $1\frac{3}{7}^6a''$, $\frac{6}{3}^4a''$, and $\frac{7}{3}^0a''$ are obtained. The intervals in the middle column are obtained by calculating constants a' and a'' from $^4F_{\frac{9}{2}}$ and $^4F_{\frac{7}{2}}$ and using these for the other two levels.

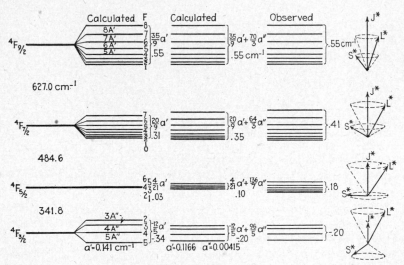

Fig. 18.9.—Calculated and observed hfs intervals for d^2s, ^4F, in lanthanum.

Although agreement with experiment is not so good as one would like, it is certain from the above considerations that the orbital motion of the two $5d$ electrons contributes considerably to the coupling of the electron resultant J with the nuclear moment I. The vector diagrams at the right in Fig. 18.9 show graphically how the stronger coupling of the s electron, acting through the spin resultant S^*, inverts the hfs of $^4F_{\frac{9}{2}}$.

Not all wide hfs patterns arise from configurations involving a single tightly bound s electron. This fact is illustrated by the $3d^94s^2, {}^2D_{\frac{5}{2},\frac{3}{2}}$ terms of copper and the $6p^3,(\frac{1}{2}\ \frac{3}{2}\ \frac{3}{2})_{\frac{3}{2},\frac{3}{2}}$ terms of bismuth. In all such cases the binding of the p, d, or f electrons, as the case may be, will be large for at least one electron. This is shown by the fact that the terms lie deep on the energy level diagram and the electrons contribute equally to the coupling of J^* with I^*. Equations for the interaction of two or more

[1] ANDERSON, O. E., Phys. Rev., Vol. 46, 1934.

arbitrary electrons with a nucleus have been derived by Goudsmit using the principle of energy sums.[1] Although the calculations from these equations are in good agreement with some *hfs* terms, Goudsmit points out that there are unaccountable discrepancies in others. Breit and Wills[2] have brought some of these discrepancies into agreement with experiment by a quantum-mechanical treatment of the same problem for coupling intermediate between *LS* and *jj*. For these rather complicated cases of nuclear interaction the reader is referred to the original articles.

18.8. Nuclear g_I Factors.—A nuclear g_I factor is a number expressing the ratio between the magnetic moment of the nucleus in *nuclear magnetons* $(eh/4\pi Mc)$ and the mechanical moment of the nucleus in quantum units of $h/2\pi$. From Eqs. (18.28) and (18.28a), the following may be written:

For arbitrary electron orbits,

$$g_I = \frac{a'Z_i j(j + 1)(l + \frac{1}{2})\,1838}{\Delta \nu l(l + 1)} \cdot \frac{\lambda}{\kappa};\tag{18.43}$$

and for s electrons,[3]

$$g_I = \frac{3a'n_o^3 1838}{8R\alpha^2 Z_i Z_o^2} \cdot \frac{1}{\kappa}.\tag{18.44}$$

As an example of the application of these equations we shall first apply Eq. (18.44) to the *hfs* of Tl II, where the very large separations are due chiefly to the penetrating s electron. The average value of a' for the 6s electron is calculated for the values given in Table 18.2 Using only the outside triplet separations $a' = 5.90$ cm^{-1}. As pointed out in Sec. 18.4, Z_i for s electrons is about equal to the atomic number Z. Z_o, the effective charge outside the core, is taken as one for Tl I, two for Tl II, and three for Tl III. The effective quantum number n_o is given by the term value of 6s,^2S in Tl III, where the 6s electron is the only valence electron. The relation $T = RZ_o^2/n_o^2$, applied to this state, with $T = 240600$ cm^{-1} and $Z_o = 3$, yields $n_o = 2.02$. Substituting these values in Eq. (18.44),

$$g_I = \frac{3 \times 5.9 \times 8.3 \times 1838}{8 \times 5.8 \times 81 \times 9} \cdot \frac{1}{2.31} = 3.5.\tag{18.45}$$

Although the exact value obtained here may not be correct, it is significant that the value is of the right order of magnitude on the assumption that nuclear moments arise from protons in the nucleus. Values of g_I computed for a number of elements by Breit, Wills, and

[1] GOUDSMIT, S., *Phys. Rev.*, **37**, 663, 1931.

[2] BREIT, G., and L. A. WILLS, *Phys. Rev.*, **44**, 470, 1933.

[3] These equations have been given by S. A. Goudsmit as fair approximations for the g_I factors, *Phys. Rev.*, **43**, 636, 1933.

Goudsmit, and independently by Fermi and Segré by a somewhat different method, are given in Table 18.3, along with values of nuclear moments. The values of I determined from band-spectrum intensities alone are given in parentheses. In many cases, only a lower limit for I has been set. A negative g_I factor suggests the possibility that the nuclear spin is due to negative charges, although this is not necessary.

TABLE 18.3.—TABLE OF NUCLEAR MOMENTS

Element and atomic number	Isotope	I	g_I	μ_I'	Element and atomic number	Isotope	I	g_I	μ_I'
H 1	1	$(\frac{1}{2})$	5.0?	2.5?	Cb 41	93	$\frac{9}{2}$	0.8	3.5
	2	$(\frac{3}{2})$	0.7?	0.7?	Rh 45	103	$\frac{5}{2}$		
He 2	4	0			Cd 48	110, 12, 14, 16,	0		
Li 3	7	$\frac{3}{2}$	2.2	3.3		111, 13	$\frac{1}{2}$	-1.0	-0.5
C 6	12	(0)			In 49	115	$\frac{9}{2}$	1.2	5.4
N 7	14	$(\frac{2}{3})$			Sn 50	117, 119	$\frac{1}{2}$	-1.8	-0.9
O 8	16	(0)			Sb 51	121	$\frac{5}{2}$	1.1	2.7
F 9	19	$\frac{1}{2}$				123	$\frac{7}{2}$	0.6	2.1
Ne 10	20, 22	0			I 53	127	$\frac{9}{2}$		
Na 11	23	$\frac{3}{2}$	1.4	2.1	Cs 55	133	$\frac{7}{2}?$	0.7	2.6
Al 13	27	$\frac{1}{2}$	4.2	2.1	Ba 56	136, 38	0		
P 15	31	$(\frac{1}{2})$				135, 37	$\frac{5}{2}?$	0.4	1.0
S 16	32	0			La 57	139	$\frac{7}{2}$		
Cl 17	35	$(\frac{5}{2})$			Pr 59	141	$\frac{5}{2}$		
Ca 20	40	0			Eu 63		$\geqq\frac{1}{2}?$		
V 23	51	$\geqq\frac{5}{2}$			Tb 65		$\geqq\frac{5}{2}$		
Mn 25	55	$\frac{5}{2}$			Ho 67		$\geqq\frac{5}{2}$		
Co 27	59	$\frac{7}{2}$	0.8	2.8	Lu 71		$\geqq\frac{3}{2}$		
Cu 29	63, 65	$\frac{3}{2}$	1.5	2.3	Ta 73	181	$\frac{7}{2}$		
Zn 30	67	$\frac{3}{2}$			W 74	182, 4, 6	0		
Ga 31	69	$\frac{3}{2}$	1.4	2.1		183	?		
	71	$\frac{3}{2}$	1.8	2.7	Re 75	185, 87	$\frac{5}{2}$		
As 33	75	$\frac{3}{2}$			Au 79	197	$\frac{3}{2}$	1.2	1.8
Br 35	79, 81	$\frac{3}{2}$			Hg 80	198, 200, 202, 204	0		
Kr 36	83	$\geqq\frac{7}{2}$				199	$\frac{1}{2}$	1.1	0.5
Rb 37	85	$\frac{5}{2}$	0.5	1.3		201	$\frac{3}{2}$	-0.4	-0.6
	87	$\frac{3}{2}$	1.9	2.8	Tl 81	203, 05	$\frac{1}{2}$	2.8	1.4
Sr 38	87	$\frac{3}{2}?$			Pb 82	207	$\frac{1}{2}$	1.0	0.5
					Bi 83	209	$\frac{9}{2}$	0.8	3.5

Just how far the above equations can be expected to give correct g_I factors is a question that will be answered when we know more concerning the structure of the nucleus. From the recent experiments of

Frisch, Stern, and Estermann as well as Rabi, Kellogg, and Zacharias[1] there is some evidence that the magnetic moment of the neutron is negative. This should play an important rôle in any new theory of nuclear structure.

18.9. Zeeman Effect in Hyperfine Structure.—We now turn to the Zeeman effect of *hfs*, a subject which had its beginning with a study of the bismuth spectrum by Back and Goudsmit. The paper published by them in 1928 is considered a classic in the annals of spectroscopy.[2] At this early stage in the development of *hfs*, in general, it was shown by Back and Goudsmit that all of the simple classical derivations and formulas for the anomalous Zeeman effect and the Paschen-Back effect could be carried over to *hfs* by making the following substitutions:

$$I, J, F, g_I, g_J, g_F, M_I, M_J, \text{ and } M_F$$
$$\text{for } S, L, J, g_S, g_L, g_J, M_S, M_L, \text{ and } M_J, \text{ respectively.}$$

Unfortunately the so-called Zeeman effect of *hfs* has not yet been observed, chiefly because of the lack of sufficient resolving power in the optical instruments thus far employed. What has been observed by Back and Goudsmit, however, is an effect similar to the so-called Paschen-Back effect in fine structure. Since there is good reason to believe that the *hfs* Zeeman effect will be observed and studied in the near future, a simple treatment of the subject will be given here.

In a very weak magnetic field the atom may be thought of as precessing as a whole around the field direction H subject to the quantum conditions that the projection of the mechanical resultant $F^*h/2\pi$ on H is equal to $M_F h/2\pi$. The magnetic quantum number M_F takes values differing from each other by unity ranging from $M_F = -F$ to $M_F = +F$. A classical vector model for very weak field is shown in Fig. 18.10. To calculate the magnetic energy it is necessary that we first compute the magnetic moment of the atom as a whole. This moment will be made up of two parts or components: μ_J, the magnetic moment of the extranuclear electrons, and μ_I, the magnetic moment of the nucleus. These moments [see Eqs. (13.1) and (13.6)] should be given by

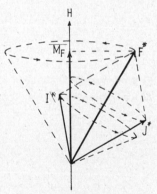

FIG. 18.10. Vector model of an atom with a nuclear spin in a *very weak* magnetic field (*hfs* Zeeman effect).

[1] FRISCH, R., and O. STERN, *Zeits. f. Phys.*, **85**, 4, 1933; ESTERMANN, I., and O. STERN, *Zeits. f. Phys.*, **85**, 17, 1933; RABI, I. I., J. M. B. KELLOGG, and J. R. ZACHARIAS, *Phys. Rev.*, **45**, 769, 1934; **46**, 157, 1934.

[2] BACK, E., and S. A. GOUDSMIT, *Zeits. f. Phys.*, **47**, 174, 1928.

$$\mu_J = g_J J^* \frac{eh}{4\pi mc} \qquad \text{and} \qquad \mu_I = g_I I^* \frac{eh}{4\pi mc}. \qquad (18.46)$$

Since it is the mechanical moments I^* and J^* that are quantized, the total magnetic moment of the atom is just the projection of these magnetic moments on F^* (see Sec. 10.3). As μ_I and I^* are parallel to each other, and μ_J and J^* are oppositely directed, the resultant atomic magnetic moment μ_F becomes

$$\mu_F = \mu_J \cos (J^*F^*) - \mu_I \cos (I^*F^*). \qquad (18.47)$$

Upon substituting from Eq. (18.46),

$$\mu_F = [g_J J^* \cos (J^*F^*) - g_I I^* \cos (I^*F^*)] \frac{eh}{4\pi mc}. \qquad (18.48)$$

As in the Zeeman effect of fine structure, the term in brackets is placed equal to F^* times a constant g_F, i.e.,

$$g_F F^* = g_J J^* \cos (J^*F^*) - g_I I^* \cos (I^*F^*). \qquad (18.49)$$

This gives

$$\mu_F = g_F F^* \frac{eh}{4\pi mc}. \qquad (18.50)$$

Referring to the vector model again, we may now evaluate the cosines in terms of the mechanical vectors and obtain, for Eq. (18.49),

$$g_F = g_J \frac{F^{*2} + J^{*2} - I^{*2}}{2F^{*2}} - g_I \frac{F^{*2} + I^{*2} - J^{*2}}{2F^{*2}}. \qquad (18.51)$$

Because of the general observation that hfs separations are many times smaller than the fine structure the g_I factor for the nucleus must also be very small compared with the g_J factor for the extranuclear electrons. If we make the assumption that $g_I << g_J$, we may write

$$g_F = g_J \frac{F^{*2} + J^{*2} - I^{*2}}{2F^{*2}}. \qquad (18.52)$$

If the nuclear spin is due to one or more particles with the mass of protons, the nuclear g_I factors should be in the neighborhood of one or two thousandths of those for electrons. By Eq. (18.50) the ratio between the magnetic and mechanical moments of the entire atom is therefore closely represented by

$$\frac{\mu_F}{\frac{F^*h}{2\pi}} = g_F \frac{e}{2mc} = g_J \frac{e}{2mc} \cdot \frac{F^{*2} + J^{*2} - I^{*2}}{2F^{*2}}. \qquad (18.53)$$

According to Larmor's theorem, F^* in a very weak field will carry out a classical precession around the field direction, the angular velocity of which should be given by H times the ratio between the magnetic and mechanical moments:

$$\omega_F = H \cdot g_F \frac{e}{2mc}. \tag{18.54}$$

The energy of this precession is given by ω_F times the component of the mechanical resultant $F^*h/2\pi$ along H:

$$\Delta W = \omega_F \frac{F^*h}{2\pi} \cos (F^*H) = H \cdot g_F \frac{e}{2mc} \frac{F^*h}{2\pi} \cos (F^*H). \tag{18.55}$$

In terms of the magnetic quantum number M_F,

$$\Delta W = H \cdot g_F \frac{e}{2mc} M_F \frac{h}{2\pi} = g_F \cdot M_F \cdot H \frac{eh}{4\pi mc}. \tag{18.56}$$

Dividing by hc, the energy in wave numbers becomes

$$-\Delta T_F = g_F \cdot M_F \frac{He}{4\pi mc} \text{ cm}^{-1} = g_F \cdot M_F \cdot L \text{ cm}^{-1}. \tag{18.57}$$

As an example of the magnetic splitting given by these equations, consider the transition $^2S_{\frac{1}{2}} - {}^2P_{\frac{3}{2}}$ in an atom where the nuclear spin

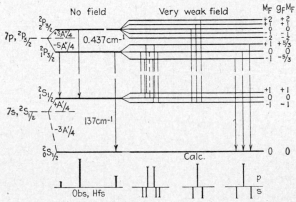

FIG. 18.11.—Zeeman effect of hfs in a very weak magnetic field.

$I = \frac{1}{2}$. Specifically the fine structure arising from the transition $7s$, $^2S_{\frac{1}{2}} - 7p, {}^2P_{\frac{3}{2}}$ in doubly ionized thallium is shown at the left in Fig. 18.11. The g_J factor for $^2P_{\frac{3}{2}}$ is $\frac{4}{3}$, which substituted in Eq. (18.52) gives the two values $g_F = 1$ for $^2_2P_{\frac{3}{2}}$ and $g_F = \frac{5}{3}$ for $^2_1P_{\frac{3}{2}}$. Similarly the g_J factor of two for $^2S_{\frac{1}{2}}$ gives $g_F = 1$ for $^2_1S_{\frac{1}{2}}$ and $g_F = \frac{0}{0}$ for $^2_0S_{\frac{1}{2}}$. Multiplying each g_F by the possible values of M_F [see Eq. (18.57)], the magnetic splitting shown at the extreme right in the figure is obtained. For any given field strength, L is a constant.

By analogy with fine structure the selection rules for hfs are

$$\Delta M_F = 0 \text{ for } p \text{ components},$$
$$\Delta M_F = \pm 1 \text{ for } s \text{ components}. \tag{18.58}$$

Similarly the relative intensities should be given by the fine-structure equations (13.21), by replacing J by F and M by M_F.[1]

In a *very weak field* the *hfs* lines each break up into symmetrical patterns similar to the anomalous Zeeman patterns of fine structure in a *weak field*. Because the complete resolution of *hfs* patterns in zero field is accomplished only for the very widest and simplest structures, it is now quite clear why the so-called Zeeman effect of *hfs* has not been observed.

If now the field is increased to a point where the ordinary anomalous patterns of fine structure would be observed, each of the *hfs* patterns, like those in the figure, will begin to overlap and something analogous to the Paschen-Back effect sets in. This is the subject to be treated in the next section.

18.10. Back-Goudsmit Effect in Hyperfine Structure.—If the magnetic field strengths commonly used in studying the Zeeman effect are employed in a study of the spectrum of an element having a nuclear magnetic and mechanical moment, a phenomenon analogous to the Paschen-Back effect in fine structure is observed. Because this effect was first observed and accounted for by Back and Goudsmit[2] the phenomena will here be referred to as the *Back-Goudsmit effect*.

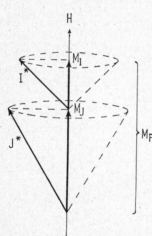

Fig. 18.12.—Independent precession of the nuclear moment I^*, and electron moment J^*, in a *weak* magnetic field (Back-Goudsmit effect).

A magnetic field that is called a *weak field* for fine structure is in reality a *strong field* for *hfs*. In such a weak field the coupling between the nuclear moment I^* and the electron resultant J^* will be broken down, and each will be quantized separately with the field direction. Classically each will precess separately around H as shown in Fig. 18.12. Under these conditions the magnetic energy will be made up of the sum of the following energies; (1) the energy due to the interaction between I^* and H; (2) the energy due to the interaction between J^* and H; (3) the energy due to the interaction between I^* and J^*. By Larmor's theorem the two precessional angular velocities are given by H times the ratio between the magnetic and mechanical moments [see Eqs. (3.58), (10.23), and (13.23)]:

$$\omega_I = H \cdot g_I \cdot \frac{e}{2mc}, \qquad \omega_J = Hg_J \cdot \frac{e}{2mc}. \qquad (18.59)$$

[1] For *hfs* intensity formulas derived by the quantum mechanics, see E. L. Hill, *Proc. Nat. Acad. Sci.*, **15**, 779, 1929.

[2] BACK, E., and S. A. GOUDSMIT, *Zeits. f. Phys.*, **47**, 174, 1928.

Multiplying each of these angular velocities by the corresponding angular-momentum components along H, the following two energy contributions are obtained:

$$\Delta W_{IH} = -H \cdot g_I \cdot \frac{e}{2mc} I^* \frac{h}{2\pi} \cos (I^*H) = -H \cdot g_I \cdot \frac{e}{2mc} M_I \frac{h}{2\pi},$$

$$\Delta W_{JH} = H \cdot g_J \cdot \frac{e}{2mc} \cdot J^* \frac{h}{2\pi} \cos (J^*H) = H \cdot g_J \cdot \frac{e}{2mc} \cdot M_J \frac{h}{2\pi}. \tag{18.60}$$

The sum of these two energies gives the main energy shift from the fine-structure term from which it sprang, *i.e.*, from the center of gravity of the *hfs* terms arising from a given fine-structure term. This sum may be written

$$\Delta W_H = (-g_I M_I + g_J M_J) H \frac{eh}{4\pi mc}. \tag{18.61}$$

Dividing by hc, the energy in wave numbers becomes

$$-\Delta T_H = (-g_I M_I + g_J M_J) \frac{He}{4\pi mc^2} = (-g_I M_I + g_J M_J)\mathbf{L} \text{ cm}^{-1}. \tag{18.62}$$

The third interaction mentioned above has still to be added to this equation. By exactly the same treatment as that given for a single electron in Sec. 10.7, and for several electrons in Sec. 13.7, this energy is given by

$$\Gamma = A' I^* J^* \overline{\cos (I^*J^*)} \text{ cm}^{-1}. \tag{18.63}$$

Referring to Fig. 18.12 it is seen that the angle between I^* and J^* is continually changing so that it must be averaged. In the usual manner the average cosine is given by

$$\overline{\cos (I^*J^*)} = \cos (I^*H) \cos (J^*H). \tag{18.64}$$

Substituting in Eq. (18.63),

$$\Gamma = A' I^* \cos (J^*H) \cdot J^* \cos (J^*H). \tag{18.65}$$

In terms of the magnetic quantum numbers these projections are

$$\Gamma = A' M_I M_J. \tag{18.66}$$

Adding this to Eq. (18.62), the total magnetic energy in a weak field becomes

$$-\Delta T = (-g_I M_I + g_J M_J)\mathbf{L} + A' M_I M_J. \tag{18.67}$$

Now the g_I factor for the nucleus is so small compared with g_J for the external electrons that the first term in the parentheses may be dropped. Neglecting this term,

$$-\Delta T = g_J M_J \mathbf{L} + A' M_I M_J \text{ cm}^{-1}. \tag{18.68}$$

Let us now apply this equation to the specific example of one of the resonance lines of thallium, $\lambda = 5349$, $6p,{}^2P_{\frac{1}{2}} - 7s,{}^2S_{\frac{1}{2}}$ (see Fig. 8.1).

For the lower level $^2P_{3/2}$, $g_J = \tfrac{4}{3}$, $M_J = \tfrac{3}{2}, \tfrac{1}{2}, -\tfrac{1}{2}, -\tfrac{3}{2}$, and $M_I = \tfrac{1}{2}$ and $-\tfrac{1}{2}$. The energies in very weak and in weak fields are readily calculated by tabulating them as in Table 18.4. Starting at the left the values of each column are written down in the order given.

TABLE 18.4.—Magnetic-energy Factors for the Terms $^2P_{3/2}$ and $^2S_{1/2}$, in an Atom Where the Nuclear Spin $I = \tfrac{1}{2}$

No field		Very weak field (hfs Zeeman effect)			Weak field (Back-Goudsmit effect)				
Term	Γ_F	M_F	g_F	$g_F M_F$	M_I	M_J	g_J	$g_J M_J$	$A M_I M_J$
		2		2	$\tfrac{1}{2}$	$\tfrac{3}{2}$		$\tfrac{6}{3}$	$\tfrac{3}{4}A''$
		1		1	$\tfrac{1}{2}$	$\tfrac{1}{2}$		$\tfrac{2}{3}$	$\tfrac{1}{4}A''$
$^2_2P_{3/2}$	$+A\tfrac{3}{4}''$	0	1	0	$\tfrac{1}{2}$	$-\tfrac{1}{2}$		$-\tfrac{2}{3}$	$-\tfrac{1}{4}A''$
		-1		-1	$\tfrac{1}{2}$	$-\tfrac{3}{2}$	$\tfrac{4}{3}$	$-\tfrac{6}{3}$	$-\tfrac{3}{4}A''$
		-2		-2	$-\tfrac{1}{2}$	$\tfrac{3}{2}$		$\tfrac{6}{3}$	$-\tfrac{3}{4}A''$
					$-\tfrac{1}{2}$	$\tfrac{1}{2}$		$\tfrac{2}{3}$	$-\tfrac{1}{4}A''$
$^2_1P_{3/2}$	$-\tfrac{5}{4}A''$	1		$\tfrac{5}{3}$	$-\tfrac{1}{2}$	$-\tfrac{1}{2}$		$-\tfrac{2}{3}$	$\tfrac{1}{4}A''$
		0	$\tfrac{5}{3}$	0	$-\tfrac{1}{2}$	$-\tfrac{3}{2}$		$-\tfrac{6}{3}$	$\tfrac{3}{4}A''$
		-1		$-\tfrac{5}{3}$					
		1		1	$\tfrac{1}{2}$	$\tfrac{1}{2}$		1	$\tfrac{1}{4}A'$
$^2_1S_{1/2}$	$+\tfrac{1}{4}A'$	0	1	0	$\tfrac{1}{2}$	$-\tfrac{1}{2}$		-1	$-\tfrac{1}{4}A'$
		-1		-1	$-\tfrac{1}{2}$	$\tfrac{1}{2}$	2	1	$-\tfrac{1}{4}A'$
$^2_0S_{1/2}$	$-\tfrac{3}{4}A'$	$\tfrac{0}{0}$	$\tfrac{0}{0}$	$\tfrac{0}{0}$	$-\tfrac{1}{2}$	$-\tfrac{1}{2}$		-1	$\tfrac{1}{4}A'$

After the table is completed, the energies are plotted as shown in Fig. 18.13 starting with the field-free levels on the left and ending with weak-field levels on the right. Calculations of the interaction energies for field strengths between the two extreme cases of weak and very weak fields have been carried out by Goudsmit and Bacher,[1] and by Inglis.[2] Their calculations show that the following rules can be applied for the transitions between very weak and weak fields: (1) the total projection of the mechanical moment of the entire atom on H remains the same in all field strengths, i.e.,

$$M_F = M_I + M_J \tag{18.69}$$

and (2) levels with the same value of M_F never cross.

Selection rules for *hfs* transitions between levels in a weak field are similar to those for fine structure in strong fields and may be written

$$\Delta M_I = 0,$$
$$\Delta M_J = \begin{cases} 0 & \text{for } p \text{ components,} \\ \pm 1 & \text{for } s \text{ components.} \end{cases} \tag{18.70}$$

[1] Goudsmit, S. A., and R. F. Bacher, *Phys. Rev.*, **34**, 1499, 1929.
[2] Inglis, D. R., *Zeits. f. Phys.*, **84**, 466, 1933.

The schematic diagram of the Tl I *hfs* pattern λ5349 is shown in Fig. 18.14. In a very weak field each *hfs* line breaks up into an anomalous but symmetrical pattern. (These have not been observed.) In

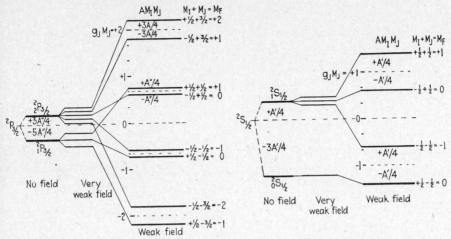

FIG. 18.13.—Splitting of *hfs* terms in *weak* and *very weak* magnetic fields (Back-Goudsmit effect).

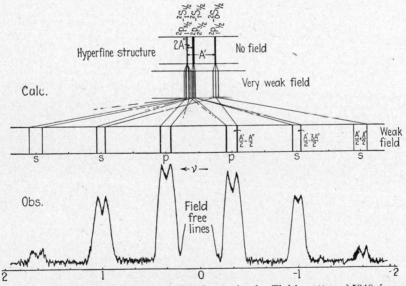

FIG. 18.14.—Schematic diagram of the change in the Tl *hfs* pattern λ5349 from no field to *very weak* field to *weak* field Back-Goudsmit effect). (*Observed pattern after Wulff*). In reproducing the microphotometer curve the field-free lines have been left out as shown by the break at the center of the figure.

the weak field where the coupling between *I* and *J* is broken down, the lines have crossed each other to form a pattern resembling closely the Zeeman pattern of the same transition in an atom where the nuclear moment is zero (see Fig. 10.8). A comparison of Fig. 18.14 with Fig. 13.11 for the Paschen-Back effect of the fine structure in jj-coupling is of interest. With $I = \frac{1}{2}$ it is to be noted that each line of the Zeeman pattern should theoretically be double, and that the separations should be of the same order of magnitude as the field-free hfs. The microphotometer curve at the bottom of the figure has been obtained in a field of 43350 gauss by Wulff.[1]

A similar calculation for any spectral line where I has an integral or half-integral value will lead to a pattern resembling closely the Zeeman pattern for the same line if I were zero. Due to the interaction energy term $A'M_IM_J$ in Eq. (18.68) each of the Zeeman terms will be split up into $2I + 1$ equally spaced levels, and each line in the observed Zeeman pattern will be split into $2I + 1$ equally spaced lines. This may be seen to better advantage from the following description of an atom where I is large. In weak field, I^* and J^* precess independently around H. For each orientation of J^*, as shown in Fig. 18.15, there will be $2I + 1$ orientations of the nuclear moment I^*. In Fig. 18.15 the I value, as in bismuth, is taken as $\frac{9}{2}$. Since the coupling of I^* with H, as measured by the energy factor $g_I M_I$, is negligibly small, I^* is coupled to, and precesses around, the magnetic component of J^* along H. Like the ordinary Zeeman effect this energy of interaction is proportional to M_I. Since the field for the precession of I^* is furnished by J^*, and its magnitude by M_J, the energy of the splitting will be proportional to M_IM_J, or equal to $A'M_IM_J$, as already shown.

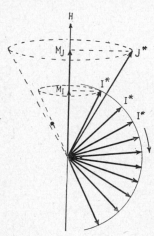

Fig. 18.15.—Vector diagram showing the $2I + 1$ orientations of the nuclear moment I^* for a fixed orientation of the electron moment J^*. Drawn for the special case where $I = \frac{9}{2}$ (Back-Goudsmit effect).

As an example of this effect a diagram of a weak-field pattern observed by Back and Goudsmit in bismuth is reproduced in Fig. 18.16. Each of the four middle groups has been resolved by Back and Goudsmit and found to have exactly 10 components. The two center groups of lines marked a have been reproduced and published by Zeeman, Back, and Goudsmit.[2] Figure 18.17 has been enlarged and reproduced from the halftone reproduction in their published paper. To obtain the lower half of the figure, the photographic paper was moved parallel to the lines

[1] Wulff, J., *Zeits. f. Phys.*, **69**, 74, 1931; see also Green, J. B., and J. Wulff, *Phys. Rev.*, **38**, 2176, 1931; **38**, 2186, 1931.

[2] Zeeman, P., E. Back, and S. A. Goudsmit, *Zeits. f. Phys.*, **66**, 11, 1930.

during exposure thus enabling the 10 components to be easily distinguished. The effect is much the same as a microphotometer trace. That there are 10 components in each group furnishes conclusive evidence that, for the Bi nucleus, $I = \frac{9}{2}$.

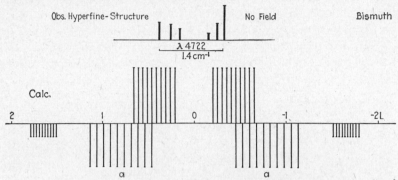

FIG. 18.16.—Calculated pattern for the bismuth line λ4722 in a weak field (Back-Goudsmit effect).

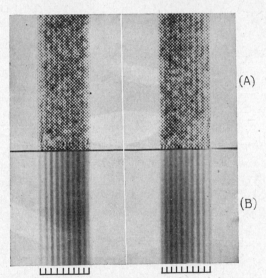

FIG. 18.17.—Observed patterns, by Back and Goudsmit, of the two center components marked (a) in Fig. 18.16. (A) Enlarged from the halftone reproduction in the published paper of Zeeman, Back, and Goudsmit. (B) Photographic paper moved parallel to the lines during enlargement.

Intensity rules for *hfs* in weak fields are the same as those for the Zeeman effect in weak fields and are given by Eq. (13.21). From the assumption that M_I does not change in any transition the intensities will be independent of the value of M_I. This means that for each component of an ordinary Zeeman pattern the intensity will be divided equally between the $2I + 1$ components due to the nuclear moment.

This means that Eq. (13.21) should be valid and that M, as given there, is the M_J as given here.   This is in fair agreement with the observations in Tl.   In Bi the appearance of so-called *forbidden transitions* ($\Delta M_I = \pm 1$) shows that the field is not strong enough for these simple rules to hold. Calculated intervals and intensities have been shown by Goudsmit and Bacher,[1] and by Back and Wulff[2] to be in excellent agreement with observed patterns in Tl and Bi in different intermediate field strengths.

18.11. Isotope Structure.—It is now known with certainty that the *hfs* observed in the spectrum lines of some elements is due to small differences in the energy levels of two or more isotopes and not to a

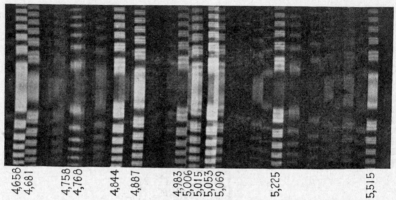

FIG. 18.18.—Isotope structure observed in the spectrum lines of tungsten. (*After Grace, More, and White.*)

nuclear spin of one isotope.   A good example of such structure is to be found in the spectrum of tungsten, one section of which, taken with Fabry and Perot étalons, is reproduced in Fig. 18.18.   Each line, it is noted, shows three components, each of which corresponds, respectively, to one of the isotopes of even mass 182, 184, and 186.   Although these patterns are distinctly different from the very commonly observed *hfs flag patterns* as shown in Fig. 18.1, one cannot always distinguish *isotope structure* from *hfs* by appearances.   Some *hfs* patterns and some isotope patterns look much alike.

In tungsten as in other elements where isotope structure predominates, many lines appear to be sharp, *i.e.*, the lines arising from the different isotopes fall on top of each other.   This fact indicates that the relative shifts of a set of terms belonging to one isotope are practically the same as the relative shifts of the same levels in another isotope. Where isotope structure is observed the relative shifts are materially different.   This latter means that the nucleus by itself is not entirely responsible for the structure and that the interaction between the

---

[1] GOUDSMIT, S. A., and R. F. BACHER, *Zeits. f. Phys.*, **66**, 13, 1930.
[2] BACK, E., and J. WULFF, *Zeits. f. Phys.*, **66**, 31, 1930.

nucleus and the extranuclear electrons must be taken into account. Because there are no combinations between the levels of one isotope and those of another one cannot say how much one system has been shifted from the other but only how levels shift relative to others. As shown by the tungsten lines, as well as the lines in other elements, the relative shifts, where observed, are found to be approximately proportional to the mass differences.

The suggestion that isotope shift may be due to a change in the Rydberg constant (see Sec. 2.13) is occasionally but not always in agreement with observation. In singly ionized lithium, for example, the observed shift of Li^6 $1s2p$ and $1s2s$ from Li^7 $1s2p$ and $1s2s$ is several times that expected. Hughes and Eckart[1] have shown, however, that with two electrons a change in the nuclear mass may alter the energy by a greater amount than in the case when there is but one electron, as in hydrogen. Their calculations for Li^6 and Li^7 are in excellent agreement with experimental observations.

Attempts to calculate isotope displacements in heavy elements have been made by Breit.[2] These calculations, based upon a change in the size of the nucleus, are in fair agreement with the relative shifts observed in Hg, Tl, and Pb.

The slight differences in the relative intensities of the tungsten isotope lines in each pattern of Fig. 18.18 are due to the presence of a fourth isotope of *odd* mass 183. Having a nuclear spin, this isotope gives rise to *hfs* which divides into components differently in different patterns. This subject of isotope structure and *hfs* together is taken up in the next section. As a matter of fact isotope structure is seldom observed in an element alone.

18.12. Isotope Structure and Hyperfine Structure Combined.—Perhaps the most complicated line patterns in all the periodic table are those observed in the spectrum of mercury. Since mercury is a heavy element, and since the mercury arc is a convenient light source for the adjustment and demonstration of interferometers, the mercury lines have been investigated by many experimenters. In such elements with high atomic weight, the Doppler broadening does not interfere in ordinary light sources to the extent that some lines were known over two decades ago to contain as many as 10 to 15 components.

In the very excellent hands of Schüler, Keyston and Jones,[3] these patterns have now been analyzed. Their analysis shows that of the six

---

[1] HUGHES, D. S., and C. ECKART, *Phys. Rev.*, **36**, 694, 1930.

[2] BREIT, G., *Phys. Rev.*, **42**, 348, 1933; see also ROSENTHAL, J. E., and G. BREIT, *Phys. Rev.*, **41**, 459, 1932; and RACAH, G., *Nature*, **129**, 723, 1932.

[3] SCHÜLER, H., *Naturwissenschaften*, **19**, 950, 1931; SCHÜLER, H., and J. E. KEYSTON, *Zeits. f. Phys.*, **72**, 423, 1931; SCHÜLER, H., and E. G. JONES, *Zeits. f. Phys.*, **74**, 631, 1932; **77**, 801, 1932.

mercury isotopes,

Mass	196	198	199	200	201	202	204	
Abundance	0.10	9.89	16.45	23.77	13.67	29.27	6.85	per cent,

the five with even mass have either a zero magnetic or a zero mechanical moment,[1] and the two with odd mass have mechanical moments as follows: for Hg 199, $I = \frac{1}{2}$ and for Hg 201, $I = \frac{3}{2}$. The magnetic moments of these two isotopes are opposite in sign and quite different in magnitude. For Hg 199, $g_I \cong 1.1$ and for Hg 201, $g_I \cong -0.41$ nuclear magnetons.

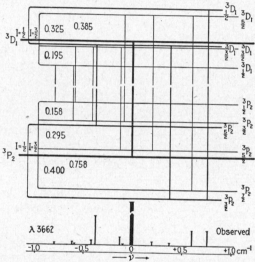

FIG. 18.19.—Hyperfine structure of the mercury isotopes as observed in the transition $6s6p$, $^3P_2 - 6s6d$, $^3D_1$, $\lambda3662$. (*After Schüler, Westmeyer, and Jones.*)

Hfs terms for two energy levels in mercury are shown in Fig. 18.19. The heavy lines near the center of both the upper and lower levels represent the even isotopes 196, 198, 200, 202, and 204. The very light lines represent the levels of the odd isotope 201, and the remaining levels belong to 199. The observed pattern is shown at the bottom, and the corresponding transitions are given directly above. The relative abundance of the isotopes as given by Aston's mass-spectrograph measurements is in agreement with the observed *hfs* in that the center line contains about 70 per cent of the total intensity. If there were an

---

[1] Since we know relatively little about nuclear structure at the present time, it is difficult to say whether one, or both, of the nuclear moments, magnetic or mechanical, is zero. If a nucleus has a large magnetic moment, but no mechanical moment, there can be no space quantization with J^* and hence no *hfs*. If a mechanical moment exists, but no magnetic moment, there will be quantization but no splitting. Such cases of one or the other moment equal to zero are known to exist in extranuclear electron structure.

appreciably different isotope shift in the initial or final states, as there is in the resonance line $^1S_0 - {}^3P_1$ at $\lambda 2536$, this line would not be single as observed but would reveal five components. The relative positions of the levels belonging to different isotopes are arbitrary, for, if one system of levels is moved up or down, the radiated lines remain unchanged.

Returning to Eqs. (18.34) and (18.35), the observed *hfs* in mercury may be used to calculate the coupling coefficient for the deeply penetrating and tightly bound $6s$ electron. For the $^3P_2$ state the calculated values are as follows:

$$\begin{array}{cc}
\text{Hg 199} & \text{Hg 201} \\
A' = +0.303 & A' = -0.114 \\
a' = +1.212 & a' = -0.456
\end{array}$$

Since a' is negative for Hg 201, the g_I factor [by Eq. (18.24)] is negative. For Hg 199, the g_I factor is positive and by the ratio of the a' coefficients is about 2.66 times as large. If the same calculations are made for the upper term $^3D_1$, a smaller ratio is obtained. This may be attributed to perturbations of certain of the *hfs* terms by those of a $^1D_2$ term, only three wave numbers away. When the perturbation corrections shown in Fig. 19.15 are made, the ratio of the a's, and hence the ratio of the g_I factors, comes out to be 2.79, in very good agreement with similar calculations for six or more other terms.

In addition to mercury, line patterns of a number of other elements have been sufficiently analyzed to show the presence of both isotope structure and *hfs*. In Cd, for example, there are six isotopes of mass 110, 111, 112, 113, 114, and 116. Like mercury the even isotopes are observed to have a nuclear moment of zero, and both of the odd isotopes to have the same mechanical moment $I = \frac{1}{2}$ and the same magnetic moment $g_I = -1.0$.

Problems

1. Show that the interaction energy of two s electrons with a nuclear moment I is given by Eq. (18.38).

2. Construct a diagram similar to Fig. 18.9 for the term $d^3s, {}^5F$. Assume $a' = 2$ cm^{-1} and $I = \frac{5}{2}$.

3. Construct a diagram similar to Fig. 18.13 for the Bi levels given in Fig. 18.5. Assume g_J factors of 2 and $\frac{5}{4}$ for the upper and lower levels, respectively. Calculations are most easily made by tabulating as in Table 18.4. Note that, for the lower level, A' is negative.

4. From the levels derived in Prob. 3, construct a diagram similar to Fig. 18.14.

CHAPTER XIX

SERIES PERTURBATIONS AND AUTOIONIZATION

It was pointed out in Chap. I that certain well-established spectral series show abnormalities of one kind or another. Of particular importance are the anomalies of the type found in one of the calcium series shown in Fig. 1.13. In this one instance the diffuse series behaves in the usual fashion by contracting after the first member to very narrow patterns. This contraction is soon disturbed, however, and the patterns expand anomalously reaching an apparent maximum at the seventh member; then decreasing again to narrow patterns, they approach the series limit.

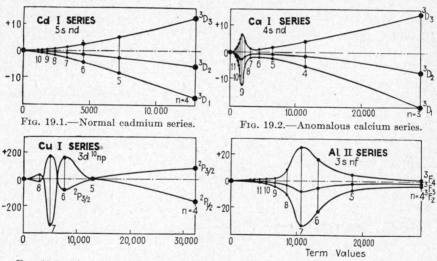

FIG. 19.1.—Normal cadmium series.

FIG. 19.2.—Anomalous calcium series.

FIG. 19.3.—Anomalous copper series.

FIG. 19.4.—Anomalous aluminum series.

In terms of the energy levels, themselves, this anomaly is to be attributed to the series of initial $^3D_{1,2,3}$ states and not in any way to the common final $^3P_{0,1,2}$ states. Of the surprisingly large number of well-known anomalous series found in other elements, those of aluminum and copper are particularly notable.

19.1. Observed Abnormal Series.—To start with, let us consider several observed series where the causes of the irregularities are now well known. Although it is the anomalous progression of spectral lines that is observed, we are here concerned with the derived energy levels themselves. In Figs. 19.1, 19.2, 19.3, and 19.4, the fine structures of four series of terms are shown for cadmium, calcium, copper, and aluminum, respectively. In each figure the fine structure is plotted vertically and the term values horizontally. The dotted center lines represent the center of gravity of each series member, each level being assigned the quantum weight $2J + 1$. The cadmium series in the first figure represents a series of triplets approaching in a regular fashion the series limit.

The $^3F_{2,3,4}$ series in singly ionized aluminum, like the $^3D_{1,2,3}$ series in calcium, expands abnormally and contracts again as it approaches the single limit. The copper series discovered by Shenstone[1] is of particular interest: the first term is right side up ($^2P_{\frac{3}{2}}$ above $^2P_{\frac{1}{2}}$), the second term is very narrow (both terms falling practically together), the third term is inverted, the fourth term is right side up and very wide, and the fifth term is inverted. The beautiful way in which each of these anomalous series has been explained by Shenstone and Russell[2] is the subject of the following sections of this chapter.

19.2. Energy Level Perturbations.—In the early chapters of this book we have seen that the term values of hydrogen-like atoms are given by the simple Bohr formula

$$T_n = \frac{RZ^2}{n^2} \tag{19.1}$$

where Z is the nuclear charge, R the Rydberg constant $= 109737 \ cm^{-1}$, and n the total quantum number. If Z is replaced by the effective nuclear charge Z_o (see Sec. 7.4) and n by the effective quantum number n^*, one obtains Rydberg's general formula for series of many electron atoms,

$$T_n = \frac{RZ_o^2}{n^{*2}} = \frac{RZ_o^2}{(n - \mu)^2}. \tag{19.2}$$

Here the integral valued quantum number n is retained by writing $n^* = n - \mu$, where μ is the so-called *quantum defect*. For all neutral atoms $Z_o = 1$, for singly ionized atoms $Z_o = 2$, etc. Using this formula, three aluminum series are shown in Fig. 19.5 with values of $\mu = n - n^*$ plotted vertically and the term values plotted horizontally. Series following Rydberg's formula [Eq. (19.2)] are represented on such a diagram by a straight horizontal line. A refinement of Rydberg's formula by Ritz in which n^* is replaced by $n - \mu - \alpha T_n$ is necessary for a series like $^1F_2$:

$$T_n = \frac{RZ_o^2}{n^{*2}} = \frac{RZ_o^2}{(n - \mu - \alpha T_n)^2} \tag{19.3}$$

On the diagram such a series is represented by a straight line with intercept μ and a slope given by α.

[1] Shenstone, A. G., *Phys. Rev.*, **34**, 1623, 1929.

[2] Shenstone, A. G., and H. N. Russell, *Phys. Rev.*, **39**, 415, 1932.

Now in the anomalous ^3F series of aluminum the fourth term is a foreign term and rightfully belongs to another ^3F series.[1]   When this term is omitted, the n values of the following terms will all be lowered by one.   A replot of the series with corrected n values is shown in Fig. 19.6, along with the anomalous ^3D series of calcium in Fig. 19.7.   The

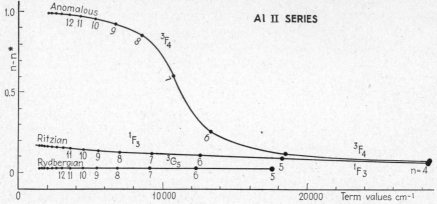

Fig. 19.5.—The quantum defect $\mu = n - n^*$ for three aluminum series.

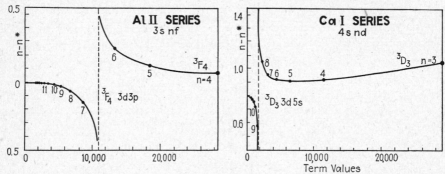

Fig. 19.6.—Aluminum series showing per-   Fig. 19.7.—Calcium series showing perturbations.   turbations.

resemblance between these curves and anomalous dispersion curves is quite striking.

A generalized form of the Rydberg-Ritz formula, derived from perturbation theory and the quantum mechanics, has been given by Langer.[2]

$$T_n = \frac{RZ_o^2}{\left[n + \Sigma\left(\dfrac{\beta_{in}}{T_n - T_i}\right)\right]^2}. \tag{19.4}$$

[1] In a study of this series Schrödinger attributed the anomalous behavior to a sort of polarization of the atom and assigned the third and fourth members of the series to the same total quantum number; *Ann. d. Phys.*, **77**, 43, 1925.

[2] Langer, R. M., *Phys. Rev.*, **35**, 649, 1930.

Here T_n represents as usual the successive terms of the series and T_i a foreign perturbing term not belonging to the series. Although Langer's formula does not adequately account for all series details, it does account for the existing anomalies in many series and its success is much beyond the expectations of a first approximation.

Langer's formula, modified by Shenstone and Russell to fit the anomalous series taken up in this and the last section, takes the form

$$T_n = \frac{RZ_o^2}{n^{*2}} = \frac{RZ_o^2}{\left[n - \mu - \alpha T_n + \left(\dfrac{\beta}{T_n - T_o} \right) \right]^2} \qquad (19.5)$$

where the effective quantum number is

$$n^* = n - \mu + \alpha T_n + \frac{\beta}{T_n - T_o}. \qquad (19.6)$$

This equation postulates that under certain conditions (to be specified later) a term T_o foreign to the series in question will perturb the series, causing it to deviate from the ordinary progression expected. Because of the form of the perturbation term $\beta/(T_n - T_o)$, this formula is analogous to the formula used in anomalous dispersion theory. This analogy, as seen in Fig. 19.6, is closer than might at first be expected.

As an example of the use of Eqs. (19.5) and (19.6), the observed term values and the computed constants of the $^3D_1$ series of calcium are given in the following table.

TABLE 19.1.—SERIES CALCULATIONS FOR THE ANOMALOUS $4snd, {}^3D_1$, SERIES OF CALCIUM

(After Shenstone and Russell)

Term value observed	Configuration	n	n^*	$n - n^*$	Term value calculation	T(obs.) $- T$ (calc.)
28969.1	$4s3d$	3	1.9463	1.0537	26465	2504
11556.4	$4s4d$	4	3.0815	0.9185	11556	0
6561.4	$4s5d$	5	4.0896	0.9104	6562	−1
4255.5	$4s6d$	6	5.0780	0.9220	4252	+3
3002.4	$4s7d$	7	6.0456	0.9544	3002	0
2268.3	$4s8d$	8	6.9552	1.0448	2287	−19
1848.9	$3d5s$	Foreign term				
1551.3	$4s9d$	9	8.4105	0.5895	1551	0
1273.1	$4s10d$	10	9.2840	0.7160	1276	−3
1045.6	$4s11d$	11	10.2445	0.7555	1048	−2
869.8	$4s12d$	12	11.2323	0.7677	873	−3
734.0	$4s13d$	13	12.2273	0.7727	737	−3
628.0	$4s14d$	14	13.2190	0.7810	630	−2

$\mu = 0.8705$, $\alpha = 0.00000339$, $\beta = -85$, $T_o = 1848.9$.

With the exception of the first series member, the agreement between the observed and calculated term values is very good. The origin of the foreign term is discussed in Sec. 19.5.

19.3. The Nature of and Conditions for Term Perturbations.—A first-order perturbation treatment and calculation of atomic energy levels have been given by Slater[1] and by Condon.[2] Including electron spin in the calculations, Condon shows that under certain conditions terms belonging to different electron configurations will perturb each other. If two levels have the same characteristic quantum numbers, and lie close together, second-order terms of the perturbation correction become large and cannot be neglected in the calculation of the energy of either level. A large second-order correction implies that the eigenfunctions for each of the respective levels contain components of the eigenfunction of the other level. Thus both levels belong in part to both electron configurations. The assignment of a given level to a definite electron configuration is therefore only approximate and becomes more exact when the levels are far apart.

The nature of the perturbation between the two levels in question reveals itself essentially as a repulsion. This apparent repulsion may be thought of as being due to a sort of resonance phenomenon, there being a certain probability that the atom will jump back and forth between the two characteristic states without the radiation of energy. The frequency of this interchange, and hence the repulsion, increases as the interval between the levels decreases.

The quantum conditions for term perturbations may be stated as follows: *Two levels belonging to the same or to different electron configurations will perturb each other when* (1) *both electron configurations are of the same parity, i.e., both even or both odd,*[3] *and* (2) *both levels have the same J value.* In addition to these necessary conditions, observation shows that the greatest effect is to be expected when the two levels have the same L and S values in LS-coupling, or the same j_1 and j_2 values in jj-coupling. For intermediate coupling schemes the more nearly alike the coupling schemes the greater will be the effect.

Consider as a simple example two neighboring sets of $^3D_{1,2,3}$ terms arising from different electron configurations of different parity, *i.e.*, one configuration odd and the other even. In the ideal case of LS-coupling these levels will be represented as shown at the left in Fig. 19.8. If now the configurations are of the same parity, *i.e.*, both even or both odd, a sort of resonance will be set up tending to repel corresponding levels. These are shown at the right in the figure. The nearer two

---

[1] Slater, J. C., *Phys. Rev.*, **34**, 1293, 1929.

[2] Condon, E. U., *Phys. Rev.*, **36**, 1121, 1930.

[3] An electron configuration or term is said to be *odd* when the sum of the l values of the electrons is odd, and *even* when the sum is even.

corresponding levels are to each other, the greater is the repelling effect (see Figs. 19.6 and 19.7). In Fig. 19.8 the $^3D_3$ terms, being the nearest to each other, undergo the greatest displacement, with the result that the narrow triplet is widened and the wide triplet is narrowed. This same result is to be expected when the unperturbed wide triplet is above the narrow triplet.

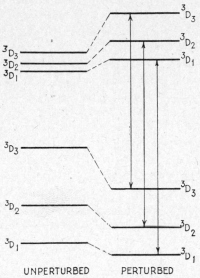

FIG. 19.8.—Schematic representation of term perturbations.

19.4. The Anomalous Diffuse Series of Calcium.—We now return to the anomalous ^3D ($4snd$) series of neutral calcium discussed in the preceding section. Referring to the calcium energy level diagram in Fig. 11.9, it is seen that the first member of the diffuse series $4snd$ is also the first member of another ^3D series $3dns$. Now the seventh member of the anomalous series is without doubt an extra member and should be called the second member of the $3dns$ series. If this assignment is correct the first two terms of the latter series should have as a limit the first excited ^2D state ($3d$) of the ionized atom. Term values taken with respect to ^2D as a limit give Rydberg denominators 1.60 and 2.64, in good agreement with the assignment.

A more detailed study of the fine structure of the two ^3D series is to be seen in Fig. 19.9. At the extreme left and right in this figure the two series are shown as they would occur without perturbation. In the center the observed series is shown. It should be pointed out that the unperturbed $3dns$ triplets should have a total separation of approximately 60 wave numbers, the same as that of the series limit ^2D (see Sec. 11.5), and that the higher members of the $4snd$ series should be very narrow. The effect of the perturbation is to widen the triplets on the left and to narrow those on the right, as observed. The third member of the right-hand series, shown by dotted lines, because it lies above the first series limit, should not be observed. This will be discussed in Sec. 19.9.

19.5. The Anomalous Principal Series in Copper.—The fine structure of the anomalous ^2P series in copper is shown in Fig. 19.3. This very irregular series, probably the most distorted series known, was discovered by Shenstone and now has a very beautiful and simple explanation. Although the first term of the series, $3d^{10}4p, {}^2P_{\frac{1}{2},\frac{3}{2}}$, in combination with $3d^{10}4s, {}^2S_{\frac{1}{2}}$, gives rise to the strongest lines in the copper arc spectrum,

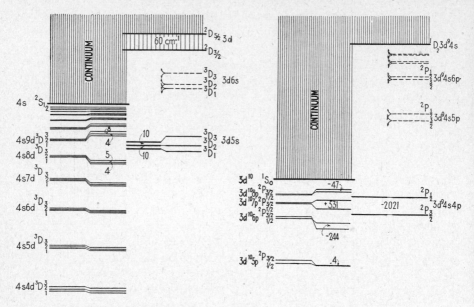

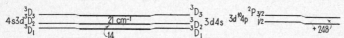

Unperturbed Perturbed   Perturbed Unperturbed   Unperturbed Perturbed   Perturbed Unperturbed

FIG. 19.9.—Perturbed diffuse series in   FIG. 19.10.—Perturbed principal series in
            calcium.   copper.

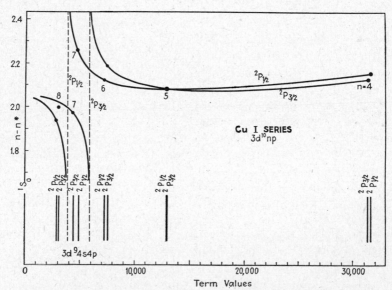

FIG. 19.11.—Showing perturbations in the principal series of copper.

it was not until the spectrum had been so thoroughly analyzed and every-thing else was accounted for, that the higher members of the series were definitely identified.

It is now known that the irregularities in this series are due to the perturbing influences of a foreign, widely spaced, inverted ^2P term. As shown in Fig. 19.10 these two fine-structure terms, 3952 cm^{-1} and 5973 cm^{-1}, respectively, are due to the odd electron configuration $3d^94s4p$, and the perturbed series of terms are due to the odd configurations $3d^{10}np$. Plotting the quantum defect $n - n^*$ against the term values, Fig. 19.11 results. It is observed that, as the series approaches the perturbing terms from either side, the mutual repulsions between cor-responding terms (*i.e.*, terms with the same J values) increase slowly at first, then more rapidly.

19.6. The Inverted Alkali Doublets.—It may be shown from the quantum mechanics or from the classical model of the atom that the doublet levels of the alkali metals should be normal, *i.e.*, of the two levels $j = l + \frac{1}{2}$ and $j = l - \frac{1}{2}$ the level $j = l - \frac{1}{2}$ should lie deeper. While this is observed to be generally true, it is well known that the ^2D and ^2F terms of some of the alkalies are inverted. In caesium, for example, the first ^2P and ^2D terms are normal and the second ^2F term is inverted.[1] In rubidium the ^2P terms are normal and the ^2D and ^2F terms are inverted.[2] In potassium the ^2P terms are normal and the ^2D terms are inverted.[3] In view of the anomalous turning over of the normal copper doublets, dis-cussed in the preceding section, it seems highly probable that the inver-sion of the narrow alkali doublets might be due to the perturbing influ-ence of widely spaced inverted doub-let terms lying high above the series limit.[4] This inverting effect is shown schematically in Fig. 19.12.

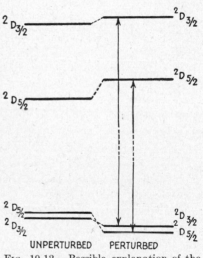

FIG. 19.12.—Possible explanation of the inversion of alkali doublets.

Inverted doublet terms arise in general from electron shells lacking but one electron to complete them. Consequently the excitation of an electron from one of the completed electron shells to an outer orbit may give rise to several of the desired doublets. Consider, for

[1] MEISSNER, K. W., *Ann. d. Phys.*, **50**, 713, 1916; **65**, 378, 1921.

[2] RAMB, R., *Ann. d. Phys.*, **10**, 311, 1931.

[3] MEISSNER, K. W., and O. MASAKI, *Ann. d. Phys.*, **10**, 325, 1931.

[4] WHITE, H. E., *Phys. Rev.*, **40**, 316, 1932.

example, the normal rubidium atom with the electron configuration

$$\text{Rb 37, } 1s^2 2s^2 2p^6 3s^2 3p^6 3d^{10} 4s^2 4p^6 5s. \qquad (19.7)$$

The excitation of the $5s$ valence electron to any of the unoccupied d orbits $4d$, $5d$, $6d$, etc., should give rise to a series of very narrow but normal ^2D levels. The excitation of a $4p$ electron from the completed $4p^6$ subshell to a $5p$ orbit, on the other hand, will result in the even configuration (*leaving off the completed subshells*) $4p^5 5s 5p$, giving rise among other terms to one inverted ^2D term and one normal ^2D term. Similarly a double excitation of two electrons to the even configuration $4p^5 4d 5p$ gives rise to three inverted ^2D terms and three normal ^2D terms. Due to the spin-orbit interaction of the $4p^5$ subshell these levels, whatever the coupling scheme, will be very wide. Furthermore the inverted doublets should lie deepest. Although these terms have not been observed in the alkali spectra, they certainly do exist and their position may be predicted fairly accurately from x-ray spectra to be high above the regular series limit of the chief optical series. Even at so great a distance, the inverted terms tend to invert the narrow doublet terms far below and the normal terms tend to restore them. The net second-order effect of these two opposing actions, although small, is great enough to cause inversion.[1]

19.7. Autoionization.—The atomic process of autoionization put forward by Wentzel and Shenstone[2] is of considerable importance in atomic spectra, for it clears up a great many of the difficulties previously unexplained. Above the limit of any series (see the calcium series in Fig. 19.9) lies a continuum of possible energy states characterized by the same quantum numbers as the series of discontinuous levels below the limit, *i.e.*, the same L, S, and J values and the same odd or even parity of the electron configuration. An atom excited to a hypothetical energy state like the even ^3D ($3d6s$) state of calcium, above the first series limit and into a region accompanied by an even ^3D continuum, is in a condition for resonance of the type discussed in Sec. 19.3. Before the atom has time to reach any stationary state and return to a lower state giving rise to radiation $h\nu$, there will be a spontaneous transition into the continuum equivalent to the ejection of an electron with kinetic energy $\frac{1}{2}mv^2$ and the return of the atom to the series limit $^2S_{\frac{1}{2}}$. This process of autoionization clearly shows why the third and succeeding members of the calcium series $3dns$ are not observed and postulates

---

[1] These actions at so great a distance have been calculated by M. Phillips, *Phys. Rev.*, **44**, 644, 1933, and shown to be great enough to produce the observed inversion.

[2] Autoionization has long been known for x-rays as the *Auger effect*. In giving a quantum-mechanical treatment of the effect, G. Wentzel (*Zeits. f. Phys.*, **43**, 524, 1927), first suggested its possible application to optical spectra. Direct application to optical spectra was made by Shenstone, *Phys. Rev.*, **38**, 873, 1931.

that these hypothetical levels are not discrete in the usual sense but are spread out over the continuum.

In some instances the quantum condition for resonance between a given discrete level and continuum are only partly satisfied (*i.e.*, there is a weak resonance coupling between the discrete state and the continuum, see Sec. 19.3) so that the process of either *spectral emission* or *autoionization* may take place.   This is the subject of the following sections.

19.8. Autoionization in Copper.—It has long been known that the copper arc spectrum, unlike most spectra, consists of many spectrum

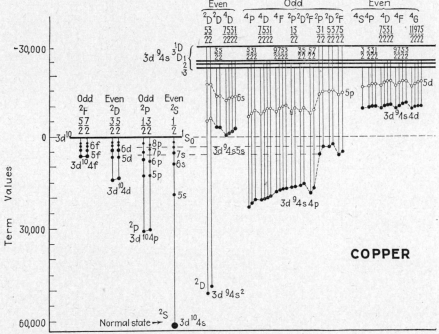

FIG. 19.13.—Energy level diagram of copper.

lines half of which are sharp and the other half unusually broad and diffuse.   A thorough investigation ·of these lines by Allen[1] has shown that the diffuseness is not due to a pressure or temperature effect but to a natural breadth of the energy levels.   Such broad levels immediately suggest that we are dealing with short mean lives and with the process of autoionization.

A thorough analysis of the copper arc spectrum by Shenstone[2] reveals, in addition to the well-known series of normal doublets, a system of inverted doublet and quartet levels.   From the energy level diagram of copper in Fig. 19.13 it is observed that several of the inverted doublet

[1] ALLEN, C. W., *Phys. Rev.*, **39**, 42, 55, 1932.
[2] SHENSTONE, A. G., *Phys. Rev.*, **28**, 449, 1926; **34**, 1623, 1929.

and quartet levels lie above the series limit of the normal doublets and in the continua of *even* ^2S and ^2D and *odd* ^2P and ^2F terms. Of these high levels the inverted $^4D_{\frac{7}{2},\frac{5}{2},\frac{3}{2},\frac{1}{2}}$ terms $(3d^94s5s)$ are of particular interest. In combination with a number of lower levels it is observed that all lines with $^4D_{\frac{7}{2}}$ or $^4D_{\frac{1}{2}}$ as initial levels are narrow sharp lines whereas those with $^4D_{\frac{5}{2}}$ or $^4D_{\frac{3}{2}}$ as initial levels are very broad and diffuse. Photographs of the combinations $^4F_{\frac{9}{2},\frac{7}{2},\frac{5}{2},\frac{3}{2}} - {}^4D_{\frac{7}{2},\frac{5}{2},\frac{3}{2},\frac{1}{2}}$ $(3d^94s4p - 3d^94s5s)$ are shown in Fig. 19.14 and the wave-lengths are given in Table 19.2.

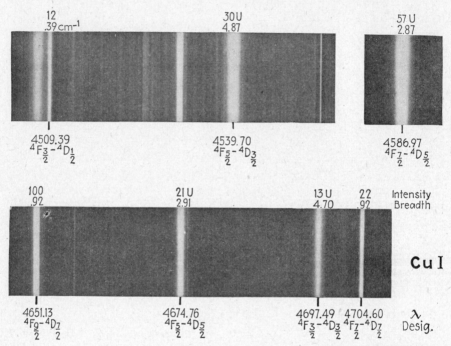

FIG. 19.14.—Broad and narrow lines in the same multiplet in the arc spectrum of copper.

The intervals between the ^4D terms, as well as the intercombinations with lower doublet levels, show that the coupling is not Russell-Saunders but something between LS- and jj-*coupling*. Now the two broad levels $^4D_{\frac{5}{2}}$ and $^4D_{\frac{3}{2}}$ are not strictly quartet levels with $S = \frac{3}{2}$ but are nearly enough like $^2D_{\frac{5}{2}}$ and $^2D_{\frac{3}{2}}$ terms to permit, at times, autoionization. The $^4D_{\frac{7}{2}}$ and $^4D_{\frac{1}{2}}$ levels, on the other hand, are strictly quartet levels, for with $3d^94s5s$ the spins of each of the s electrons and the S of $3d^9$ must take the so-called *parallel* positions to produce, with the L value 2, the J values $\frac{7}{2}$ and $\frac{1}{2}$, respectively. The observed and calculated g factors of 0 and $\frac{7}{2}$ from the Zeeman effect confirm this. In this latter case autoionization is not to be expected, and the sharp lines arising from these two levels indicate that it does not occur.

Table 19.2.—Quartet Multiplet in Copper

	$^4D_{7/2}$ 545.0	$^4D_{5/2}$ 636.2	$^4D_{3/2}$ 887.8	$^4D_{1/2}$
$^4F_{9/2}$	**100** 4651.13 *21494.2*			
244.3				
$^4F_{7/2}$	**22** 4704.60 *21249.9*	**57 U** 4586.97 *21794.8*		
409.4				
$^4F_{5/2}$	**2** 4797.04 *20840.4*	**21 U** 4674.76 *21385.5*	**30 U** 4539.70 *22021.7*	
739.7				
$^4F_{3/2}$		**2 U** 4842.20 *20646.0*	**13 U** 4697.49 *21282.0*	**12** 4509.39 *22169.8*

For want of a picture of the spreading out of an energy level, the following process is suggested. By the absorption of energy the atom is raised toward an excited state, *e.g.*, toward $^4D_{5/2}$ of the above given example. Because of the resonance phenomenon discussed in Sec. 19.3 there will be a certain probability that the atom will go over into the continuum and self-ionize before it has time to reach any stationary state. Thus in absorption the energy level in question will not be discrete but will be broadened by an amount depending upon the probability of self-ionization. The emission of radiation being the reverse of absorption, the observed spectral lines are broad.

The other diffuse lines in the copper spectrum all start from initial states that lie above the first series limit and have, without doubt, the same explanation as that given above for the $^4D_{3/2,5/2}$ states of $3d^94s5s$.

19.9. Autoionization in Calcium, Strontium, and Barium.—In the early development of complex-spectrum analysis, Russell and Saunders[1] discovered the now famous series of p' terms. These terms which they designated as $np'_{1,2,3}$, where $n = 2, 3, 4,$ and 5, are now designated as $^3P_{0,1,2}$ and are attributed by Russell[2] to the electron configurations $3d3d$, $3d4d$, $3d5d$, and $3d6d$. All but the first member of this series (see Fig. 11.9) lie above the first series limit $4\,^2S$ of the four chief series of singlets and triplets. The continuum above these four chief series corresponds to *even* S and D terms and to *odd* P and F terms. Russell's ^3P terms ($3dmd$), being characteristically *even*, enable the electron in any one of these states to have a mean life sufficiently great to combine normally with *odd* lower terms and give rise to the respectably sharp

[1] Russell, H. N., and F. A. Saunders, *Astrophys. Jour.*, **61**, 38, 1925.

[2] Russell, H. N., *Astrophys. Jour.*, **66**, 13, 1927.

spectrum lines observed. The *even* ^3S term $3d4d$ combining with $^3P_{0,1,2}$, $4s4p$ in a double electron jump gives rise to three hazy lines at λ 2757.40, λ 2749.34, and λ 2745.49. The broadness of these lines is due to the broad $^3S_1$ level and indicates that (1) the quantum conditions for auto-ionization are not far from satisfied (with respect to the $^3S_1$ continuum), (2) the mean life of the atom is long enough to permit some atoms to return to lower levels giving rise to radiation, and (3) that some of the atoms starting toward this state go over into the continuum and self-ionize.

In strontium a $^3F^\circ$ term $4d6p$ [the corresponding term in calcium (see Fig. 11.9) is $^3F^\circ$, $3d5p$] lies just above the 5^2S limit and, as in calcium, is in a continuum of $^3F^\circ$ terms $5smf$. These negative $^3F^\circ{}_{2,3,4}$ terms $4d6p$ combine with lower $^3D_{1,2,3}$ terms $5s4d$, giving rise to five very diffuse lines (see Table 19.3).

TABLE 19.3

Strontium, hazy lines (short mean life)			Barium, sharp lines (long mean life[1])		
Interval	λ	Designation	Interval	λ	Designation
$4n$	3189.23	$^3D_3 - {}^3F^\circ_4$	10	3586.50	$^3D_3 - {}^3F^\circ_4$
$3n$	3189.93	$^3D_2 - {}^3F^\circ_3$	10	3561.94	$^3D_2 - {}^3F^\circ_3$
$2n$	3198.99	$^3D_1 - {}^2F^\circ_2$	10	3566.66	$^2D_1 - {}^3F^\circ_2$
$2n$	3200.22	$^3D_3 - {}^3F^\circ_3$	15	3610.96	$^3D_3 - {}^3F^\circ_3$
$1n$	3205.13	$^3D_2 - {}^3F^\circ_2$	3	3589.95	$^3D_2 - {}^3F^\circ_2$
			2	3639.72	$^3D_3 - {}^3F^\circ_2$

[1] White, H. E., *Phys. Rev.*, **38**, 2016, 1931.

In barium these same $^3F^\circ{}_{2,3,4}$ terms $5d7p$ lie just below the series limit 6^2S so that autoionization is not possible. Combining with lower $^3D_{1,2,3}$ terms $6s5d$, six relatively sharp lines are expected and observed (see Table 19.3). Where the mean life in a given state is long the lines will have a very narrow natural breadth, and where the mean life is relatively small the lines will have wide natural breadth. This question of the breadths of spectral lines will be taken up in Chap. XXI.

19.10. Hyperfine-structure Term Perturbations.—In the early development of *hfs* and nuclear spin it was observed that the Landé interval rule was always valid. This observation is in complete agreement with the present-day atomic models, and, were it not for one fairly well-established case in mercury, found by Schüller and Jones,[1] the rule might be laid down as infallible. Since the one known departure from the interval rule is attributed by them to the same type of perturbation phenomena as those discussed in the first sections of this chapter, a discussion of this single known example is not out of place here.

[1] Schüler, H. and E. G. Jones, *Zeits. f. Phys.*, **74**, 631, 1932; **77**, 801, 1932.

The first member of the diffuse series in mercury consists of four terms $^3D_1$, $^3D_2$, $^3D_3$, and $^1D_2$, arising from the electron configuration $6s6d$ (see Fig. 11.6). Contrary to what one would expect from LS- or jj-coupling, the $^1D_2$ term lies about three wave numbers below $^3D_1$. Since the triplet intervals 60 and 35 cm^{-1} have the ratio 5:3 in place of 2:3 for LS-coupling, only the $^3D_1$ and $^3D_3$ levels can be assigned definite S and L values. Due to the close proximity of the two levels $^3D_1$ and

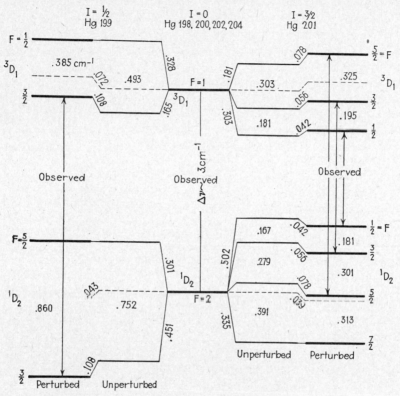

Fig. 19.15.—Hyperfine-structure term perturbations in the arc spectrum of mercury. (*After Schüler and Jones.*)

$^1D_2$, their respective *hfs* terms perceptibly perturb each other. These perturbations are shown schematically in Fig. 19.15.

Due to the relatively large number of mercury isotopes (198, 199, 200, 201, 202, and 204) the *hfs* patterns of a majority of the spectrum lines are very complex. As stated in Sec. 18.12 the very interesting and praiseworthy analysis of many of these patterns by Schüler and Jones has led to the assignment of different nuclear spins to the different isotopes:

Mercury $\begin{cases} \text{Isotope} & 198 \quad 199 \quad 200 \quad 201 \quad 202 \quad 204 \\ \text{Nuclear spin} & 0 \quad \frac{1}{2} \quad 0 \quad \frac{3}{2} \quad 0 \quad 0 \end{cases}$

Starting with the even isotopes with zero spin in the center column of Fig. 19.15, the two terms $^3D_1$ and $^1D_2$ will, for the 199 isotope, each be split into two hyperfine levels. The same two terms for the 201 isotope will be split into three and four hyperfine levels, respectively. The dotted lines represent the centers of gravity of each set of levels (each level is assigned the quantum weight $2F + 1$), and the arrows indicate the levels that repel each other. It is assumed that there is no isotope displacement.

By analogy with the perturbation rules given in Sec. 19.3 the quantum conditions for hyperfine term perturbations may be postulated as follows: Two levels belonging to the same or to different electron configurations will perturb each other (1) when both electron configurations are of the same sign, and (2) when both levels have the same F value. The I value being always the same for every energy level of each atom, the greatest effect is to be expected when the two levels have the same J value. (In the case of mercury the J's are different.) Schüler and Jones point out that the repulsion is not only a function of the distance between the levels but also a function of the F and I values. Though the $F = \frac{5}{2}$ levels are farther apart than the $F = \frac{1}{2}$ levels, the shift is greater. Furthermore the shift of the $F = \frac{3}{2}$ levels for $I = \frac{1}{2}$ is twice as great as for $I = \frac{3}{2}$. A possible explanation lies in the relative magnitudes of the nuclear factors.

It is to be noted that the levels for $I = \frac{3}{2}$ are inverted with respect to the levels for $I = \frac{1}{2}$. Whatever the coupling scheme may be for the $6s6d$ configuration, the $^3D_1$ term can only be LS-coupling with $S = 1$, $L = 2$, and $J = 1$. With a positive g factor and a strong coupling between the $6s$ electron and the nucleus, the hfs terms of $^3D_1$ will be large and inverted as observed for $I = \frac{1}{2}$. With a negative nuclear g factor they will be normal as observed for $I = \frac{3}{2}$. The magnitude of the hyperfine separations shows that the positive g factor is 2.7 times the negative g factor.

CHAPTER XX

THE STARK EFFECT

20.1. Discovery of the Stark Effect.—Although the splitting up of spectral lines in a magnetic field was discovered by Zeeman as early as 1897, some 16 years elapsed before anyone succeeded in showing that a similar effect is produced when a source of light is placed in an electric field. In 1913 Stark[1] demonstrated that every line of the Balmer series of hydrogen, when excited in a strong electric field of at least 100000 volts per centimeter, is split into a number of components. When viewed perpendicular to the field, some of the components of each line pattern are observed to be plane-polarized with the electric vector parallel to the field (*p* components), and the others polarized with the electric vector normal to the field (*s* components). When viewed parallel to the field only the *s* components appear, now unpolarized.

There is at least one good reason why early attempts to observe the splitting of spectrum lines in an electric field were not successful, *viz.*, the production of very high potential gradients along a discharge tube is a very difficult task. Soon after Stark's discovery, Lo Surdo[2] observed the splitting of lines excited in the cathode dark space of a discharge tube. These two sets of observations mark the beginning of a very interesting, and at the same time complex, field of investigation.[3]

20.2. The Stark Effect of Hydrogen.—If one were to ask, What was the most outstanding success of the early Bohr quantum theory?, the reply would be, The first satisfactory treatment of the hydrogen atom in an electric field, by Epstein[4] and by Schwarzschild.[5] It is interesting to point out that these early results, coming as they did at a time before the spinning electron made its début, have been little altered by the more satisfactory quantum mechanics as given by the Schrödinger wave equation[6] and by the Dirac theory of the electron.[7]

[1] Stark, J., *Berl. Akad. Wiss.*, **40**, 932, 1913; *Ann. d. Phys.*, **43**, 965, 1919.

[2] Lo Surdo, A., *Accad. Lincei Atti*, **22**, 665, 1913; **23**, 83, 256, 326, 717, 1914.

[3] A rather complete bibliography and account of the Stark effect is given by R. Minkowski in H. Geiger and K. Scheel, *Handbuch der Physik*, Vol. 21, p. 389, 1929.

[4] Epstein, P. S., *Ann. d. Phys.*, **50**, 489, 1916; also *Phys. Zeits.*, **17**, 148, 1916.

[5] Schwarzschild, K., *Sitz-ber. Berl. Akad. Wiss.*, 1916, p. 548.

[6] Schrödinger, E., *Ann. d. Phys.*, **80**, 437, 1926; Epstein, P. S., *Phys. Rev.*, **28**, 695, 1926.

[7] Schlapp, R., *Proc. Roy. Soc.*, A, **119**, 313, 1928.

We shall not attempt to derive any of the equations for the Stark effect but shall begin by first writing down the general energy relations for a hydrogen atom in an electric field and then proceed to interpret them in terms of atomic models and the observed spectrum lines. The interaction energy of a hydrogen-like atom in an electric field is given by

$$\Delta T = AF + BF^2 + CF^3 + \cdots \qquad (20.1)$$

Here ΔT represents the change in the term value of the atom in wave numbers, i.e., the shift in the energy levels from the field-free states to the states in the electric field, and F is the strength of the field in electrostatic units. The coefficients A, B, and C, in this equation, have been calculated from classical and quantum-mechanical considerations by Epstein, Wentzel, Waller, Van Vleck, S.Doi, Schrödinger, and others, and are given by

$$A = \frac{3h}{8\pi^2 mec} n(n_2 - n_1),$$

$$B = \frac{h^5}{2^{10}\pi^6 m^3 e^6 c} n^4 \{17n^2 - 3(n_2 - n_1) - 9m_l^2 + 19\}, \qquad (20.2)$$

$$C = \frac{3h^9}{2^{15}\pi^{10} m^5 e^{11} c} n^7 \{23n^2 - (n_2 - n_1)^2 + 11m_l^2 + 39\}.$$

Here n is the usual total quantum number, and n_1, n_2, and m_l are *electric quantum numbers*, subject to the condition

$$m_l = n - n_2 - n_1 - 1. \qquad (20.3)$$

The allowed values are

$$n = 1, 2, 3, \cdots \infty, \qquad\qquad n_1 = 0, 1, 2, 3, \cdots n - 1,$$
$$\qquad\qquad\qquad\qquad\qquad\qquad\qquad\qquad (20.4)$$
$$m_l = 0, \pm 1, \pm 2, \cdots \pm (n - 1), \qquad n_2 = 0, 1, 2, 3, \cdots n - 1.$$

If the field is expressed in volts per centimeter the independent constants preceding the quantum numbers in these expressions are 6.42×10^{-5}, 5.22×10^{-16}, and 1.53×10^{-25} for A, B, and C, respectively. The first term in Eq. (20.1), involving F to the first power, is called *the first-order Stark effect;* the second term, involving F to the second power, is called *the second-order Stark effect;* etc. The values of A, B, and C indicate that, if the field is not too large ($F < 100000$ volts per centimeter), the lower states of the hydrogen atom (n small) would be expected to show only a first-order Stark effect. Such fields result in a symmetrical splitting of the energy levels about their field-free positions. The second-order effect, which is always present and becomes large for higher states and higher fields, results in a unidirectional displacement of each line. One peculiar result should be pointed out before going further, *viz.*, that the first-order Stark effect is observed first in hydrogen-like atoms, whereas the second-order Stark effect predominates in most others. The latter will be considered more in detail in Sec. 20.8.

20.3. Early Orbital Model of Hydrogen in an Electric Field.[1]—The early treatment by Epstein and Schwarzschild of the hydrogen atom in an electric field is shown schematically in Fig. 20.1. We have seen in Chap. III how the Bohr-Sommerfeld orbits, in field-free space, are quantized, and how the size and shape of each orbit are given by the total quantum number n, the azimuthal quantum number l (or k), and the radial quantum number r. In a magnetic field we have seen how

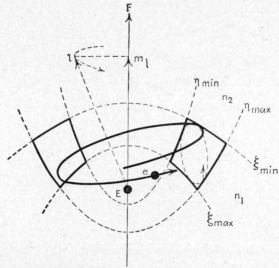

Fig. 20.1.—The orbital model of hydrogen in an electric field.

the orbit becomes oriented, or space-quantized, and how the magnetic quantum number m_l is introduced.

Now the action of an external electric field on an orbital electron is quite different from the action due to a magnetic field. So different in fact is the new motion that a different system of coordinates is required for a solution of the problem. The required solutions are found in parabolic coordinates, and the quantum numbers describing the motion are those given in Eq. (20.2). The quantum number m_l, which gives the projection of the orbital angular momentum (*i.e.*, $m_l h/2\pi$), on the electric axis, is to be compared with the magnetic quantum number m_l. It should be pointed out that in an electric field the orbital angular momentum is not necessarily constant as it is in a magnetic field.

[1] For a treatment of the Stark effect in terms of electron orbits, see A. Sommerfeld, "Atomic Structure," p. 276, 1923; see also A. E. Ruark and H. C. Urey, "Atoms, Molecules and Quanta," p. 149, 1930.

The quantum numbers n_1 and n_2, called the *parabolic quantum numbers*, are closely analogous to and replace the radial and azimuthal quantum numbers of field-free space. Just as r and l determine the range of the electron-nuclear distance r_{min} (perihelion) to r_{max} (aphelion), so n_1 and n_2 determine the range of the electron's motion in the electric-field coordinates as shown in Fig. 20.1. While n_1 limits the motion to the region between the two paraboloids of revolution ξ_{min} and ξ_{max}, n_2 limits the motion to the region between the two paraboloids of revolution η_{min} and η_{max}. The region intersected by the two pairs of paraboloids is shown in cross section only. Confined to this region the electron has three periodic motions, one around the field direction given by m_l, and one each along the ξ and η coordinates given by n_1 and n_2. Since the last two periods are not necessarily the same, the electron will in time have covered every point in the cross-sectional area shown.[1] If $m_l \neq 0$, $n_1 \neq 0$, and $n_2 = 0$, then $\eta_{min} = \eta_{max}$ and the motion is confined to move along a paraboloid given by $\eta = $ constant between the limits ξ_{min} and ξ_{max}. If n_1 and n_2 are both zero, $\eta_{min} = \eta_{max}$ and $\xi_{min} = \xi_{max}$, and the electron moves in a circle with $m_l = n - 1$.

Although quantum-mechanical models in the form of electron-cloud pictures have not been made for hydrogen-like atoms in an electric field, there is little doubt but what they closely resemble the orbital model just as they do for the field-free states shown in Chaps. IV and IX. It will be seen in Sect. 20.5 that in a strong electric field the spin of the electron adds very little to the orbital picture presented above. This is to be contrasted with the large contribution of the spin to the energy in a magnetic field, as shown by the anomalous Zeeman effect.

20.4. Weak-field Stark Effect in Hydrogen.—A treatment of the hydrogen atom in a weak electric field has been given for the orbital model, neglecting electron spin, by Kramers,[2] and for the quantum-mechanical model, including spin, by Schlapp.[3] This latter treatment employs the Dirac electron theory and is therefore to be preferred. Although Schlapp's derivations will not be given here, we may nevertheless form some picture of the atom in a weak field and see in a qualitative way how the energy levels and spectrum lines should split up according to his results.

By a *weak electric field* in hydrogen is meant one in which the interaction energy between the electron resultant j^* and the field F is considerably less than the magnetic interaction energy between l^* and s^*. In other words we have a weak field when the Stark splitting is small

---

[1] Attempts to represent the various possible motions of an orbital electron in an electric field have been made by R. W. Wood, *Phys. Rev.*, **38**, 346, 1931; see also A. Sommerfeld, "Atombau."

[2] Kramers, H. A., *Zeits. f. Phys.*, **3**, 199, 1920.

[3] Schlapp, R., *Proc. Roy. Soc.*, A, **119**, 313, 1928.

compared with the fine-structure splitting.   In a weak field the spinning
electron, which may be thought of classically as a small magnet, does
not interact with the field so that the coupling of j^* with F is due only to
the interaction of l^* with F.   On the classical picture of a precessing
atom the electron mechanical resultant $j^*h/2\pi$ precesses around the
field F, somewhat as shown in Fig. 20.2.   The projection of j^* on the
field direction F is given by m_j, where m_j takes values differing from each
other by unity from $+j$ to $-j$.

The important difference between the Zeeman effect and the Stark
effect is that each pair of levels $+m_j$ and $-m_j$ arising from a given level
have the same energy when in an electric field but different energies

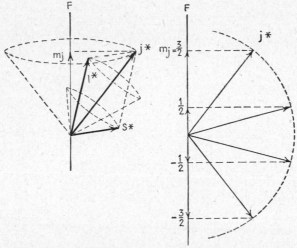

FIG. 20.2.—Classical vector model for the hydrogen atom in a weak electric field.

when in a magnetic field.   The state $m_j = \frac{3}{2}$ in Fig. 20.3, for example,
has the same energy as the state $m_j = -\frac{3}{2}$.   Similarly the states $m_j = +\frac{1}{2}$
and $m_j = -\frac{1}{2}$ have the same energy.   Instead of a level $j = \frac{3}{2}$ being
split up into four components as in the Zeeman effect, there are but two
levels.   The reason for this can best be understood by referring to the
classical orbital model, or to the quantum-mechanical model of electron
clouds (see Figs. 9.8 and 9.10).   The nature of the forces acting on the
electron are purely electrostatic so that the energy of the electron in an
orbit of given n and l depends only on the inclination of the orbit plane
with respect to the electric field, or to the distribution of charge on the
quantum-mechanical model, and not on the direction of rotation or
motion of the electron in its orbit.   The states with $+m_j$ and $-m_j$
correspond to the same inclination of the orbital plane, or to the same
charge distributions, and therefore have the same distortion, or energy
change, due to the applied field.   In a magnetic field, on the other hand,

the energy depends on the direction of rotation, and the energies change sign when m_j changes sign.   It should be noted in Fig. 9.8 that for given n, l, and j each pair of states $\pm m_j$ have the same charge distributions. Again each pair of states with the same n, j, and m_j but different l have the same angular distribution but different radial distribution.

The energy levels of the hydrogen atom for the two states $n = 2$ and $n = 3$ are shown in Fig. 20.3.   The field-free levels and theoretical pattern for H_α are given at the left and the weak-field levels and pattern are given at the right.   Theoretical treatments of the Stark effect show that wherever two or more levels with the same n and j but different

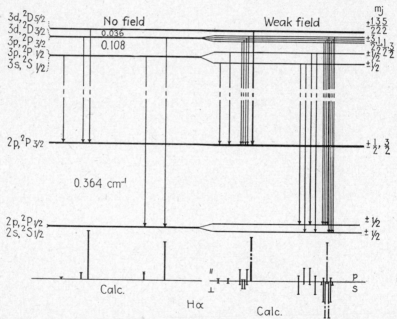

Fig. 20.3.—Fine structure and weak-field Stark effect for hydrogen H_α.   (*After Schlapp.*)

l lie close together the first-order Stark effect predominates over the second-order Stark effect.   At the left in the figure it is to be noted that states for which n and j are equal fall together (see Fig. 9.3), and that these same levels at the right show a large first-order splitting.   The only unpaired state for each n is in each case the one at the top, $2p$, $^2P_{\frac{3}{2}}$, and $3d, ^2D_{\frac{5}{2}}$, and these show only second-order splittings too small to show in the figure.   The reason why a first-order effect occurs in the double levels and not in the single may be explained as follows: Owing to the overlapping of angular wave functions, and the mutual energy shared by the two states, the atom in either one of the shared states will possess a net electric moment.   When a state is unpaired, there can be no appreciable electric moment and hence only a second-order effect.

Due to the space quantization of the mechanical moments, as shown in Fig. 20.2, the electric moment interacts with F to give $j + \frac{1}{2}$ equally spaced levels. The quantum numbers for weak-field Stark effect are n, j, and m_j. Although l is no longer a quantum number, Schlapp arbitrarily assigns the upper levels of each parent j to the higher l value $l = j + \frac{1}{2}$, and the lower levels to $l = j - \frac{1}{2}$. All weak-field levels arising from the same fine-structure term j retain the same j value.

The selection rules for the weak-field Stark effect are the same as those for the Zeeman effect:

$$\Delta m_j = 0 \text{ gives } \mathbf{p} \text{ } components,$$
$$\Delta m_j = \pm 1 \text{ gives } \mathbf{s} \text{ } components. \tag{20.5}$$

The relative intensities of the various components shown at the lower right in Fig. 20.3 are those calculated by Schlapp. Each fine-structure component in H_α should show a symmetrical pattern. Since the fine structure without field has never been completely resolved, these patterns have never been observed. Due to the falling together of levels with the same m_j, the s components when viewed parallel to F will (since each arises from two opposite circular polarizations) be unpolarized.

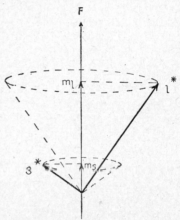

20.5. Strong-field Stark Effect in Hydrogen.—A *strong electric field* for hydrogen may be defined as one for which the interaction energy between the electron and the field F is greater than the interaction energy between the electron spin and orbit. In other words when the splitting of the energy levels due to the

Fig. 20.4.—Classical vector model for the hydrogen atom in a strong electric field. Space quantization for the Stark effect.

field is greater than the fine-structure splitting, the field is said to be *strong*. In such a field the magnetic coupling between l^* and s^* is broken down, and l^* is quantized with respect to (and on the classical model precesses independently around) the field direction F as shown in Fig. 20.4. While the spin is not acted on by the external electric field, it does interact with the magnetic field of the orbital motion l^*. This interaction takes place even though s^* is no longer coupled with the orbit to form j^*. Resolving the magnetic field due to l^* into two components, one along F and the other normal to F, the normal component will average to zero. As a result of this, s^* will precess around the component parallel to F. As in a strong magnetic field the spin s^* therefore precesses around

the electric field direction but for a different reason. We may, therefore, ascribe quantum numbers m_l and m_s to these two motions where
m_l takes values from $+l$ to $-l$, and m_s takes the values $+\frac{1}{2}$ and $-\frac{1}{2}$.
[This is the m_l of Eq. (20.3).]

In such a strong field Epstein and Schwarzschild, and others, have
shown that the first-order Stark effect is many times larger than the
so-called second-order Stark effect (see Sec. 20.2), and that the interaction energy of l^* with F is given by the first term of Eq. (20.1).

$$\Delta T = AF = 6.42 \times 10^{-5}n(n_2 - n_1)F. \tag{20.6}$$

Although the coupling between l^* and s^* has been broken down
in a strong field, there is still a magnetic interaction between the two
vectors which is of the same order of magnitude as the fine structure
in no field, and this must be added to Eq. (20.6). Just as in the Zeeman
effect this energy is given by Eq. (10.29) as

$$\Gamma = al^*s^* \cos (l^*s^*) \text{ cm}^{-1}. \tag{20.7}$$

Even though l is not a quantum number, the cosine when averaged
should give [see Eq. (10.33)]

$$\Gamma = am_lm_s \text{ cm}^{-1}. \tag{20.8}$$

Adding this energy to Eq. (20.6), each strong-field term is shifted by

$$\Delta T = 6.42 \times 10^{-5}n(n_2 - n_1)F + am_lm_s, \tag{20.9}$$

where a is the l^*s^* coupling coefficient (see Sec. 8.6) determined from the
fine structure, and where F is measured in volts per centimeter.

Let us now apply Eq. (20.9) to the specific example of the first three
states of hydrogen and then the selection rules to the first member
of the Balmer series H_α. The energies for each quantum state are
easily calculated by tabulating as in Table 20.1.

The allowed values of n, n_1, and n_2 are first written down in columns
to insure obtaining all possible combinations. The quantities $n(n_2 - n_1)$
are next computed. From Eq. (20.3) the values of m_l are obtained.
For every possible state m_l there are the two possibilities $m_s = +\frac{1}{2}$
and $m_s = -\frac{1}{2}$. The a coefficients in the last column are not all equal
as each is a measure of the spin-orbital interactions and there are several
different l's. We see from this table that there is exactly the same
number of possible states of the atom as in the Zeeman effect. In the
Stark effect, however, certain levels fall together. Plotting the energies
as given by Cols. 5 and 8, each weak-field level m_j is connected to a
strong-field level with the same m_j, such that no two levels with the same
m_j cross.

TABLE 20.1.—ENERGY FACTORS FOR THE STARK EFFECT IN HYDROGEN

n	n_2	n_1	$n_2 - n_1$	$n(n_2 - n_1)$	m_l	m_s	am_lm_s
1	0	0	0	0	0	$\pm\frac{1}{2}$	0
2	+1	+1	0	0	-1	$\pm\frac{1}{2}$	$\mp a/2$
	+1	0	+1	+2	0	$\pm\frac{1}{2}$	0
	0	+1	-1	-2	0	$\pm\frac{1}{2}$	0
	0	0	0	0	+1	$\pm\frac{1}{2}$	$\pm a/2$
3	+2	+2	0	0	-2	$\pm\frac{1}{2}$	$\mp a$
	+2	+1	+1	+3	-1	$\pm\frac{1}{2}$	$\mp a/2$
	+2	0	+2	+6	0	$\pm\frac{1}{2}$	0
	+1	+2	-1	-3	-1	$\pm\frac{1}{2}$	$\mp a/2$
	+1	+1	0	0	0	$\pm\frac{1}{2}$	0
	+1	0	+1	+3	+1	$\pm\frac{1}{2}$	$\pm a/2$
	0	+2	-2	-6	0	$\pm\frac{1}{2}$	0
	0	+1	-1	-3	+1	$\pm\frac{1}{2}$	$\pm a/2$
	0	0	0	0	+2	$\pm\frac{1}{2}$	$\pm a$

As in the Paschen-Back effect the selection rules for a strong electric field may be stated as follows:

$$\Delta m_s = 0,$$
$$\Delta m_l = 0 \text{ for } p \text{ components}, \qquad (20.10)$$
$$\Delta m_l = 1 \text{ for } s \text{ components}.$$

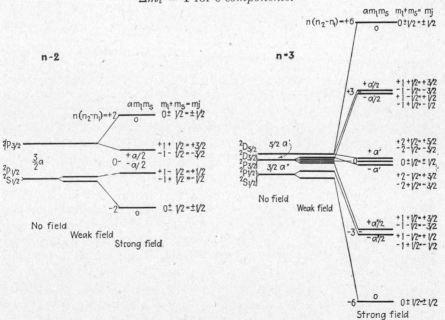

FIG. 20.5.—Stark effect of hydrogen, showing weak- and strong-field energy levels for $n = 2$ and $n = 3$.

Intensity rules have been worked out from the quantum mechanics by a number of investigators. Those shown in Fig. 20.6 have been calculated by Schlapp using as a model the Dirac electron as applied to hydrogen. Although the weak-field patterns have not been observed, the strong-field pattern for each line has been observed and found to be in good agreement with theory, in both the intensities and the relative separations. It should be pointed out that under different electrical conditions in different types of sources the relative intensities of the components are different. The microphotometer curve shown for H_α in Fig. 20.6, taken from the work of Mark and Wierl,[1] is observed

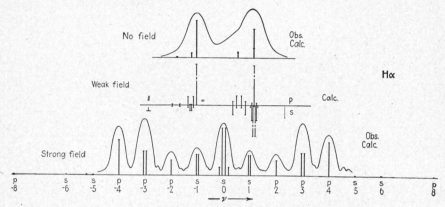

FIG. 20.6.—Stark effect of hydrogen, showing calculated and observed structure for H_α. (*Observed field-free pattern after Spedding, Shane, and Grace; observed strong-field pattern after Mark and Wierl.*)

to be in excellent agreement. The fine-structure splitting due to the magnetic l^*s^* interaction is not resolved. The lower figure if plotted to the scale of the field-free line above would be many times wider than shown. A reproduction of Mark and Wierl's published photograph of H_α is given in Fig. 20.7. In enlarging this photograph the photographic paper was moved in the direction of the lines during the exposure.

20.6. Second-order Stark Effect in Hydrogen.—In field strengths of over 100000 volts per centimeter the Stark components of the hydrogen line patterns show deviations from the shifts given by the formulas for the *first-order Stark effect*. This effect, which is found experimentally to shift different components to the red or violet by an amount proportional to the square of the field strength, is called the *second-order Stark effect*. In other than hydrogen-like atoms the same phenomenon is called the *quadratic Stark effect*.

The first observations of the second-order effect in hydrogen were made by Takamine and Kokubu[2] in the Stark pattern of H_γ when

[1] MARK, H., and R. WIERL, *Zeits. f. Phys.*, **55**, 156, 1929.

[2] TAKAMINE, T., and N. KOKUBU, *Proc. Tokyo Math. Phys. Soc.*, **9**, 394, 1918.

the spectrum was produced in a field of 147000 volts per centimeter.   In this field the middle s component of H_γ was observed to be shifted toward the red by only 0.8 Å.   These experiments were followed up by extensive investigations in fields of several hundred thousand volts per centimeter by Kiuti,[1] Foster,[2] Ishida and Hiyama,[3] Rausch von Traubenberg and Gebauer,[4] and others.

The theoretical relation giving the second-order shift of the energy levels in hydrogen-like atoms is given by the second equation in Eq.

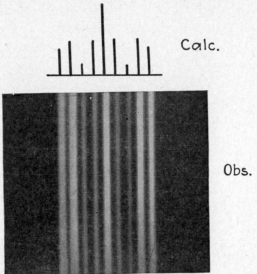

FIG. 20.7.—Observed Stark pattern for hydrogen $H\alpha$.   (*After Mark and Wierl.*)

(20.2).   Early derivations of this formula, using the orbital model of the atom, did not include the constant term 19.   Recent comparisons of theory and experiment show better agreement with the newer formula as it is given in Eq. (20.2).   This may be shown by the observations of Rausch von Traubenberg and Gebauer for two of the s components of H_γ in Fig. 20.8.   The circles represent the observed shifts as measured from the photographic plates, the solid lines the theoretical shifts according to Eq. (20.2), and the dotted lines the shifts according to the older theory.   Equally good agreement has been found in other components and other line patterns in hydrogen.

In measuring the second-order shifts of various components of a given Stark pattern better agreement with theory is found by taking

[1] KIUTI, M., *Japan. Jour. Physics*, **4**, 13, 1925.

[2] FOSTER, J. S., *Astrophys. Jour.*, **63**, 191, 1926.

[3] ISHIDA, Y., and S. HIYAMA, *Inst. Phys. Chem. Research, Tokyo, Sci. Paper* 9, Vol. 152, 1928.

[4] VON TRAUBENBERG, H. RAUSCH, and R. GEBAUER, *Zeits. f. Phys.*, **54**, 307, 1929; **56**, 254, 1929.

symmetrical pairs of lines and measuring the shift of their center of gravity from the field-free lines. The wave-length shift is given by

$$\Delta\lambda = \frac{\lambda_r + \lambda_v}{2} - \lambda_0, \tag{20.11}$$

where λ_r is the wave-length of the red component, λ_v is the wave-length of the violet component, and λ_0 the wave-length of the field-free line.

20.7. Stark Effect for More than One Electron.—As compared with the Stark effect in hydrogen the effect of an electric field on atoms containing more than one electron is in many cases quite complicated. One of the most important features to be mentioned is the unexpected appearance of so-called *forbidden lines*. These lines, involving what

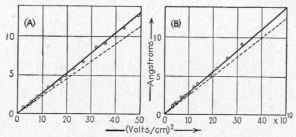

Fig. 20.8.—Second-order Stark effect in hydrogen. (*After Rausch von Traubenberg and Gebauer.*) *A.* Wave-length shift of the middle *s* component of H_γ. *B.* Shift of the *s* components, ± 3, of H_γ.

in field-free space would correspond to a change in the azimuthal quantum number of zero, two, three, four, etc., are often the strongest lines in a pattern. The reason for this is that in an electric field the quantum conditions are quite different and the selection rules apply to a new set of quantum numbers.

Although the splitting up of the energy levels for different atoms is different from level to level and from atom to atom, the formulas derived from the quantum mechanics for hydrogen are found to apply in many cases. To be more exact, the more nearly hydrogen-like a given term happens to be, the more nearly the Stark splitting will follow the hydrogen formulas [Eqs. (20.1) and (20.2)]. Hydrogen-like states in complex atoms are those for which the effective quantum number n_0 is nearly an integer, and the quantum defect (see Sec. 7.4) is practically zero. Such terms arise when the excited electron, or *running electron* as it is sometimes called, is in a nonpenetrating orbit like $2p$, $3d$, $4f$, $5f$, $5g$, $6f$, $6g$, $6h$, etc.

If the excited electron moves in a penetrating orbit, the state will not show, in ordinary fields, a first-order Stark effect. A classical explanation that has been given for this is as follows: Owing to the rapid precession of a penetrating orbit when in a non-Coulomb force field the electric moment will precess rapidly in the orbit plane so that its time average in any direction will vanish. With no electric moment there should be no first-order Stark effect. In an electric field, however, the orbit will be displaced as a whole in one direction and this will give rise to a quadratic, or second-order, Stark effect. On the quantum mechanics one might say, just as in hydrogen, that, due to the overlapping of wave functions and the mutual sharing of energy of two close neighboring states, the atom in either of the two states will possess a net electric moment. This moment, due to the space quantization of mechanical moments, will interact with the field in such a way as to give rise to equally spaced levels, the intervals between which will be proportional to the first power of the field F. The farther removed a state is from other hydrogen-like states, the smaller will be the net electric moment

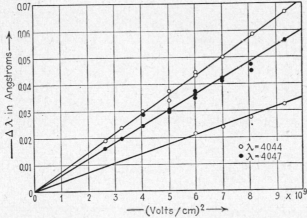

FIG. 20.9.—Quadratic Stark effect for the potassium doublet $4s, {}^2S_{\frac{1}{2}} - 5p, {}^2P_{\frac{1}{2},\frac{3}{2}}$, $\lambda4047$ and $\lambda4044$. (*After Grotrian and Ramsauer.*)

and the smaller the first-order splitting. Just as in hydrogen we can now say that, if the excited electron is in a hydrogen-like orbit and there are no other hydrogen-like orbits with the same n, the state will show no first-order effect.

As an example of the practical application of the above principles, let us consider the sodium D lines arising from the transitions $3s, {}^2S_{\frac{1}{2}}-3p$, ${}^2P_{\frac{1}{2},\frac{3}{2}}$. Here these states, arising from electron orbits with the same total quantum number n, are thousands of wave numbers apart as well as a long way from the almost hydrogen-like $3d, {}^2D_{\frac{3}{2},\frac{5}{2}}$ states. These lines have been studied in strong electric fields by Ladenburg[1] and found to show only a quadratic Stark effect. In a field of 160000 volts cm^{-1} the various components for the two lines were displaced to the red by a small fraction of an Ångström unit. Again in potassium, Grotrian and

[1] LADENBURG, R., *Phys. Zeits.*, **22**, 549, 1921; *Zeits. f. Phys.*, **28**, 51, 1924; *Ann. d. Phys.*, **78**, 675, 1925.

Ramsauer[1] have observed similar shifts, with slight splitting into components of the doublet $4s, {}^2S_{\frac{1}{2}} - 5p, {}^2P_{\frac{1}{2},\frac{3}{2}}$. A reproduction of their measurements on this doublet is shown in Fig. 20.9.

If a given orbit is not far from hydrogen-like, the term will show only a quadratic Stark effect in a weak field. As the field increases, and the levels from the hydrogen-like orbits of the same n begin to overlap the one in question, the term will begin to show a first-order Stark effect. An electric field which, for a given level, gives only a quadratic effect is sometimes called a *weak field*. A field strong enough to give a first-order effect is also called a *strong field*. We therefore see that what may be called a weak field for one energy level may be a strong field for other levels of the same atom. (It should be noted that this reference to weak and strong fields cannot be applied to hydrogen, for there the first-order effect is observed first in weak fields and then the second-order effect in strong fields.) A pure quadratic Stark effect arises when the conditions for weak field are satisfied for both the initial and final states. These are the conditions under which Fig. 20.9 was obtained. As the field increases, the initial state usually goes over to the strong-field case long before the final state does. When the field is strong for both the initial and final states the Stark separations are given by $AF + BF^2$ [see Eqs. (20.1) and (20.2)], and the resultant Stark patterns will resemble those of hydrogen. We shall now apply these principles to the Stark effect of helium.

20.8. The Stark Effect in Helium.—The appearance of forbidden lines in helium when the spectrum is produced in an electric field was first observed by Koch.[2] Following Koch's discovery, Stark[3] and his coworkers were able to produce long series of forbidden lines like $1s2s, {}^3S - 1sns, {}^3S$, $1s2p, {}^3P - 1snp, {}^3P$, etc., where $\Delta l = 0$ and $1s2s, {}^3S - 1snd, {}^3D$, $1s2p, {}^3P - 1snf, {}^3F$, etc., where $\Delta l = 2$. Later experiments by Foster[4] and others extended the observations and, under improved experimental conditions, brought out the significance of these new lines. The correlation between the Stark patterns of helium with its two electrons and the Stark patterns of hydrogen with its one electron is one of the most interesting and remarkable achievements of our modern theory of atomic spectra.

As a specific example of the Stark effect in helium let us consider the spectrum line $\lambda 3705$, arising from the transition $1s2p, {}^3P - 1s7d, {}^3D$, and examine the various energy levels, transitions, and observed Stark components associated with it. From the energy level diagram of

---

[1] Grotrian, W., and G. Ramsauer, *Phys. Zeits.*, **28**, 846, 1927.

[2] Koch, J., *Ann. d. Phys.*, **48**, 98, 1915.

[3] Stark, J., *Ann. d. Phys.*, **48**, 210, 1915; **56**, 577, 1918.

[4] Foster, J. S., *Phys. Rev.*, **23**, 667, 1924; *Proc. Roy. Soc.*, A, **114**, 47, 1927; A, **117**, 137, 1927.

helium in Fig. 12.14, it is seen that both of these terms are nearly hydrogen-like. By hydrogen-like is meant that the term value is within a
few wave numbers of the corresponding term value in a hydrogen-like
atom. In such a state the excited electron is in an orbit not greatly
different from one of the hydrogen orbits. (Compare the He 2p curve
in Fig. 12.15 with that of H in Fig. 4.6.)

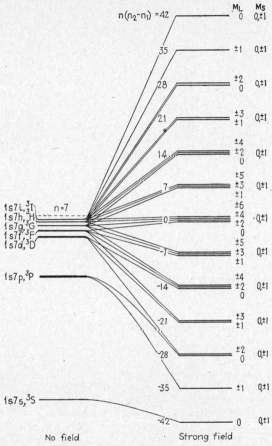

Fig. 20.10.—Theoretical Stark splitting for the $1s7l$ states of helium, where $l = 0, 1, 2, 3,$
4, 5, and 6, for s, p, d, f, g, h, and i electrons respectively.

Turning first to the final state $1s2p,{}^3P$, we find that the only other
near-by states are ${}^1S$ and ${}^3S$, arising from $1s2s$ several thousand wave
numbers lower. From the discussion in the previous section one should
therefore expect only a quadratic Stark effect for both the ${}^1P$ and ${}^3P$
terms of $1s2p$. Even the very highest fields yet attained would not be
strong enough to bring the $1s2s$ and $1s2p$ sets of levels near enough
together to give rise to a first-order Stark splitting. We may therefore
assume little or no splitting and a very small shift in the final state ${}^3P$
for all ordinary fields.

Turning now to the $1s7d,^3D$ initial state which is almost hydrogen-like, we find $1s7p,^3P$ 42 cm^{-1} lower and $1s7s,^3S$ 159 cm^{-1} still lower. Above $1s7d,^3D$, and within but a few wave numbers, must lie the states arising from the configurations $1s7f$, $1s7g$, $1s7h$, and $1s7i$ (see Fig. 20.10). Although not observed in connection with the ordinary spectral series, these levels certainly do exist as possible states of the helium atom. Due to the close proximity of these latter states, an electric field will not have to be very strong to produce a first-order Stark splitting of ^3D. At first the ^3P and ^3S states will show a second-order Stark splitting. As the field is increased, and the components of the upper levels approach those of ^3P, the levels will begin to show a first-order effect. Finally,

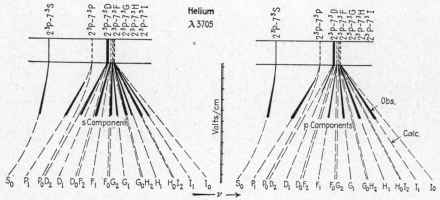

FIG. 20.11.—Theoretical and observed Stark patterns for the helium line λ3705 in different field strengths.

when the field and splitting are large enough, the ^3S term will show a first-order splitting. In these strong fields the spin-orbit interaction SL is broken down and the quantum number L no longer has meaning. Only the projections of the orbital and spin momenta on the field direction are quantized, and we have as quantum numbers M_L and M_S in place of m_l and m_s as in hydrogen. For each quantum value of M_L there will be three possible values of M_S, viz., 1, 0, and −1. These are indicated at the right in Fig. 20.10. Although there is no coupling between the spin resultant S and the field F, S will interact with the orbital magnetic moment projected on F (see Sec. 20.5) and give rise to splittings of the same order of magnitude as the fine structure of each triplet. This splitting is too small to show in the figure. The small separations appearing at the right are shown for the purpose of correlation with field-free states.

Mention should be made at this point of the singlet terms arising from each of the configurations shown in Fig. 20.10. These singlets in field-free space lie just above each corresponding triplet, and these go over in an electric field to an array of levels almost identical with the one shown for the triplets.   Due to the spin-spin interaction this set of levels will be just above but almost superposed upon the triplet array.

In considering the allowed transitions between two sets of levels the selection rules,

$$\Delta M_S = 0,$$
$$\Delta M_L = 0 \text{ for } p \text{ components,} \qquad (20.12)$$
$$\Delta M_L = 1 \text{ for } s \text{ components}$$

must be applied.   With the set of levels shown at the right in Fig. 20.10 as initial states, and the states $M_L = 1$, 0, and -1 (from $1s2p,{}^3P$)

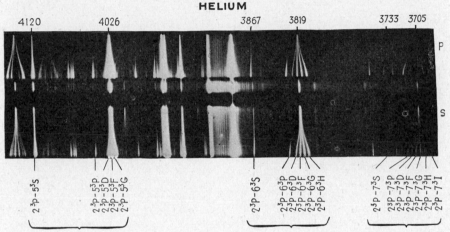

FIG. 20.12.—Stark effect in helium.   (*Enlarged from a section of a plate taken by J. S. Foster.*)   The field-free spectrum is shown between the *p* components above and the *s* components below.

as final states, transitions from the states $M_L = 0$, ± 1, and ± 2 are the only ones allowed.   Since the final levels show only a quadratic effect, the three lower levels will be superposed and the observed spectrum lines should follow the dotted lines in Fig. 20.11.   The observed patterns, as photographed by Foster, are reproduced in Fig. 20.12.   These observed lines are drawn as heavy lines in Fig. 20.11.   In very weak fields only certain of the lines from levels with higher L values appear.   Most of these in zero field are forbidden transitions.   As the field increases, the $2{}^3P - 7{}^3P$ transition appears.   Quantum-mechanical calculations for the tracing of various levels from zero field to strong field have been carried out by Foster[1] and shown to be in good agreement with experiment.

[1] FOSTER, J. S., *Proc. Roy. Soc.*, **A**, **117**, 137, 1927.

CHAPTER XXI

THE BREADTH OF SPECTRUM LINES

It is well known from experiment that many spectrum lines have an observable breadth that is independent of any optical system used to observe them. In many cases narrow and broad lines are observed simultaneously in the same spectrum. The *sharp* and *diffuse series* of each of the alkali metals are good examples of this. Oftentimes it is found that suitable methods of excitation will sharpen the lines to within the limits of the resolving power of the best spectrographs. Other lines are known, however, where all of the general methods used for sharpening lines have failed to produce fine sharp lines. The copper arc lines discussed in Chap. XIX, and reproduced in Fig. 19.14, are good examples of this. In this chapter we are concerned with the general causes of, and where possible the theoretical calculations for, the observed breadth of spectrum lines. We shall start by writing down the known causes and types of spectrum-line breadths and then proceed, in the following sections of this chapter, to treat each one more or less independently:[1]

    A. Doppler effect.

    B. Natural breadth.

    C. External effects:

        a. Collision damping.

        b. Asymmetry and pressure shift.

        c. Stark effect.

The first of these, the *Doppler effect*, has to do with the distribution of frequencies observed from many atoms moving at random as they do according to the kinetic theory of gases. This simplest of all broadening effects will be treated first in this chapter (see Sec. 21.1).

The second of these, *natural breadth*, treats of an inherent property of the atom, independent of all external effects. The quantum mechanics shows, for example, that the energy levels of an isolated atom are not sharp, as given by Bohr's simple theory, but have a finite natural breadth. This will be treated in Secs. 21.2 and 21.3.

The third and perhaps the least understood of the causes for the broadening of spectrum lines includes all *external effects* produced by (1) collisions between atoms and (2) fields of neighboring atoms and

---

[1] For a more detailed account of, and references to the subject of, the breadth of spectrum lines the reader is referred to the article published by V. Weisskopf, *Phys. Zeits.*, **34**, 1, 1933, and also to Max Born, "Optik," pp. 421–455, 1933.

molecules. These effects will be treated in the last three sections of this chapter.

21.1. The Doppler Effect.—Apparently one of the most classical of all atomic phenomena is the effect of the Doppler principle as it applies to the observed frequency of a radiated line. This is perhaps best shown by the different stellar spectra and by the solar spectrum as observed from the limbs of the sun (see Fig. 21.1). Here, where the velocities of the stars and their emitting gases, with respect to the observer, are high, the observed shifts of the spectrum lines are large. Quite similar effects are well known to exist in the case of a gaseous discharge where, due to thermal agitation, the atoms emitting light have relatively

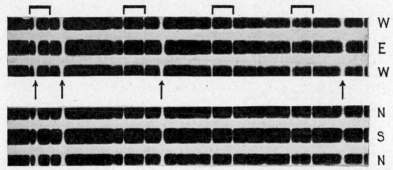

Fig. 21.1.—Solar spectra of the east and west limbs, and the north and south poles, of the sun. Arrows indicate solar lines showing the Doppler shift. Bracketed lines, showing no shift, are part of the oxygen A band produced by absorption in the earth's atmosphere.

high velocities. The random motions of the atoms or molecules in a gas, however, produce a net broadening of the line with no apparent shift of its central maximum. As one might well expect, this broadening is found experimentally to (1) *increase with temperature and* (2) *decrease with increasing atomic weight.*

For an appreciable Doppler effect the atom must have an appreciable velocity at the time of radiation. If v is the velocity of the atom, and θ is the angle between v and the direction of observation, the frequency of the light will be changed by an amount $\Delta\nu$, given simply by the classical expression

$$\frac{\Delta\nu}{\nu_0} = \frac{\nu - \nu_0}{\nu_0} = \frac{v\cos\theta}{c} = \frac{u}{c}, \qquad (21.1)$$

where ν_0 is the frequency of the line for $v = 0$, ν the observed frequency,

$$u = v\cos\theta \qquad (21.2)$$

the component of the velocity v in the direction of observation, and c the velocity of light. Unlike the closely analogous Compton effect this relation does not involve h and is exactly the relation given by the quantum mechanics. Assuming a Maxwellian distribution of the velocities the probability that the velocity will lie between u and $u + du$ is given by

$$dw = \sqrt{\frac{\beta}{\pi}}\, e^{-\beta u^2} du, \tag{21.3}$$

where

$$\beta = \frac{\mu}{2RT}. \tag{21.4}$$

Here μ is the molecular weight, R the universal gas constant, and T the absolute temperature. Substituting the value of u from Eq. (21.1) we get for the relative intensity I as a function of the frequency ν,

$$I(\nu) = \text{constant } e^{-\beta \frac{c^2}{\nu^2}(\nu - \nu_0)^2}. \tag{21.5}$$

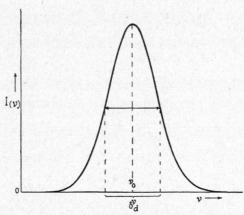

FIG. 21.2.—Intensity-frequency contour for the Doppler broadening of a spectrum line.

This general equation is plotted in Fig. 21.2 for the purpose of showing the general shape of a spectrum line which has been broadened by the so-called Doppler effect. To find the two frequencies at which the intensity drops to half its maximum value[1] the exponential term in Eq. (21.5) is set equal to one-half. Solving this for $\nu - \nu_0$ and multiplying by two we get for the *half-intensity breadth*, in absolute frequency units,

$$\delta_d^\nu = 2\frac{\nu_0}{c}\sqrt{\frac{2RT}{\mu}\ln 2} = 1.67\frac{\nu_0}{c}\sqrt{\frac{2RT}{\mu}}. \tag{21.6}$$

This equation shows that *the Doppler broadening is* (1) *proportional to the square root of the temperature,* (2) *proportional to the frequency ν_0, and* (3) *inversely proportional to the square root of the molecular weight.*

---

[1] The half-intensity breadth of a spectrum line is here defined as the interval between two points where the intensity drops to half its maximum value. (Some authors take half of this interval and call it the half breadth.)

Remembering that $\Delta\nu/\nu = \Delta\lambda/\lambda$, the half-intensity breadth in terms of absolute wave-length units is

$$\delta_d^\lambda = 2\frac{\lambda_0}{c}\sqrt{\frac{2RT}{\mu}\ln 2} = 1.67\frac{\lambda_0}{c}\sqrt{\frac{2RT}{\mu}}. \tag{21.7}$$

As an example of the application of this equation, consider the sodium D lines at $\lambda 5893$ Å. For a temperature of 500° Abs., Eq. (21.6) gives a half-intensity breadth of 0.056 cm^{-1} or 0.02 Å, a value 200 times as large as the natural half-intensity breadth (see the following section).

While Eq. (21.6) shows that the half-intensity breadth in frequency units increases with frequency, Eq. (21.7) shows that, in wave-length units,

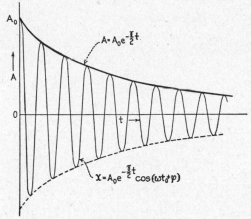

Fig. 21.3.—Amplitude-time curve of a single electric charge oscillating about a fixed point. A damped oscillator.

it decreases. The latter would show that the x-ray region of the spectrum might be suitable for the measurement of natural breadths (see Sec. 21.4).

21.2. Natural Breadths from Classical Theory.—According to classical electromagnetic theory a vibrating electric charge is continually damped by the radiation of energy. The energy E of such an oscillator decreases exponentially by

$$E = E_0 e^{-\gamma t} \tag{21.8}$$

and the amplitude (see Fig. 21.3) by

$$A = A_0 e^{-\frac{\gamma}{2}t}, \tag{21.9}$$

where E_0 is the initial energy at time $t = 0$, E the energy at any later time t, A and A_0 the corresponding amplitudes, and γ a constant given by

$$\gamma = \frac{2}{3}\cdot\frac{e^2}{mc^3}\omega_0^2 = \frac{8\pi^2 e^2 \nu_0^2}{3mc^3}. \tag{21.10}$$

Here ω_0 is equal to 2π times the frequency of the oscillation ν_0. The displacement x of the oscillator at any time t is given by

$$x = A_0 e^{-\frac{\gamma}{2}t} \cos(\omega_0 t + \varphi). \qquad (21.11)$$

An ordinary Fourier analysis of the damped wave emitted by the oscillator gives for the energy, or better the intensity which is proportional to the energy radiated, as a function of the frequency,

$$I(\nu) = \frac{\gamma}{2\pi} \cdot \frac{1}{4\pi^2(\nu_0 - \nu)^2 + \left(\dfrac{\gamma}{2}\right)^2}. \qquad (21.12)$$

The general contour of such a distribution is shown in Fig. 21.4. The half-intensity breadth δ_n^ν of this symmetrical distribution, like the

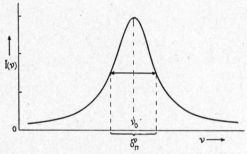

FIG. 21.4.—Intensity-frequency contour for the natural breadth of a spectrum line.

Doppler half-intensity breadth, is here defined as *the interval between the two points where the intensity drops to half its maximum value.* As seen from Eq. (21.12) the intensity will drop to half its maximum when the two terms in the denominator are equal, *i.e.*, when

$$\nu_0 - \nu = \frac{\gamma}{4\pi} = \frac{1}{2}\delta_n^\nu = \Delta\nu, \qquad (21.13)$$

which gives for the natural half-intensity breadth

$$\delta_n^\nu = \frac{\gamma}{2\pi} = \frac{4\pi e^2 \nu_0^2}{3mc^3}. \qquad (21.14)$$

Since $\Delta\nu/\nu = \Delta\lambda/\lambda$, and $c = \nu\lambda$, the half-intensity breadth, in terms of wave-length, is

$$\delta_n^\lambda = \Delta\lambda = \frac{2\pi c}{\omega_0^2}\gamma = \frac{c}{2\pi\nu^2}\gamma = \frac{4\pi e^2}{3mc^2} = 1.16 \times 10^{-12} \text{ cm} \qquad (21.15)$$

which is constant and equal to 0.000116 Å for all wave-lengths, a value many times too small to be measured by ordinary spectroscopic methods.

21.3 Natural Breadths and the Quantum Mechanics.—According to quantum-mechanical principles an energy level diagram of an atom is not to be thought of as a set of discrete levels but as a sort of continuous term spectrum in which the probability distribution is concentrated in regions where the terms are observed (see Fig. 21.5). With such probability distributions for the different levels of a given atom the transitions between levels will not give rise to infinitely sharp lines. From Heisenberg's uncertainty principle, expressed in terms of energy and time,

$$\Delta E \Delta t \sim h, \tag{21.16}$$

it is not difficult to understand how it is that the energy levels are not discrete. Writing for ΔE the uncertainty in the energy $h \Delta T$, and for the time Δt the mean life τ, the uncertainty in the breadth of an atomic state in absolute frequency units is of the order

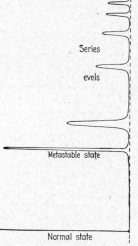

$$\Delta T \sim \frac{1}{\tau}. \tag{21.17}$$

Series

evels

This may be interpreted to mean that the greater the mean life of an atom in a given state the smaller will be the half-intensity breadth of the state. It follows therefore that normal states, or metastable states, of atoms will be sharp whereas other states will be broad.

Metastable state

It is not surprising to find that the quantum mechanics leads to an expression for the half-intensity breadth of spectrum lines which, although different for different levels, is of the same order of magnitude as that given by the classical theory of radiation damping. The probability distribution $I(T)$ of an energy state for an atom on the quantum mechanics has been given by

Normal state

FIG. 21.5.—Schematic diagram illustrating natural breadths of energy levels.

$$I(T) = \frac{\gamma_n}{2\pi} \frac{1}{4\pi^2(T_n - T)^2 + (\gamma_n/2)^2}, \tag{21.18}$$

where T_n is the term value of the center of gravity of the term distribution, and

$$\gamma_n = \sum_m C_{n,m} \frac{8\pi^2 e^2 (T_n - T_m)^2}{3mc^3} = \frac{1}{\tau}. \tag{21.19}$$

Here T_m is the term value of any lower level to which a transition may take place. $T_n - T$ represents small $\Delta \nu$ intervals in the initial term and $T_n - T_m$ the mean radiated frequency $\nu_{n,m}$ corresponding to transitions between the two levels. With the above value of γ_n the term half-intensity breadth δ_n^T is given [see Eq. (21.14)] by

$$\delta_n^T = \sum_m C_{n,m} \frac{4\pi e^2 (T_n - T_m)^2}{3mc^3} = \frac{1}{2\pi\tau}. \tag{21.20}$$

Now the coefficient $C_{n,m}$ varies from level to level and depends for its value on all other states of the atom lower than the one in question:

$$C_{n,m} = 3 \sum_m f_{n,m} \cdot \frac{g_m}{g_n}. \qquad (21.21)$$

Here g_n and g_m are the quantum weights $(2J + 1)$ of the levels for the transition $n \rightarrow m$, and $f_{n,m}$ is the number of so-called *dispersion electrons* for the same transition. The sum is to be taken over all levels m which lie deeper than the level n.

Although not easily determined the f factors in the above given equation are a measure of the intensity of a spectrum line and in a few simple cases have been calculated[1] and measured.[2]

London has shown from Schrödinger's theory that the number of dispersion electrons to be associated with any state of the atom is equal to unity. This means that, if we sum up the f's for all transitions into and out of a given state,

$$\Sigma f = 1. \qquad 1.22)$$

The f's for transitions *into* a state are taken with a plus sign and those *out of* a state with a minus sign. The table of f values given in Table 21.1 will serve as a simple example of this rule. Since these are all transitions into the normal state, $3s,{}^2S$, and there are no transitions out, the sum, including the rest of the series and the small sum con-

Table 21.1.—Dispersion Electrons, f Factors. Observed Values to Be Associated with the Principal Series of Sodium
(*After Filippov and Prokofjew*)[1]

Transition	λ_{air}	$f_{n,m}$	Transition	λ_{air}	$f_{n,m}$
$3s,{}^2S - 3p,{}^2P$	5893	0.9755	$3s,{}^2S - 11p,{}^2P$	2476	0.0000384
$3s,{}^2S - 4p,{}^2P$	3303	0.01403	$3s,{}^2S - 12p,{}^2P$	2464	0.0000284
$3s,{}^2S - 5p,{}^2P$	2853	0.00205	$3s,{}^2S - 13p,{}^2P$	2456	0.0000217
$3s,{}^2S - 6p,{}^2P$	2680	0.000631	$3s,{}^2S - 14p,{}^2P$	2449	0.0000173
$3s,{}^2S - 7p,{}^2P$	2594	0.000256	$3s,{}^2S - 15p,{}^2P$	2444	0.0000140
$3s,{}^2S - 8p,{}^2P$	2544	0.000134	$3s,{}^2S - 16p,{}^2P$	2440	0.0000116
$3s,{}^2S - 9p,{}^2P$	2512	0.0000811	$3s,{}^2S - 17p,{}^2P$	2437	0.0000092
$3s,{}^2S - 10p,{}^2P$	2491	0.0000537	$3s,{}^2S - 18p,{}^2P$	2434	0.0000075

[1] Filippov, A., and W. Prokofjew, *Zeits. f. Phys.*, **56**, 458, 1929.

tributed by the continuum above the series limit, should add up to unity. It is to be noted that almost the entire sum in this case comes from the resonance lines $\lambda5890$ and $\lambda5896$ (average 5893) due to the

[1] London, F., *Zeits. f. Phys.*, **39**, 322, 1926; Hargreaves, J., *Proc. Camb. Phil. Soc.*, **25**, 323, 1929; Trumpy, B., *Zeits. f. Phys.*, **54**, 372, 1929; **61**, 54, 1930; **66**, 720, 1930.

[2] Filippov, A., *Zeits. f. Phys.*, **69**, 526, 1931; Minkowski, R., *Zeits. f. Phys.*, **36**, 839, 1926; Ladenburg, R., and E. Thiele, *Zeits. f. Phys.*, **72**, 697, 1931.

transitions $3s,^2S_{\frac{1}{2}} - 3p,^2P_{\frac{3}{2}}$ and $3s,^2S_{\frac{1}{2}} - 3p,^2P_{\frac{1}{2}}$. Taking this fine structure into account the f factors for each of these two lines separately are 0.3252 and 0.6503, respectively. Using these values we shall now return to the calculation of half-intensity breadths. Remembering that the summation of the f's for a given state is to be taken over those levels lying deeper than the one in question, the value of C for $3p,^2P_{\frac{1}{2}}$ and for $3p,^2P$ [Eq. (21.21)] is practically unity. For $^2P_{\frac{1}{2}}$, $\Sigma f_{n,m} = 0.3252$, $g_n = 2$, and $g_m = 2$. For $^2P_{\frac{3}{2}}$, $\Sigma f_{n,m} = 0.6503$, $g_n = 4$, and $g_m = 2$. These levels, for these particular lines, have just the classical half-intensity breadth of 0.000116Å. By Eq. (21.20) this corresponds to a mean life of

$$\tau = \frac{3mc^3}{8\pi^2 e^2 \nu^2} = 1.6 \times 10^{-8} \text{ sec.} \quad (21.23)$$

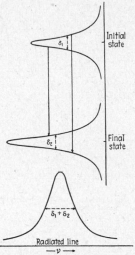

FIG. 21.6.—Showing the relation between the natural breadth of a spectrum line and the natural breadths of the corresponding energy levels.

It is not difficult to show that, if $\delta_1 = \gamma_1/2\pi$ and $\delta_2 = \gamma_2/2\pi$ represent the respective half-intensity breadths of the initial and final states for a given transition, the intensity distribution of the observed spectrum line will be given by

$$I(\nu) = \frac{\gamma_1 + \gamma_2}{2\pi} \cdot \frac{1}{4\pi^2(\nu_{1,2} - \nu)^2 + \left(\dfrac{\gamma_1 + \gamma_2}{2}\right)^2}. \quad (21.24)$$

From this relation we observe that the line drops to half its maximum intensity when the first and second terms in the second denominator are equal, *i.e.*, when

$$2\pi(\nu_{1,2} - \nu) = \frac{\gamma_1 + \gamma_2}{2}. \quad (21.25)$$

From this we see that the half-intensity breadth of the radiated line,

$$\delta_n^\nu = \nu_{1,2} - \nu = \frac{\gamma_1 + \gamma_2}{2\pi} = \delta_1 + \delta_2, \quad (21.26)$$

is just equal to the sum of the half-intensity breadths of the initial and final states. This is shown schematically in Fig. 21.6, where both the initial and final states have been drawn with relatively large breadths. For the sodium D lines, discussed above, the final state with an almost infinite mean life is sharp so that the natural breadths of the observed lines will be due almost entirely to the spread of the initial states. Measurements of the half-intensity breadths of spectrum lines will be discussed in Sec. 21.4.

21.4. Observed Natural Breadths and Doppler Broadening.—In the preceding section we have seen that the *Doppler breadths* of the sodium *D* lines at normal temperatures and pressures are many times the *natural breadths* as given by Eq. (21.26). In spite of this observed fact fruitful attempts to measure the natural breadths of many lines have been made. In order to see how this is possible the two types of curve are superposed in Fig. 21.7. One represents the natural breadth of a line and the other the Doppler breadth for the same total intensity. Each curve assumes all other broadening effects are absent. It is observed that, while the Doppler intensity drops off sharply and becomes negligibly small in a very short frequency interval, the natural breadth remains fairly large at considerable distances from the center. If the

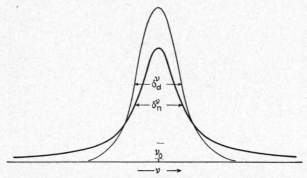

Fig. 21.7.—Comparison of natural breadth and Doppler breadth of two lines with the same half-intensity breadth and the same total intensity.

Doppler breadth is not too large it is easy to see how one might measure the intensity contours far out on the wings and from these calculate the half-intensity breadth. This has been done for the sodium *D* lines by Minkowski.[1] In this particular instance almost perfect agreement between theory and experiment was found. Many measurements of other lines have been made in this indirect way with varying degrees of agreement.

In hydrogen the Doppler effect has been the chief limiting factor in all attempts to resolve the fine structure of the Balmer series lines (see Fig. 9.5). For H_α, at temperatures between 250° and 300° Abs., the Doppler half-intensity breadth is about 0.2 cm^{-1}, or 0.09Å, a value of the same order of magnitude as the largest fine-structure interval. By operating a hydrogen-discharge tube in a liquid air bath the H_α^1 and H_α^2 lines have been considerably sharpened. Attempts to excite the lines with the tube cooled in liquid hydrogen have been unsuccessful. The effect of atomic mass on the Doppler breadth is very beautifully brought out by the comparison of the H_α lines reproduced in Fig. 9.5. The H_α^1 lines

[1] Minkowski, R., *Zeits. f. Phys.*, **36**, 839, 1926.

are 1.4 times as broad as those of H_a^2. The measured contours of these and other lines as well as their increase in breadth with temperature are in excellent agreement with Eq. (21.24).

Mention should be made at this point of the several attempts that have been made to measure the *natural breadths of x-ray lines*. The results thus far obtained in this region of the spectrum show that, while the shapes of the lines studied are not far from that expected, the half-intensity breadths are several times larger than is predicted by theory.

Experimental verification of the natural contour of a spectrum line has been made in the case of the anomalously broad lines so well known in the copper arc spectrum (see Fig. 19.14). The intensity

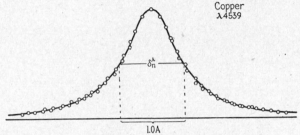

FIG. 21.8.—Observed natural breadth contour of one of the anomalous copper arc lines. See Fig. 19.14.   (*After Allen.*)

contour of one of these lines, as measured by Allen,[1] is reproduced in Fig. 21.8. For this as well as many other broad lines in copper the mean life of the atom in the upper state has been greatly reduced by the probability of *autoionization*, a phenomenon discussed in Chap. XIX. Although this particular type of broadening is not due to exactly the same effect as a natural breadth, it is here classified as such in that it takes the place of natural breadth and is an inherent property of the atom independent of all external effects. The observed half-intensity breadths show that the mean life of the atom in such broad upper states is of the order of 10^{-13} sec.

With the exception of a few special cases, such as the broad copper lines, the natural breadth of a spectrum line may be neglected in comparison with the Doppler breadth at ordinary temperatures. The importance of the subject of natural breadths lies in its application to the dispersion of a gas and to dispersion theory in general, a field of investigation which has developed largely in the hands of Ladenburg and Kopfermann.[2]

21.5. Collision Damping.—One of the important external causes in the broadening of spectral lines is the process called *collision damping*.

[1] ALLEN, C. W., *Phys. Rev.*, **39**, 42, 55, 1932.

[2] LADENBURG, R., *Zeits. f. Phys.*, **65**, 167, 189, 1930.   For other references see H. Kopfermann and R. Ladenburg, *Zeits. f. Phys.*, **48**, 26, 1928.

This is but one of the effects produced by the collision of two atoms, one of which is in the process of emitting or absorbing radiation. Following the early suggestion of Michelson[1] in 1895, and Lorentz[2] in 1905, the phenomenon is based upon the following assumptions: *If, during the time an atom is emitting or absorbing radiation of frequency ν_0 it collides elastically with another atom, the phase and amplitude of the radiation have a chance of undergoing a considerable change.*

If one assumes that the time two atoms are in collision is large compared with the *mean time between collisions*, the emitting or absorbing atoms will most of the time be under the influence of strong atomic fields. These conditions, which exist in a gas at relatively high pressures, give rise in general to a red shift of the spectrum lines. This phenomenon will be discussed in the following section under the heading of Asymmetry and Pressure Shift.

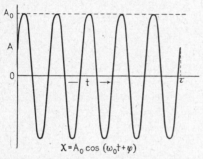

$$X = A_0 \cos (\omega_0 t + \varphi)$$

FIG. 21.8a.—Undamped oscillation instantly stopped after a short interval of time. Ideal model for collision damping.

In this section we are concerned with the damping effect, or broadening of a spectrum line, produced by the sudden change in the atomic radiation by collision. The assumptions usually made are: (1) the *mean time between collisions* is large compared with the *collision time*, and (2) with every impact the oscillations are either completely cut off, or they are momentarily interrupted during impact only to resume the same frequency again with possibly a phase and amplitude change (see Fig. 21.10). That the phase of the oscillations may be changed in the short collision time may be seen from the following rough calculation. For normal temperatures and normal-effective-collision cross sections the collision time is of the order of 10^{-13} sec. For ordinary visible light with a period of about 10^{-15} sec. there will be some hundred modified oscillations during impact.

In giving a classical treatment of the phenomenon of collision damping, it is customary to assume the radiation to be an undamped oscillation of the form shown in Fig. 21.8a, and given by

$$x = A_0 \cos (\omega_0 t + \varphi) \qquad (21.27)$$

(where $\omega_0 = 2\pi\nu_0$), which is instantly stopped after an interval of time τ. Now τ is the interval between the time the atom begins radiating and the time a collision occurs. A Fourier analysis of a single finite wave

[1] MICHELSON, A. A., *Astrophys. Jour.*, **2**, 251, 1895.

[2] LORENTZ, H. A., *Koninklijke. Akad. Wetenschappen Amsterdam, Versl.*, **14**, 518, 577, 1905–1906.

like this leads, strangely enough, to an intensity distribution which has the contour of a single-slit diffraction pattern. The shorter the *wave train*, or the longer the wave-length, the broader the central maximum of this pattern. Now for each atom of a gas, τ will have a different value so that for the gas as a whole there will be a certain probability distribution of the τ's. If we assume the same distribution for τ as is usually assumed for the *free paths* of the same gas atoms, the probability that τ will lie between τ and $\tau + d\tau$ is given by

$$dw = \frac{1}{\tau_0}e^{\frac{-\tau}{\tau_0}}d\tau, \tag{21.27a}$$

where τ_0 is the *mean flight time*, i.e., the average time between collisions. When a Fourier analysis of the set of wave trains has been made, the relative intensity I, as a function of the frequency ν, is found to be given by the relation

$$I(\nu) = \text{constant} \frac{1}{(\omega_0 - \omega)^2 + (1/\tau_0)^2}. \tag{21.28}$$

This equation gives the same intensity contour as *radiation damping* shown in Fig. 21.4. The intensity drops to half its value when

$$\omega_0 - \omega = \frac{1}{\tau_0} = 2\pi(\nu_0 - \nu) \tag{21.29}$$

and gives for the *collision-damping half-intensity breadth*,

$$\delta_c^\nu = \frac{1}{\pi\tau_0}. \tag{21.30}$$

This result is to be compared with Eq. (21.20). It should be noted that in the derivation of this equation the small effect of natural breadth due to radiation damping has been neglected. Further consideration of this problem shows that, if the radiation starts again after impact with a new phase and amplitude, and radiation during impact is neglected, exactly the same intensity distribution is obtained as given above.

Let us now find the order of magnitude of the line broadening due to collision damping. To do this we must first find a value of τ_0. From the kinetic theory of gases the average velocity of an atom or molecule is given by

$$v_0 = \sqrt{\frac{8RT}{\pi\mu}}, \tag{21.31}$$

where R is the universal gas constant $= 8.3 \times 10^7$ ergs mole^{-1}, T the absolute temperature, and μ the molecular weight. The mean free path l_0 is just

$$l_0 = v_0\tau_0, \tag{21.32}$$

so that the half-intensity breadth

$$\delta_c^\nu = \frac{1}{\pi \tau_0} = \frac{1}{\pi l_0} \sqrt{\frac{8RT}{\pi \mu}}. \tag{21.33}$$

If a foreign gas is present, the molecular weight μ is replaced by $mM/(m + M)$, where m is the molecular weight of the emitting gas and M that of the foreign gas. The mean free path, as given by the Maxwellian formula, is also written

$$l_0 = \frac{kT}{\sqrt{2}\pi\rho^2 p} = \frac{RT}{\sqrt{2}N\pi\rho^2 p}, \tag{21.34}$$

where ρ is the *optical cross section*, or *collision diameter*, *i.e.*, the average distance between nuclear centers at closest approach, and p is the pressure. This gives for the half-intensity breadth, in terms of the Avogadro number $N = 6.06 \times 10^{23}$ mole^{-1}, and the pressure p or density d,

$$\delta_c^\nu = \frac{4N\rho^2 p}{\sqrt{RT\mu\pi}} = 4N\rho^2 d\sqrt{\frac{RT}{\mu^3\pi}}. \tag{21.35}$$

The only unknown factor in this expression is the collision diameter ρ. Instead of assuming the kinetic-theory values of ρ and attempting to check theoretically the observed line breadths for different pressures, it is customary to compute values of ρ from the observed lines. The following values, for example, were obtained by Schütz for the sodium D lines excited in an atmosphere of different foreign gases (see Table 21.2).

TABLE 21.2.—OPTICAL CROSS SECTION, OR COLLISION DIAMETER ρ, FOR THE SODIUM D LINES ABSORBED IN MIXTURES WITH A FOREIGN GAS
(*After Schütz*)

Source		H_2	He	Ne	A	N_2
Schütz[1]	ρ_{opt}	5.8	5.6	6.15	9.0	8.3 Å
Kinetic theory	ρ_{kin}	2.3	1.9	2.3	2.8	3.1

[1] SCHÜTZ, W., *Zeits. f. Phys.*, **45**, 30, 1927.

Since the observed values ρ_{opt} are from two to three times those calculated from kinetic theory the term *optical cross section* has been applied in the one case and *kinetic cross section* in the other.

In some instances the effect of a foreign gas on the spectrum lines of a given element is to give very broad lines and large optical cross sections. In favorable cases ρ_{opt} may be from 10 to 100 times ρ_{kin}. This is interpreted to mean that even at great distances another gas atom may act on the radiating atom strongly enough to change the phase of the oscillation. Such large actions often arise when no foreign gases are present.

A comparison of Doppler half-intensity breadths with collision half-intensity breadths [Eqs. (21.6) and (21.35)] shows that for visible light, and room temperature and pressure, the two effects are of the same order of magnitude.   In mercury, Fabry and Perot reduced the pressure to 1 mm in order to measure the Doppler broadening without large distortions from collision damping.   With increased pressures, on the other hand, collision damping becomes the predominant cause for the broadening of lines.   The effect of pressure or density [see Eq. (21.35)] on the breadth of a line is shown in the specific case of the mercury resonance line λ2537 in Fig. 21.9.   Here the half-intensity breadth, as it is observed in absorption, is plotted against the *relative density*, the latter being defined as the density of the gas relative to its density at normal tem-

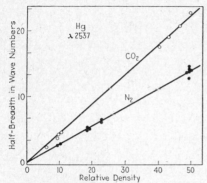

FIG. 21.9.—Observed pressure broadening of the mercury resonance line λ2537 in absorption. (*After Füchtbauer, Joos, and Dinkelacker.*)

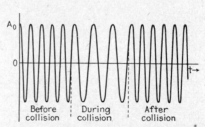

FIG. 21.10.—Schematic diagram of the change in frequency at the time of collision between two atoms one of which is radiating.

perature and pressure.   The largest readings correspond to values taken at a pressure of 50 atm.   The foreign gas mixed with the mercury vapor to obtain the upper curve was CO_2, and to obtain the lower curve, N_2.

21.6. Asymmetry and Pressure Shift.—In the previous section we have seen how the broadening of a spectrum line due to pressure has been attributed to the sudden change in phase of the emitted radiation by collision, a phenomenon called *collision damping*.   Since collision damping takes into account only that part of the radiation given out before and after collision, we have yet to consider the radiation that takes place during collision.   This is shown schematically in Fig. 21.10. In this very ideal model it is assumed that the frequency of the oscillation changes suddenly when the emitting atom first comes under the influence of the colliding atom.   After collision the original frequency is resumed again.   Asymmetry and pressure shift are attributed to the modified radiation indicated at the center of the figure.

The explanation has been given that at close approach of a foreign atom the energy levels of the excited or radiating atoms in question are altered, due chiefly to polarization effects (see Fig. 7.5).[1]   It is convenient

[1] This is quite similar to a quadratic Stark effect and might well be classified as such (see Sec. 21.7).

in this explanation, following Jablónski,[1] to represent the energy levels by means of potential curves for the two atoms considered as a molecule. In Fig. 21.11 the initial and final states of the pseudo molecule are plotted

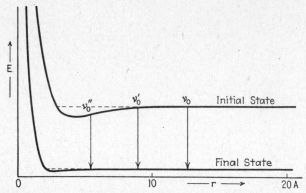

FIG. 21.11.—Potential curves for two states of an atom at close approach of another atom. Illustrating the cause for asymmetry and red shift. (*After Jablónski and Weisskopf.*)

as functions of the distance between the atomic centers, r. Due to the polarization of one atom at close approach of another, an excited or outer state will be lowered more than a tightly bound lower state. The frequency distribution during this time of close approach is added to the collision-damping distribution. The result is that the spectrum line

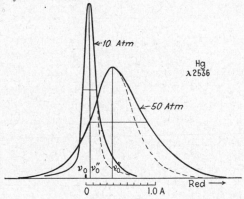

FIG. 21.12.—Asymmetry and broadening of the mercury resonance line λ2536 with increased pressure. (*After Füchtbauer, Joos, and Dinkelacker.*)

observed is spread out more on the long wave-length side than it is on the short (see Fig. 21.12).

At normal temperatures and pressures the collision times are small, and the broadening and shift are small. With increasing pressure the *mean collision time* increases and the time between collisions decreases

[1] JABLÓNSKI, A., *Zeits. f. Phys.*, **70**, 723, 1931; see also MARGENAU, H., *Phys. Rev.*, **43**, 129, 1933.

with the result that, as the line is shifted to the red, it is broadened asymmetrically. The mercury resonance line λ2537 is shown in Fig. 21.12, as observed in absorption by Füchtbauer, Joos, and Dinkelacker,[1] at a pressure of 10 and 50 atm., respectively. The foreign gas used in these observations was nitrogen. To show that the pressure shift depends upon the foreign gas used, curves have been reproduced in Fig. 21.13. In general it is observed that the shift of a line is very closely proportional to the relative density. The relative density is here defined as the density of the gas relative to the density at normal temperature and pressure.

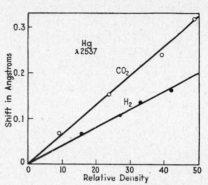

FIG. 21.13.—Pressure shift of the mercury resonance line λ2537, in absorption. (*After Füchtbauer, Joos, and Dinkelacker.*)

That the lowering of an energy level due to pressure effects is greater for high levels than it is for the low is confirmed by Babcock's[2] interferometer measurements on the iron lines. The well-known spectrum of iron was investigated at pressures below 1 atm. for the purpose of determining how reliable the different lines may be as wave-length standards. At low pressures the lines are very sharp, and the pressure

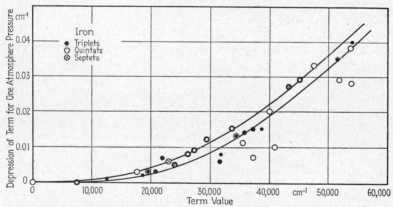

FIG. 21.14.—Relative shifts of the energy levels of iron as a function of their term values. (*After Babcock.*)

shift is extremely small. Employing Fabry-Perot étalons, however, shifts accurate to thousandths of an Ångström or better were measured. Since an observed spectrum line gives only the difference between two

[1] FÜCHTBAUER, C., G. JOOS, and O. DINKELACKER, *Ann. d. Phys.*, **71**, 204, 1923.
[2] BABCOCK, H. D., *Astrophys. Jour.*, **67**, 240, 1928.

term values, relative shifts are all that can be determined. The results from over 100 lines are best shown by the graph reproduced in Fig. 21.14, where each term is plotted relative to the ground state as zero. Weighting each plotted point, Babcock expresses the belief that the quintet and septet terms are depressed slightly more than the triplets. Whether this is a real effect or not, the major effect is in good agreement with what one would expect from polarization effects explained above.

21.7. Stark Broadening.—In an ordinary arc of high current density many ions are produced which upon collision with other atoms give rise to strong electric fields. The effect of these intermolecular fields is to produce a Stark-effect broadening of the observed spectrum lines. In addition to this effect by *ion* fields, *dipole* or *quadrupole moments* of gas atoms or molecules may also produce relatively strong intermolecular electric fields. The hydrogen atom and molecule are good examples of a dipole and quadrupole, respectively. Being of the same order of magnitude as collision damping and Doppler broadening (see Secs. 21.5 and 21.1), the Stark effect plays a relatively important part in the general subject of the breadth of spectrum lines. In attempting to calculate Stark-effect broadening one is immediately confronted with the problem of continually changing, inhomogeneous, electric fields. At the approach of two atoms in collision the electric field at each of the respective atoms increases, reaches a maximum at closest approach, and then diminishes as the two atoms recede.

Since the Stark effect for an inhomogeneous electric field has never been worked out, Holtsmark[1] and Debye[2] made the simplifying assumption that there will be an average intermolecular field F to which, one can assume, the ordinary Stark-effect formulas apply. The problem of calculating *average fields* has been divided into three classes, (1) the field due to charged atoms or molecules, *i.e.*, *ions*, (2) the field due to *dipole moments*, and (3) the field due to *quadrupole moments*. Although the theoretical treatment of each of these three possibilities is out of place here, we shall write down the derived formulas for the three average field strengths:

(For ions) $F = a_1 e n^{\frac{2}{3}}.$ (21.36)

(For dipoles) $F = a_2 \mu n.$ (21.37)

(For quadrupoles) $\bar{F} = a_3 q n^{\frac{4}{3}}.$ (21.38)

Here the a's are constants, e is the ionic charge, μ the dipole moment, q the quadrupole moment, and n the number of corresponding particles per cubic centimeter.

Holtsmark made the next simplifying assumption that a spectrum line is spread out symmetrically into a continuous frequency band, the

[1] Holtsmark, J., *Phys. Zeits.*, **20**, 162, 1919; **25**, 73, 1924.
[2] Debye, P., *Phys. Zeits.*, **20**, 160, 1919.

total breadth of which is given by the outermost components of the first-order Stark effect (see Chap. XX). The total spread of the levels will be

$$\Delta T_{max} = A_{max}F. \tag{21.39}$$

In general there will be a statistical distribution of the fields and a resultant distribution of bands of different breadths. The summing up of these distributions, in the case of dipole fields for example, leads to an intensity distribution having the same form as that for natural breadths.

For dipole moments, $$I = I_0\frac{\delta_s}{2\pi} \cdot \frac{1}{(\nu - \nu_0)^2 + (\delta_s/2)^2}, \tag{21.40}$$

where δ_s is the half-intensity breadth,[1]

(for dipole) $$\delta_s = A_{max}\bar{F} = 4.54A_{max}\mu n. \tag{21.41}$$

The intensity contours for ions and for quadrupole moments have almost the same form as those for the dipole moments (see Fig. 21.4).

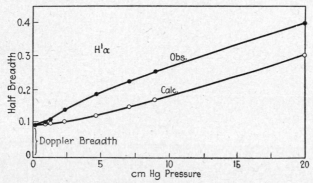

FIG. 21.15.—Observed half-intensity breadth of hydrogen H_α, $\lambda 6563$, in angstroms. (*After Michelson.*) Calculated half-intensity breadth due to Stark effect from intermolecular quadrupole fields. (*After Holtsmark.*)

The essential features of the above given equations are the expressions for the half-intensity breadths of the observed spectrum lines. For the latter two types of field these are:

For ion $$\delta_s = 3.25A_{max}en^{\frac{2}{3}}. \tag{21.42}$$

For quadrupole $$\delta_s = 5.52A_{max}qn^{\frac{4}{3}}. \tag{21.43}$$

As one might well expect, all half-intensity breadths are functions of the density n.

Of the many attempts made to check these formulas with observation those made by Holtsmark are perhaps the best. Of these his comparison of Eq. (21.43) with Michelson's observations on the hydrogen

---

[1] For a derivation of the equations given here the reader is referred to M. Born, "*Optik*," 1933; also V. Weisskopf, *Phys. Zeits.*, **34**, 1, 1933.

line H_α has been pointed out by several investigators as giving the best general agreements. The quadrupole moment of the hydrogen molecule is known from theory (by Debye) to be 3.2×10^{-26} gm$^{\frac{1}{2}}$ cm$^{\frac{7}{2}}$ sec.$^{-1}$. This value substituted in Eq. (21.43) gives the half-intensity breadth as a function of n. A_{max} is calculated from Eq. (20.2). In Fig. 21.15 both the calculated and observed half-intensity breadths have been plotted for comparison. Subtracting the Doppler breadth the agreement, even here, is not very good.

In general the first-order Stark effect will account for the broadening of many spectrum lines. The second-order, or quadratic, Stark effect which only becomes appreciably large in strong fields must also produce an observable effect.

One of the best confirmations of Stark-effect broadening may be found in the chief series of the alkali atoms where historically the terms *sharp* and *diffuse* series originated. Due to the penetration of the s and p orbits involved in the sharp-series lines, both in the initial S states and in the final P states show no first-order Stark effect. As a result the lines, despite strong intermolecular electric fields, are sharp. For the diffuse series, however, the d and f orbits are nearly hydrogen-like and, being not far removed from the hydrogen-like $f, g, h, \ldots$ orbits, show a first-order Stark effect. Under suitable excitation conditions even the diffuse and fundamental series have been observed as sharp lines.

Finkelnburg[1] has studied the Balmer series under pressures of from 1 to 30 atms. of hydrogen. Using a high-voltage condensed-spark discharge, between metal electrodes placed very close together, each member of the series is observed as a very broad line. At a pressure of about 2 atms. the H_α, H_β, and H_γ lines are symmetrically broadened, without an appreciable shift of the maximum, to the extent that the half-intensity breadths are about 25, 100, and 200 Å, respectively. At from 10 to 30 atms. the lines are so broad that they overlap one another and form a continuous spectrum. These enormous breadths are attributed by Finkelnburg to a Stark effect, the enormous fields being produced by the very high ion density in the spark discharge. That the Stark effect is chiefly responsible for the broadening is confirmed by (1) the general contour of the lines, (2) the symmetrical broadening without appreciable shift, and (3) the increased broadening with higher members of the series.

It should be pointed out that *asymmetry* and *pressure shift*, discussed in Sec. 21.6, may well be classified as a *second-order Stark effect*. At close approach of a foreign atom the associated electric field causes a polarization and a displacement of the energy levels of the atom in question (see Fig. 21.11).

[1] Finkelnburg, W., *Zeits. f. Phys.*, **70**, 375, 1931.

APPENDIX

TABLE I.—VALUES OF THE PHYSICAL CONSTANTS
(After Birge)[1]

Velocity of light.............. $c = (2.99796 \pm 0.00004) \times 10^{10}$ cm sec.$^{-1}$

Mass of the electron (spectroscopic)..................... $m_0 = (9.035 \pm 0.010) \times 10^{-28}$g

Mass of the proton........... $M_p = (1.6608 \pm 0.0017) \times 10^{-24}$g

Charge on the electron........ $e = (4.770 \pm 0.005) \times 10^{-10}$ abs-e.s.u.

Planck's constant............. $h = (6.547 \pm 0.008) \times 10^{-27}$ erg. sec.

Rydberg constant (hydrogen[1]). $R_H{}^1 = (109677.759 \pm 0.05)$ cm^{-1}

Rydberg constant (hydrogen[2]). $R_H{}^2 = (109707.56 \pm 0.05)$ cm^{-1}

Rydberg constant (helium)..... $R_{He} = (109722.403 \pm 0.05)$ cm^{-1}

Rydberg constant (infinite. mass)..................... $R = (109737.42 \pm 0.06)$ cm^{-1}

Ratio M_p/m_0 (spectroscopic).... 1838 ± 1

Wave number per absolute volt. (8106 ± 3) cm^{-1} abs-volt^{-1}

Wave-length per absolute volt.. $(12336 + 5) \times 10^{-8}$ cm^{-1} abs-volt^{-1}

Energy of one abs-volt electron.. $(1.5910 \pm 0.0016) \times 10^{-12}$ erg

Speed of one abs-volt electron.. $(5.9346 \pm 0.0017) \times 10^{7}$ cm sec.$^{-1}$

Fine-structure constant......... $\alpha = 2\pi e^2/hc = (7.283 \pm 0.006) \times 10^{-3}$

.... $\alpha^2 = (5.305 \pm 0.008) \times 10^{-5}$

.... $1/\alpha = 137.29 \pm 0.11$

Unit angular momentum....... $h/2\pi = (1.0419 \pm 0.0013) \times 10^{-27}$ erg. sec.

Magnetic moment (one Bohr magneton)................ $\mu_1 = (0.9174 \pm 0.0013) \times 10^{-20}$ erg gauss^{-1}

Magnetic moment (one nuclear magneton)................ $\mu_1/1838 = 4.991 \times 10^{-24}$ erg gauss^{-1}

Zeeman displacement per gauss. $= (4.674 \pm 0.003) \times 10^{-5}$ cm^{-1} gauss^{-1}

Ratio $\dfrac{\text{Bohr magneton}}{\text{Bohr mechanical moment}} = \dfrac{\mu_1}{h/2\pi} = (0.8805 \pm 0.0005) \times 10^{7}$ gauss^{-1} sec^{-1}

[1] BIRGE, R. T., *Phys. Rev.*, Supplement, **1**, 1, 1929.

TABLE II.—EQUIVALENT ELECTRONS
(After Gibbs, Wilber, and White)[1]

p Electrons

(6)	p^1 —	^2P					
(15)	p^2 —	^1S	^1D	^3P			
(20)	p^3 —	^2P	^2D	^4S			
(15)	p^4 —	^1S	^1D	^3P			
(6)	p^5 —	^2P					
(1)	p^6 —	^1S					

d Electrons

(10)	d^1 —	$^2(D)$					
(45)	d^2 —	$^1(SDG)$	$^3(PF)$				
(120)	d^3 —	$^2(D)$	$^2(PDFGH)$	$^4(PF)$			
(210)	d^4 —	$^1(SDG)$	$^3(PF)$	$^1(SDFGI)$	$^3(PDFGH)$	$^5(D)$	
(252)	d^5 —	$^2(D)$	$^2(PDFGH)$	$^4(PF)$ $^2(SDFGI)$		$^4(DG)$	$^6(S)$
(210)	d^6 —	$^1(SDG)$	$^3(PF)$	$^1(SDFGI)$	$^3(PDFGH)$	$^5(D)$	
(120)	d^7 —	$^2(D)$	$^2(PDFGH)$	$^4(PF)$			
(45)	d^8 —	$^1(SDG)$	$^3(PF)$				
(10)	d^9 —	$^2(D)$					
(1)	d^{10} —	$^1(S)$					

[1] GIBBS, R. C., D. T. WILBER, and H. E. WHITE, *Phys. Rev.*, **29**, 790, 1927.

TABLE II.—EQUIVALENT ELECTRONS.—(*Continued*)

f Electrons

(14) f^1 — $^2(F)$		
(91) f^2 — $^1(SDGI)$	$^3(PFH)$	
(364) f^3 — $^2(PD_2F_2G_2H_2IKL)$	$^4(SDFGI)$	
(1001) f^4 — $^1(S_2D_4FG_4H_2I_3KL_2N)$	$^3(P_3D_2F_4G_3H_4I_2K_2LM)$	$^5(SDFGI)$
(2002) f^5 — $^2(P_4D_5F_7G_6H_7I_5K_5L_3M_2NO)$	$^4(SP_2D_3F_4G_4H_3I_3K_2LM)$	$^6(PFH)$
(3003) f^6 — $^1(S_4PD_6F_4G_5H_4I_7K_3L_4M_2N_2Q)$	$^3(P_6D_5F_9G_7H_9I_6K_6L_3M_3NO)$	$^5(SPD_3F_2G_3H_2I_2KL)$ $^7(F)$
(3432) f^7 — $^2(S_2P_5D_7F_{10}G_{10}H_9I_9K_7L_5M_4N_2OQ)$	$^4(S_2P_2D_6F_5G_7H_5I_5K_3L_3MN)$	$^6(PDFGHI)$ $^8(S)$
(3003) f^8 — $^1(S_4PD_6F_4G_5H_4I_7K_3L_4M_2N_2Q)$	$^3(P_6D_5F_9G_7H_9I_6K_6L_3M_3NO)$	$^5(SPD_3F_2G_3H_2I_2KL)$ $^7(F)$
(2002) f^9 — $^2(P_4D_5F_7G_6H_7I_5K_5L_3M_2NO)$	$^4(SP_2D_3F_4G_4H_3I_3K_2LM)$	$^6(PFH)$
(1001) f^{10} — $^1(S_2D_4FG_4H_2I_3KL_2N)$	$^3(P_3D_2F_4G_3H_4I_2K_2LM)$	$^5(SDFGI)$
(364) f^{11} — $^2(PD_2F_2G_2H_2IKL)$	$^4(SDFGI)$	
(91) f^{12} — $^1(SDGI)$	$^3(PFH)$	
(14) f^{13} — $^2(F)$		
(1) f^{14} — $^1(S)$		

The subscripts to the right of each term type in the table for *f* electrons are not inner quantum numbers but indicate the number of such terms. For example f^7 — $^2(S_2P_5,$ etc.,) indicates that there are two ^2S terms, five ^2P terms, etc., arising from seven *f* electrons.

TABLE III.—RELATIVE INTENSITY TABLES FOR MULTIPLETS, FOR FINE STRUCTURE IN *LS* OR *jj*-COUPLING, AND FOR HYPERFINE STRUCTURE.[1]

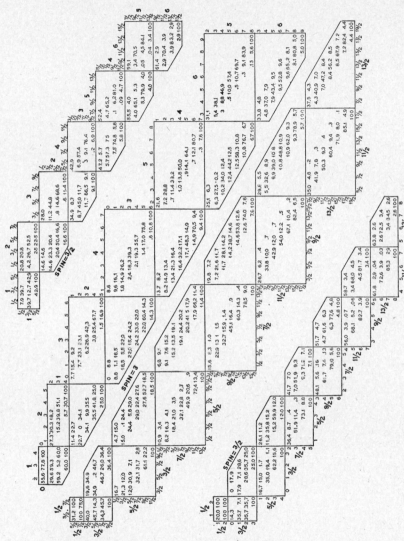

[1] After H. E. WHITE and A. Y. ELIASON, *Phys. Rev.*, **44**, 753, 1933.

TABLE III.—(Continued)

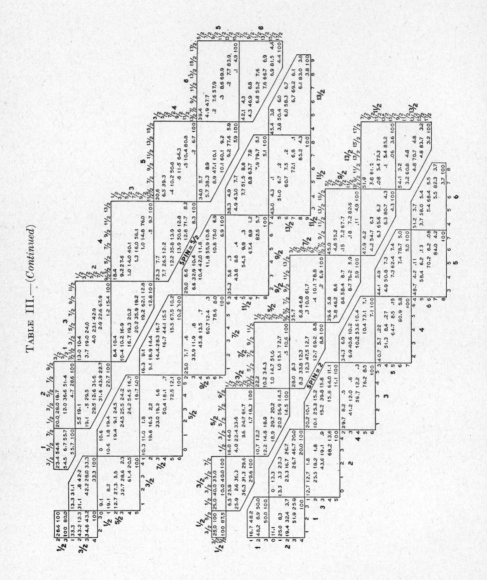

TABLE III.—(*Continued*)

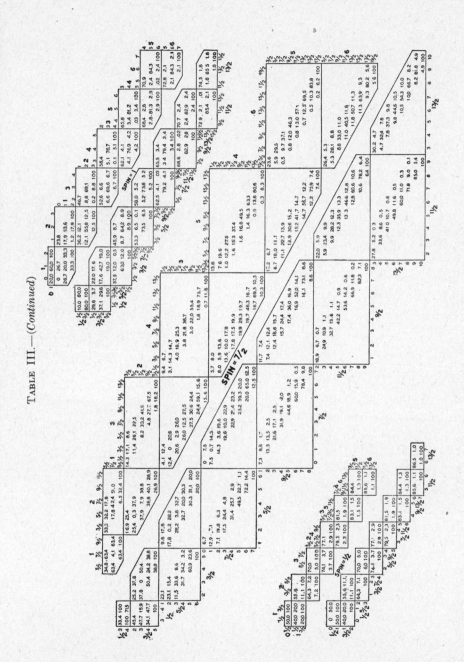

TABLE IV.—LANDÉ g FACTORS FOR LS-COUPLING

Singlets, $S=0$ / Doublets, $S=\frac{1}{2}$

J	0	1	2	3	4	5	6	7	$\frac{1}{2}$	$\frac{3}{2}$	$\frac{5}{2}$	$\frac{7}{2}$	$\frac{9}{2}$
L													
$S\,0$	0/0								2				
$P\,1$		1							$\frac{2}{3}$	$\frac{4}{3}$			
$D\,2$			1							$\frac{4}{5}$	$\frac{6}{5}$		
$F\,3$				1							$\frac{6}{7}$	$\frac{8}{7}$	
$G\,4$					1							$\frac{8}{9}$	$\frac{10}{9}$

Triplets, $S=1$ / Quartets, $S=\frac{3}{2}$

J	0	1	2	3	4	5	6	7	$\frac{3}{2}$	$\frac{5}{2}$	$\frac{7}{2}$	$\frac{9}{2}$	$\frac{11}{2}$	$\frac{13}{2}$	$\frac{15}{2}$
$S\,0$		2							2						
$P\,1$	0/0	$\frac{3}{2}$	$\frac{3}{2}$						$\frac{8}{3}$	$\frac{26}{15}$	$\frac{8}{5}$				
$D\,2$		$\frac{1}{2}$	$\frac{7}{6}$	$\frac{4}{3}$					0	$\frac{6}{5}$	$\frac{48}{35}$	$\frac{10}{7}$			
$F\,3$			$\frac{2}{3}$	$\frac{13}{12}$	$\frac{5}{4}$					$\frac{2}{5}$	$\frac{36}{35}$	$\frac{78}{63}$	$\frac{4}{3}$		
$G\,4$				$\frac{3}{4}$	$\frac{21}{20}$	$\frac{6}{5}$					$\frac{4}{7}$	$\frac{62}{63}$	$\frac{116}{99}$	$\frac{14}{11}$	

Quintets, $S=2$ / Sextets, $S=\frac{5}{2}$

J	0	1	2	3	4	5	6	7	$\frac{5}{2}$	$\frac{7}{2}$	$\frac{9}{2}$	$\frac{11}{2}$	$\frac{13}{2}$	$\frac{15}{2}$
$S\,0$			2						2					
$P\,1$		$\frac{5}{2}$	$\frac{11}{6}$	$\frac{5}{3}$					$\frac{12}{5}$	$\frac{66}{35}$	$\frac{12}{7}$			
$D\,2$	0/0	$\frac{3}{2}$	$\frac{3}{2}$	$\frac{3}{2}$	$\frac{3}{2}$				$\frac{10}{3}$	$\frac{28}{15}$	$\frac{58}{35}$	$\frac{100}{63}$	$\frac{14}{9}$	
$F\,3$	0	1	$\frac{5}{4}$	$\frac{27}{20}$	$\frac{7}{5}$				$-\frac{2}{3}$	$\frac{16}{15}$	$\frac{46}{35}$	$\frac{88}{63}$	$\frac{142}{99}$	$\frac{16}{11}$
$G\,4$		$\frac{1}{3}$	$\frac{11}{12}$	$\frac{23}{20}$	$\frac{19}{15}$	$\frac{4}{3}$			0	$\frac{6}{7}$	$\frac{8}{7}$	$\frac{14}{11}$	$\frac{122}{143}$	$\frac{18}{13}$

Septets, $S=3$ / Octets, $S=\frac{7}{2}$

J	0	1	2	3	4	5	6	7	$\frac{7}{2}$	$\frac{9}{2}$	$\frac{11}{2}$	$\frac{13}{2}$	$\frac{15}{2}$
$S\,0$				2					2				
$P\,1$		$\frac{7}{3}$	$\frac{23}{12}$	$\frac{7}{4}$					$\frac{16}{7}$	$\frac{122}{63}$	$\frac{16}{11}$		
$D\,2$		3	2	$\frac{7}{4}$	$\frac{33}{20}$	$\frac{8}{5}$			$\frac{14}{5}$	$\frac{72}{35}$	$\frac{38}{21}$	$\frac{56}{33}$	$\frac{18}{11}$
$F\,3$	0/0	$\frac{3}{2}$	$\frac{3}{2}$	$\frac{3}{2}$	$\frac{3}{2}$	$\frac{3}{2}$	4	2	$\frac{12}{7}$	$\frac{34}{21}$	$\frac{52}{33}$	$\frac{222}{143}$	$\frac{20}{13}$
$G\,4$		$-\frac{1}{2}$	$\frac{5}{6}$	$\frac{7}{6}$	$\frac{13}{10}$	$\frac{41}{30}$	$\frac{59}{42}$	$\frac{10}{7}$	$\frac{14}{15}$	$\frac{44}{35}$	$\frac{86}{63}$	$\frac{140}{99}$	$\frac{206}{143}$

(With $-\frac{4}{3}$ and further octet values $\frac{284}{195}$, $\frac{22}{15}$ in the highest J columns.)

TABLE V.—LANDÉ g FACTORS FOR TWO ELECTRONS IN jj-COUPLING
(Values in parenthesis are excluded if electrons are equivalent)

		$j=$ 0	1	2	3	4		$j=$ 0	1	2	3	4	5	6	7
ss	$j_1=\frac{1}{2},\,j_2=\frac{1}{2}$	0/0	(2)												
sp	$j_1=\frac{1}{2},\,j_2=\frac{1}{2}$	0/0	$\frac{4}{3}$				**pf**								
	$j_1=\frac{1}{2},\,j_2=\frac{3}{2}$		$\frac{7}{6}$	$\frac{8}{5}$											
sd	$j_1=\frac{1}{2},\,j_2=\frac{3}{2}$		$\frac{1}{2}$	$\frac{16}{10}$											
	$j_1=\frac{1}{2},\,j_2=\frac{5}{2}$			$\frac{12}{10}$	$\frac{4}{3}$		**dd**								
sf	$j_1=\frac{1}{2},\,j_2=\frac{5}{2}$			$\frac{2}{3}$	$\frac{22}{21}$										
	$j_1=\frac{1}{2},\,j_2=\frac{7}{2}$				$\frac{32}{28}$	$\frac{4}{3}$									
pp	$j_1=\frac{1}{2},\,j_2=\frac{1}{2}$	0/0	$(\frac{2}{3})$				**df**								
	$j_1=\frac{1}{2},\,j_2=\frac{3}{2}$		$\frac{2}{3}$	$\frac{7}{6}$											
	$j_1=\frac{3}{2},\,j_2=\frac{1}{2}$		$(\frac{2}{3})$	$(\frac{7}{6})$											
	$j_1=\frac{3}{2},\,j_2=\frac{3}{2}$	0/0	$(\frac{4}{3})$	$\frac{4}{3}$	$(\frac{4}{3})$										
pd	$j_1=\frac{1}{2},\,j_2=\frac{3}{2}$		$\frac{2}{3}$	$\frac{32}{30}$			**ff**								
	$j_1=\frac{1}{2},\,j_2=\frac{5}{2}$			$\frac{52}{45}$	$\frac{10}{9}$										
	$j_1=\frac{3}{2},\,j_2=\frac{3}{2}$	0/0	$\frac{12}{10}$	$\frac{12}{10}$											
	$j_1=\frac{3}{2},\,j_2=\frac{5}{2}$		$\frac{16}{10}$	$\frac{102}{90}$	$\frac{223}{180}$	$\frac{5}{4}$									